This second volume of James Clerk Maxwell's correspondence and manuscript papers begins in July 1862 with his first referee reports for the Royal Society, and concludes in December 1873 shortly before the formal inauguration of the Cavendish Laboratory at Cambridge. The volume documents his involvement with the wider scientific community in Victorian Britain, and the period of his scientific maturity. In the years 1862–73 Maxwell wrote the classic works on statistical molecular theory and field physics, including the *Treatise on Electricity and Magnetism*, which established his special status in the history of science. His letters and drafts of this period provide unique insight into this work, which remains fundamental to modern physics. Few of the manuscripts reproduced here have received prior publication in other than truncated form; and the volume includes Maxwell's correspondence with G. G. Stokes, Kelvin and P. G. Tait. The edition is annotated with a full historical commentary.

Note on this Paperback Re-issue:

This is Part One of Volume Two of the Scientific Letters and Papers of James Clerk Maxwell. Volume Two was first published as a single hardback volume in 1995.
This paperback impression of Volume Two is printed in two parts, the first of which contains pages i-469 of the original hardback, the second pages 470-999 of the original hardback.

THE SCIENTIFIC LETTERS AND PAPERS OF
JAMES CLERK MAXWELL

$$k \nabla^2 \mu\alpha = 4\pi\mu \frac{d^2}{dt^2}\mu\alpha$$
$$k \nabla^2 \mu\beta = 4\pi\mu \frac{d^2}{dt^2}\mu\beta \quad\quad\quad (69)$$
$$k \nabla^2 \mu\gamma = 4\pi\mu \frac{d^2}{dt^2}\mu\gamma$$

If we assume that α, β, γ are functions of $lx + my + nz - Vt = w$ the first equation becomes

$$k\mu \frac{d^2\alpha}{dw^2} = 4\pi\mu^2 V^2 \frac{d^2\alpha}{dw^2} \quad\quad (70)$$

or
$$V = \pm \sqrt{\frac{k}{4\pi\mu}} \quad\quad (71)$$

The other equations give the same value for V so that the wave is propagated in either direction with a velocity V.

This wave consists entirely of magnetic disturbances, the direction of magnetization being in the plane of the wave. No magnetic disturbance whose direction of magnetization is not in the plane of the wave can be propagated as a plane wave at all.

Hence magnetic disturbances propagated through the electromagnetic field agree with light in this, that the disturbance at any point is transverse to the direction of propagation, and such waves may have all the properties of polarized light.

The only medium in which experiments have been made to determine the value of k is air, in which $\mu = 1$ and therefore by equation (46)

$$V = v \quad\quad (72)$$

By the electromagnetic experiments of M. M. Weber & Kohlrausch

$$v = 310\,740\,000 \text{ meters per second}$$

is the number of electrostatic units in one electromagnetic unit of electricity and this according to our result should be equal to the velocity of light in air or vacuum.

Velocity of light in air by M. Fizeau's experiments

$$V = 314\,858\,000$$

Leipzig Trans V (1857) p 260 or Poggendorff's Annalen Aug 1856 p 10
Comptes Rendus vol XXIX (1849) p 90

The electromagnetic theory of light. From 'A dynamical theory of the electromagnetic field', October 1864 (Number 239).

THE SCIENTIFIC LETTERS AND PAPERS OF
JAMES CLERK MAXWELL

VOLUME II
1862–1873
Part I
1862–1868

EDITED BY

P. M. HARMAN

Professor Emeritus of the History of Science, Lancaster University

CAMBRIDGE UNIVERSITY PRESS
Cambridge, New York, Melbourne, Madrid, Cape Town, Singapore, São Paulo, Delhi

Cambridge University Press
The Edinburgh Building, Cambridge CB2 8RU, UK

Published in the United States of America by Cambridge University Press, New York

www.cambridge.org
Information on this title: www.cambridge.org/9780521256261

© Cambridge University Press 1995

This publication is in copyright. Subject to statutory exception
and to the provisions of relevant collective licensing agreements,
no reproduction of any part may take place without the written
permission of Cambridge University Press.

First published 1995
This digitally printed version 2008

A catalogue record for this publication is available from the British Library

Library of Congress Cataloguing in Publication data
Maxwell, James Clerk, 1831–1879.
The scientific letters and papers of James Clerk Maxwell/edited by P. M. Harman
Includes bibliographical references and index.
1. Electromagnetic theory. 2. Light, Wave theory of. 3. Molecular theory – Statistical methods.
I. Harman, P. M. (Peter Michael), 1943– . II. Title.
QC670.M385 1990   530.1′41   89–452

ISBN 978-0-521-10135-6 paperback (Volume 1)
ISBN 978-0-521-25625-4 hardback (Volume 1)
ISBN 978-0-521-10136-3 paperback (Volume 2 Set)
ISBN 978-0-521-74607-6 paperback (Volume 2 Part 1)
ISBN 978-0-521-74610-6 paperback (Volume 2 Part 2)
ISBN 978-0-521-25626-1 hardback (Volume 2)
ISBN 978-0-521-10137-0 paperback (Volume 3 Set)
ISBN 978-0-521-74614-4 paperback (Volume 3 Part 1)
ISBN 978-0-521-74617-5 paperback (Volume 3 Part 2)
ISBN 978-0-521-25627-8 hardback (Volume 3)
ISBN 978-0-521-75794-2 paperback (3 Volume Set)
ISBN 978-0-521-80952-8 hardback (3 Volume Set)

For Tim and Rosie

CONTENTS
Part I

Preface	*page* xi
List of texts	xiv
Editorial note	xxiv
List of plates	xxvii
Abbreviated references	xxix
Introduction	1
TEXTS 1862-1868	39

Appendix

Index

Part II

Preface	*page* xi
List of texts	xiv
Editorial note	xxiv
List of plates	xxvii
Abbreviated references	xxix
TEXTS 1869-1873	470
Appendix	971
Index	977

PREFACE

This second volume of James Clerk Maxwell's scientific letters and papers documents the period of his maturity. These manuscripts provide substantive evidence of the process in which the brilliant innovations of his scientific youth were transformed into the Maxwellian physics transmitted to posterity. The volume covers the years 1862–73, when Maxwell wrote the classic works on statistical molecular theory and field physics, including the *Treatise on Electricity and Magnetism*, which established his unique status in the history of science. The volume begins with his first referee reports for the Royal Society, signalling his involvement with the wider scientific community, and ends shortly before the inauguration of the Cavendish Laboratory at Cambridge.

Only a small number of the manuscripts reproduced in this volume have received prior publication in other than truncated form. Letters received by Maxwell, of which few are now extant, are reproduced on a selective basis, and third-party correspondence is also included. All the letters from his major correspondents – George Gabriel Stokes, William Thomson (later Lord Kelvin) and Peter Guthrie Tait – are reproduced complete, the correspondence with Tait being of especial interest.

This volume prints all of Maxwell's extant autograph letters from the period 1862–73. While these and other manuscripts provide profuse documentation of the evolution of Maxwell's science, his intellectual development, and the course of his public career, little information can be gleaned about his private affairs. Campbell and Garnett's *Life of Maxwell* contains no more than a very sparse selection of the documents, still extant at the time of his death, which related to his personal life in this period.

Much of the work on this volume has been carried out in the Cambridge University Library and the Harvard College Library. I am grateful to the President and Fellows of Clare Hall, Cambridge, and the Department of the History of Science, Harvard University, for hospitality in providing facilities for this work.

The edition owes much to the support of Cambridge University Press. Sir Alan Cook has taken a kind interest in the progress of my work on behalf of the Syndics. Richard Ziemacki, Simon Capelin, James Deeny and Fiona Thomson have been generous with advice and assistance. I am very grateful to Alan Winter and Richard Schermerhorn: the completion of this volume owes much to the help they kindly proffered. It is a pleasure to thank Susan

Bowring for her meticulous contribution as copy-editor; and to gratefully acknowledge the work of Pauline Ireland and of the draughtsmen and typesetters at the Press in the presentation of the edition in such an elegant form.

I have benefited from the helpfulness of archivists and librarians in many libraries. I thank especially Godfrey Waller of the Manuscripts Room of the Cambridge University Library and Alan Clark of the Library of the Royal Society, for their kindness and efficiency over many years.

I am grateful to many friends and colleagues who have been helpful in providing information about the location of manuscripts, in offering advice, and in fostering my work by various acts of kindness. I thank especially Jed Buchwald, I. Bernard Cohen, Francis Everitt, Tom Fuller, Ivor Grattan-Guinness, Erwin Hiebert, Bruce Hunt, Lord Jenkin, Robert Kargon, Martin Klein, Anne Kox, Sir Brian Pippard, A. I. Sabra, Robert Schulmann, Sam Schweber, Alan Shapiro, Daniel Siegel, Thomas Simpson, John Stachel, Carlene Stephens, The Hon. Guy Strutt, Garry J. Tee, Paul Theerman, Charles Webster, Tom Whiteside, L. Pearce Williams and David Wilson.

I am grateful to Ethel Dunkerley for typing the entire manuscript (from my handwritten transcriptions) with such dedication; to Isabel Matthews for valuable assistance in drawing the figures; and to Keith Papworth of the Cavendish Laboratory for his enthusiasm in preparing photographs of Maxwell's experimental apparatus.

It would have proved impossible to prepare this volume for publication without the opportunity to spend extended periods working in a research library. I am grateful to the Royal Society for awarding me a succession of research grants, and I thank Norman Robinson and Sheila Edwards for their interest. I am especially grateful to the National Science Foundation for substantial grants which supported two years work at Harvard; to thank Ronald J. Overmann for his generous interest and kindness, I can only say that without such support this volume would not have been completed.

For permission to reproduce manuscripts I am grateful to Lord Rayleigh; Professor Sydney Ross; Miss Margaret Tait; the Syndics of the Cambridge University Library; the Master and Fellows of Trinity College, Cambridge; the Master and Fellows of Peterhouse, Cambridge; the Cavendish Laboratory, Cambridge; the Librarian of Glasgow University Library; St Andrews University Library; Edinburgh University Library; the Trustees of the National Library of Scotland; the Royal Society; the Royal Institution; Imperial College London Archives; King's College London Archives; the University of London Library and the Athenæum; the Institution of Electrical Engineers, London; the Greater London Record Office; the Bodleian Library, Oxford; the Royal Greenwich Observatory; The General

Electric Company, p.l.c.; The Queen's University of Belfast Library; Columbia University Library; The Johns Hopkins University Library; the Smithsonian Institution Libraries; Harvard University Archives; and the Akademie-Archiv, Berlin.

I am grateful to the Cavendish Laboratory and the Whipple Museum of the History of Science, Cambridge for permission to reproduce photographs of Maxwell's apparatus, and to Dr I. B. Hopley for use of his photograph of the governor; and to the Syndics of the Cambridge University Library, the Librarian of Glasgow University Library, and the Royal Society for permission to reproduce photographs of documents.

To end on a very personal note, my deepest thanks are to Juliet, Tim and Rosie for so good-humouredly tolerating my absorption in this work.

LIST OF TEXTS

Part I and Part II

197	Letter to William Sharpey, 8 July 1862	page 41
198	Letter to George Gabriel Stokes, 14 July 1862	43
199	Letters to George Gabriel Stokes, 16 July 1862	46
200	Letter to George Gabriel Stokes, 21 July 1862	50
201	On a paper by Thomas Romney Robinson on the spectra of electric sparks, 10 September 1862	54
202	Letter to George Gabriel Stokes, 10 September 1862	58
203	On diagrams of forces, c. November 1862	60
204	Letter to John William Cunningham, 5 December 1862	61
205	On a paper by George Biddell Airy on stress in beams, late December 1862	62
206	Letter to George Gabriel Stokes, 29 December 1862	70
207	On the conduction of heat in gases, c. Spring 1863	72
208	Letter to John William Cunningham, 24 March 1863	86
209	Letter to George Biddell Airy, 14 May 1863	87
210	Letter to William Thomson, 29 May 1863	88
211	Letter to William Thomson, June 1863	93
212	Letter to George Gabriel Stokes, 9 June 1863	95
213	Letter to John William Cunningham, 27 June 1863	97
214	Letter to William Thomson, 31 July 1863	98
215	Letter to John William Cunningham, 10 August 1863	102
216	Letter to Robert Dundas Cay, 21 August 1863	103
217	Letter to George Phillips Bond, 25 August 1863	104
218	Letter to Fleeming Jenkin, 27 August 1863	110
219	Letter to William Thomson, 11 September 1863	112
220	On a paper by Charles Chambers on the magnetic action of the sun, late October 1863	117
221	On the equilibrium and stiffness of a frame, c. January 1864	119
222	Letter to Katherine Mary Clerk Maxwell, 28 January 1864	122
223	On a paper by William John Macquorn Rankine on fluid motion, late February 1864	123
224	On the theory of Saturn's rings, 1864	128
225	Letter to Hermann Helmholtz, 12 April 1864	146
226	Letter to John Tyndall, 20 April 1864	147
227	On the motion of the earth through the ether, c. 24 April 1864	148

List of texts

228	Letter to George Gabriel Stokes, 6 May 1864	*page* 154
229	Letter to Robert Dundas Cay, 12 July 1864	157
230	On the determination of coefficients of self-induction, *c.* Summer 1864	158
231	Draft of 'A dynamical theory of the electromagnetic field', *c.* Summer 1864	160
232	Letter to Charles Hockin, 7 September 1864	164
233	On the determination of the number of electrostatic units in one electromagnetic unit of electricity, *c.* September 1864	165
234	Letter to William Thomson, 27 September 1864	172
235	Letter to William Thomson, 15 October 1864	176
236	On the explanation of the reflection and refraction of light by the electromagnetic theory of light, October 1864	182
237	Letter to George Gabriel Stokes, 15 October 1864	186
238	A dynamical theory of the electromagnetic field (abstract), [27 October 1864]	189
239	Cancelled passages in the manuscript and proofs of 'A dynamical theory of the electromagnetic field', October 1864	197
240	Letter to Charles Hope Cay, 5 January 1865	202
241	On the determination of the number of electrostatic units in one electromagnetic unit of electricity, *c.* February 1865	204
242	Letter to William Thomson, 25 February 1865	207
243	Torsion balance to compare an electrostatic attraction with an electromagnetic repulsion, 1 March 1865	213
244	Letter to Peter Guthrie Tait, 7 March 1865	214
245	Letter to Peter Guthrie Tait, 3 April 1865	216
246	Letter to William Thomson, 17 and 18 April 1865	218
247	Letter to Robert Dundas Cay, 28 April 1865	221
248	Letter to Thomas Graham, 1 May 1865	222
249	Letter to Peter Guthrie Tait, 17 June 1865	224
250	Letter to Henry Richmond Droop, 19 July 1865	226
251	Letter to Lewis Campbell, 21 November 1865	228
252	On the viscosity or internal friction of air and other gases (abstract), [23 November 1865]	230
253	On James Thomson's vortex turbine, *c.* late 1865	236
	Appendix I: On the stability of vortex motion, *c.* late 1865	239
	Appendix II: Letter to Robert Dundas Cay, 8 December 1865	240
254	On the stability of fluid motion, *c.* 1865	241
255	On a paper by John Tyndall on calorescence, 1 January 1866	245
256	Letter to Charles Benjamin Tayler, 2 February 1866	249
257	Letter to Hugh Andrew Johnstone Munro, 7 February 1866	250

258	On a paper by John Tyndall on radiation, 22 February 1866	*page* 253
259	Drafts of 'On the dynamical theory of gases', late 1865 – early 1866	254
260	Letter to William Thomson, 27 February 1866	267
261	On a paper by Joseph David Everett on the rigidity of glass, 1 March 1866	272
262	Letter to Peter Guthrie Tait, 4 April 1866	276
263	On the dynamical theory of gases (abstract), [16 May 1866]	279
264	On a paper by Thomas Graham on the absorption and separation of gases, 17 July 1866	285
265	On a paper by Edward Wyndham Tarn on the stability of domes, 18 December 1866	288
266	Letter to George Gabriel Stokes, 18 December 1866	291
267	Letter to James Joseph Sylvester, 21 December 1866	294
268	Letter to George Gabriel Stokes, 27 February 1867	298
269	On a paper by Joseph David Everett on the determination of rigidity, 4 March 1867	300
270	Reported comments on Brodie's chemical calculus, 6 June 1867	304
271	Letter to William Huggins, 10 June 1867	306
272	British Association paper on a stereoscope, [September 1867]	312
273	On reciprocal figures and diagrams of forces, *c.* September 1867	313
	Appendix: British Association paper on diagrams of forces, [September 1867]	317
274	Letter to William Thomson, 14 September 1867	318
275	Letter to Peter Guthrie Tait, 13 November 1867	321
276	Letter to Peter Guthrie Tait, 4 December 1867	323
277	Letter to Peter Guthrie Tait, 11 December 1867	328
278	Letter to Peter Guthrie Tait, 23 December 1867	335
279	On the principles of stereoscopic vision, *c.* 1867	340
	Appendix: exhibition of stereograms to the London Mathematical Society, 23 January 1868	342
280	Question to the London Mathematical Society on governors, 23 January 1868	343
	Appendix: draft on governors, *c.* January 1868	344
281	Letter to William Thomson, 20 February 1868	346
282	On a paper by Joseph David Everett on the rigidity of metal rods, *c.* 25 February 1868	348
283	Letter to George Biddell Airy, 12 March 1868	351
284	Letter to Peter Guthrie Tait, 12 March 1868	353
285	Letter to William Robert Grove, 27 March 1868	356
286	Letter to Mark Pattison, 7 April 1868	358

List of texts xvii

287	Letter to Mark Pattison, 13 April 1868	*page* 362
288	On papers by Francis Bashforth, James Atkinson Longridge and Charles Watkins Merrifield on the motion of projectiles, 19 May 1868	369
289	On a method of making a direct comparison of electrostatic with electromagnetic force; with a note on the electromagnetic theory of light (abstract), [10 June 1868]	375
290	On a paper by Alfred Des Cloiseaux on the optical properties of crystals, *c.* late May 1868	380
291	On a paper by Robert Moon on the impact of compressible bodies, 8 July 1868	383
292	On the measurement of surface tension, *c.* Summer 1868	386
293	Letter to Peter Guthrie Tait, 14 July 1868	389
294	Letter to Peter Guthrie Tait, 18 July 1868	391
	Appendix: comments on Thomson and Tait's *Natural Philosophy*, Chapter II, July 1868	395
295	Letter to William Thomson, 18 July 1868	398
296	Letter to Peter Guthrie Tait, *c.* 20 July 1868	407
297	Letter to John Tyndall, 23 July 1868	409
	Appendix: stability criteria for governors of the fifth order, *c.* late July 1868	410
298	On a paper by George Gabriel Stokes on the communication of vibration to a gas, 28 July 1868	412
299	Letter to Peter Guthrie Tait, 3 August 1868	416
300	On the absorption and dispersion of light, *c.* August 1868	419
	Appendix: Mathematical Tripos question, *c.* late 1868	420
301	Letter to William Thomson, 19 August 1868	422
302	Letter to William Thomson, 5 September 1868	424
303	Letter to William Thomson, 12 September 1868	428
304	On topology, *c.* September 1868	433
305	On continuity and topology, *c.* September 1868	439
306	Letter to William Thomson, 28 September 1868	443
307	Letter to William Thomson, 6 October 1868	446
308	Letter to William Thomson, 7 October 1868	449
	Appendix: on hollow solids, *c.* October 1868	450
309	Letter to William Huggins, 13 October 1868	451
310	Letter to William Thomson, 16 October 1868	453
311	Letter to William Thomson, 30 October 1868	457
312	Letter to Lewis Campbell, 3 November 1868	460
313	Letter to William Robert Grove, 7 November 1868	461
314	Letter to George Biddell Airy, 9 November 1868	462

315	Letter to William Thomson, 9 November 1868	page 463
316	Letter to William Thomson, 7 December 1868	464
317	On the topology of surfaces, 29 December 1868	466
318	On J. B. Listing's paper 'Der Census räumlicher Complexe', 11 February 1869	470
319	On a paper by Henry Moseley on the motion of glaciers, 2 March 1869	472
320	Letter to Arthur Cayley, 12 April 1869	476
321	Letter to William Thomson, 12 May 1869	479
322	Letter to William Thomson, 5 June 1869	483
323	Letter to George Gabriel Stokes, 26 June 1869	487
324	Letter to George Gabriel Stokes, 8 July 1869	489
325	On a paper by Norman Macleod Ferrers on the motion of a rigid body, 14 August 1869	492
326	Letter to William Thomson, 17 August 1869	496
327	Letter to William Thomson, 1 October 1869	498
328	Letter to William Thomson, 5 October 1869	501
329	Contents of the *Treatise on Electricity and Magnetism*, c. October 1869	502
330	Letter to the London Mathematical Society on the potential of a disc, November 1869	508
331	On a paper by George Oldham Hanlon on the *vena contracta*, November 1869	510
332	Letter to William Thomson, 16 November 1869	513
333	Letter to Peter Guthrie Tait, 10 December 1869	516
334	On reciprocal figures, frames, and diagrams of forces (abstract), [17 December 1869]	519
335	Drafts relating to Part IV of the *Treatise*, c. late 1869	522
336	Letter to Katherine Mary Clerk Maxwell, 3 January 1870	528
337	On a paper by William John Macquorn Rankine on fluid motion, 2 March 1870	529
338	On a paper by William John Macquorn Rankine on the thermodynamic theory of waves, 26 March 1870	535
339	Letter to William Thomson, 14 April 1870	541
340	Letter to John William Strutt, 18 May 1870	545
341	Letter to Cecil James Monro, 6 July 1870	550
342	On a paper by Charles Bland Radcliffe on animal electricity, c. July 1870	554
343	On the chromatic effects of polarised light on double refracting crystals: addition to a paper by Francis Deas, c. Summer 1870	559

List of texts

344	Draft of the 1870 Presidential Address to Section A of the British Association, *c.* Summer 1870	*page* 564
345	British Association paper on hills and dales, [September 1870]	566
346	Letter to Peter Guthrie Tait, 7 November 1870	568
347	On the application of quaternions to electromagnetism, November 1870	570
348	Letter to Peter Guthrie Tait, 14 November 1870	577
349	Letter to John Hutton Balfour, 28 November 1870	580
350	Letter to John William Strutt, 6 December 1870	582
	Appendix: from the manuscript of the *Theory of Heat, c.* late 1870	584
351	Letter to George Gabriel Stokes, 11 January 1871	589
352	Draft letter to Peter Guthrie Tait, 23 January 1871	590
353	Letter to Peter Guthrie Tait, 23 January 1871	593
354	On a paper by John William Strutt on the theory of resonance, 31 January 1871	598
355	Letter to John William Strutt, 4 February 1871	605
356	Postcard to Peter Guthrie Tait, 14 February 1871	609
357	Draft letter to Edward William Blore, 15 February 1871	611
358	Letter to John William Strutt, 15 March 1871	614
359	Letter to Cecil James Monro, 15 March 1871	617
360	On colour blindness, *c.* March 1871	621
361	Letter to Katherine Mary Clerk Maxwell, 20 March 1871	623
362	Letter to William Thomson, 21 March 1871	624
363	Letter to Katherine Mary Clerk Maxwell, 22 March 1871	629
364	Plans for the physical laboratory, *c.* March 1871	630
365	Postcard to William Thomson, 30 March 1871	632
366	Postcard to Peter Guthrie Tait, 4 April 1871	634
367	Postcard to Peter Guthrie Tait, 3 May 1871	636
368	Postcard to Peter Guthrie Tait, 8 May 1871	637
369	Postcard to Peter Guthrie Tait, 11 May 1871	639
370	Question to the London Mathematical Society on spatial relations, 11 May 1871	641
	Appendix: note on spatial relations, 11 May 1871	642
371	Postcard to Peter Guthrie Tait, 12 May 1871	644
372	Postcard to Peter Guthrie Tait, 25 May 1871	645
373	Postcard to Peter Guthrie Tait, 27 May 1871	646
374	Postcard to Peter Guthrie Tait, 27 May 1871	648
375	Postcard to Peter Guthrie Tait, 3 June 1871	650
376	Postcard to Peter Guthrie Tait, 14 June 1871	652
377	On the history of the kinetic theory of gases: notes for William Thomson, *c.* Summer 1871	654

378	Letter to Charles William Siemens, 23 June 1871	*page* 661
379	Letter to John William Strutt, 8 and 10 July 1871	664
	Appendix: letter of reference for William Kingdon Clifford, *c.* July 1871	666
380	Postcard to Peter Guthrie Tait, 13 July 1871	667
381	Letter to James Thomson, 13 July 1871	668
382	Letter to James Thomson, 24 July 1871	670
383	Note for William Thomson and Peter Guthrie Tait, late August 1871	675
384	Postcard to Peter Guthrie Tait, 5 September 1871	677
385	Note for Fleeming Jenkin on electric circuits, *c.* September 1871	678
	Appendix: annotation on proof of Jenkin's *Electricity and Magnetism*, *c.* September 1871	680
386	Letter to Peter Guthrie Tait, 19 October 1871	681
387	Postcard to Peter Guthrie Tait, 23 October 1871	682
388	Letter to Peter Guthrie Tait, 2 November 1871	683
389	Postcard to Peter Guthrie Tait, 7 November 1871	686
390	Postcard to William Thomson, 7 November 1871	689
391	Letter to Robert Dundas Cay, 23 November 1871	690
392	Reported comments on the strains of an iron structure, 5 December 1871	691
393	Postcard to Peter Guthrie Tait, 7 December 1871	692
394	Postcard to Peter Guthrie Tait, 12 December 1871	694
395	On the geometrical mean distance of two figures on a plane, *c.* December 1871	695
396	Letter to Peter Guthrie Tait, 21 December 1871	699
397	Letter to William Milner Fawcett, 1 January 1872	701
398	Postcard to Peter Guthrie Tait, 1 January 1872	702
399	Postcard to Peter Guthrie Tait, *c.* 4 January 1872	704
400	Letter to George Gabriel Stokes, 8 January 1872	706
401	Postcard to Peter Guthrie Tait, 19 January 1872	707
402	Postcard to William Thomson, 8 February 1872	708
403	Postcard to Peter Guthrie Tait, 12 February 1872	710
404	Letter to George Gabriel Stokes, 12 February 1872	711
405	Abstract of paper on Arago's rotating disc, *c.* 15 February 1872	712
406	Letter to William Huggins, 2 May 1872	714
407	Letter to Peter Guthrie Tait, *c.* early May 1872	715
408	Postcard to Peter Guthrie Tait, 9 May 1872	716
409	Postcard to Peter Guthrie Tait, 14 May 1872	717

410	On a paper by George Biddell Airy on the magnetic properties of iron and steel, 17 May 1872	*page* 718
411	Letter to Peter Guthrie Tait, 24 May 1872	727
412	Letter to Robert Dundas Cay, 27 May 1872	729
	Appendix: theorem on the potential function for the 1873 Mathematical Tripos, *c.* Summer 1872	730
413	Note to Peter Guthrie Tait, *c.* late June 1872	731
414	Postcard to Peter Guthrie Tait, 29 June 1872	732
415	On a paper by Latimer Clark on a standard of electromotive force, *c.* 2 July 1872	734
416	Letter to George Gabriel Stokes, 8 July 1872	738
417	Postcard to Peter Guthrie Tait, 15 July 1872	739
	Appendix: postcard to Peter Guthrie Tait, 7 August 1872	741
418	Letter to Latimer Clark, 16 July 1872	742
419	On the interpretation of Lagrange's and Hamilton's equations of motion, *c.* July 1872	744
420	Letter to William Thomson, 10 August 1872	748
421	Letter to James Thomson, 2 September 1872	751
422	Postcard to Peter Guthrie Tait, 4 October 1872	755
423	Letter to Peter Guthrie Tait, 9 October 1872	756
424	Letter to George Biddell Airy, 16 October 1872	758
425	Letter to Lewis Campbell, 19 October 1872	760
426	Letter to George Biddell Airy, 28 October 1872	761
427	Note to Peter Guthrie Tait, 12 November 1872	763
428	Letter to Peter Guthrie Tait, late 1872 – early 1873	764
429	Notes to Peter Guthrie Tait, *c.* December 1872	766
430	On electromagnetism, late 1872 – early 1873	767
431	On Forbes' work on colours, *c.* 1872	774
432	On the classification of the physical sciences, late 1872 – early 1873	776
433	Letter of reference for James Thomson, 7 January 1873	783
434	Postcard to William Thomson, 22 January 1873	784
435	Draft letter to the Duke of Devonshire, late January – early February 1873	785
436	On a problem in the calculus of variations in which the solution is discontinuous, February 1873	787
437	Lecture on Faraday's lines of force, early 1873	790
	Appendix: on dynamical principles, *c.* 1873	811
438	Letter to Henry Bence Jones, 4 February 1873	813
439	Essay for the Eranus Club on science and free will, 11 February 1873	814

440	Postcard to Peter Guthrie Tait, 12 February 1873	*page* 824
441	Letter to Peter Guthrie Tait, *c.* early 1873	825
442	On a paper by Frederick Guthrie on the electrical properties of hot bodies, *c.* 25 February 1873	827
443	Postcard to Peter Guthrie Tait, 3 March 1873	831
444	Postcard to Peter Guthrie Tait, 5 March 1873	832
445	Letter to Peter Guthrie Tait, 10 March 1873	833
446	Postcard to Peter Guthrie Tait, 12 March 1873	835
447	On a paper by James Jago on experiments on vision, *c.* 24 March 1873	836
448	Letters to William Thomson, 25 March 1873	839
449	Letter to Lewis Campbell, 3 April 1873	840
450	Review of Fleeming Jenkin, *Electricity and Magnetism*, *c.* April 1873	842
451	Letter to Peter Guthrie Tait, 2 May 1873	845
452	Letter to Peter Guthrie Tait, 7 May 1873	846
453	Letter to George Gabriel Stokes, 13 May 1873	847
454	Letter to Peter Guthrie Tait, 15 May 1873	848
455	On a paper by Dugald M'Kichan on the determination of the number of electrostatic units in one electromagnetic unit of electricity, *c.* 20 May 1873	849
456	Letter to Robert Dundas Cay, 22 May 1873	852
457	On the effect of gravity on the temperature of a column of gas, *c.* 25 May 1873	853
458	Letter to John William Strutt, 26 May 1873	856
459	Letter to Charles Tomlinson, 29 May 1873	858
460	On a paper by John William Strutt on theorems relating to vibrations, 26 June 1873	860
461	On the theory of anomalous dispersion, *c.* 1873	864
462	On a paper by Latimer Clark on a standard voltaic battery, 26 June 1873	866
463	Fixtures and instruments in the Cavendish Laboratory, June 1873	868
464	Draft letter to Henry Wilkinson Cookson, 5 July 1873	876
465	Postcard to Peter Guthrie Tait, *c.* 8 July 1873	877
466	Letter to Henry Augustus Rowland, 9 July 1873	879
467	Letter to Henry Augustus Rowland, 12 July 1873	881
468	Letter to Peter Guthrie Tait, 22 July 1873	884
469	Postcard to Peter Guthrie Tait, 24 July 1873	888
470	Draft of 'On Loschmidt's experiments on diffusion', late July 1873	890

471	Postcard to Peter Guthrie Tait, 30 July 1873	*page* 897
472	Drafts of 'On the final state of a system of molecules in motion subject to forces of any kind', *c.* August 1873	898
473	Draft of 'On the final state of a system of molecules in motion subject to forces of any kind', August 1873	911
474	Letter to Peter Guthrie Tait, *c.* August 1873	915
475	On atoms and ether, 13 August 1873	917
476	Letter to John William Strutt, Lord Rayleigh, 28 August 1873	919
477	Note to Peter Guthrie Tait, late August – early September 1873	921
478	Drafts of lecture on 'Molecules', *c.* August – September 1873	922
479	Postcard to Peter Guthrie Tait, 2 September 1873	934
480	British Association paper on geometrical optics, [September 1873]	935
481	On the effect of gravity on the temperature of a column of gas, October 1873	937
482	Letter to John William Strutt, Lord Rayleigh, 22 November 1873	940
483	Letter to Peter Guthrie Tait, 1 December 1873	944
484	Letter to William Grylls Adams, 3 December 1873	949
485	On quaternions, December 1873	951
486	Letter to Herbert Spencer, 5 December 1873	956
487	Letter to Herbert Spencer, 17 December 1873	962
488	Examiner's report on the Natural Sciences Tripos (Physics) 1873, December 1873	964
489	The equation of continuity and physical analogy, 1873	965
490	On a paper by Osmond Fisher on the elevation of mountains, *c.* December 1873	968

EDITORIAL NOTE

The terms of reference of this edition of Maxwell's scientific letters and papers are described in the General introduction and Editorial note to the first volume. Maxwell's extant autograph letters and papers are supplemented by documents drawn from the *Life of Maxwell*, and by his shorter publications – letters, reviews, abstracts of contributed and published papers, and contributions to discussions – which were omitted from the memorial edition of his *Scientific Papers* published by Cambridge University Press in 1890. The texts are reproduced in chronological sequence, so far as can be determined. In the case of postcards, where there is generally no date written by Maxwell, the convention is adopted (in the absence of any other evidence) of dating the cards by their postmarks. In the case of abstracts of contributed and published papers the convention is adopted either of citing the date when the paper was read, or (in the case of papers read to the Royal Societies of London and Edinburgh) the date the paper was received by the Secretary.

The primary intention of this edition is the reproduction of an accurate text of all Maxwell's scientific letters and substantive manuscript papers. Manuscript fragments and jottings have been included on a selective basis. Special mention should be made of a series of six notebooks[1] that Maxwell kept during the years spanned by this volume. These notebooks, each of which was in use for two or three years, contain drafts of examination questions, journal references, calculations, and a miscellany of fragmentary jottings and notes. Some materials drawn from these notebooks have been reproduced as texts, and additional manuscript jottings have been included in the editorial annotations.

As already mentioned, the edition includes publications omitted from the *Scientific Papers*. Two classes of such published works have of necessity not been included: reports of the British Association Committee on electrical standards, of which Maxwell was a member[2] (the report for the year 1863

---

(1) There are three notebooks in the Maxwell Papers in the King's College London Archives; one in ULC Add. MSS 7655, V, k/9; one in the Cavendish Laboratory, Cambridge (of which there is a photocopy in ULC Add. MSS 7655, V, n/1); and one in ULC Add. MSS 7655, V, n/2).

(2) In the British Association *Reports* for 1863, 1864 and 1869; reprinted in Fleeming Jenkin, *Reports of the Committee on Electrical Standards appointed by the British Association for the Advancement of Science* (London, 1873).

including his paper, written with Fleeming Jenkin, on electrical units and dimensional relations);[3] and his series of questions set during five years as an examiner and moderator for the Cambridge Mathematical Tripos,[4] though some of these questions (being of special relevance) have been reproduced as texts or included in the editorial annotations.

Letters addressed to Maxwell are listed in the appendix. Because of the limited scope of these documents (as described in the General introduction to the first volume of the edition) these letters are reproduced on a selective basis. In the present volume all the letters written by his major correspondents, George Gabriel Stokes, Peter Guthrie Tait, and William Thomson, are printed *in extenso*. Other letters are reproduced complete, in extract, or are merely cited, as judged appropriate. Because of the generally patchy nature of the extant incoming correspondence, these letters are reproduced as annotations to the Maxwell texts. Third-party letters and other documents that contain information bearing on Maxwell's writings and work are included, generally in selective extract.

In accordance with the principles of modern scholarship the reproduction of the texts faithfully follows the manuscripts in spelling, punctuation, capitalization, and in preserving contractions; endpoints to sentences have been silently inserted. Where the texts are reproduced from printed sources the style of the original is followed. Trivial cancellations have been omitted without comment, but corrections deemed significant have been recorded. Minor deletions are placed within angle brackets ⟨...⟩ preceding the revised text; longer cancelled passages are reproduced by setting a double vertical bar against them in the left-hand margin. Appended passages are reproduced with a single vertical bar in the left-hand margin; appended phrases by corners ⌞...⌟ which enclose the added words. Annotations which were subsequently appended by Maxwell or by his correspondents are recorded. The name enclosed by brackets {...} denotes the annotator. The very few editorial insertions to the text, which have been introduced for the sake of clarity, are enclosed within square brackets.

In general I have attempted to preserve the layout of the manuscripts in their transformation to the printed page, but some necessary adjustments have been made for reasons of clarity. This applies especially to the reproduction of figures, which, like the transcription of handwriting, requires editorial interpretation. Some of Maxwell's figures are clearly drawn, but

---

(3) J. Clerk Maxwell and Fleeming Jenkin, 'On the elementary relations between electrical measurements', *Phil. Mag.*, ser. 4, **29** (1865): 436–60, 507–25; in Jenkin, *Reports of the Committee*: 59–96.

(4) In the *Cambridge University Calendar* for 1866, 1867, 1869, 1870 and 1873.

most are rough sketches. The aim has been to elucidate Maxwell's intentions as determined by study of both the figure and the corresponding text. The aim has been clarity rather than the precise reproduction of the originals. Figure numbers have been added; the captions are Maxwell's. In printing documents in the annotations to the texts, the convention is adopted of marking paragraph divisions and lines of poetry by a solidus.

The editorial commentary – the historical and textual notes and the Introduction – is intended to aid the reader in following Maxwell's arguments and his allusions to concepts, events and personalities. The Introduction provides a broad account of his intellectual development and career in the period covered by this volume, and an outline review of the texts here reproduced. In addition to clarifying obscurities in the texts, the historical notes seek to establish the context within which the documents were written, employing contemporary published as well as manuscript sources, including letters written to Maxwell, third-party correspondence, and fragmentary manuscript jottings not reproduced as texts. Reference to the first volume of the edition is made in the form 'Volume I: 438', meaning Volume I: [page] 438.

LIST OF PLATES

Part I

From 'A dynamical theory of the electromagnetic field', October 1864 (The Royal Society, PT.72.7, folio 62) (Number 239) *frontispiece*

I	The 'compound' governor, after 1863 (Cavendish Laboratory, Cambridge) (Number 219)	*facing page* 114
II	From a letter to William Thomson, 15 October 1864 (Glasgow University Library) (Number 235)	178
III	Drawing of torsion balance, 1 March 1865 (ULC Add. MSS 7655, V, c/14 (i)) (Number 243)	212
IV	Apparatus to determine the viscosity of gases, 1865 (Cavendish Laboratory, Cambridge) (Number 252)	230
V	Real image stereoscope, 1867 (Cavendish Laboratory, Cambridge) (Number 272)	312
VI	Stereograms of icosihedron in octahedron, lines of curvature of elliptic paraboloid and lines of curvature of hyperbolic paraboloid, 1867 (ULC Add. MSS 7655, V, i/11) (Number 274)	318
VII	Stereograms of lines of curvature of ellipsoid and Fresnel's wave surface, 1867 (ULC Add. MSS 7655, V, i/11) (Number 274)	319
VIII	Stereograms of conical point of wave surface and centres of curvature of ellipsoid, 1867 (ULC Add. MSS 7655, V, i/11) (Number 275)	322
IX	Stereograms of Gordian knots, 1867 (ULC Add. MSS 7655, V, i/11) (Number 277)	330
X	Stereograms of confocal spherical ellipses and concyclic spherical ellipses, 1867 (ULC Add. MSS 7655, V, i/11) (Number 277)	331
XI	Electrical torsion balance, 1868 (Cavendish Laboratory, Cambridge) (Number 289)	376
XII	Surface-tension microscope, 1868 (Whipple Museum, Cambridge) (Number 292)	386
XIII	Zoetrope or 'wheel of life' showing Helmholtz's rings, 1868 (Cavendish Laboratory, Cambridge) (Number 307)	446

XIV	Zoetrope or 'wheel of life' showing motion through a fluid, 1868 (Cavendish Laboratory, Cambridge) (Number 310)	456

Part II

XV	Postcard to Peter Guthrie Tait, 7 November 1871 (ULC Add. MSS 7655, I, b/36) (Number 389)	686

ABBREVIATED REFERENCES

Ann. Chim. Phys.	*Annales de Chimie et de Physique* (Paris).
Ann. Phys.	*Annalen der Physik und Chemie* (Leipzig).
Boase	*Modern English Biography containing Many Thousand Concise Memoirs of Persons who have Died since the Year 1850*. By Frederic Boase, 3 vols. and supplement (3 vols.) (Truro, 1892–1921).
Camb. & Dubl. Math. J.	*Cambridge and Dublin Mathematical Journal* (Cambridge).
Camb. Math. J.	*Cambridge Mathematical Journal* (Cambridge).
Comptes Rendus	*Comptes Rendus Hebdomadaires des Séances de l'Académie des Sciences* (Paris).
DNB	*Dictionary of National Biography*. Ed. L. Stephen and S. Lee, 63 vols. and 2 supplements (6 vols.) (London, 1885–1912).
Electricity	Michael Faraday, *Experimental Researches in Electricity*, 3 vols. (London, 1839–55).
Electrostatics and Magnetism	William Thomson, *Reprint of Papers on Electrostatics and Magnetism* (London, 1872).
Knott, *Life of Tait*	Cargill Gilston Knott, *Life and Scientific Work of Peter Guthrie Tait. Supplementing the two Volumes of Scientific Papers Published in 1898 and 1900* (Cambridge, 1911).
Larmor, *Correspondence*	*Memoir and Scientific Correspondence of the Late Sir George Gabriel Stokes, Bart.* Ed. J. Larmor, 2 vols. (Cambridge, 1907).
Larmor, 'Origins'	'The origins of Clerk Maxwell's electric ideas, as described in familiar letters to W. Thomson'. Communicated by Sir Joseph Larmor, in *Proc. Camb. Phil. Soc.*, **32** (1936): 695–750. Reprinted separately (Cambridge, 1937).
Life of Maxwell	Lewis Campbell and William Garnett, *The Life of James Clerk Maxwell. With a Selection from his Correspondence and Occasional Writings and a Sketch of his Contributions to Science* (London, 1882).
Life of Maxwell (2nd edn)	Lewis Campbell and William Garnett, *The Life of James Clerk Maxwell with Selections from his Correspondence and Occasional Writings*, new edition, abridged and revised (London, 1884).
Math. & Phys. Papers	William Thomson, *Mathematical and Physical Papers*, 6 vols. (Cambridge, 1882–1911).
Molecules and Gases	*Maxwell on Molecules and Gases*. Ed. Elizabeth Garber,

	Stephen G. Brush and C. W. F. Everitt (Cambridge, Massachusetts/London, 1986).
OED	*The Oxford English Dictionary*, 12 vols. (Oxford, 1970).
Papers	George Gabriel Stokes, *Mathematical and Physical Papers*, 5 vols. (Cambridge, 1880–1905).
Phil. Mag.	*Philosophical Magazine* (London).
Phil. Trans.	*Philosophical Transactions of the Royal Society of London* (London).
Proc. Camb. Phil. Soc.	*Proceedings of the Cambridge Philosophical Society* (Cambridge).
Proc. Roy. Soc.	*Proceedings of the Royal Society of London* (London).
Proc. Roy. Soc. Edinb.	*Proceedings of the Royal Society of Edinburgh* (Edinburgh).
Scientific Memoirs	*Scientific Memoirs, Selected from the Transactions of Foreign Academies of Science and Learned Societies, and from Foreign Journals.* Ed. Richard Taylor, 5 vols. (London, 1837–52).
Scientific Papers	*The Scientific Papers of James Clerk Maxwell.* Ed. W. D. Niven, 2 vols. (Cambridge, 1890).
Thomson and Tait, *Natural Philosophy*	Sir William Thomson and Peter Guthrie Tait, *Treatise on Natural Philosophy. Vol. 1* (Oxford, 1867).
Trans. Camb. Phil. Soc.	*Transactions of the Cambridge Philosophical Society* (Cambridge).
Trans. Roy. Soc. Edinb.	*Transactions of the Royal Society of Edinburgh* (Edinburgh).
Treatise	James Clerk Maxwell, *A Treatise on Electricity and Magnetism*, 2 vols. (Oxford, 1873).
ULC	Manuscripts in the University Library, Cambridge.
Venn	*Alumni Cantabrigienses. A Biographical List of all Known Students, Graduates and Holders of Office at the University of Cambridge, from the Earliest Times to 1900.* Compiled by J. A. Venn. Part II. From 1752 to 1900, 6 vols. (Cambridge, 1940–54).
Wiener Berichte	*Sitzungsberichte der Mathematisch-Naturwissenschaftlichen Classe der Kaiserlichen Akademie der Wissenschaften* (Vienna).
Wilson, *Stokes–Kelvin Correspondence*	*The Correspondence between Sir George Gabriel Stokes and Sir William Thomson, Baron Kelvin of Largs.* Edited with an introduction by David B. Wilson, 2 vols. (Cambridge, 1990).

INTRODUCTION

This second volume of James Clerk Maxwell's scientific letters and manuscript papers begins in mid-1862 with his first referee reports for the Royal Society, and concludes in December 1873 shortly before the formal inauguration of the Cavendish Laboratory. In the period encompassed by this volume Maxwell took his place among the élite of Victorian science. Though his sense of duty prompted him to accept university appointments and to shoulder responsibilities within the scientific community, his ultimate commitment was that of a natural philosopher. As Lewis Campbell, his lifelong friend and biographer expressed it, 'with sacred devotion [he] continued in mature life the labours which had been his spontaneous delight in boyhood'.[1]

Two topics dominated his research and writing in this period of his scientific maturity: the electromagnetic field and the electromagnetic theory of light, and statistical molecular physics, on which he wrote the classic works which established his unique status in the history of science. His search for rigorous analytical foundations was balanced by an enduring concern with geometrical representation and analogy; and the simple apparatus of his experiments on colour vision in the 1850s yielded to the precision instruments

---

(1) *Life of Maxwell*: 431. There is a biographical study by C. W. F. Everitt, *James Clerk Maxwell: Physicist and Natural Philosopher* (New York, 1975), based on his article on 'Maxwell' in *Dictionary of Scientific Biography*, ed. C. C. Gillispie, 16 vols. (New York, 1970–80), **9**: 198–230. Several of the documents included in this volume shed light on Maxwell's early interests and career. A letter to J. J. Sylvester (Number 267) is informative about Maxwell's knowledge of the geometrical and optical properties of ovals at the time of his first work in mathematics in 1846–7 (Volume I: 35–62). Information about his candidacy for a fellowship at Trinity College, Cambridge in 1854 and 1855 is given in a letter to Lewis Campbell (Number 251). The significance of the two geometrical problems in the *Camb. & Dubl. Math. J.* in 1853 (Volume I: 230–6) is described in letters to Tait and James Thomson: the problem on the motion of particles in a circle (Number 398) and that on the path of rays of light in a medium of continuously variable index of refraction (Numbers 249, 380 and 421). In 1870 he commented on 'gorgeous entanglements of colour', the chromatic effects of polarised light on doubly refracting crystals (Number 343) which had fascinated him in 1848 (Volume I: 97–100). A brief review of J. D. Forbes' contribution to the theory of colours (Number 431) gives a recollection of his own introduction to the subject by Forbes (see Volume I: 300–3); he continued his experiments on colour vision in the 1860s (Numbers 202, 341, 358, 359 and 360).

fashioned for his measurement of electrical units and experiments on the viscosity of gases.

An important feature of his writings in this period is a concern with the philosophical problems generated by his physics. These include the disjunction between the reversible laws of mechanics and the irreversibility of natural processes; his expression of the essentially statistical nature of the second law of thermodynamics (as illustrated by the 'demon' paradox); and his discussion of problems of atomism, determinism and free will. Maxwell's letters and manuscript drafts afford glimpses of the breadth of scholarship which sustained his reflections on these philosophical issues; and more generally, provide substantive evidence of the process in which the brilliant innovations of scientific youth were transformed into the enduring mature achievement which established his pre-eminence in the 'classical' physics of the nineteenth century.

London scientific society

Maxwell was appointed Professor of Natural Philosophy at King's College, London in July 1860, and he held the post until April 1865. The move to London fostered his induction into the wider scientific community of Victorian Britain. In the 1850s his work had been shaped by the scientific culture of the two universities where he had received his education, Edinburgh and Cambridge. The decision to continue his academic career in London, after his enforced redundancy from Marischal College, Aberdeen and the failure of his quest to succeed James David Forbes at Edinburgh University, was capped by his election as a Fellow of the Royal Society and the award of the Society's Rumford Medal.[2] On his arrival in London in October 1860 he was soon introduced into metropolitan scientific society. In his journal entry of Sunday, 24 March 1861 Thomas Archer Hirst recorded his first acquaintance with Maxwell: '[I was] at an evening party at Dr Carpenters and was introduced to Helmholtz and Maxwell...the latter talkative with a Scotch brogue, he took great interest in my ripples'.[3] The

---

(2) On Maxwell's nomination for and award of the Royal Society's Rumford Medal in 1860, and election as a Fellow of the Royal Society on 2 May 1861, see *Minutes of Council of the Royal Society from December 16th 1858 to December 16th 1869*, **3** (London, 1870): 63, 72 and 85; and *Proc. Roy. Soc.*, **11** (1860–1): 19–21, 193. See Volume I: 647n.

(3) *Natural Knowledge in a Social Context: the Journals of Thomas Archer Hirst FRS*, eds. W. H. Brock and R. M. MacLeod [Mansell microform] (London, 1980): f. 1572 (Sunday, 24 March 1861). On Hirst see Number 369 note (6); the reference is to his paper 'On ripples, and their relation to the velocities of currents', *Phil. Mag.*, ser. 4, **21** (1861): 1–20, 188–98. William Benjamin Carpenter, FRS 1844, was Registrar of the University of London (*DNB*).

following May he delivered his first Friday evening discourse to the Royal Institution 'On the theory of the three primary colours'.[4]

During his early years in London Maxwell was burdened with teaching duties at King's College. The syllabus for his lectures in his first session in 1860 broadly followed the curriculum of his predecessor, Thomas Minchin Goodeve, but with some stronger emphasis on the coverage of fundamental principles. For his elementary course for first-year students he offered lectures on mechanics, the properties of matter and heat, to be supplemented by a more detailed mathematical study of these topics; and the course concluded with some experimental demonstrations and lectures on light. For the lecture course for second- and third-year students, where Goodeve had discussed applied mechanics and astronomy, Maxwell announced an advanced course which was significantly more mathematical in scope; he proposed the study of rigid body dynamics, the motion of an incompressible fluid and its application to electricity and magnetism, of astronomy, and of waves and their application to sound and light. These lectures required Maxwell's attendance at King's College for three mornings a week during term, when he delivered one hour-long lecture to each of these two classes; and there was in addition the requirement to teach a separate course on experimental physics, an evening class which met once a week. In his second session in 1861–62 he abandoned the more mathematical lectures in the elementary class.[5]

This basic pattern of lecturing continued during Maxwell's subsequent sessions at King's College, though there was some modification in the content of the lecture courses. In 1862–63 the evening class was given on the subject of 'Sound, light, and radiant heat'; in 1863–64 on the 'Properties of bodies as affected by pressure and heat'; and in 1864–65 on 'Magnetism and electricity'.[6] In these two final sessions of his teaching at King's College, the demonstrations on optics were removed from the elementary course and included in the curriculum for the advanced class, where the lectures on mathematical physics were abandoned in favour of a more rigorous coverage of the basic topics taught in the elementary course.[7] An important development was the appointment of a lecturer in October 1861; having

---

(4) See Volume I: 675–9.

(5) *The Calendar of King's College, London for 1859–60*: 99–100; *Calendar for 1860–61*: 115–17, 268–70; *Calendar for 1861–62*: 113–15. See also C. Domb, 'James Clerk Maxwell in London 1860–1865', *Notes and Records of the Royal Society of London*, **35** (1980): 67–103.

(6) *The Calendar of King's College, London for 1862–63*: 288–90; *Calendar for 1863–64*: 294–6; *Calendar for 1864–65*: 299–301.

(7) *The Calendar of King's College, London for 1863–64*: 131–3; *Calendar for 1864–65*: 135–8.

noted that the duties of teaching were 'too heavy for one person properly to discharge'[8] the College Council appointed George Robarts Smalley (Numbers 204 and 208). On Smalley's resignation in July 1863 the post was filled by William Grylls Adams, who ultimately succeeded Maxwell as professor in April 1865.[9]

As early as October 1864 Maxwell signalled to William Thomson that it was his intention to resign from King's College, indicating his desire to pursue research unrestricted by academic duties (Number 235); and he declared subsequently that it was for this reason that he had resigned (Number 256). This was no doubt his motive: at the time of his resignation he was planning experiments to determine the ratio of electrical units (Numbers 242 and 243), and was very soon heavily engaged in measuring gas viscosity (Numbers 244, 245 and 246). Nevertheless, a resignation accepted on 10 February 1865 and which was intended to take effect in mid-session is curious, though the College Council minutes record Maxwell's readiness to 'continue his work until the appointment of his successor'.[10] The College Council proceeded to resolve the situation promptly: Adams was appointed to the professorship on 10 March 1865. On 21 March the Council abolished the lectureship, Adams having agreed to carry out all the teaching duties in natural philosophy for a salary enhanced from that advertised for the professorship;[11] the Council minutes record that this arrangement would result in a 'considerable saving' to the College.[12] The circumstances of Maxwell's resignation from King's College and of Adams' rapid succession to his post are not entirely clear.[13]

Maxwell remained in academic retirement until his return to Cambridge in 1871, although he was a candidate in 1868 for appointment as Principal of

---

(8) King's College London Archives, King's College Council Vol. I, minute 42, 11 October 1861.

(9) See Numbers 209 note (2) and 256 esp. note (4).

(10) According to the terms of Maxwell's letter of resignation as recorded in the minutes of the meeting of the King's College Council on 10 February 1865 (King's College London Archives, King's College Council Vol. I, minute 410); see Number 235 note (20). The post was advertised to take effect from 25 April 1865 (King's College London Archives, Special Committees N°. 2, f. 305, 15 February 1865).

(11) King's College London Archives, King's College Council Vol. I, minutes 415, 423.

(12) The advertised salary for the post of Professor of Natural Philosophy was four guineas per student *per annum* (King's College London Archives, Special Committees N°. 2, f. 305, 15 February 1865). Adams' salary as lecturer had been two guineas per student *per annum* (King's College Council Vol. I, minute 373, 18 November 1864). On the abolition of the lectureship he agreed to undertake all the teaching duties in natural philosophy for five guineas per student *per annum*, with the consequence that a 'considerable saving would be effected' (King's College Council Vol. I, minute 423, 21 March 1865).

(13) See also Domb, 'James Clerk Maxwell in London': 92–5, 101–3.

the United Colleges of St Andrews (Numbers 311 to 315). Despite his resignation from King's College, during the 1860s he continued to live in London for some of the winter months. As a Fellow he attended meetings of the Royal Society and acted as a referee on papers submitted for publication in the *Philosophical Transactions*. His most substantial memoirs of the period were published in the Society's *Transactions*: 'A dynamical theory of the electromagnetic field' (Numbers 238 and 239); 'On the viscosity or internal friction of air and other gases', the Bakerian Lecture for 1866 (Number 252); 'On the dynamical theory of gases' (Number 263); and 'On a method of making a direct comparison of electrostatic with electromagnetic force' (Number 289). He read several shorter papers at meetings of the Royal Society; these included papers on the dynamo (Number 268), on governors (Numbers 280, 283 and 297: Appendix), and on Arago's rotating disc (Numbers 400, 404 and 405). In April 1864 he was elected a member of the select Philosophical Club of the Royal Society (Number 226), which had been founded in 1847 to 'promote...the scientific objects of the Royal Society'.[14] His attendance is recorded at eight of the monthly meetings of the Philosophical Club in the years 1864–73; and the minutes record that on 18 December 1873 'Professor Clerk Maxwell exhibited an instrument for applying polarized light to detect the state of strain in a moving viscous fluid', this being the subject of a paper which he read to a meeting of the Royal Society the same day.[15]

In April 1867 Maxwell was elected a member of the newly formed London Mathematical Society,[16] presenting papers (see Numbers 279, 311, 318 and 345) and participating in discussions (Numbers 330 and 331), most notably when he raised questions on the condition for the stability of governors in January 1868 (Number 280) and on the convention regarding spatial relations in May 1871 (Number 370). His involvement in London scientific life was capped by two Friday evening discourses at the Royal Institution: 'On colour vision' in 1871 (Number 360) and 'On action at a distance' in 1873 (Numbers 437 and 438), the easy social relations prevailing on these occasions being recorded by Thomas Archer Hirst.[17] Maxwell was ac-

---

(14) See Number 226 note (2).

(15) T. G. Bonney, *Annals of the Philosophical Club of the Royal Society* (London, 1919): 193; and see Number 259 note (12).

(16) *Proceedings of the London Mathematical Society*, 2 (1867): 26.

(17) *Journals of Thomas Archer Hirst*: f. 1896 (24 March 1871): 'At Spottiswoode's to dinner; present Clerk Maxwell (lectured at Royal Inst.) Tyndall, Odling, Mr and Mrs Birkbeck. After the lecture on Colour Maxwell, Odling and Sir F. Pollock smoked a pipe in Tyndall's rooms.'; and *Journals of Thomas Archer Hirst*: f. 1969 (21 February 1873): 'After the lecture...Sir F. and

quainted with W. R. Grove,[18] a senior figure in London science (Numbers 285 and 313), and in 1869 he was nominated by Grove and Hirst for election to the Athenæum Club.[19] While he was not aloof to Tait's urging[20] to contribute papers to the Royal Society of Edinburgh (Numbers 334 and 395), the London scientific milieu, where he established relations with the astronomer William Huggins (Numbers 271, 309 and 406) and with the chemistry community (Number 270), proved more compelling. He was not however an intimate of the vocal circle of metropolitan scientists which included Hirst, Thomas Henry Huxley and John Tyndall[21] (Numbers 226, 297 and 477). He was hostile to their secularist outlook; and his opposition to the formation of the Physical Society of London (Number 484) suggests his lack of sympathy with their cultivation of the role of the scientific professional.

Standards of electrical resistance

At the 1861 meeting of the British Association for the Advancement of Science Latimer Clark and Sir Charles Bright called for the establishment of a system of units of electrical potential, current and resistance.[22] William Thomson urged the formation of the British Association Committee on standards of electrical resistance; its aim was to determine the most convenient unit of resistance and to discover the most suitable material for the standard unit.[23] Maxwell was co-opted as a member of the Committee in 1862, and in May and June 1863 he joined Fleeming Jenkin and Balfour

---

Lady Pollock... and others collected in Tyndall's rooms'. William Spottiswoode, FRS 1853, was President of the London Mathematical Society and Treasurer of the Royal Society in 1871 (*DNB*).

(18) William Robert Grove, FRS 1840, judge and physical scientist, leading member of the Royal Society Philosophical Club (*DNB*).

(19) *Journals of Thomas Archer Hirst*: f. 1843 (16 March 1869), an unsuccessful proposal; *Journals of Thomas Archer Hirst*: f. 1845 (13 April 1869), Maxwell elected to the Athenæum Club.

(20) Peter Guthrie Tait to Maxwell, 6 and 13 December 1867; see Number 277 notes (2) and (22).

(21) John Tyndall, Professor of Natural Philosophy at the Royal Institution, FRS 1852 (*DNB*). See R. M. MacLeod, 'The x-club: a social network of science in late-Victorian England', *Notes and Records of the Royal Society of London*, **24** (1970): 305–22.

(22) Latimer Clark and Sir Charles Bright, 'On the formation of standards of electrical quantity and resistance', *Report of the Thirty-first Meeting of the British Association for the Advancement of Science* (London, 1862), part 2: 37–8.

(23) 'Provisional report of the Committee appointed by the British Association on standards of electrical resistance', *Report of the Thirty-second Meeting of the British Association for the Advancement of Science* (London, 1863): 125–63. See Crosbie Smith and M. Norton Wise, *Energy and Empire. A Biographical Study of Lord Kelvin* (Cambridge, 1989): 687–94.

Stewart in an accurate measurement of electrical resistance in absolute units, employing a method devised by William Thomson.[24]

These experiments were carried out at King's College, London (Numbers 210 to 216). By 'absolute' units was meant reference to 'fundamental' units of time, mass and space, so that 'all the units form part of a coherent system', and hence avoiding 'useless coefficients in passing from one kind of measurement to another'. The determination of electrical units was based on the 'natural relations existing between the various electrical quantities, and between these and the fundamental units of time, mass and space'. The inspiration for this approach came from the classic experiments of Wilhelm Weber; and the 'natural' relations included Ohm's law and Joule's law of the work performed by a current in a circuit. These relations would yield an 'electrostatic' system of units; but the 'chief applications of electricity are dynamic, depending on electricity in motion, or on voltaic currents with their accompanying electromagnetic effects'. The expression of electrical quantities in 'electromagnetic' units would require the introduction of the effects of electricity in motion, such as the force exerted on the pole of a magnet by a current. Measurement of work and force would have required complex experiments; and Thomson therefore devised a method in which the resistance of a rotating coil was calculated from the measurement of the deflection of a magnet placed at its centre, the resistance of the coil being compared with that of an arbitrary standard.[25]

In working with precision apparatus designed by William Thomson these experiments embodied a distinct advance in experimentation over Maxwell's work on colour vision in the 1850s. The technique which was employed in the electrical experiments – 'studying oscillations of magnets by aid of mirrors' – had important implications, for it suggested, as Maxwell remarked to Stokes in June 1863, 'the determination of gaseous friction by means of a disc oscillating in a gas' using the same method (Number 212). His subsequent

---

(24) 'Report of the Committee appointed by the British Association on standards of electrical resistance', *Report of the Thirty-third Meeting of the British Association for the Advancement of Science* (London, 1864): 111–76; see Number 210 note (2). Balfour Stewart, Edinburgh University 1845, was Director of the Kew Observatory 1859–70 (*DNB*). Fleeming Jenkin (P. G. Tait's class-mate at the Edinburgh Academy, where Maxwell was his senior) was an engineer in partnership with William Thomson (*DNB*); see Smith and Wise, *Energy and Empire*: 698–702, and William Thomson, 'Note on the contributions of Fleeming Jenkin to electrical and engineering science', in *Papers Literary, Scientific, &c by the Late Fleeming Jenkin*, ed. S. Colvin and J. A. Ewing, with a Memoir by Robert Louis Stevenson, 2 vols. (London, 1887), **1**: clv–clix.

(25) 'Report of the Committee appointed by the British Association on standards of electrical resistance', *Report of the Thirty-third Meeting of the British Association*: 111–16.

measurement of the viscosity of gases depended on the application of this experimental arrangement (Number 252).

The centrifugal governor designed by Fleeming Jenkin, which was used to control the speed of the revolving coil in the experiments on electrical standards, also sparked off Maxwell's imagination. He immediately began to investigate the dynamical principles that regulate the operation of governors, reporting his conclusions to Thomson (Numbers 214 and 219). The mathematical method he suggested to establish the conditions for the stability of governors is identical in form to the argument that he had used to determine the conditions of stability of the rings of Saturn in his Adams Prize memoir *On the Stability of the Motion of Saturn's Rings*.[26] He followed this procedure in his 1868 paper 'On governors' (Number 280). This interest in the stability of governors forms a strand in his continuing concern with stability problems, including that of the motion of Saturn's rings (Number 224).

A third important development from the work on electrical standards was a paper written in collaboration with Fleeming Jenkin, 'On the elementary relations of electrical quantities', which was included in the Committee's 'Report' in 1863.[27] Here Maxwell introduced the dimensional notation, which was to become standard, expressing dimensional relations as products of powers of Mass, Length and Time. For every quantity the ratio of the two absolute definitions (of the electrostatic unit based on forces between electric charges and the electromagnetic unit based on forces between magnetic poles) is a power of a constant with dimensions $[LT^{-1}]$ and magnitude very nearly the velocity of light.[28] The argument established a phenomenological link between electromagnetic quantities and the velocity of light, which no doubt fostered the strategy of his Royal Society paper 'A dynamical theory of the electromagnetic field' (Numbers 238 and 239). In this paper he set out a formulation of his 'Electromagnetic Theory of Light'[29] where the theory was detached from the mechanical ether model in which it had been embedded in his paper 'On physical lines of force' (Numbers 232 and 240).

The study of dimensional relations also revealed the different classes of experiments from which the ratio of electrostatic and electromagnetic units of electricity, and hence the velocity of propagation of electromagnetic waves,

---

(26) See Number 219 note (17); and O. Mayr, 'Maxwell and the origins of cybernetics', *Isis*, **62** (1971): 425–44, esp. 428–9.

(27) See Number 218 note (3).

(28) See the *Treatise*, **2**: 239–43 (§§620–7); and Everitt, *James Clerk Maxwell*: 100–1.

(29) An expression first used in 'A dynamical theory of the electromagnetic field'; see Number 238 and *Scientific Papers*, **1**: 577.

could be obtained (Number 218). His correspondence with William Thomson in the autumn and winter of 1864–65 is filled with discussion of various experiments which could be deployed to determine this ratio (Numbers 233, 234, 235, 241, 242 and 243). This interest culminated in the experiments on the direct comparison of electrostatic and electromagnetic forces which he carried out with Charles Hockin in 1868 (Number 289); these measurements, which formed the capstone to his work as a member of the Committee on electrical standards in the 1860s, established a value for the velocity of propagation of electromagnetic waves, a key element in his theory of the electromagnetic field. Maxwell's work with the Committee on electrical standards was marked by his appointment as President of Section A (mathematics and physics) of the British Association in 1870 (Number 344).

The electromagnetic theory of light and the ether

Maxwell's heady statement in the third part of his paper 'On physical lines of force' in 1862, that '*light consists in the transverse undulations of the same medium which is the cause of electric and magnetic phenomena*',[30] stated the unification of optics and electromagnetism in terms of a mechanical theory of the ether. His concern to explore the implications of an ether which had optical and electromagnetic correlates led him to highlight two critical problems: the effect of motion in the ether, and the explanation of optical reflection and refraction by means of the electromagnetic theory. In the course of writing his paper 'A dynamical theory of the electromagnetic field' (Numbers 238 and 239) in 1864 he considered both of these questions.[31]

In April 1864 he set up an 'Experiment to determine whether the Motion of the Earth influences the Refraction of Light' (Number 227). This investigation was suggested by the experiments of Hippolyte Fizeau on the detection of the ether wind.[32] Maxwell suggested that the Fresnel drag (of the ether) could affect the refraction of light by a glass prism; but in calculating the displacement arising from the drag he ignored the compensating change in the density of the transparent medium. According to Fresnel's theory, the ether and refractive medium satisfy a continuity equation at their boundary; this has the consequence that the retardation due to the medium is not affected by the motion of the earth.[33] Stokes drew

---

(30) *Scientific Papers*, **1**: 500. See Daniel M. Siegel, *Innovation in Maxwell's Electromagnetic Theory: Molecular Vortices, Displacement Current and Light* (Cambridge, 1991): 120–43.
(31) See Everitt, *James Clerk Maxwell*: 114, 118–23.
(32) See Number 227 notes (4) and (7).
(33) See Number 227 note (5).

Maxwell's attention to the error when he submitted his paper to the Royal Society (Number 228). Indeed, in 1846 Stokes had himself considered this problem, and had concluded that the motion of the ether would have no effect on the refraction of light.[34]

Maxwell withdrew the paper in response to Stokes' criticism of its argument, but he gave an account of his experiment in a letter written in 1867 to the astronomer William Huggins (Number 271). Here he reported the result of his aborted 1864 paper, that his experiment had failed to find any effect of the motion of the earth on the refraction of light; but he now pointed out that Stokes had already established this conclusion. Maxwell's subsequent discussion of the problem – notably in a letter to the American astronomer David Peck Todd[35] – led A. A. Michelson in the 1880s to undertake his famous experiments to attempt to detect ether drag.

On writing to Stokes in May 1864 Maxwell remarked that 'I am not inclined and I do not think I am able to do the dynamical theory of reflexion and refraction on different hypotheses' (Number 228), alluding to his paper in preparation on 'A dynamical theory of the electromagnetic field'. But he did make an attempt to derive the laws of optical reflection and refraction from his electromagnetic theory of light; a fragmentary draft (Number 236) records his substitution of electromagnetic analogues for the elastic variables employed in theories of the luminiferous ether. In the event this derivation remained abortive: writing to Stokes in October 1864 (Number 237) he criticised the selectivity of the physical assumptions and boundary conditions which were required, an endemic difficulty of dynamical ether theories. Thus he told Stokes that 'I have written out so much of the theory as does not involve the conditions at bounding surfaces'; and his paper 'A dynamical theory of the electromagnetic field', which he was about to forward to the Royal Society, does not include discussion of optical reflection and refraction.

It might have been anticipated that he would broaden the scope of the electromagnetic theory of light in his *Treatise on Electricity and Magnetism*, to encompass an electromagnetic theory of optical reflection and refraction. But he did not do so, explaining (in February 1879) that 'In my book I did not attempt to discuss reflexion at all. I found that the propagation of

---

(34) See Number 228 note (4). Maxwell subsequently set a Mathematical Tripos question on this problem: see Number 228 note (5).

(35) Maxwell's letter of 19 March 1879 to D. P. Todd (to be reproduced in Volume III) was published posthumously as 'On a possible mode of detecting a motion of the solar system through the luminiferous ether', *Proc. Roy. Soc.*, **30** (1880): 108–10 (= *Nature*, **21** (1880): 314–15); and see Number 271 note (17).

Introduction

light in a magnetized medium was a hard enough subject'.[36] The inherent complexity of the problem, aggravated by his lack of easy familiarity with ether dynamics, led him to restrict the scope of his explication of the electromagnetic theory of light.

Maxwell's limitation of the range of his electromagnetic theory of light as a general theory of optics is paralleled by his apparent failure to consider the question of the production of electromagnetic waves.[37] He conceived the generation of light to be a mechanical rather than an electromagnetic process, a phenomenon of molecular motion in the ether. This was consonant with his interpretation of the Faraday magneto-optic effect in the *Treatise* (Numbers 434, 441 and 468): that the magneto-optic rotation implied the rotation of vortices in the ether. Writing to Thomson in January 1873, shortly before the publication of the *Treatise*, he noted that 'Faradays twist of polarized light will not come out without what the schoolmen call local motion' (Number 434). The relation between optics and electromagnetism was expressed in terms of the molecular connection between ether and matter. This was therefore, as he explained in February 1879, a 'hybrid theory' based on 'the bodily motion of the medium', not a 'purely electromagnetic hypothesis'.[38]

This approach to optics is manifest in several drafts which relate to an examination question he set for the 1869 Cambridge Mathematical Tripos, where he explores the implication for physical optics of the mechanical relation between ether and matter. He supposes that the forces acting on the particles of matter originate in the ether, these particles being assumed to be independent of each other. This would, he noted in a draft in 1868, entail an 'irregularity of refraction' (Number 300). Returning to the subject in 1873, after the public discussion of anomalous dispersion,[39] he concluded that his

---

(36) ULC Add. MSS 7656, M 439, printed in part in Larmor, *Correspondence*, **2**: 40–3 (to be reproduced in Volume III).

(37) See Bruce J. Hunt, *The Maxwellians* (Ithaca/London, 1991): 28–30; and Thomas K. Simpson, 'Maxwell and the direct experimental test of his electromagnetic theory', *Isis*, **57** (1966): 411–32.

(38) See note (36). On Maxwell's theory of molecular vortices and the Faraday effect see Siegel, *Innovation in Maxwell's Electromagnetic Theory*: 29–84, 144–67; and Ole Knudsen, 'The Faraday effect and physical theory, 1845–1873', *Archive for History of Exact Sciences*, **15** (1976): 235–81, esp. 248–61.

(39) See Number 460 note (15); Jed Z. Buchwald, *From Maxwell to Microphysics. Aspects of Electromagnetic Theory in the Last Quarter of the Nineteenth Century* (Chicago/London, 1985): 233–7; and E. T. Whittaker, *A History of the Theories of Aether and Electricity*, 2 vols. (London, 1951–3), **1**: 261–5.

The kinetic theory of gases and molecular physics

In November 1857, while engaged in revising for publication his Adams Prize essay *On the Stability of the Motion of Saturn's Rings*, Maxwell remarked to William Thomson that 'the general case of a fortuitous concourse of atoms each having its own orbit & excentricity is a subject above my powers at present'. He amplified the point in the memoir: 'When we come to deal with collisions among bodies of unknown number, size, and shape, we can no longer trace the mathematical laws of their motion with any distinctness'.[40] Concern with the problem of calculating the trajectories of particles in a complex dynamical system helped to alert his interest in the kinetic theory of gases. On reading a paper on the subject by Rudolf Clausius in 1859 he was led to a study of the collisions of particles as a means of establishing the properties of gases. The statistical method of his theory of gases provided a means of describing the complex pattern of the motion of gas molecules. The problem of stability (of the rings of Saturn) was transformed into a problem of molecular regularity represented by a statistical law. The success of his statistical method in the theory of gases led him in 1864 to a vain attempt to apply the method to compute the collisions of the particles constituting Saturn's rings, so as 'to throw some light on the theory of a confused assemblage of jostling masses whirling round a large central body' (Number 224).

In his paper 'Illustrations of the dynamical theory of gases' Maxwell had advanced on Clausius' use of a statistical argument to calculate the probability of a molecule travelling a given distance (the 'mean free path') without collision. He had introduced a statistical function for the distribution of velocities among the gas molecules.[41] This description of physical processes

---

(40) Maxwell to William Thomson, 14 November 1857 (Volume I: 555); J. Clerk Maxwell, *On the Stability of the Motion of Saturn's Rings* (Cambridge, 1859): 53 (= *Scientific Papers*, **1**: 354). See P. M. Harman, 'Maxwell and Saturn's rings: problems of stability and calculability', in *The Investigation of Difficult Things. Essays on Newton and the History of the Exact Sciences in Honour of D. T. Whiteside*, ed. P. M. Harman and Alan E. Shapiro (Cambridge, 1992): 477–502.

(41) Maxwell's and Clausius' papers are cited in Number 207 notes (5) and (7). On Maxwell's theory of gases see especially the introductory essay by Elizabeth Garber, Stephen G. Brush and C. W. F. Everitt, 'Kinetic theory and the properties of gases: Maxwell's work in its nineteenth-century context', in *Molecules and Gases*: 1–63; Stephen G. Brush, *The Kind of Motion We Call Heat: a History of the Kinetic Theory of Gases in the Nineteenth Century*, 2 vols. (Amsterdam/New York, 1976); and Everitt, *James Clerk Maxwell*: 131–63.

by a statistical function was a major innovation in the science of physics. However his treatment of the conduction of heat in gases was criticised by Clausius, who pointed out that Maxwell had disregarded the additional kinetic energy associated with motion in the direction of the temperature gradient, and had assumed an isotropic distribution function.[42] In attempting to meet Clausius' critique Maxwell introduced a variable path length (depending on the position of a particle between collisions), so as to consider particle collisions where the properties of the gas vary from place to place; but his attempt to draft a paper on these lines (Number 207) proved inconclusive, and was abandoned.

This failure to resolve Clausius' criticisms may have prompted Maxwell to a decision to undertake an investigation of transport phenomena. His experimental study of gas viscosity was suggested by the apparatus used in the determination of the standard of electrical resistance, using magnets to vibrate discs suspended in gases and measuring the oscillations by mirrors attached to the suspension (Number 212). He apparently began some experiments in late 1863;[43] but his correspondence indicates that systematic work, using the apparatus described in his Royal Society paper on gas viscosity (Number 252), was established in spring 1865 (Numbers 240, 242 and 244 to 249). The elastic-sphere model for gas molecules that he had assumed in his paper 'Illustrations of the dynamical theory of gases' implied that viscosity would vary as the square root of the temperature;[44] but he found that the viscosity was a linear function of the absolute temperature (Numbers 249 and 252). The hypothesis that gas molecules could be represented as colliding elastic spheres was therefore in question; and in drafting his paper 'On the dynamical theory of gases' he replaced this model by the concept of considering gas molecules as centres of force subject to a law of repulsion (Number 250).

The experiments on gas viscosity thus initiated a radical reconstruction of Maxwell's kinetic theory of gases. He computed the motions of molecules travelling in complicated trajectories by using the methods of orbital dynamics (Number 259). To describe gas viscosity he abandoned the notion of a 'mean free path' and in its place introduced the concept of the 'time of relaxation' of stresses in the gas.[45] He found that if the force law of repulsion between the molecules was an inverse fifth-power law, the viscosity varied directly with temperature, a result which was in agreement with his experiments and consistent with his definition of viscosity in terms of the

---

(42) See Number 207 notes (9) and (39).
(43) See Number 212 note (11). (44) See Number 246 note (7).
(45) See Number 259 note (12), and Everitt, *James Clerk Maxwell*: 143–4.

relaxation time. This theory was developed in his paper 'On the dynamical theory of gases' (Number 263), where he presented a new derivation of the statistical distribution law, demonstrating that the velocity distribution would maintain a state of equilibrium unchanged by collisions. The equilibrium distribution provided the basis for calculating the properties of gases.

In drafting 'On the dynamical theory of gases' Maxwell considered the question of the equilibrium of temperature in a vertical column of gas under gravity (Number 259). He found that, according to his theory, the temperature of the gas would diminish as the height increased: the condition of final equilibrium would therefore be one of 'mechanical instability', and 'the energy thus developed could be transferred to machinery so as to convert the invisible agitation of the gas into any other form of energy and thus form a perpetual motion'. Maxwell's theory seemed to have the consequence that energy could be abstracted from a gas acted on by gravity while the gas cooled, a result which he found 'directly opposed to the second law of Thermodynamics'. On writing to William Thomson in February 1866 he emphasised the conclusion which he had drawn: 'by means of material agency mechanical effect is derived from the gas under gravity by cooling it below the temperature of the coldest of the surrounding objects' (Number 260), explicitly evoking the language of Thomson's own statement of the second law of thermodynamics.

By the time Maxwell submitted the paper to the Royal Society in May 1866 he had discovered one of the errors in his analysis, a mistake in mathematical reasoning;[46] but this partial correction led to the conclusion that the temperature would increase with the height (Number 263). Thomson reviewed the paper for the Royal Society, but was unable to detect the error that still compromised its argument. However, in December 1866 Maxwell reported to Stokes (the Secretary of the Royal Society) that he had located the error in his statistical reasoning: 'I now make the temperature the same throughout' (Number 266), a revision incorporated in an 'addition' which was appended to the paper prior to its publication in the *Philosophical Transactions*.[47]

Maxwell returned to this subject in 1873 (Numbers 457 and 481) in response to correspondence in the journal *Nature* on his statement in his *Theory of Heat* that gravity had no effect on the temperature of a column of gas. He re-examined the question (Numbers 472 and 473), confirming the conclusion presented in the 'addition' to his paper 'On the dynamical theory

---

(46) See Number 259 note (33).   (47) See Number 266 note (8).

of gases'. He reformulated the presentation of the statistical foundations of his theory of gases, employing a method derived from a paper by Ludwig Boltzmann on the general Maxwell–Boltzmann distribution law for complex molecules in the presence of an external field of force (Number 474).[48]

Maxwell's kinetic theory of gases, which provided an explanation of the transport properties of gases, had other important implications for molecular physics. One of its consequences was his derivation of 'Avogadro's hypothesis' (Number 259).[49] In a discussion following Benjamin Collins Brodie's presentation of his symbolic calculus of chemical operations at a meeting of the Chemical Society in June 1867, Maxwell emphasised that the derivation of Avogadro's hypothesis from the kinetic theory of gases provided important support for the molecular theory of matter (Number 270). His concern with understanding the nature of matter led also to an interest in molecular forces. This is apparent in his construction of apparatus to measure the surface tension of liquids, a study of the physics of capillary action (Numbers 292 and 293).

In 1873 he made a further advance in the application of the kinetic theory of gases to molecular physics. He developed Loschmidt's attempt to gain an estimate of molecular diameters from a study of the diffusion of gases, and obtained values which were in agreement with calculations based on viscosity (Numbers 469, 470 and 471). He gave a broad summary of his work on gases, on molecular physics and his method of statistical representation, in a lecture on 'Molecules' delivered to the meeting of the British Association for the Advancement of Science in September 1873 (Number 478). His application of mathematical methods to the study of gases had led him to a major innovation in mathematical physics, and to important results in molecular science. The lecture on 'Molecules' provided a suitable capstone to this work, which established Maxwell's international reputation in the 1860s.

Maxwell's text on the *Theory of Heat* was an outgrowth from his work on the theory of gases. The circumstances under which he undertook the commission from Longmans are not clear, and its writing led to an intermission in his work on the *Treatise on Electricity and Magnetism*. His letters written in late 1869 (Numbers 332 and 333) show that this work was well advanced at that time, but was apparently only resumed in the following autumn (Number 346). It seems that he wrote the *Theory of Heat* in 1870: in a letter to Thomson in April

---

(48) See Number 472 note (12). See also Stephen G. Brush, 'Foundations of statistical mechanics, 1845–1915', *Archive for History of Exact Sciences*, **4** (1967): 145–83 (= Brush, *The Kind of Motion We Call Heat*, **2**: 335–85).

(49) See Number 259 notes (13) and (14).

1870 concerned with the conduction of heat he states that 'I am boiling all this down for my chapter on Conduction' (Number 339). It is in this letter that he first signed himself *dp/dt*, his thermodynamic signature.[50]

The origins of his interest in writing a text on heat may perhaps lie in his friend Peter Guthrie Tait's request in December 1867 that he read draft chapters of Tait's *Sketch of Thermodynamics*. His immediate response (Number 277) and the course of reviewing Tait's work (Numbers 278 and 284) may have helped to foster a more general interest in thermodynamics, apparent in his letters of April 1868 to Mark Pattison (Numbers 286 and 287). Tait's partialities did however have an adverse effect on the argument of the *Theory of Heat*, leading Maxwell to become confused about the significance of Clausius' contributions to thermodynamics, notably over the meaning of 'entropy'.[51] The concepts that Clausius had introduced to explicate his thermodynamic theory – entropy, disgregation, ergal and virial – were for Maxwell the butt of jocular barbs (Numbers 356, 402 and 403). But as he finally came to realise (Number 483), his confusion over the meaning of 'entropy' had disfigured the text of his book.

By April 1871 Maxwell was beginning to correct the proofs of the *Theory of Heat*. On writing to Tait in April and May 1871 (Numbers 366, 367, 372, 373 and 374) he mentioned points which arose during his proof-reading of the early chapters of the book; this also prompted a letter to C. W. Siemens on thermo-electricity (Number 378). Two letters to James Thomson (Numbers 381 and 382), bearing on the account in the *Theory of Heat* of Thomas Andrews' work on the continuity of the liquid and gaseous states, raised questions that Maxwell was anxious to resolve during the correction of proofs. He was concerned to establish the conditions determining the pressure at which gas and liquid can coexist at equilibrium. The problems about molecular forces raised by Andrews' and Thomson's work on the continuity of the gas–liquid transition were central to Maxwell's endeavour to understand the phenomena of molecular physics.

The paradoxes of dynamics and thermodynamics

Maxwell's initial discussion in early 1866 of the equilibrium of temperature in a column of gas had led him to a 'paradox': 'a collision between Dynamics & thermodynamics' (Number 260). He confessed in 1873 that until he had

---

(50) See Number 339 note (17).

(51) See Number 483 notes (19) to (22); Martin J. Klein, 'Gibbs on Clausius', *Historical Studies in the Physical Sciences*, **1** (1969): 127–49; and Edward E. Daub, 'Entropy and dissipation', *ibid.*, **2** (1970): 321–54.

resolved it, the problem 'nearly upset my belief in calculation' (Number 457). The paradox highlighted the issue of the relation between Maxwell's statistical theory of molecular motions and the second law of thermodynamics. This law had been first stated by Clausius and Thomson in the early 1850s, and its interpretation – as a law denoting the tendency of heat to pass from warmer to colder bodies – was still under debate.

It is likely that reflection on the problem of the equilibrium of temperature in a column of gas led Maxwell to consider the bearing of his statistical theory of the distribution of velocities among gas molecules on the interpretation of the second law of thermodynamics. It was in immediate response to Tait's request to read draft chapters of his *Sketch of Thermodynamics* that Maxwell first formulated the famous 'demon' paradox in December 1867 (Number 277).[52] The purpose of Maxwell's 'finite being' was to 'pick a hole' in the second law of thermodynamics, by exposing the problem of explaining the irreversible flow of heat from warmer to colder bodies in terms of the statistical regularities that describe the motion of gas molecules. As he later explained to Tait, his purpose was 'To show that the 2nd law of Thermodynamics has only a statistical certainty'.[53] Because of the statistical distribution of molecular velocities in a gas at equilibrium there will be spontaneous fluctuations of individual molecules, fluctuations that take heat from a cold body to a hotter one. While it would require the action of the 'finite being' to select individual molecules and produce an observable flow of heat from a cold body to a hotter one, this process occurs spontaneously at the molecular level. If it were possible to manipulate the molecules individually then the second law of thermodynamics could be violated; this law is therefore a statistical law which applies to systems of molecules, not to the fluctuations of individual molecules.

---

(52) The term 'demon' was apparently first used by William Thomson. But see William Thomson, 'The kinetic theory of the dissipation of energy', *Nature*, **9** (1874): 441–4, on 442n (= *Math. & Phys. Papers*, **5**: 12n), where he defines 'a "demon"', according to the use of this word by Maxwell'. The term 'demon' did not receive Maxwell's approbation. In his letter of 6 December 1870 to J. W. Strutt (Number 350, and see note (55) below) he described his 'finite being' as a 'self-acting' device; and in an undated note to P. G. Tait headed 'Concerning Demons' (ULC Add. MSS 7655, V, i/11a, to be published in Volume III; the MS is printed in part in Knott, *Life of Tait*: 214–15) he declared: 'Call him no more a demon but a valve', observing: 'Who gave them this name? Thomson', unequivocally ascribing the term 'demon' to Thomson.

(53) In the MS 'Concerning Demons': see note (52). For analysis see Martin J. Klein, 'Maxwell, his demon, and the second law of thermodynamics', *American Scientist*, **58** (1970): 84–97; and also Stephen G. Brush, 'The development of the kinetic theory of gases. VIII. Randomness and irreversibility', *Archive for History of Exact Sciences*, **12** (1974): 1–88 (= Brush, *The Kind of Motion We Call Heat*, **2**: 543–654).

Maxwell subsequently amplified his argument to highlight the disjunction between the laws of dynamics and the second law of thermodynamics. In a letter to William Thomson in 1857[54] he had first considered the dynamical implications of time-reversal on the motion of particles; writing to Mark Pattison in April 1868 he brought together his discussion of the perfect reversibility of particle motions with his understanding of the essential irreversibility of natural processes. Dynamical laws allow that everything could 'happen backwards', he told Pattison, but 'our experience of irreversible processes...leads to the doctrine of a beginning & an end instead of cyclical progression for ever' (Number 286). He illustrates irreversible processes by the jumbling together of black and white balls in a box, where 'the operation of mixing is irreversible' (Number 287).

He conjoined his arguments on the perfect reversibility of the laws of dynamics, the irreversibility of natural processes, and the statistical interpretation of the second law of thermodynamics, in a letter to John William Strutt (later Lord Rayleigh)[55] in December 1870. He argued that the perfect reversibility allowed for by the laws of mechanics is constrained by the irreversibility of natural processes. The 'finite being' – now described as a 'mere guiding agent', a 'self-acting' device which could select molecules – was introduced to illustrate his statistical interpretation of irreversible processes as described by the second law of thermodynamics, which 'has the same degree of truth as the statement that if you throw a tumblerful of water into the sea you cannot get the same tumblerful of water out again' (Number 350).

Maxwell's insistence on the disjunction between the laws of mechanics and the second law of thermodynamics led him to be severely critical of attempts, notably by Boltzmann and Clausius, to reduce the second law of thermodynamics to a theorem in dynamics. The second law of thermodynamics was a fundamentally statistical law; to attempt to give it a purely mechanical interpretation, he joked to Tait in December 1873, was in the realm of 'cloud-cuckoo-land' where the 'German Icari flap their waxen wings', doomed to catastrophic disappointment in the pursuit of an illusion (Number 483).[56]

Maxwell's contrast between the reversible laws of mechanics and the

---

(54) Maxwell to William Thomson, 24 November 1857 (Volume I: 561–2).

(55) John William Strutt, Trinity 1861, senior wrangler 1865, third Baron Rayleigh 1873 (*DNB*).

(56) See Klein, 'Maxwell, his demon, and the second law of thermodynamics'; and Günter Bierhalter, 'Von L. Boltzmann bis J. J. Thomson: die Versuche einer mechanischen Grundlegung der Thermodynamik (1866–1890)', *Archive for History of Exact Sciences*, **44** (1992): 25–75, esp. 28–48.

Introduction

irreversibility of natural processes bore on the problems of materialism and determinism that exercised his circle in this period.[57] As he explained to Mark Pattison, a 'strict materialist believes that everything depends on the motion of matter'; and while the perfect reversibility of particle motions was consistent with the doctrine of materialism, 'in the present dispensation there remain a number of irreversible processes' (Number 286). The second law of thermodynamics, an irreducibly statistical law, was inconsistent with the supposition of a wholly mechanical universe.

In his lecture on 'Molecules' to the British Association in 1873 (Number 478) he appealed to Lucretius 'who attempted to burst the bounds of Fate by making his atoms deviate from their courses at quite uncertain times and places, thus attributing to them a kind of irrational free will'.[58] At the time of writing 'On the dynamical theory of gases' in February 1866 he had sought to clarify the meaning of Lucretius' atomism, making specific allusion to the swerve of the atoms (Number 257); and he quoted the passage in *De Rerum Natura* on the swerve of atoms and free will in his memorandum written for William Thomson in 1871 on the history of the 'kinetic theory of gases' (Number 377).[59] This theme is explored in some detail in his 1873 essay on 'the progress of Physical Science... and the Freedom of the Will' (Number 439). Here he argued that the universe was fundamentally causal yet not deterministic, citing the swerve of Lucretian atoms in illustration of the instability of a dynamical system at 'singular points'. Such instabilities were not uncaused but were incalculable; there were therefore limits to the perfect predictability of the Laplacian deterministic universe, which contrasted with 'a world like this, in which the same antecedents never again concur, and nothing ever happens twice'.[60]

His critique of materialism included scrutiny of the concept of matter. He explained to Pattison in April 1868 that he found it unacceptable to define matter as 'that which is perceived by the senses' or to conceive inertia as 'metaphysical passivity' (Number 287). These definitions, intended to provide foundations for the science of dynamics, had been stated by Thomson and Tait in their recently published *Treatise on Natural Philosophy*. Provoked

---

(57) See Theodore M. Porter, *The Rise of Statistical Thinking 1820–1900* (Princeton, 1986): 194–208; and Smith and Wise, *Energy and Empire*: 621–33.

(58) *Scientific Papers*, **2**: 373; and see Number 439 note (19).

(59) See Numbers 257 esp. note (10) and 377 esp. note (5).

(60) In a letter to Francis Galton of 26 February 1879 (to be reproduced in Volume III) he refers to the 'bifurcation of path' of a mechanical system at a point of singularity, referring to Joseph Boussinesq, *Conciliation du Véritable Déterminisme Mécanique avec l'Existence de la Vie et de la Liberté Morale* (Paris, 1878), where the phrase 'lieux de bifurcation' is used (on p. 50). See Harman, 'Maxwell and Saturn's rings: problems of stability and calculability': 496–501.

by their discussion (Number 294: Appendix), he cited a passage from Torricelli's *Lezioni Accademiche* in support of his contention that, in physics, matter should be defined in relation to energy and momentum; the concept of a material substratum endowed with inertia did not provide the basis for the science of dynamics.[61] In the *Treatise* he refers to the 'fundamental dynamical idea of matter', which he defines as being 'capable by its motion of becoming the recipient of momentum and of energy'.[62] He maintained that speculations about matter as a passive entity defining substances belonged to metaphysics rather than to the science of dynamics (Numbers 287 and 437: Appendix). Maxwell thus aimed to establish the conceptual basis of his dynamical theory of the electromagnetic field, and to refute the claim that the doctrines of materialism were sanctioned by the science of physics.

Maxwell endeavoured to present his physics in terms which evoked continuity with classical debates in the philosophy of science. An important example of this style of argument, where he sought to give his ideas the pedigree of historical tradition, is in his presentation of the theory of the electromagnetic field. In a lecture in early 1873 (Number 437) he stressed that the theory had as its aim the resolution of the enigma in Newton's natural philosophy, the problem of action at a distance. He had indeed sought to broaden his field theory to embrace the explanation of gravity, but without success (Numbers 238 and 287). The analogy of the tails of comets led him to envision lines of gravitational force spreading through space (Numbers 217 and 309), a representation of gravity that he had suggested to Michael Faraday in 1857;[63] but the imagery, though powerful, merely remained suggestive.

Geometry, mechanics and optics: the principle of duality

As a boy, Maxwell's scientific imagination had been aroused by geometry, leading to his first mathematical papers on the description of ovals and on the theory of rolling curves. The study of geometrical problems remained a

---

(61) On Torricelli see Numbers 287, esp. note (12); 294: Appendix, esp. note (29); and 437: Appendix, esp. note (48). On inertia, the definition of matter and Thomson and Tait's *Natural Philosophy*, see Numbers 287, esp. note (10); 294: Appendix, esp. notes (27) and (31); and 437: Appendix, esp. note (47).

(62) *Treatise*, **2**: 181 (§550). See P. M. Harman, *Metaphysics and Natural Philosophy. The Problem of Substance in Classical Physics* (Brighton, 1982): 127–50; Harman, 'Newton to Maxwell: the *Principia* and British physics', *Notes and Records of the Royal Society of London*, **42** (1988): 75–96, esp. 88–92.

(63) Maxwell to Michael Faraday, 9 November 1857 (Volume I: 550–1).

lifelong concern (Numbers 320, 407 and 409), and included an abiding interest in understanding the mathematical properties of Cartesian ovals (Number 267). In the 1850s the analogy between the geometry of lines and surfaces and the imagery of Faraday's lines of force had shaped the geometrical expression of his field theory in his paper 'On Faraday's lines of force'. The commitment to geometrical representation was incorporated into his *Treatise on Electricity and Magnetism*, where topological ideas form an important element in the work's mathematical style.

Geometrical analogy continued to play a significant role in shaping his physics, especially in the application of contemporary methods of projective geometry. He first used these ideas in applying graphical analysis to the theory of frameworks; this theory formed an important element of his work in this period. He lectured on the theory of engineering structures to his class at King's College, London (Number 203), leading to a paper 'On reciprocal figures and diagrams of forces';[64] and he subsequently extended this theory of reciprocal diagrams in statics (Numbers 273 and 334). This work drew on projective geometry (termed the 'geometry of position' or 'modern geometry'),[65] especially the concept of geometrical correspondence between reciprocal figures. This method, as he explained in applying it to geometrical optics, was based on the 'principle of duality...the leading idea of modern geometry' (Number 480). He conceived this to be a general geometrical method, and by the process that he later termed the 'cross-fertilization of the sciences',[66] he applied the principle of reciprocity to the study of electrical potential (Number 274); to the depiction of the velocities of molecules in a gas by means of Hamilton's geometrical representation of the paths of particles, the hodograph (Number 472);[67] and to geometrical optics, where the 'object and image were homographic figures' (Number 480).[68]

Maxwell had been interested in optical instruments and geometrical optics

---

(64) See Number 203 note (4). See T. M. Charlton, *A History of the Theory of Structures in the Nineteenth Century* (Cambridge, 1982): 58–66; and Erhard Scholz, *Symmetrie, Gruppe, Dualität. Zur Beziehung zwischen theoretischer Mathematik und Anwendungen in Kristallographie und Baustatik des 19. Jahrhunderts* (Basel/Boston/Berlin, 1989): 181–201.

(65) For Maxwell's use of these terms see Numbers 472 §1, 480 and 482. The term 'geometry of position' was also applied to topology: see Number 373, and note (82).

(66) *Scientific Papers*, **1**: 744.

(67) On the hodograph see Number 472 note (6); and Thomas L. Hankins, *Sir William Rowan Hamilton* (Baltimore/London, 1980): 327–33.

(68) See Number 273 note (2); and also Lorraine J. Daston, 'The physicalist tradition in early nineteenth-century French geometry', *Studies in History and Philosophy of Science*, **17** (1986): 269–95; and Joan L. Richards, 'Projective geometry and mathematical progress in mid-Victorian Britain', *ibid.*: 297–325.

in the 1850s, when he had expounded a theory of optical instruments in terms of geometrical relations divorced from consideration of the dioptrical properties of lenses. In 1867 he constructed a real image stereoscope (Number 272), which he used to project stereograms of surfaces (Numbers 274, 275, 277 and 279); and the following year he developed the popular zoetrope or 'wheel of life', which he used to illustrate Helmholtz's vortex rings and motion in a fluid (Numbers 306, 307 and 310). His application of the principle of duality to geometrical optics enlarged on his earlier work, enabling him to present the subject within a general mathematical framework, as he announced to the meeting of the British Association for the Advancement of Science in September 1873 (Number 480). As he subsequently explained to Lord Rayleigh, 'I am getting more light on Geometrical Optics', having grasped that the 'geometry of the subject is the geometry of position' (Number 482). The principle of duality served as a method of geometrical analogy, linking the graphical analysis of frames, geometrical optics, electrical circuits, and the kinetic theory of gases.

Reports for the Royal Society

Following his election as a Fellow of the Royal Society in 1861 Maxwell began to be asked to referee papers submitted for publication in the *Philosophical Transactions*. By the 1860s the Royal Society had regularised the process of reviewing papers.[69] Many of the papers read at meetings of the Society were submitted for publication in the *Transactions*. One of the Secretaries of the Society (in 1862, William Sharpey and George Gabriel Stokes, Sharpey being succeeded by Thomas Henry Huxley in 1872) would secure reports by (generally) two Fellows judged to have appropriate expertise. These reports were then considered by the Committee of Papers. If the paper was accepted, publication in the *Transactions* would follow; if rejected, its manuscript would be preserved in the archives of the Society. Abstracts of the papers read at meetings were printed in the Society's *Proceedings* (where short papers were also included), but publication in the *Transactions* was subject to the reviewing process.[70]

---

(69) Marie Boas Hall, *All Scientists Now. The Royal Society in the Nineteenth Century* (Cambridge, 1984): 68.

(70) The MSS of papers accepted for publication in the *Phil. Trans.* were sometimes, for years up to 1865, preserved in the archives of the Royal Society: see Numbers 200 note (7), 206 note (5), 212 note (6), 223 notes (9) and (15), and 239. An example of the form letter issued by the Secretaries of the Royal Society to invite a report from a referee is reproduced in Wilson, *Stokes–Kelvin Correspondence*, **1**: 323–4, this example being the paper 'On the viscosity of gases by Mr J. C. Maxwell'; for Thomson's report on Maxwell's paper see Number 252 note (3).

Maxwell's referee reports cover a wide range of subjects: optics, mechanics, hydrodynamics, elasticity, thermodynamics, gas theory, electricity, magnetism, electro-physiology, and visual perception. This breadth of coverage no doubt demonstrates Stokes' opinion of his competence and critical acuity over the entire range of physics. These reports are generally substantive essays offering significant commentary on the papers reviewed. The reports are informative about Maxwell's grasp of the topics reviewed; and in many cases the request to referee papers elicited his comments on problems not discussed elsewhere in his writings. He consistently maintained a commitment to the intellectual value of the refereeing process, to standards of rigorous and informative comment. Even when his conclusions are wholly negative, for example in his severely critical report on Robert Moon's theory of elastic impact (Number 291), his comments are substantive and suggestive, not briefly dismissive. When a paper strikes him as in some way confused, for example Frederick Guthrie on the electrical properties of hot bodies (Number 442) and Henry Moseley on glacier motion (Number 319), his comments are nevertheless informative, clearly intended to be helpful to the author.

On some occasions, as in his reviews of Des Cloiseaux on the optical properties of crystals (Number 290) and Bland Radcliffe on animal electricity (Number 342), he mentions his lack of specialised knowledge of these fields of research. The boundaries of his expertise are interesting in their own right. Thus his report on Samuel Haughton's paper on the reflection of polarised light (Number 199) clearly indicates his lack of familiarity with the intricacies of the wave theory of light (Number 200), a limitation that is also apparent in his attempt to discuss the motion of the earth through the ether (Numbers 227 and 228) and to elaborate an electromagnetic theory of optical reflection and refraction (Numbers 236 and 237). Several of the reports bear on topics that had been of major interest to him earlier in his career: on Jago on vision (Number 447), Everett's experiments on elasticity (Numbers 261, 269 and 282), Airy on the theory of elasticity (Numbers 205, 206 and 212), and Ferrers on the theory of rotating bodies (Number 325). His reports on these papers provided him with an arena for the expression of his current outlook on problems on which he would not otherwise have written so substantively, and his comments are often informative about his early work on these topics.

Many of the reports are on fields of research which connected more directly with his current interests and writing: on Chambers on the sun's magnetism (Number 220), Rankine on potential theory and hydrodynamics (Numbers 223 and 337) and on the thermodynamics of waves (Number 338), Airy on magnetism (Numbers 410 and 453), Latimer Clark on a standard of electromotive force (Numbers 415 and 462; and see Numbers 416, 418 and 420), M'Kichan on the ratio of electrical units (Number 455), Strutt

(Rayleigh) on potential theory and acoustics (Numbers 354 and 355), Stokes on wave propagation in a gas (Number 298) and Graham on the absorption of gases (Number 264). These reports provide insight into the development and scope of his physics, supplementing his letters and manuscript drafts.

There are several reports on papers concerned with experimental topics that have a less immediate relevance to Maxwell's own current work: on papers by Stokes, Robinson and Miller on spectra (Numbers 197, 198, 199 and 201), and by Tyndall on radiant heat (Numbers 255 and 258). Here his discussion reveals his grasp of the contemporary literature and his understanding of broader developments in physical science. His report on papers by Bashforth, Longridge and Merrifield on the motion of projectiles (Number 288) demonstrates his command over a traditional problem in dynamics; while his review of Tarn's paper on the stability of domes (Number 265) illustrates his knowledge of the subject of vaulted structures and elastic systems, an interest which forms a strand of his work in this period (Numbers 221 and 392).[71] On occasion the task of reviewing papers may have directly stimulated his own research, as in his development (Number 334) of Airy's function of stress, a concept that he had encountered and discussed in the course of writing a report (Number 205).

The *Treatise on Electricity and Magnetism*

Maxwell's correspondence with Tait, late in 1867, provides the first indication of his intention to write a treatise on electricity and magnetism.[72] In a letter to William Thomson in February 1868 (Number 281) he emphasised from the outset the mathematical style of his work, specifically mentioning potential theory (Green's theorem and spherical harmonic analysis). It is likely that the project was suggested by the publication of Thomson and Tait's *Treatise on Natural Philosophy* in 1867. Late that year he stated an interest in the application of potential theory to electrostatics (Number 274), and in spherical harmonics and in the symbolism appropriate to the representation of the Laplacian operator (Number 277); and it may be surmised that he had commenced work on the *Treatise* at this time.

His correspondence with William Thomson and Peter Guthrie Tait in the period 1868–71 enables his progress in writing the *Treatise* to be charted. The

---

(71) See Charlton, *History of the Theory of Structures*: 77–81; and Edoardo Benvenuto, *An Introduction to the History of Structural Mechanics*, 2 vols. (New York/Berlin/Heidelberg/London, 1991), **2**: 499–507.

(72) P. G. Tait to Maxwell, 27 November 1867 (Number 276 note (2)) and 6 December 1867 (Number 277 note (2)).

topics discussed in these letters (and from 1871 postcards, taking advantage of the new halfpenny postage) reflect Maxwell's perception of his correspondents' interests and special competence. The letters to Thomson in 1868–69 are dense with discussion of electrostatics and magnetism; while the correspondence with Tait (especially after November 1870) focuses especially on mathematical methods. While only a few of Thomson's letters to Maxwell are extant, the Maxwell–Tait correspondence is much more complete, and the nature of their relationship can be readily gauged. For Tait, Maxwell served as an inexhaustible fount of knowledge and critical insight across the range of physics; while Maxwell drew upon Tait's expertise in spherical harmonics and quaternions, mathematics that he sought to apply in the *Treatise*.

Maxwell's relationship with Thomson at this time was more complex. Thomson was currently engaged in preparing his *Reprint of Papers on Electrostatics and Magnetism*. One problem which he was re-working for the volume, on the distribution of electricity on the surface of a spherical bowl – 'the most remarkable problem of electrostatics hitherto solved', as Maxwell later acclaimed it[73] – is discussed in some detail (Numbers 310, 326 and 327); and the tone of Maxwell's letters makes abundantly clear his respect for Thomson's mastery of the mathematical theory of electrostatics. But Maxwell's general limitation of his correspondence with Thomson to these topics suggests his perception of the likely boundary of Thomson's interests and expertise. Correspondence between Tait, Thomson and Maxwell in July 1868 is suggestive of Thomson's view of Maxwell's conceptual acumen and command of mathematical physics. Thomson wrote to Tait puzzling over problems in the theory of vortex motion,[74] and suggested that Tait forward his letter to Maxwell in the hope that Maxwell might be able to shed light on the problems with which he was grappling unavailingly. Maxwell responded with an extraordinarily rich analysis (Number 295), expounding the mathematical analogy between vortex motion in a fluid and electromagnetism. Thomson apparently felt an element of competition with Maxwell at this time, describing one instance of their separate endeavours, on the axis of a magnet (Number 383), as a 'race'.[75]

Maxwell did on occasion communicate to Thomson his ideas on some of the deeper issues lying at the foundations of his theory of the electromagnetic field. A crucial feature of Maxwell's field theory, which differentiates the

---

(73) *Scientific Papers*, **2**: 303 (in his review of *Electrostatics and Magnetism*); see Number 310 note (2).

(74) William Thomson to P. G. Tait, 5 July 1868 (Number 295 note (2)).

(75) William Thomson to P. G. Tait, 21 August 1871 (Number 383 note (1)).

theory from continental electrodynamics (based on the motion of point charges), is his concept of charge as the manifestation of the electromagnetic field. The final enunciation of this theory in the *Treatise*[76] was the product of considerable conceptual development and clarification during the 1860s;[77] his conceptualisation of the field theory of electric charge (in a form preliminary to that expounded in the *Treatise*) is described in a letter to Thomson in June 1869 (Number 322). This theory of electric charge is based on the concept of a 'displacement of electricity' leading to the manifestation of charge; on the analogy between electricity and the flow of an incompressible fluid; and on electromotive force as the cause of the polarisation of dielectrics.

Maxwell described the oddities of Carl Neumann's theory of the 'transmission of Potentials' in a letter to Thomson in October 1869 (Number 327). But it was for Tait that he drew pointed contrast between his own theory of the electromagnetic field and the various versions of action at a distance electrodynamics proposed by German physicists: on Riemann (Number 284) and on Helmholtz's critique of Weber (Number 389). In the *Treatise* he presented his theory of the electromagnetic field as fulfilling the programme bequeathed to Wilhelm Weber by Carl Friedrich Gauss: to form a 'consistent representation' (Maxwell's translation of Gauss' *construirbare Vorstellung*) of the propagation of electrodynamic forces, which were 'not instantaneous, but propagated in time, in a similar manner to that of light'.[78]

Maxwell seems to have written the *Treatise* in the sequence of the four-part structure of its published text. His letters to Tait and Thomson in July 1868 give evidence of work on spherical harmonics (Numbers 293, 294 and 295) which was basic to his application of potential theory in Part I of the text, on 'Electrostatics'. In letters to Thomson in September and October 1868 he discussed the theory of electrostatic instruments and problems in potential theory (Numbers 302, 303, 306, 310 and 311). By May 1869 he reported to Thomson that he was completing this first part of the text, and described his use of Thomson's method of electric images in explaining the distribution of electricity on the surfaces of intersecting spheres (Number 321). The

---

(76) See Number 322 note (8); and Buchwald, *From Maxwell to Microphysics*: 20–40.

(77) Siegel, *Innovation in Maxwell's Electromagnetic Theory*: 85–119; Joan Bromberg, 'Maxwell's electrostatics', *American Journal of Physics*, **36** (1968): 142–51.

(78) *Treatise*, **2**: 435 (§861), translating Gauss' letter to Weber of 19 March 1845 in *Carl Friedrich Gauss Werke*, **5** (Göttingen, 1867): 627–9, on 629; see P. M. Heimann, 'Maxwell and the modes of consistent representation', *Archive for History of Exact Sciences*, **6** (1970): 171–213.

expression of the potential of an electrified grating was discussed in letters to Stokes and Thomson in the summer of 1869 (Numbers 323, 324 and 326); and in May 1870 he gave John William Strutt an account of his treatment of the potential between parallel electrified plates (Number 340), both these problems arising in the theory of electrostatic instruments.

The work of writing Part II of the *Treatise*, on 'Electrokinematics', had also progressed. He described his chapter on electric conduction to Thomson in August 1868 (Number 301), and a year later this part of the text was also nearing completion (Numbers 322 and 326). By October 1869 he was able to report on his work in writing Part III, on 'Magnetism' (Number 327); a month later he was raising points in the theory of electromagnetism (Numbers 330 and 332). This rapid progress in writing is confirmed in a letter to Tait in December 1869, where he states that he was 'at the 4th of the 4 parts of my book namely Electrodynamics' (Number 333). The few extant preliminary drafts of this part of the *Treatise* (Number 335) were probably written at this time, as was an outline of the contents of the book (Number 329), which lists the chapters of its first three parts in detail, and terminates with the introductory chapters of Part IV, on 'Electromagnetism'.

It would seem likely that, by the time he abandoned work on the *Treatise* to write the *Theory of Heat* sometime early in 1870, he had progressed further in drafting the fourth part of the book. His later correspondence and publications establish that sections of its text, including his treatment of the mutual induction between coils (Numbers 395 and 396) and of Arago's rotating disc (Numbers 400, 404 and 405), were first written subsequent to his resumption of work on the *Treatise* in late 1870. But this correspondence does not suggest that he was then engaged in writing the substantive part of his account of 'Electromagnetism'. In his letters to Tait in November 1870 (Numbers 346 and 348), which signal his resumption of work on the *Treatise*, he declares his intention to introduce quaternions into his exposition of electromagnetic theory (Number 347). Judging by his subsequent correspondence with Tait, his major concern was with the revision and amplification of the mathematical argument of the book.

A key feature of the *Treatise* is the style of mathematical physics that pervades it, a style that emphasises the mathematical expression of physical quantities freed from their direct representation by a mechanical model. While this method preserved the Lagrangian analytical mechanics of his paper 'A dynamical theory of the electromagnetic field' (Number 238) rather than the physical mechanics of 'On physical lines of force', he did not adopt the algebraic form of Lagrange's *Mécanique Analytique* but emphasised the physical interpretation of the symbols of the Lagrangian calculus. The mathematical style of the *Treatise* also incorporates the physical geometry of his paper 'On Faraday's lines of force', where he had grounded his theory of lines of force on the geometrical analogy of lines of flow of an incompressible fluid. The analytical and geometrical style of the *Treatise* draws together and enlarges upon his own earlier methods, and embraces four fundamental mathematical ideas: quaternions (vector concepts), integral theorems, topology, and the Lagrange–Hamilton method of analytical dynamics.[79]

Topological arguments and integral theorems provided more rigorous expression for his representation of the electromagnetic field in geometrical terms. In 'On Faraday's lines of force' he had formulated field equations in terms of relations between electric and magnetic 'quantities' (acting through surfaces) and 'intensities' (acting along lines), making informal use of Stokes' theorem, which transforms line into surface integrals.[80] In the *Treatise* he gave these concepts analytical expression; and wrote to Stokes in January 1871 (Number 351) and to Tait the following April (Number 366) to inquire about the provenance of this theorem, published by Stokes in his Smith's Prize examination of February 1854, in which Maxwell had been placed equal Smith's Prizeman.[81]

Maxwell discussed the topology of knots and its electromagnetic analogue in two letters to Tait in November and December 1867 (Numbers 275 and 276), at the outset of embarking on the writing of the *Treatise*. His interest in topology, which he terms the 'geometry of position',[82] had been stimulated by Thomson's work on vortex motion, which drew upon Helmholtz's classic study on the subject. There use had been made of Riemann's classification of surfaces by their topological connectivity, a treatment of the properties of surfaces which he had developed in the course of his work on complex function theory.[83] Maxwell noted the use of integral theorems to express the topological properties of surfaces, and emphasised their application to theories of electromagnetism and the motion of fluid vortices (Numbers 276

---

(79) See P. M. Harman, 'Mathematics and reality in Maxwell's dynamical physics', in *Kelvin's Baltimore Lectures and Modern Theoretical Physics*, ed. Robert Kargon and Peter Achinstein (Cambridge, Mass./London, 1987): 267–97.

(80) Volume I: 257–8, 365, 371–5.

(81) See Numbers 351 note (3) and 366 note (3); and J. J. Cross, 'Integral theorems in Cambridge mathematical physics, 1830–55', in *Wranglers and Physicists. Studies on Cambridge Physics in the Nineteenth Century*, ed. P. M. Harman (Manchester, 1985): 112–48, esp. 139–45.

(82) See Numbers 276 note (8), 304 note (3), and 373. The term 'geometry of position' was also used to denote projective geometry: see note (65) and Number 373 esp. note (10); and Johann Benedict Listing, 'Vorstudien zur Topologie', in *Göttinger Studien. 1847. Erste Abtheilung: Mathematische und naturwissenschaftliche Abhandlungen* (Göttingen, 1847): 811–75, esp. 813–14.

(83) See Numbers 304 note (4) and 305 note (8).

and 305). He explored the relation between Helmholtz's theorems of vortex motion and the theory of electromagnetism (Numbers 295 and 296) and discussed the topology of curves and surfaces (Numbers 304, 305, 306, 308 and 317).

In February 1869 he gave the London Mathematical Society an account of Johann Benedict Listing's 'Der Census räumlicher Complexe', a study of the topology of geometrical figures (Number 318); and he applied these ideas to a study of topographical geometry (Number 345). In clarifying the mathematical argument of the *Treatise* he drew upon Listing's 'Vorstudien zur Topologie' to define the convention specifying the direction of linear and rotational motions, a problem crucial to understanding the relation between lines of force and electrical circuits (Number 385). He discussed the issue with Tait in May 1871, and raised it for discussion at a meeting of the London Mathematical Society (Numbers 368, 369, 370 and 371). In the *Treatise* he made explicit the enlargement of his physical geometry to include the topological treatment of lines and surfaces.[84]

In November 1870 he wrote to Tait, signalling a keen interest in quaternion ideas, methods and notation (Numbers 346 and 348). These letters give the first indication of his resumption of work on the *Treatise* and of an intention to remould its mathematical argument. His correspondence with Tait at this time also provides evidence of his first serious interest in quaternions. He aimed to demonstrate the application of vectors to the mathematics of electromagnetism (Number 347). William Rowan Hamilton had developed his calculus of quaternions from his work on algebra. In his study of complex numbers he sought to extend the complex number system to three dimensions, and in 1843 he invented 'quaternions', hypercomplex numbers with one real and three (imaginary) complex parts. He interpreted the three imaginary numbers as 'vectors' directed along three mutually perpendicular lines in space; the real part of the quaternion was the 'scalar'.[85] In the *Treatise* Maxwell emphasises the conceptual role of vectors as a means of representing physical quantities geometrically. This method provides a direct representation of electrical quantities congruent with their 'physical meaning'; it is a 'mode of contemplating geometrical and physical quantities' which is 'more primitive and more natural' than the method of Cartesian coordinates.[86]

His enthusiasm for quaternions was encouraged by Tait's declaration, in his paper 'On Green's and other allied theorems', of the 'promise of

---

(84) *Treatise*, 1: 16–27 (§§18–24).

(85) See Number 346 notes (2) and (5). See Hankins, *Hamilton*: 283–325; and Michael J. Crowe, *A History of Vector Analysis. The Evolution of the Idea of a Vectorial System* (Notre Dame/London, 1967). (86) *Treatise*, 1: 8–9 (§10).

usefulness in physical applications'[87] of Hamilton's operator ∇ (Number 346). In this paper, which Maxwell eulogised as 'really great' (Number 349), Tait expressed Green's and Stokes' theorems in quaternion form, and emphasised the 'simplicity and expressiveness of quaternions' in establishing the 'mutual relationship' of the properties of the 'analytical and physical magnitudes which satisfy... Laplace's equation'.[88] Maxwell's rapid grasp of the advantages in applying quaternion concepts to electricity and magnetism is revealed in his correspondence with Tait in early 1871 (Numbers 352, 353 and 356).

From the first Maxwell placed great emphasis on the value of the 'ideas of the calculus of quaternions...[as] distinguished from its operations and methods' (Number 347),[89] an opinion that he later repeated in his review of Kelland and Tait's *Introduction to Quaternions* (Number 485). His representation of the 'Vector Functions of the Electromagnetic Field' (Number 347) was the immediate consequence of his incorporation of ideas drawn from quaternions. He assured Tait that 'the value of Hamiltons idea of a Vector is unspeakable'; and it was in placing emphasis on the separate vector and scalar parts of Hamilton's quaternion that he sought to 'leaven my book with Hamiltonian ideas without casting the operations into a Hamiltonian form' (Number 348).[90] In pursuit of this objective he continued to raise questions of quaternion expression and notation for Tait's appraisal, as the *Treatise* proceeded to publication (Numbers 396, 401, 422, 423, 443 and 465).

The mathematical argument of the *Treatise* also encompasses a development of the generalised Lagrangian theory of the electromagnetic field (Numbers 408, 414, 417, 419 and 430) as first presented in 'A dynamical theory of the electromagnetic field'. There he had expounded the theory from analytical equations of mechanical systems, deploying the Lagrangian formalism of dynamics without reference to a specific mechanical model of the ether. As he explained to Tait in December 1867, the ether model of

---

(87) P. G. Tait, 'On Green's and other allied theorems', *Trans. Roy. Soc. Edinb.*, **26** (1870): 69–84, on 69; and see his letter to Maxwell of 13 December 1867 (Number 277 note (22)) and his card of 5 April 1871 (Number 366 note (5)).

(88) Tait, 'On Green's and other allied theorems': 70.

(89) See also the *Treatise*, **1**: 9 (§10).

(90) In adopting this approach he was encouraged by Bartholomew Price, Secretary of the Delegates of the Clarendon Press, Oxford. In a letter to Maxwell of 4 January 1871 (ULC Add. MSS 7656, P 659; and see note (95)) he argued: 'Quaternion Methods and Quaternion Notation are only just beginning to be used in this place: and the exclusive use of them in your book would therefore much curtail its usefulness, so I think you had better always express the analysis in the ordinary Cartesian form, and repeat it when desirable to do so in the Quaternion form.'

his paper 'On physical lines of force' had been 'built up to show that the phenomena are such as can be explained by mechanism', but that the 'nature of this mechanism is to the true mechanism what an orrery is to the Solar System' (Number 278).[91] In the *Treatise* he maintained this preference for abstract rather than concrete representation, and emphatically refrained from speculating about a hypothetical ether model which could be invoked as a mechanical explanation: 'The problem of determining the mechanism...admits of an infinite number of solutions'.[92]

In postcards to Tait in May and June 1872 (Numbers 408 and 414) he indicated the scope of the revision of his application of analytical dynamics. He proposed to follow the method adopted by Thomson and Tait in their *Natural Philosophy*, deriving the generalised equations of motion from impulsive forces, scorning the algebraic Lagrangian approach where physical concepts are 'supplanted by symbols'[93]. He stressed the importance of the link between the mathematical formalism of dynamics and the physical reality depicted. In a draft he explained his preference for the form of the equations of motion as given by Hamilton over that by Lagrange. The Hamiltonian form of the equations was based on the concept of momentum rather than (as with Lagrange) on velocity; and Maxwell suggested that Newton's second law of motion would thus determine the meaning of the dynamical theory of the electromagnetic field (Number 419). As Maxwell explained in the *Treatise*, it was his aim to translate the mathematical symbols 'from the language of the calculus into the language of dynamics', so that this language should express 'some property of moving bodies'.[94]

Having commenced the revision of the text of the *Treatise* in autumn 1870, Maxwell wrote to Bartholomew Price, Secretary of the Delegates of the Clarendon Press, Oxford, to report his progress. Price's response (in early January 1871) indicates that the work was sufficiently advanced for the Press to 'begin printing'.[95] A contract was not however signed until 10 May 1871,[96] Maxwell having reported to Tait that 'I have been at the Clarendon & they are to go a head' (Number 367). Shortly afterwards he was struck by the need to revise the convention on spatial relations that he had adopted (Numbers 368, 369 and 370), sending Tait a revise of *Treatise* §23 with the

---

(91) On Maxwell's likely source for this analogy see Number 278 note (13).
(92) *Treatise*, **2**: 417 (§831).   (93) *Treatise*, **2**: 194 (§567).
(94) *Treatise*, **2**: 185 (§554).
(95) Price to Maxwell, 4 January 1871 (note (90)): 'I am pleased to hear that you are so far on with the work that we may begin printing.' (and see Number 367 note (3)).
(96) See Number 367 note (3).

urgent request: 'Will this do? Tell me that I may print' (Number 371). Type-setting commenced promptly; the first proof sheets were available in June 1871, and by the following August this work was well advanced,[97] with Maxwell continuing to revise his account of spherical harmonics (Numbers 387 and 388).

Tait and Thomson (Number 390) assisted in the correction of proofs, their 'many valuable suggestions made during the printing' being acknowledged in the Preface to the *Treatise*.[98] Thomson was currently engaged in publishing the reprint of his papers on *Electrostatics and Magnetism*, and Maxwell repaid the service by reading his proofs (Numbers 383, 402, and 420). From spherical harmonics Maxwell's correspondence with Tait turned towards Tait's current interest in thermo-electricity (Numbers 393, 394, 396 and 401), and then to his own new application of Thomson's theory of electrical images to the explanation of Arago's rotating disc (Numbers 399, 400, 403, 404 and 405), both topics being discussed in the *Treatise*. The errors of Weber and Carl Neumann were duly noted (Numbers 411 and 428). As the book proceeded through the press during 1872, Maxwell raised questions for Tait's comment on quaternions (Numbers 401, 422 and 423) and on Lagrangian dynamics (Numbers 408, 414 and 419). Proofs of the final sections of the text are dated January 1873,[99] and the Preface is dated 1 February 1873; the book was published the following March.[100]

The *Treatise* was reviewed (anonymously) by Tait in the journal *Nature*.[101] Describing Maxwell as having 'a name which requires only the stamp of antiquity to raise it almost to the level of that of Newton', Tait placed emphasis on the power and novelty of Maxwell's mathematical physics. He drew attention to Maxwell's use of quaternion concepts and notation, to the role of the Lagrange–Hamilton formalism of dynamics in his dynamical theory of the electromagnetic field, and to the treatment of spherical harmonics in his exposition of the mathematical theory of electrostatics. Tait declared however that the main object and achievement of the work was in expounding a transformation in the very foundations of physical theory, 'simply to upset completely the notion of *action at a distance*'; and this had led Maxwell to demonstrate 'the connection between radiation and electrical phenomena'.[102] The formulation of the concept of the electromagnetic field

---

(97) See Numbers 383 note (5) and 386 note (2).   (98) *Treatise*, **1**: x note.
(99) See Number 434 note (7).   (100) See Number 448 esp. note (5).
(101) Confirmed by Knott, *Life of Tait*: 356. See also David B. Wilson, 'P. G. Tait and Edinburgh natural philosophy, 1860–1901', *Annals of Science*, **48** (1991): 267–87.
(102) [P. G. Tait,] 'Clerk-Maxwell's Electricity and Magnetism', *Nature*, **7** (24 April 1873): 478–80.

Cambridge and the Cavendish Laboratory

and the expression of the electromagnetic theory of light were thus highlighted as the major features of the *Treatise*.

In 1849 the Board of Mathematical Studies at Cambridge had recommended that 'the Mathematical Theories of Electricity, Magnetism, and Heat, be not admitted as subjects of examination',[103] a reform that was in line with current practice, though questions on these topics were set in the papers for the Smith's Prizes for which the high wranglers in the Mathematical Tripos competed. During the 1860s there was a movement for reform of the Tripos, with advocacy of the introduction of physical subjects into the examination. This process of reform of the Mathematical Tripos was gently fostered by Maxwell (Number 316) on his appointment as an examiner and moderator in 1866, 1867, 1869 and 1870 (Numbers 253, 254 and 300); and he served as additional examiner in 1873 (Numbers 412 and 436). Maxwell introduced a few questions on electricity, magnetism and heat into the examination, these topics being the major fields of research in mathematical physics since the 1840s; and he also suggested that questions on physical problems be set for the Adams Prize competition (Number 362).

George Biddell Airy wrote to the Vice-Chancellor of the University in 1866 urging reform of the Mathematical Tripos. Subsequent discussion by the Board of Mathematical Studies led to the appointment of a Physical Sciences Syndicate, which in its report of 27 February 1869 recommended 'providing public instruction in Heat, Electricity and Magnetism', these subjects to be added to the examination for the Mathematical Tripos in 1873. The Syndicate recommended that a new professorship be established for offering lectures in these subjects, and also urged the foundation of a physical laboratory. The University's scientific professors had already concluded that a new professorship would be required to provide effective teaching in the new subjects.[104] These recommendations had uncomfortable financial implications; but the Chancellor of the University, the Duke of Devonshire, intervened with an offer 'to provide the funds required for the building and apparatus, as soon as the University shall have in other respects completed its arrangements for teaching Experimental Physics, and shall have approved

---

(103) Report of the Board of Mathematical Studies, 19 May 1849, ULC, Cambridge University Archives, Minute V, 7. See David B. Wilson, 'Experimentalists among the mathematicians: physics in the Cambridge Natural Sciences Tripos, 1851–1900', *Historical Studies in the Physical Sciences*, **12** (1982): 325–71.

(104) *Cambridge University Reporter* (16 November 1870): 93–7.

34   *Introduction*

the plan of the building'.⁽¹⁰⁵⁾ This had immediate effect: a Professorship of Experimental Physics was established, the regulations to which it was to be subject approved, and the post was advertised on 14 February 1871, the election being announced for 8 March.⁽¹⁰⁶⁾

William Thomson was invited to stand for election; and after declining he was prompted by Stokes (as Lucasian Professor of Mathematics) to write to Helmholtz in an unavailing attempt to arouse his interest.⁽¹⁰⁷⁾ Maxwell was then invited by Stokes and by E. W. Blore (of Trinity), and urged by Strutt, to offer himself for election to the professorship. Blore and Stokes assured him that Thomson would not come forward, and Stokes asserted that 'I think you would most likely be elected'.⁽¹⁰⁸⁾ Expressing tentative initial interest (Number 357) Maxwell decided to stand and was duly elected, 'on the understanding', according to Lewis Campbell, 'that he might retire at the end of a year, if he wished to do so'.⁽¹⁰⁹⁾ Maxwell's position as third choice for the professorship, after Thomson and Helmholtz, may well reflect a ranking as judged in 1870; but his resignation from King's College, London may have led his Cambridge colleagues to surmise his likely disinterest in an academic post. Campbell's statement indicates that there was some uncertainty about his future commitment; but whatever his private doubts, Maxwell began immediately to draw up plans for the design of the laboratory and the acquisition of apparatus (Numbers 364 and 365). He drew on the expertise of Thomson at Glasgow and Tait at Edinburgh (Numbers 362, 365, 366, 367 and 374), and on R.B. Clifton's recent experience in planning a physical laboratory at Oxford.⁽¹¹⁰⁾ Work on the construction of the laboratory soon began to proceed (Numbers 397, 425 and 449).⁽¹¹¹⁾

---

(105) The (seventh) Duke of Devonshire to the Vice-Chancellor, John Power, 10 October 1870, ULC, V. C. Corr. I. 2; printed in the *Cambridge University Reporter* (19 October 1870): 13.

(106) *Cambridge University Reporter* (30 November 1870): 125–6; *ibid.* (8 February 1871): 175; *ibid.* (15 February 1871): 188. See Number 357 note (3) and D. A. Winstanley, *Later Victorian Cambridge* (Cambridge, 1947): 194–8.

(107) S. P. Thompson, *The Life of William Thomson, Baron Kelvin of Largs*, 2 vols. (London, 1910), **1**: 563–6.

(108) G. G. Stokes to Maxwell, 16 February 1871 (Number 357 note (3)).

(109) *Life of Maxwell*: 348; on Maxwell's election see Number 357 note (5).

(110) Number 365 note (4). See R. Sviedrys, 'The rise of physical science at Victorian Cambridge', *Historical Studies in the Physical Sciences*, **2** (1970): 127–51; Sviedrys, 'The rise of physics laboratories in Britain', *ibid.*, **7** (1976): 405–36.

(111) See 'The new physical laboratory of the University of Cambridge', *Nature*, **10** (1874): 139–42. The doors of the 'Cavendish Laboratory' (as the laboratory came to be known: see Number 463 notes (3) and (4)) bear the inscription 'Magna opera Domini exquisita in omnes voluntates ejus', the Vulgate version of Psalm 111, v. 2, 'The works of the Lord are great, sought out of all them that have pleasure therein' (Authorised Version). The inscription was placed

Maxwell delivered his inaugural lecture at Cambridge on 25 October 1871,[112] and immediately commenced regular lecturing duties. Stokes had informed him in February 1871 that his lectures would be 'subject to the approval of the board of Mathematical Studies'; it was anticipated that candidates for the Mathematical Tripos who opted for physical subjects, as well as candidates for the Natural Sciences Tripos, would attend.[113] Maxwell's correspondence with Tait indicates that he envisaged his lectures as being addressed to candidates reading for the Mathematical Tripos; thus in October 1872 he declared his intention 'to sow [quaternion] seed at Cambridge' (Number 423). In fulfilling the requirement that his professorship meet the scope of the Mathematical Tripos when the new regulations came into force in 1873, Maxwell lectured on 'Heat' in Michaelmas term 1871, on 'Electrostatics and Electrokinematics' in Lent term 1872, and on 'Electromagnetism' in Easter term 1872, the titles of these courses being modified slightly in subsequent years.[114] In Michaelmas term 1871 he recorded the attendance of 19 students (including Horace Lamb, W. W. Rouse Ball and W. M. Hicks), with attendance swelling to 26 in Lent term 1872 but falling to 10 in the Easter term. In Michaelmas term 1873 he recorded the attendance of a mere eight students, though these included George Howard Darwin (who had graduated as second wrangler in 1868 and was a Fellow of Trinity) and George Chrystal.[115] With very few exceptions, these students were candidates for the Mathematical Tripos.

there on the initiative of the architect William Milner Fawcett; see his letter of 16 December 1873 to the Vice-Chancellor, H. W. Cookson (ULC, CUR, 55.2 (192)): 'I am sorry to hear any adverse criticism on the Inscription on the door of the Cavendish Laboratory. / I am solely responsible for it and was careful to refer to an old Vulgate that there might be no mistake, but that the Latin might be correct. / I did feel a difficulty in the translation in our authorized English but a friend recommended me that the Vulgate Latin tho' not good had a certain authority and I would not be wrong in quoting from it. / It is unfortunate that the Hebrew is not correctly rendered, but we are not responsible for the Vulgate translation and the text seems to me so appropriate that I hope no serious objection will be taken to it.'

(112) J. Clerk Maxwell, *Introductory Lecture on Experimental Physics*, October 25, 1871 (London/Cambridge, 1871) (= *Scientific Papers*, 2: 241–55). The MS of the lecture is preserved in ULC Add. MSS 7655, V, h/7.

(113) Stokes to Maxwell, 18 February 1871 (Number 357 note (4)).

(114) *Cambridge University Reporter* (18 October, 1871): 16–17. In 1872–3 the lectures were on 'Heat and Elasticity', 'Electrostatics and Electrokinematics', and 'Electromagnetism'; see *Cambridge University Reporter* (16 October 1872): 8; *ibid.* (24 January 1873): 29; and *ibid.* (29 April 1873): 22. In 1873–4 the lectures were on 'Heat and Elasticity', 'Electricity and Magnetism', and 'Electromagnetism'; see *Cambridge University Reporter* (14 October 1873): 23; *ibid.* (14 January 1874): 185; and *ibid.* (14 April 1874): 315.

(115) In a notebook, ULC Add. MSS 7655, V, n/2.

G. H. Darwin's notes on Maxwell's lectures on 'Heat and Elasticity', delivered in the new lecture room of the Cavendish Laboratory in Michaelmas term 1873, and his more fragmentary notes on the lectures on 'Electricity and Magnetism' delivered in Lent term 1874,[116] have been preserved.[117] These notes show that Maxwell lectured on mathematical physics, and that his presentation was at an advanced level. In the lectures on 'Heat and Elasticity' he began by reviewing some of the topics described in his *Theory of Heat*, on liquid–gas exchanges, the Carnot cycle, Joule's paddle wheel experiment, Maxwell's thermodynamic relations, isothermal surfaces and Fourier's theory of the conduction of heat. His presentation was however at a deeper level of mathematical sophistication than that adopted in his text. On turning to more complex topics in mathematical physics he discussed the analogy between electricity and heat based on the mathematics of potential theory, and introduced the application of spherical harmonic analysis, taxing Darwin's comprehension.[118] His presentation of the kinetic theory of gases is of special interest, as the lectures followed the argument of his most recent work on the subject (Number 472). The severely analytical presentation was softened by the introduction of the geometrical analogy of the hodograph to represent the distribution of molecular velocities in space. His discussion of the statistical law of the distribution of velocities among molecules led to an account of his recent derivation of the distribution law for complex molecules in the presence of an external field of force, to which Darwin made reference.[119] Maxwell was an examiner for the Natural Sciences Tripos in 1873 (Number 488), but his lectures were not directed at the concerns of students about to sit the Cambridge examination in physics.[120]

As the new Cavendish Laboratory[121] neared completion early in 1873 (Number 449) Maxwell gave attention to the equipment which would be needed, and drew up a list of laboratory fittings and apparatus to be acquired (Numbers 463 and 464). The direction of the Laboratory and the encouragement of research by Cambridge Fellows, as in urging Strutt (Rayleigh) to write a book on the 'Theory of Sound' (Number 458), and his review of a dissertation (Number 489), were to be important duties during the last years of his life. Other dimensions of the final part of his career were broached in 1873: the planning and writing of articles for the ninth edition

---

(116) See note (114).   (117) ULC, DAR. 210.22.
(118) See Number 482 note (5).   (119) See Number 472 note (4).
(120) Coutts Trotter (see Number 361 note (2)) delivered lectures on physics attended by candidates for the Natural Sciences Tripos; see Wilson, 'Experimentalists among the mathematicians': 343–6.   (121) See note (111).

of the *Encyclopaedia Britannica* (Number 432); an interest in communicating his ideas to a wider public (Numbers 486 and 487), especially as a book reviewer for the journal *Nature* (Numbers 450 and 485); the agreement to undertake an edition of Henry Cavendish's manuscripts on electricity (Numbers 435 and 459); and his participation in the work of the Cambridge Philosophical Society (Number 490). The initiation of correspondence with Henry Rowland (Numbers 466 and 467), a member of the younger generation of physicists beyond Cambridge, whose work became deeply imbued with Maxwell's electromagnetic theory,[122] heralded the spread of Maxwellian theory and its dominance of 'classical' physics in the latter part of the nineteenth century.

---

(122) See Buchwald, *From Maxwell to Microphysics*: 73–7.

TEXTS
1862-1868

197

LETTER TO WILLIAM SHARPEY[1]

8 JULY 1862

From the original in the Library of the Royal Society, London[2]

Glenlair House
Dalbeattie
N.B.[3]
8 July 1862

Dear Sir

I now return Professor Stokes' paper 'On the Long Spectrum of Electric Light'.[4] I have read it and beg to report to the Committee of Papers that I find in it so much new information respecting the invisible rays, which constitute so large a part of the radiation from the electric spark and their relation to various substances[5] that I consider the Paper well worthy of being published in the Philosophical Transactions.

By the discovery of a substance capable of rendering visible the highly refrangible rays,[6] Professor Stokes has been enabled to make observations

---

(1) Professor of Anatomy and Physiology at University College, London; Secretary of the Royal Society 1853–72 (*DNB*).

(2) Royal Society, *Referees' Reports*, **4**: 263.

(3) North Britain (Scotland).

(4) G. G. Stokes, 'On the long spectrum of electric light', *Phil. Trans.*, **152** (1862): 599–619 (= *Papers*, **4**: 203–33). The paper was received by the Royal Society and read on 19 June 1862; see the abstract in *Proc. Roy. Soc.*, **12** (1862): 166–8 (= *Papers*, **4**: 203–4).

(5) In a paper 'On the prismatic decomposition of electrical light', *Report of the Fifth Meeting of the British Association for the Advancement of Science* (London, 1836), part 2: 11–12, Charles Wheatstone had reported his discovery that the spectra of electric sparks contain bright lines determined by the nature of the electrodes. The subject had been of some recent interest: see A. J. Ångström, 'Optical researches', *Phil. Mag.*, ser. 4, **9** (1855): 327–42; Ångström, 'On the Fraunhofer lines visible in the solar spectrum', *ibid.*, **24** (1862): 1–11; Julius Plücker, 'Ueber die Constitution der electrischen Spectra der verschiedenen Gase und Dämpfe', *Ann. Phys.*, **107** (1859): 497–539, 638–43; Gustav Kirchhoff, 'Untersuchungen über das Sonnenspectrum und die Spectren der chemischen Elemente', *Abhandlungen der Königlichen Akademie der Wissenschaften zu Berlin* (Aus dem Jahre 1861): 63–95, esp. 67–74, (trans. by Henry E. Roscoe) *Researches on the Solar Spectrum, and the Spectra of the Chemical Elements* (Cambridge/London, 1862): 8–12.

(6) Stokes recalled that following the experimental researches described in his paper 'On the change of refrangibility of light', *Phil. Trans.*, **142** (1852): 463–562 (= *Papers*, **3**: 267–409), he had anticipated that an electric spark would emit 'rays of much higher refrangibility than were found in the solar spectrum'; but that in February 1853 he had been 'perfectly astonished on subjecting a powerful discharge from a Leyden jar to prismatic analysis with quartz apparatus, to find a spectrum extending no less than six or eight times the length of the visible spectrum'. Stokes projected 'a spectrum formed by a prism and lens of quartz on a piece of uranium glass';

with the eye on these rays and has thus extended our knowledge of –

– the bright rays due to metals[7]

– the absorption of these rays by various media, and the unequal absorption of different parts of the invisible spectrum by media which do not absorb visible light, a phenomenon having the same relation to the 'long spectrum' that colour has to the visible spectrum, and, affording the same kind of assistance in the discrimination of these substances.[8]

These researches may also afford the means for a more exact knowledge of the electric spark itself,[9] and when compared with the photographic results obtained by Dr Miller,[10] may render the proof of the absolute identity of the cause of all the effects produced by these radiations more convincing to those who do not yet believe it.

I remain
Yours truly
J. CLERK MAXWELL

Dr Sharpey
Sec R.S.[11]

---

reporting that on 'changing the metals between which the spark passed, we found that the lines were changed, which showed clearly that they were due to the particular metals'. See Stokes, 'On the long spectrum of electric light': 599–600.

(7) Stokes reported observations of the spectra of platinum, palladium, gold, silver, mercury, antimony, bismuth, copper, lead, tin, nickel, cobalt, iron, cadmium, zinc, aluminium and magnesium, and exhibited in a figure the principal lines of aluminium (which 'stands at the head of the above metals for richness in rays of the very highest refrangibility') together with those of zinc and cadmium for comparison. See Stokes, 'On the long spectrum of electric light': 603–6.

(8) A point made by Stokes in discussing the 'highly characteristic' absorption by alkaloids and glucosides; see 'On the long spectrum of electric light': 607.

(9) As discussed by Stokes in his paper 'On the long spectrum of electric light': 615–19.

(10) In his paper 'On the long spectrum of electric light': 601–2, Stokes refers to a paper by William Allen Miller (see Number 199 note (12)), to which his own paper was a 'supplement'. See Miller's letters to Stokes of 2 March, 25 and 29 April, and 23 August 1862 in Larmor, *Correspondence*, **1**: 159–61.

(11) Stokes' paper was also refereed by Charles Wheatstone, in a report dated 16 July 1862 (Royal Society, *Referees' Reports*, **4**: 262). Wheatstone declared the paper to be 'a valuable addition to the numerous memoirs which have been recently published relating to the prismatic decomposition of electric light, especially as showing how the author's own original and important experiments on fluorescence can be applied to the investigation and determination of the positions of the invisible rays'. See notes (5), (6) and (10); and Numbers 198 note (2) and 199 note (12).

=198=

LETTER TO GEORGE GABRIEL STOKES

14 JULY 1862

From the original in the Library of the Royal Society, London[1]

Glenlair
Dalbeattie
July 14, 1862

Dear Stokes

I now return to you Dr Robinsons Paper 'On Spectra of Electric Light as modified by the nature of the Electrodes and the Media of Discharge'[2] and beg to report to the Committee of Papers that I have read it and consider the investigations there described as worthy to be recorded in the Philosophical Transactions.

The subject is well worthy of study, notwithstanding the number of observations that must be made and the changes of circumstance that must be tried in order to ascertain the dependence or independence of the lines upon the circumstances under which they are produced.

The results tabulated by Dr Robinson[3] will no doubt be discussed by himself in the second part of his paper,[4] and the modifications of selected lines traced through all the changes of conditions. For me to attempt this from the tables without the experience gained by making the observations would be nearly useless, and as I have not attempted it I cannot properly appreciate the evidence of the connexion of particular phenomena with particular conditions.

The conditions which are at our disposal relate to the Spark to the Electrodes and to the Medium. The Spark is a transient electric current which may vary in 'mean strength' and in 'duration' the total quantity of electricity which passes being the product of these quantities.

Weber has shown how to ascertain by the magnetic galvanometer and electric dynamometer the strength and duration of a uniform current

---

(1) Royal Society, *Referees' Reports*, **5**: 218.

(2) T. R. Robinson, 'On the spectra of electric light, as modified by the nature of the electrodes and the media of discharge', *Phil. Trans.*, **152** (1862): 939–86, esp. 939–74. The paper was received by the Royal Society and read on 19 June 1862; see the abstract in *Proc. Roy. Soc.*, **12** (1862): 202–5.

(3) Thomas Romney Robinson, astronomer at Armagh Observatory, was Stokes' father-in-law (see Larmor, *Correspondence*, **1**: 14–15; and *DNB*). On Stokes' own contemporary related work see Number 197; and for the broader context see Number 197 note (5).

(4) Robinson, 'On the spectra of electric light': 974–86; and for Maxwell's report see Number 201.

equivalent to the actual spark both in quantity and in heating effect,[5] and we can calculate from this the actual strength and variation of the spark at any part of its duration by a rough theory. This investigation would not be necessary in spectrum observations but it may serve to direct our attention to what we may know about the spark.

The path of the current is known to us by its luminosity. This arises from something in rapid vibration, whether particles of gas or metal or ether. The amount of energy spent in producing these movements is directly as the whole quantity and inversely as ⟨the square⟩ of the duration. These movements constitute heat at the place where they exist and if they are propagated elsewhere they are called radiant heat, light or invisible rays according as they are received on a thermometer, the eye, or anything else. If the vibrations were quite irregular we should have a continuous spectrum but we find bright lines indicating a tendency of the vibrations to have particular periods. Is this tendency to a particular period of vibration an inalienable property of the molecules of elementary substances or can it be modified by the action of other molecules or changes of amplitude in the vibrations.

The action of other molecules of the same substance certainly alters the effects, see the CP spectra, the R spectra and the transition spectra,[6] but we must remember that cæteris paribus the rarification diminishes the resistance and alters the nature of the spark, and the heat produced in its path.

The action of bodies chemically combined might be expected to be more powerful but it certainly does not always change the character of the lines.

As far as I am aware no change in position of a line has been observed due either to change of power of spark or chemical action, which seems to indicate that the vibrating systems are very elementary. I am not aware of lines belonging to compound bodies.

To settle disputes with regard to lines selected for their apparent variation they should first be examined with a strong train of prisms to find out whether they are broad faint lines or narrow bright ones ⌊see Kirchhoff⌋.[7] Two sparks taken under different circumstances should then be compared simultaneously by reflecting both through different parts of the same slit. The

---

(5) Wilhelm Weber, 'Elektrodynamische Maassbestimmungen', *Ann. Phys.*, **73** (1848): 193–240, esp. 215–18; (trans.) 'On the measurement of electro-dynamic forces', *Scientific Memoirs*, ed. R. Taylor, **5** (London, 1852): 489–529, esp. 506–9.

(6) Spectra obtained from gases at common pressure ('CP'), on rarefying the gas in which discharges were made ('R'), and '*transition*' spectra produced during rarefaction; see Robinson, 'On the spectra of electric light': 946, 948.

(7) Gustav Kirchhoff, *Researches on the Solar Spectrum, and the Spectra of the Chemical Elements*, trans. by Henry E. Roscoe (Cambridge/London, 1862); see Number 197 note (5).

electric circumstances may be made the same by making the same current pass through both sparks or different by drawing off part of the current from one spark &c. Electrodes may be got rid of by using a strong induction coil and a vessel with partitions or perhaps this would answer.

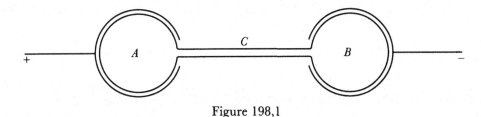

Figure 198,1

Two large globes A, B connected by a fine tube C. The balls of thin glass & covered externally with tin foil and the tin foil connected with the poles of the coil.

There would then be no metallic electrodes and the current would be a reciprocating one due to static induction, faint in the globes, but strong in the tube.

I do not understand how a line can be seen to be distinctly narrower than the image of the slit.[8] I have seen D double when I thought the slit too wide to show it. That the relative brightness of different lines in the same medium should alter is to be expected but may lead to further knowledge. That the position of a line should alter would be very remarkable and would require a readjustment of theories and probably would produce a still greater revolution in science than if the permanence of all lines were demonstrated.

Yours truly
J. CLERK MAXWELL

Professor Stokes
Sec R.S.[9]

---

(8) See Robinson's comments in 'On the spectra of electric light': 947.
(9) For Wheatstone's report on Robinson's paper see Number 201 note (8).

LETTERS TO GEORGE GABRIEL STOKES

16 JULY 1862

From the originals in the University Library, Cambridge[1]

Glenlair
Dalbeattie
July 16, 1862

My dear Stokes

I have read Professor Haughton's paper 'On the reflexion of polarized light from polished surfaces, transparent and metallic'[2] and I find that it contains many valuable observations, important to the theory of reflexion and I think the paper such as should be published in the Society's Transactions and beg to report accordingly to the Committee of Papers.[3]

Mr Haughtons experiments and observations determine for various incidences of plane polarized light on different surfaces

1st the difference of phase of the components of the reflected light, in and perpendicular to, the plane of reflexion. (A)

2nd The ratio of the amplitudes of these components, the components of the incident light being equal. (B)[4]

He has determined by experiment the angle of incidence at which the difference of phase is 90° (Principal Incidence) and the ratio of the components of the incident light so that the reflected light shall be circularly polarized.[5] The tangent of the Principal Incidence he calls 'the Coefficient

---

(1) ULC Add. MSS 7656, M 418.

(2) Samuel Haughton, 'On the reflexion of polarized light from polished surfaces, transparent and metallic', *Phil. Trans.*, **153** (1863): 81–125. The paper was received by the Royal Society on 9 June 1862, and read on 19 June 1862; see the abstract in *Proc. Roy. Soc.*, **12** (1862): 168–70.

(3) Maxwell subsequently qualified this judgment: see Number 200.

(4) On this ratio see Number 200 note (10).

(5) The terms in which Haughton's paper are couched follow those of Fresnel's theory of reflection: see A. J. Fresnel, 'Mémoire sur la loi des modifications que la réflexion imprime à la lumière polarisée', *Mémoires de l'Académie Royale des Sciences de l'Institut de France*, **11** (1832): 393–433. Fresnel obtains amplitude ratios for oscillations in and perpendicular to the plane of incidence (tangent and sine laws). He supposes that on total reflection light is shifted in phase from the incident wave; and discusses the conditions in which the light is circularly polarised, as in the 'Fresnel rhomb'. See George Biddell Airy, *Mathematical Tracts on the Lunar and Planetary Theories, the Figure of the Earth, Precession and Nutation, the Calculus of Variations, and the Undulatory Theory of Optics* (Cambridge, $_3$1842): 342–55, esp. 349, 354; where he notes that in the case of 'reflection at the surfaces of metals, the reflected ray appears to possess properties similar to those of light totally reflected within glass'; and that in 'Fresnel's rhomb' the 'effect of the two reflections...will be to accelerate the phases of vibration in the plane...more than those perpendicular to that plane by 90°'.

of Refraction' (not the Index) and the ratio of components the Coefficient of Reflexion.[6]

If Fresnels theory[7] were correct Brewsters law[8] would hold[9] and the Coefficient of refraction would be the Index of Refraction[10] and the Coefficient of Reflexion would be zero.[11] It appears that the Coefficient is less than the Index of refraction and the Coeff^t of Reflexion has values up to nearly unity.

The different series of experiments on the same substance at the various incidences will all give independent values of (A) and (B) for each incidence. A comparison of these series first with each other, and then with theory would give first a measure of the value of the observations, and then an indication of the truth of the theory. As far as I can see the author has restricted himself to determining the two coefficients which are distinguishing marks of the media and quite independent of theory, though they may be made numerical constants in a theory afterwards. They may be found to throw light on the optical character of metallic and other surfaces, and from the observations they appear to be capable of sufficiently accurate determination.

I have also read Professor Miller's Paper 'On the Photographic Transparency of Bodies &c'[12] and beg to report to the Committee of Papers that I think it should be published in the Transactions.[13]

---

(6) See Haughton, 'On the reflexion of polarized light from polished surfaces': 84.

(7) See note (5).

(8) That the condition of maximum polarisation is that the tangent of incidence is equal to the index of refraction. See David Brewster, 'On the laws which regulate the polarisation of light by reflexion from transparent bodies', *Phil. Trans.*, **105** (1815): 125–59, esp. 127; Brewster, 'On the phenomenon and laws of elliptic polarization, as exhibited in the action of metals upon light', *Phil. Trans.*, **120** (1830): 287–326, esp. 324; and Brewster, *A Treatise on Optics* (London, 1831): 169, 229–30.

(9) The relation between Fresnel's theory and Brewster's law is discussed in Airy's *Mathematical Tracts*: 343–4, 355n.   (10) See note (8).

(11) This follows from Fresnel's tangent law for oscillations in the plane of incidence when the angles of incidence and refraction are complementary; Haughton, 'On the reflexion of polarised light from polished surfaces': 87. See Fresnel, 'Mémoire sur la loi des modifications que la réflexion imprime à la lumière polarisée': 402; and Airy, *Mathematical Tracts*: 343–4, who notes, following Fresnel, that this condition gives $\tan i = \mu$ (Brewster's law) 'which defines the polarizing angle'.

(12) W. A. Miller, 'On the photographic transparency of various bodies, and on the photographic effects of metallic and other spectra obtained by means of the electric spark', *Phil. Trans.*, **152** (1862): 861–87. The paper was received by the Royal Society and read on 19 June 1862; see the abstract in *Proc. Roy. Soc.*, **12** (1862): 159–66.

(13) For Stokes' reference to Miller's paper see Number 197 note (10). Miller was Maxwell's colleague, as Professor of Chemistry, at King's College London; see Volume I: 662n. In his paper

By taking a number of photographs on the same scale Dr Miller has enabled us to compare at our leisure the spectra of the different metals and the effects of absorption on them. While the method of using a fluorescent screen (as you do)[14] ensures seeing all that is to be seen, and enables the observer to adjust his apparatus by the help of the eye, the photographic method, when once perfected, though each observation takes longer time and is done in the dark gives us permanent records of the facts without the labour of measurement or the uncertainty of memory.

At the same time the comparison of the photographs with the appearances on the fluorescent screen will afford proof that the same vibrations produce both effects.

Dr Miller has used different electrodes different media for the spark to traverse & different media for the light of the spark to traverse. I know no other variable except the substance used as the sensitive screen. As Dr Millers researches already have great optical value any extension of them with varied sensitive media would have immense importance in Photography. I do not think most photographers are sufficiently aware that the ordinary media are hardly sensitive till near the line G.

I think there is perhaps an error at the top of Page 39 where Dr Miller says your screen was made of Uranium GLASS.[15][a] I understood it to be a modified phosphate of Uranium.[16]

I remain
Yours truly
J CLERK MAXWELL

Professor Stokes
Secretary of the Royal Society[17]

(a) {Stokes} I used sometimes one & sometimes the other. G.G.S.[18]

'On the photographic transparency of various bodies': 864n he thanked Maxwell for help with some calculations.

(14) See G. G. Stokes, 'On the long spectrum of electric light', *Phil. Trans.*, **152** (1862): 599–619; and for Maxwell's report see Number 197.

(15) As mentioned by Stokes in his paper 'On the long spectrum of electric light': 600; see Number 197 note (6).

(16) The substance used as a screen whose preparation is described in detail by Stokes in 'On the long spectrum of electric light': 602–3.

(17) In a report on Miller's paper, dated 23 August 1862 (Royal Society, *Referees' Reports*, **5**: 157), Charles Wheatstone declared that: 'The great number of metallic substances in which he has determined the photographic lines from the spectra by prismatic analysis, renders it of especial value, and though the positions of these lines are only roughly ascertained, his experiments will furnish most valuable indications to the physicist who may hereafter undertake to determine accurately the index of refraction of the invisible rays.'

(18) In the published text of his paper 'On the photographic transparency of various bodies': 882, Miller refers to Stokes' use of 'a screen of uranium glass, or of a particular phosphate of uranium'.

Dear Stokes

The accompanying papers only arrived here yesterday and Dr Millers photographs are still on their way. The reason is that when I sent for the papers from London they were mistaken for another parcel which I did not wish forwarded.

Yours truly
J C. MAXWELL

= 200 =

LETTER TO GEORGE GABRIEL STOKES

21 JULY 1862

From the original in the Library of the Royal Society, London[1]

Glenlair
Dalbeattie
1862 July 21

Dear Stokes

I quite concur in your report on Mr Haughton's paper.[2] I have never read M. Jamins paper[3] though I was aware of its existence, and that he had constructed an instrument to analyze elliptically polarized light.[4] I also knew that you had constructed an instrument with a selenite plate for a similar purpose,[5] but as I had not the means of getting up the subject within the time, I assumed that Mr Haughton,[6] living in Dublin and working for

---

(1) Royal Society, *Referees' Reports*, **5**: 103.

(2) This letter was written in supplement to Maxwell's report on Haughton's paper 'On the reflexion of polarized light from polished surfaces, transparent and metallic' (Number 199). To obtain agreement between the two referees of the paper Stokes had sent Maxwell his own report, dated 30 June 1862 (Royal Society, *Referees' Reports*, **5**: 106), on receiving Maxwell's letter of 16 July 1862. Stokes was severely critical of Haughton's paper, concluding with the following recommendations: 'On the whole, I do not think the paper ought to be printed without some modifications. / 1st It would be well if the author were to modify the opening sentence, in which he appears to claim as a discovery a very simple consequence of the theory of transverse vibrations applied to the leading features of metallic reflection.... / 2nd The error or oversight of giving two different definitions of the same expression "coefficient of reflection" should be corrected. / 3rd Reference should be made to the experiments of Jamin.... / 4th Further information should be afforded as to the mode of conducting the experiments.... / 5th The author should be requested to reconsider his result that J/I depends on the azimuth of the polarizer.... / 6th It might be desirable to give at the end a comparison of the constants as determined respectively by the author and M. Jamin.... /... I am prepared, in case the other referee be decidedly favourable to the publication, to recommend that the paper be printed subject to slight modification, provided that, after communication with the author the referees should be satisfied that the numerical results were sufficiently trustworthy....'.

(3) Jules Jamin, 'Mémoire sur la réflexion à la surface des corps transparents', *Ann. Chim. Phys.*, ser. 3, **29** (1850): 263–304. Two earlier papers by Jamin were also relevant to Haughton's work: 'Mémoire sur la réflexion métallique', *ibid.*, **19** (1847): 296–342, and 'Mémoire sur la couleur des métaux', *ibid.*, **22** (1848): 311–27.

(4) Jamin, 'Mémoire sur la réflexion à la surface des corps transparents': 270–86. The phenomenon had been discussed by David Brewster, 'On the phenomenon and laws of elliptic polarization, as exhibited in the action of metals upon light', *Phil. Trans.*, **120** (1830): 287–326.

(5) G. G. Stokes, 'On a new elliptic analyser', *Report of the Twenty-first Meeting of the British Association for the Advancement of Science* (London, 1852), part 2: 14 (= *Papers*, **3**: 197–9).

(6) Haughton was a Fellow of Trinity College, Dublin, FRS 1858.

years on the subject had made the necessary inquiries and placed his experimental results before the Society simply as an addition to the mass of facts observed by various experimenters.

The opening statement claiming the discovery that plane polarized light could be made into circularly polarized light by reflexion at proper incidence and azimuth[7] must be so expressed as to be understood as a mere deduction, tolerably obvious, from the fact that the two components have a difference of phase varying with the incidence and extending sufficiently to allow of one value being $\frac{1}{4}$ undulation, while neither component vanishes.[8]

I understood the definition of the coeffts to relate to the conditions of this single experiment only, for of course it is possible that when the difference of phase is 90°,[9] $\frac{J^{(10)}}{I}$ may not be a minimum, and the second definition therefore should not stand side by side with the first[11] till their identity is proved.

From the very brief manner in which the mode of observation is described I suspected that the author had already described it but as there was no reference to any more complete description, I think that the observations lose much of their value for want of some statement of the way in which each result was obtained.[12] In a case like that of this paper, where several series

---

(7) Comparison of the manuscript of Haughton's paper 'On the reflexion of polarized light from polished surfaces, transparent and metallic' (Royal Society, PT. 68.4) with its printed text in *Phil. Trans.*, **153** (1863): 81–126, on 83, shows that Haughton left this statement unaltered. See also note (15) on Haughton's revision.

(8) On the phase difference of 90° between components, a retardation of $\frac{1}{4}$ of a wave-length, see Number 199 esp. note (5). In his report (note (2)) Stokes had made reference to the constant that 'the author calls the coefficient of refraction...defined as the tangent of the principal incidence (or that at which the difference of phase is a quarter of an undulation) and accordingly for transparent substances would agree with the index of refraction on the supposition of the exactitude of the formula of Fresnel.' See Number 199 esp. notes (8) and (11).

(9) See Number 199.

(10) In Haughton's paper I and J denote the amplitudes of the components of the reflected waves polarised in and perpendicular to the plane of incidence, respectively. These symbols had been introduced by A. L. Cauchy, 'Mémoire sur la polarisation des rayons réfléchis ou réfractés par la surface de séparation de deux corps isophanes et transparents', *Comptes Rendus*, **9** (1839): 676–91, esp. 687–91; and subsequently employed by Jamin, 'Mémoire sur la réflexion à la surface des corps transparents': esp. 274–5. See Number 199 where Maxwell denotes J/I as relation (B).

(11) See Stokes' second point in his critique of Haughton's paper (note (2)). Earlier in his report he had noted that Haughton seemed to define the 'coefficient of reflexion...at one place as the value of J/I at the principal incidence, in another as the minimum value of J/I...regarded as a function of the angle of incidence'.

(12) See Stokes' fourth point in his critique of Haughton's paper (note (2)). Earlier in his

of observations are taken under slightly different circumstances (azimuth of polarizer) which ought to give identical series of values of the retardation and $\frac{J}{I}$ for each incidence, I think the reader ought to have the means placed before him of judging the degree and reliance to be placed on each observation with deductions as to the accuracy of each element of the apparatus (polarizer compensator analyzer & graduated circles)[13] and finally a comparison of general results with different modifications of the theory showing whether the differences from the theory can be explained by errors of observation.

The variation of $\frac{J}{I}$ with the azimuth must either be erroneous or may arise from the action of the quartz of the compensator.[14] A few experiments with the compensator should have been given to prove that no rotation of plane polarization takes place.

I therefore agree with you that the author should be requested to point out

---

report he had criticised Haughton with some vehemence: 'we are not told whether the observations were taken right and left of the plane of incidence at equal azimuths, or if not in what manner the index errors of the polarizer and analyzer were determined, or whether they were determined at all. We do not know whether or not the precaution was taken of reversing in succession the polarizer and analyzer (i.e. turning them through 180°) and taking the mean of the results in the 4 different positions. We are not informed whether the results given were got by single observations, or how many they were the mean of.' See Haughton, 'On the reflexion of polarized light from polished surfaces': 83–4 for a brief account of his experimental procedure.

(13) Haughton explained that he had 'employed the quartz compensator described by M. Jamin, for the purpose of converting the elliptically-polarized reflected light into plane-polarized light, before allowing it to pass through the analyser'; Haughton, 'On the reflexion of polarized light from polished surfaces': 83; and see Jamin, 'Mémoire sur la réflexion à la surface des corps transparentes': 271–2.

(14) See Stokes' fifth point in his critique of Haughton's paper (note (2)). Earlier in the report he had stated: 'Yet on the strength of these experiments, so many important details respecting which are omitted, we are expected to believe that the ratio of J/I at a given angle of incidence changes with the azimuth of the polarizer.... But neither Fresnel's formula for reflexion nor any others are involved in the ratio of J to I when nothing but the azimuth of the polarizer is changed.... A variation in the ratio of J to I with a variation in the azimuth of the polarizer could not be accepted as a true physical result without the most rigorous scrutiny of every step of the process. In default of such we should unhesitatingly attribute it to some disturbing cause vitiating in a regular manner the result of observation.' In a document 'Remarks on Mr Stokes' Report...' (Royal Society, *Referees' Reports*, 5: 105), accompanying a letter to Stokes of 6 November 1862 (Royal Society, *Referees' Reports*, 5: 104), Haughton responded to this critique: 'With regard to J/I varying with the azimuth, while the incidence remained the same, these variations were observed, after making all due precautions against experimental error, & I cannot therefore consent to alter that portion of my paper.'

the claims of his paper to publication and to state in what relation it stands to M. Jamin's observations, whether as more correct or otherwise.[15]

If the observations were properly reduced and some proof given of their accuracy the results would be of value, though not the first of their kind, but I imagine from what you say that in the case of mere verifications and repetitions of researches the Society would not recommend publication in the Transactions.

Yours truly
J. CLERK MAXWELL

(15) Comparison of the manuscript of Haughton's paper with its printed text (see note (7)) shows that Haughton responded to Stokes' report by prefacing his paper with a resumé of Jamin's work and appending tables comparing his own results with those of Jamin. See Haughton, 'On the reflexion of polarised light from polished surfaces': 81–3, 123–5.

REPORT ON A PAPER BY THOMAS ROMNEY ROBINSON ON THE SPECTRA OF ELECTRIC SPARKS[1]

10 SEPTEMBER 1862

From the original in the Library of the Royal Society, London[2]

REPORT ON DR ROBINSONS 'CONTINUATION OF PAPER ON ELECTRIC SPECTRA'[3]

In this paper, the author, by comparing the results of the observations already described and tabulated,[4] arrives at the general conclusions to which his experiments point.

He wishes to ascertain in what circumstances connected with the production of an electric spark the position and intensity of the bright lines in its spectrum depend. He has therefore varied the electric conditions the electrodes and the medium through which the discharge takes place.

If the lines were due entirely to the independent action of the elementary bodies in the region of the spark and if each elementary body produces a group of lines each of them distinct from any line due to any other element then with very little trouble we should arrive at an ultimate analysis of all bodies. But if many lines are common to many elements, and if the lines due to compounds and mixtures differ by excess or defect from the sum of the lines due to the compounds then we have the prospect of a wider field of investigation before we reach the ultimatum of science.

It appears from the observations that a large number of lines are seen in many different cases, when both the electrodes and the gaseous medium are changed. In these cases there is either an exact coincidence between certain of the modes of vibration of different elements, or there is an unknown element common to the supposed elements or the lines do not arise from gross matter but from certain mechanical properties of an 'etherial' medium which is always present.

---

(1) See also Number 198.
(2) Royal Society, *Referees' Reports*, **5**: 219.
(3) T. R. Robinson, 'On the spectra of electric light, as modified by the nature of the electrodes and the media of discharge', *Phil. Trans.*, **152** (1862): 939–86, esp. 974–86.
(4) See Number 198 note (2).

A perfect coincidence between the periodic times of vibration of perfectly different and independent bodies would be unexpected and would require rigid proof, both with respect to the degree of coincidence and the want of anything in common between the bodies. Exact coincidence even of single lines, much more of groups whether near each other or in different parts of the spectrum would be a very strong argument in favour of identity of cause. Whether we have reason to trust to spectrum observations in attempting to reduce the number of elementary bodies, or whether we should expect rather to discover some properties of an ethereal medium, we must make use of comparisons such as those in this paper and at the same time we should study the mathematical theory of the vibrations of compound systems.

If a system is performing compound vibrations the component vibrations belonging to a given series, then the presence of another system capable of performing a series of vibrations having various relations to the first series may greatly modify the actual vibrations. If the mechanical connexion between the two systems is not very close, then only those vibrations will be much affected which are common to both systems and these will be affected in intensity but not in period.

If the connexion between the two systems is of a more intimate kind we may expect slight changes in the period as well as the intensity of the vibrations.

If any connexion could be made out between the results of a mechanical theory and the observed effects of condensation and rarefaction mixture and combination we should obtain even more insight into nature than if we had established a theory of lines peculiar to each element, and unalterable.

The weakening of a line is as remarkable a phenomenon as its intensification and is free from the suspicion which we may often feel of a line being due to an inappreciable quantity of a foreign body. I think it would add to the value of the paper if the history of a few of the more remarkable lines were exhibited in as many tables, the table for each line consisting of columns for the gases and horizontal lines for the electrodes and the body of the table indicating by marks of magnitude, as *, n.b &c,[5] the intensity for the gas and the metal corresponding. The reader would then see at one view the effect of different circumstances on the brightness of a line, without tracing it through the tables of metals in the 1st part.

The paper indicates a large field of inquiry which it would take long to work over but while it agrees with former researches in making catalogues of

---

(5) As he explained in 'On the spectra of electric light': 949, Robinson denoted by a * 'the lines which are far transcendent in brilliancy, and are not less broad than the image of the slit'.

lines and pointing out the most conspicuous as characteristic of particular substances, it shows the importance of a careful study of particular lines as influenced by the density of the medium, its composition, and that of the electrodes and the electric circumstances of the spark. The lines most worth examining are those which are visible in many cases but have variable intensity and perhaps those most important of all may be those which are broad and apparently ill defined. These would probably be most altered by change of circumstances and would therefore give most information as to the conditions of alteration.

When a few remarkable lines have been selected and examined with a powerful train of prisms it might be worth trying whether the position of a line cannot be altered by change of temperature in the medium, substitution of flame for electric spark or different combinations of the element.

By viewing a standard case and another example at once through the same slit the coincidence or defect of coincidence might be very accurately observed.

I think that Ways mercury light[6] would be a good subject for experiment because we have mercury for electrodes and nearly pure mercury vapour (very dense) for medium and we can vary the intensity of the electric current continuously and we may even by connecting the electrodes with those of an induction machine have sparks in the same place with the continuous current and simultaneously.

In the same way we might use sparks passing through an ordinary flame, to compare the effects of heat and electricity.

I do not understand however whether a molecule can be said to have a temperature of its own. If its parts have relative motion, that may constitute its selfcontained temperature, while its motion as a whole may be the condition of its temperature as observed. The first kind of motion probably is that on which the lines depend and may possibly be different when excited by electricity than when excited by communication of heat.

I do not know whether visible light can be produced by the sudden compression of a gas. Radiant heat is so produced (see Tyndall)[7] and if we could get flashes of light in this way in gases of great density, without

---

(6) Way's mercury light is described by J. H. Gladstone, 'On the electric light of mercury', *Phil. Mag.*, ser. 4, **20** (1860): 249–53, on 249.

(7) John Tyndall, 'On the absorption and radiation of heat by gaseous matter', *Phil. Trans.*, **152** (1862): 59–98, esp. 75–80.

electricity or combustion it might be an aid in eliminating the effects of particular circumstances.

JAMES CLERK MAXWELL[8]

Sept 10, 1862

---

(8) In a report dated 22 October 1862 (Royal Society, *Referees' Reports*, 5: 220), Charles Wheatstone declared Robinson's paper to be 'a very valuable contribution to that new department of optics and chemistry which has been designated "Spectral Analysis". The influence which pressure in gases has on the development of the spectral lines; and the proof that lines appear in compound gases which do not exist in their elementary components, while others which occur in the elements disappear in the compound are quite new and contrary to the prevalent opinion.'

202

LETTER TO GEORGE GABRIEL STOKES

10 SEPTEMBER 1862
From the original in the University Library, Cambridge[1]

Glenlair,
Dalbeattie
1862 Sept 10

Dear Stokes

I send you reports on Dr Robinson's papers.[2] I did not know that the reciprocating discharge in a closed glass vessel had been tried and found to exhibit the lines of the constituents of glass.

I have been comparing the results of colour observations by different eyes in order to see whether they can be reduced to a single diagram by altering the mode of projection, that is taking different units of the standard colours.[3]

I find that I get consistent results in the three cases I have tried but that the numbers by which the coordinates must be multiplied vary from 1 to 3 so that if we suppose one person to see blue 3 times stronger relative to green than another person, we get consistent results. I find that the centre and circumference of my retina differ so that white appears bluer to the retina generally than to the centre and therefore the colour complementary to red is of higher refrangibility for the retina than for its centre. I cannot perceive any difference in merely looking at white paper, but I suppose any constant difference in different parts of the retina can be discovered only by reason as it would not be an object of perception.[4] By choosing a standard eye, or taking an average I could express the facts of colour vision in two diagrams.

---

(1) ULC Add. MSS 7656, M 419. First published in Larmor, *Correspondence*, **2**: 22–3.

(2) Numbers 198 and 201.

(3) In his paper 'On the theory of compound colours, and the relations of the colours of the spectrum', *Phil. Trans.*, **150** (1860): 57–84, esp. 68–9 (= *Scientific Papers*, **1**: 424–5), Maxwell took red, green and blue as standards of spectral colour, marking the positions of the standard colours on the scale of his colour box. See Volume I: 619, 635, 638. Maxwell had corresponded with Stokes on the subject in 1859–60; see Volume I: 619–22, 632, 640, 645–53, 657–8. In a letter to C. J. Monro of 18 February 1862 Maxwell described a new instrument, based on an experimental arrangement described by Newton, for experiments on colour vision: see Volume I: 709. There are some experimental results in colour vision *c*.1862 among Maxwell's manuscripts (ULC Add. MSS 7655, V, b/13).

(4) See Maxwell's paper 'On colour-vision at different points of the retina', *Report of the Fortieth Meeting of the British Association for the Advancement of Science; held at Liverpool in September 1870* (London, 1871), part 2: 40–1 (= *Scientific Papers*, **2**: 230–2). See also Maxwell's letter to Monro of 6 July 1870 (Number 341).

1ˢᵗ a triangle of colour giving relations in the quality of colours and the same for all eyes.⁽⁵⁾

2ⁿᵈ a curve representing the intensity of colour at each point of the spectrum.⁽⁶⁾ This curve is different for different eyes and for different parts of the same eye. These differences may arise from absorption of certain rays before they reach the retina. Irregularities in the curve extending over small spaces are probably of this sort. There may also be differences in the sensibility of the nerves to particular sensations. This would account for inequalities extending over entire regions of colour in a regular manner.

The fact that all colours lie nearly in two straight lines makes it impossible to assign the exact position of the sensation defective in the colour blind.⁽⁷⁾ It lies in the production of the line joining green with the extreme red but its exact position differs according to the normal person with whom the colourblind eye is compared, and colour blind eyes differ as much with regard to intensity of different colours as normal eyes do.

Yours truly
JAMES CLERK MAXWELL

---

(5) Compare Volume I: 620; and Maxwell, 'On the theory of compound colours': 74 and Fig. 4 opposite 84 (= *Scientific Papers*, **1**: 431, 444).

(6) Compare Volume I: 650–1; and Maxwell, 'On the theory of compound colours': Figs. 6, 7 and 9, opposite 84 (= *Scientific Papers*, **1**: 444).

(7) Compare Maxwell, 'On the theory of compound colours': 81 and Fig. 10 opposite 84 (= *Scientific Papers*, **1**: 440, 444); 'The triangle of colours is reduced, in the case of dichromic vision, to a straight line'.

203

MANUSCRIPT ON DIAGRAMS OF FORCES[1]

circa NOVEMBER 1862[2]

From the original in the King's College London Archives[3]

MECHANICAL DIAGRAMS & DIAGRAMS OF FORCES[4]

A mechanical diagram is a figure of a structure in which lines are drawn between the different points of a structure indicating the *direction* of the forces which act between them.[5]

The forces which act between two points are either *Tensions* pulling them together or *Pressures* pushing them asunder. We reckon Tensions positive and Pressures negative. The action on the one point is always equal and opposite to that on the other. In the mechanical diagram each line of action is distinguished by a letter.

A Diagram of Forces is a figure in which every force in the mechanical diagram is represented in magnitude and direction by a line parallel to its line of action in the 1st Diagram and distinguished by the same letter.

Every system of forces in the mechanical diagram which $\begin{cases} \text{act at} \\ \text{pass through} \end{cases}$ one point is represented in the diagram of forces by a closed figure whose sides are parallel and proportional to the forces.

When the lines meeting at a point in either figure form a closed figure in the other the two diagrams are said to be *reciprocal*.

When a frame is loaded only at external points on one side or the other, so that no piece which forms a side of two closed figures is loaded at both ends a reciprocal figure can always be drawn.

All the loads are represented by consecutive parts of the same straight line.

---

(1) Probably notes for a lecture to the class of applied mechanics at King's College London: see Number 334.

(2) The entries following this note in Maxwell's notebook (see note (3)), class exercises for King's College London, are dated November 1862.

(3) Notebook of James Clerk Maxwell (1), King's College London Archives.

(4) In his paper 'On reciprocal figures and diagrams of forces', *Phil. Mag.*, ser. 4, **27** (1864): 250–61, on 251 (= *Scientific Papers*, **1**: 515), Maxwell states that he was indebted to a discussion by W. J. M. Rankine, *A Manual of Applied Mechanics* (London/Glasgow, 1858): 137–40, for a general statement of the method of diagrams of forces.

(5) See also Numbers 273 and 334.

204
LETTER TO JOHN WILLIAM CUNNINGHAM[1]
5 DECEMBER 1862
From the original in the King's College London Archives[2]

8 Palace Gardens Terrace
W
5 Dec 1862

Dear Sir

I am very anxious that the examination papers in Mechanics should be printed from type instead of from stone.

I find that the lithographic papers are printed so that even if everything is plain in perfect copies, uncertainties exist in other copies which are very apt to make the examination not quite a fair one.

Mr Smalley[3] has the M.S. and expects to give it in at the office today.

Yours truly
J. CLERK MAXWELL

J W Cunningham Esqre

---

(1) Secretary of King's College London.

(2) King's College London Archives, KA/IC/M 67. Previously published in C. Domb, 'James Clerk Maxwell in London, 1860–1865', *Notes and Records of the Royal Society*, **35** (1980): 67–103, on 79.

(3) George Robarts Smalley, St John's 1841, Mathematical Master at King's College School (Venn), was appointed to a College Lectureship in Natural Philosophy on 11 October 1861. The appointment was made on the grounds that the 'duties [were]...too heavy for one person properly to discharge' (King's College London Archives, King's College Council Vol. I, minute 42). Smalley had been a candidate for the Professorship of Natural Philosophy (to which Maxwell was appointed) in 1860; see Volume I: 662n. On his duties as lecturer see Number 209.

205

REPORT ON A PAPER BY GEORGE BIDDELL AIRY ON STRESS IN BEAMS

LATE DECEMBER 1862[1]

From the original in the Library of the Royal Society, London[2]

REPORT ON THE ASTRONOMER ROYAL'S PAPER ON THE STRAINS[3] IN THE INTERIOR OF BEAMS[4]

In this paper the Author investigates the conditions of equilibrium of the forces of tension and pressure acting in the interior of a heavy lamina, and applies his results to cases of beams supported and loaded in different ways.

The laws of the resolution and composition of internal pressures and tensions acting in the same plane are established, and then, by considering the equilibrium of a portion of the beam divided from the rest by an imaginary line of any form, the author arrives at a result, which, being treated by means of the Calculus of Variations, gives the equations of equilibrium of the vertical and horizontal pressures and shearing forces.

These equations are partial differential equations, one solution of which is, that these three forces are the three second differential coefficients of a single function of x and y.[5] In the general form of the solution, arbitrary functions of x and y, respectively, are added to the 2nd diffl coeffts with respect to x & y respectively. The author, however, considers that the effect of these terms is merely to express accidental distributions of pressure arising from the beam being originally in a state of strain. In this investigation which has reference to the *additional* stresses[6] due to the external applied forces, they are therefore disregarded. We shall see the effect of this hereafter.

The Author then assumes an expression containing a sufficient number of terms of powers and products of x and y as the form of the function to be found, and reduces it by the equations of condition, till it contains only three arbitrary constants.

---

(1) See Number 206. According to the Royal Society's *Register of Papers Received* Airy's paper was referred to Maxwell on 18 December 1863, and to Rankine on 31 December 1863.

(2) Royal Society's *Referees' Reports*, **5**: 6.

(3) For Maxwell's comment on Airy's use of the term 'strain' see Number 206 esp. note (7).

(4) George Biddell Airy, 'On the strains in the interior of beams', *Phil. Trans.*, **153** (1863): 49–79. The paper was received by the Royal Society on 6 November 1862, and read on 11 December 1862; see the abstract in *Proc. Roy. Soc.*, **12** (1862): 304–6.

(5) See note (10).

(6) On Maxwell's use of the term 'stress' see Number 206 esp. note (7).

To determine these three quantities the original equations are not sufficient. (We must refer to this again.)⁽⁷⁾ The Author therefore avails himself of the following hypothesis deduced from experiment by several writers on this subject (Young &c).⁽⁸⁾

That the middle point of any vertical section is a neutral point (having no horizontal pressure or tension) and that the horizontal pressures below this point are equal to the tensions at points equally distant above it.⁽⁹⁾

From this supposition he is enabled to deduce the form of the function F,⁽¹⁰⁾ and from it the nature of the forces acting at any point. Tables are given, showing the values of the principal pressures at selected points and the angles they make with the vertical, and this is done for a beam projecting from a wall, a beam supported on two piers & unloaded, centrally loaded, and excentrically loaded, a beam fixed at both ends, and a beam fixed at one end and supported at the other. Diagrams are added,⁽¹¹⁾ showing the direction of the axes of stress at every point of the beam in each of these cases and it is easy to see from these diagrams the general character of the forces in a way which will be practically useful to all who wish to understand the subject.

I therefore regard this paper as a valuable one with regard to its subject and its results but I have some remarks to make upon the physical and mathematical principles by which these results are worked out.

The objection which I have to the method of investigation is that the conditions arising from the elasticity of the beam are not taken account of at all or even mentioned.⁽¹²⁾

---

(7) See *infra* and note (21).

(8) W. J. M. Rankine, *A Manual of Applied Mechanics* (London/Glasgow, 1858): 73–4. There is a general discussion of the elasticity of beams by Thomas Young, *A Course of Lectures on Natural Philosophy and the Mechanical Arts*, 2 vols. (London, 1807), **1**: 135–52.

(9) Airy, 'On the strains in the interior of beams': 58.

(10) Maxwell subsequently developed the application of this function in his papers 'On reciprocal diagrams in space, and their relation to Airy's function of stress', *Proceedings of the London Mathematical Society*, **2** (1868): 58–60 (= *Scientific Papers*, **2**: 102–5); and 'On reciprocal figures, frames and diagrams of forces', *Trans. Roy. Soc. Edinb.*, **25** (1870): 1–40, esp. 27–31 (= *Scientific Papers*, **2**: 192–7), where he referred to Airy's 'important simplification of the theory of the equilibrium of stress in two dimensions' by means of the stress function. See Number 334. In his report on Airy's paper, dated 26 January 1863 (Royal Society, *Referees' Reports*, **5**: 1), W. J. M. Rankine observed that 'the introduction of that function F... leads to remarkably clear, simple, and certain methods of solving problems respecting the strains in the interior of beams'.

(11) Plates V, VI and VII in *Phil. Trans.*, **153** (1863).

(12) In a letter to Stokes of 22 February 1863 (Royal Society, *Referees' Reports*, **5**: 4), having been sent Maxwell's report, Airy responded: 'This remark astonishes me. The elasticity and its law, are the foundations of every one of my applications of the new theory.' In support of this

Now there are certain mechanical investigations in which it is of use to consider elasticity when the question relates altogether to forces. When we regard a beam as a mere line, and enquire into the whole moment of bending tending to break it across any given point, we obtain the result without requiring to take notice of the yielding of the beam.

Even when the question relates to a beam of finite depth as in the case before us, it seems likely, and is I believe demonstrable, that the final result, giving the value of the forces at any point, will be independent of the coefficients of elasticity, provided all parts of the beam are equally elastic. But I do not think that we can obtain the forces acting between the parts of any system without knowing the conditions under which the distance of those parts is variable, unless there are no more connexions between the parts than are just sufficient to fix each point. If there are more connexions we require to know something of the elasticity of the connexions, or the question is indeterminate.

In the present paper a system of forces is given which fulfils the conditions of internal equilibrium and the conditions of no pressure at the free surface. Such a system of forces might exist in a beam, if it could be produced in it by the straining of an elastic solid. But whether this is the system of internal forces which would be *produced* in a beam by the action of the given external forces is as yet undecided.

Conceive a beam free from weight, and projecting from a wall and having its interior in a state of strain but in equilibrium among themselves. Now let gravity act on the beam. It will produce an additional system of internal forces superimposed on the first. Will this additional system be the same as that which the author has obtained in his first example?[13] I think it is necessary to examine the question before we can decide.

Writing as in the paper $LM-Q$ for the pressure parallel to x, the shearing

---

contention he cites passages from his paper (see note (21) and also Airy, 'On the strains in the interior of beams': 49, 56, 58–9), concluding: 'in every instance, the value of the function [F] is found from a process which rests ENTIRELY on the theory of elasticity.' For Maxwell's response see Number 212, esp. note (2), Airy having acquiesced to Stokes' inquiry in a letter of 26 February 1863 (Royal Greenwich Observatory Archive, ULC, Airy Papers 6/392, 124R–125V): 'Would you have any objection to letting me forward to him your letter to me?...'. Stokes continued: 'I have not as yet myself read your paper, and therefore cannot fully enter into the report and your letter; but unless I greatly mistake I catch his meaning – that your investigation takes account of *systems of forces only* not entering into displacements; that your result is therefore necessarily FROM THE VERY PRINCIPLE OF THE PROCESS, indeterminate'.

(13) Airy, 'On the strains in the interior of beams': 57–60.

force and the pressure parallel to y ($p_{xx} p_{xy}$ and p_{yy} in Rankine)[14] then the eq^n of eq^m are

$$\frac{d}{dx}p_{xx} + \frac{d}{dy}p_{xy} = 0$$

$$\frac{d}{dx}p_{xy} + \frac{d}{dy}p_{yy} + g = 0$$

writing g for gravity that we may know what terms depend on it.[15]

Putting $M = p_{xy} = -\dfrac{d^2 F}{dx\,dy}$ we find

$$L = p_{xx} = \frac{d^2 F}{dy^2} + Y \quad \text{(a function of } y \text{ only)}$$

$$Q = p_{yy} = \frac{d^2 F}{dx^2} + X - gy \quad (X \text{ a function of } x \text{ only}).^{(16)}$$

Let us suppose the beam isotropic in its elasticity then if $\xi \eta \zeta$ be the displacements in $x\,y\,z$ and if μ & m coeffts of cubic & linear elasticity[17]

$$\frac{d\xi}{dx} = \left(\frac{1}{9\mu} + \frac{2}{3m}\right)p_{xx} + \left(\frac{1}{9\mu} - \frac{1}{3m}\right)(p_{yy} + p_{zz})^{(18)}$$

$$\frac{d\eta}{dy} = \left(\frac{1}{9\mu} + \frac{2}{3m}\right)p_{yy} + \left(\frac{1}{9\mu} - \frac{1}{3m}\right)(p_{zz} + p_{xx})$$

$$\frac{d\zeta}{dz} = \left(\frac{1}{9\mu} + \frac{2}{3m}\right)p_{zz} + \left(\frac{1}{9\mu} - \frac{1}{3m}\right)(p_{xx} + p_{yy})$$

$$\frac{d\xi}{dy} + \frac{d\eta}{dx} = \frac{2}{m}(p_{xy}).$$

---

(14) Rankine, *Applied Mechanics*: 89; in Rankine's symbolism p denotes 'intensity of a stress', and of the subscript letters he intended 'the first small letter to denote the direction perpendicular to the plane on which the stress acts, and the second to denote the direction of the stress itself'.

(15) In 'On the strains in the interior of beams': 54 Airy wrote $y - Q = 0$, y being a vertical ordinate representing gravity.

(16) Compare Airy, 'On the strains in the interior of beams': 55, where he establishes that 'L, M, O are the three partial differential equations of the second order of a function F of x and y, such that $L = d^2F/dy^2$, $M = d^2F/dx\,dy$, $O = d^2F/dx^2$'. See notes (10) and (15).

(17) Maxwell uses the symbols for these coefficients – there termed the 'moduli of cubical and linear elasticity' – which he had introduced in his paper 'On the equilibrium of elastic solids', *Trans. Roy. Soc. Edinb.*, **20** (1850): 87–120 (= *Scientific Papers*, **1**: 30–73). See Volume I: 135.

(18) The form of these equations of elasticity is drawn from those of 'On the equilibrium of elastic solids': 90–5 (= *Scientific Papers*, **1**: 34–41). See Volume I: 157–63.

Now there are two cases we may consider. 1st a very thin lamina free from pressure along z, then $p_{zz} = 0$. 2nd a very thin plank unable to expand in z, then $\zeta = 0$ and

$$p_{zz} = -\frac{\dfrac{1}{9\mu}-\dfrac{1}{3m}}{\dfrac{1}{9\mu}+\dfrac{2}{3m}}(p_{xx}+p_{yy}) = -h(p_{xx}+p_{yy}).$$

Integrating we find

$$\xi = \overset{(1-h^2)}{\left(\frac{1}{9\mu}+\frac{2}{3m}\right)}\int p_{xx}\,dx + \overset{(1-h)}{\left(\frac{1}{9\mu}-\frac{1}{3m}\right)}\left(\frac{dF}{dx}+\int X\,dx - gxy\right)$$

$$\eta = \overset{(1-h^2)}{\left(\frac{1}{9\mu}+\frac{2}{3m}\right)}\int p_{yy}\,dy + \overset{(1-h)}{\left(\frac{1}{9\mu}-\frac{1}{3m}\right)}\left(\frac{dF}{dy}+\int Y\,dy\right)$$

and the factors written above the line are to be used in case 2nd only. Differentiating and adding we find

$$\frac{d\xi}{dy}+\frac{d\eta}{dx} = \overset{(1-h^2)}{\left(\frac{1}{9\mu}+\frac{2}{3m}\right)}\left(\frac{d}{dy}\int p_{xx}\,dx + \frac{d}{dx}\int p_{yy}\,dy\right)$$

$$+\overset{(1-h)}{\left(\frac{1}{9\mu}-\frac{1}{3m}\right)}\left(2\frac{d^2F}{dx\,dy}-gx\right)$$

$$=\frac{2}{m}\frac{d^2F}{dx\,dy}.$$

$$\therefore \frac{d}{dy}\int p_{xx}\,dx - 2p_{xy} + \frac{d}{dx}\int p_{yy}\,dy - \overset{\frac{1}{1-h}}{g}hx = 0.$$

Note. The value of h does not affect the distribution of forces.

This is the equation depending on the fact that the beam was unstrained before the weight began to act. Let us examine whether the solution in the present paper fulfils it.

We have at Page 11[19]

$$p_{xx} = \frac{d^2F}{dy^2} = \frac{3}{s^2}(r-x)^2(s-2y)$$

$$\int p_{xx}\,dx = -\frac{1}{s^2}(r-x)^3(s-2y) + Y'$$

$$\frac{d}{dy}\int p_{xx}\,dx = \frac{2}{s^2}(r-x)^3 + \frac{dY'}{dy}$$

$$p_{xy} = -\frac{d^2F}{dx\,dy} = \frac{6}{s^2}(r-x)(sy-y^2)$$

$$p_{yy} = \frac{d^2F}{dx^2} - y = \frac{1}{s^2}(3sy^2 - 2y^3) - y$$

$$\int p_{yy}\,dy = \frac{1}{s^2}(sy^3 - \tfrac{1}{2}y^4) - \tfrac{1}{2}y^2 + X'$$

$$\frac{d}{dx}\int p_{yy}\,dy = \frac{dX'}{dx}.$$

The equation of condition now becomes

$$\frac{2}{s^2}(r-x)^3 - \frac{12}{s^2}(r-x)(sy-y^2) + \frac{dX'}{dx} + \frac{dY'}{dy} - ghx = 0.$$

Now $\frac{dX'}{dx}$ is a function of x and constants and $\frac{dY'}{dy}$ is a function of y and constants. These may be so assumed as to make the equation true, whatever functions of x alone or y alone enter into it. But the second term is a function of x and y and therefore the author's solution does not satisfy this equation.

Let us now introduce the terms which he has neglected in the expressions for p_{xx} & p_{yy} namely Y & X. These terms will produce terms in the equation of condition of the form $x\frac{dY}{dy} + y\frac{dX}{dx}$ so that if we make

$$\frac{dY}{dy} = -\frac{12}{s^2}(sy-y^2) \quad \text{and} \quad Y = -\frac{2}{s^2}(3sy^2 - 2y^3) + Ay + B$$

the equation of condition will be satisfied. In this case

$$p_{xx} = \frac{3}{s^2}(r-x)(s-2y) - \frac{2}{s^2}(3sy^2 - 2y^3) + Ay + B$$

---

(19) Airy, 'On the strains in the interior of beams': 59. Using the symbols introduced by Airy, r and s are the length and depth of the beam, x the horizontal abscissa, and y the vertical ordinate.

and the other forces remain as before. This solution satisfies the condition that the beam will return to a state of no strain if its weight were abolished, but it does not satisfy the condition that $p = 0$ at the end of the beam. To make the solution complete we should require to calculate the effect of a distribution of pressure represented by $\frac{2}{s^2}(3sy^2 - 2y^3) + Ay + B$ on the end of a beam fixed at the other end and unaffected by gravity. I have not been able to do this. The condition of no longitudinal pressure on any part of the free end of the beam renders the exact determination of the forces much more difficult. The difference, however, between the exact solution and that of this paper will in the case of long beams be very small, and only sensible very near the end.

If we determine A and B so as to make the *total* longitudinal pressure $= 0$ and also the *total* moment of bending in the bounding vertical surface $= 0$ we find for the value of p_{xx}

$$p_{xx} = \frac{3}{s^2}(r-x)^2(s-2y) + s\left(\frac{4y^3}{s^3} - \frac{6y^2}{s^2} + \frac{12}{5}\frac{y}{s} + \frac{1}{5}\right)$$

$$= s\left(\frac{2y}{s} - 1\right)\left\{-3\frac{r^2}{s^2}\left(1-\frac{x}{r}\right)^2 + 2\frac{y^2}{s^2} - 2\frac{y}{s} + \frac{1}{5}\right\}.$$

This is the nearest approximation to the solution of Case 1st that I can obtain. It corresponds to the case of a beam infinite in length, acted on by its own weight and by other forces at a great distance on each side of the part considered, in such a way as to make the *total* longitudinal, bending and shearing forces at the section $(r = x)$ disappear. Case 2 – the beam resting on piers at its extremities[20] – may be modified in the same way by supposing it produced both ways and such vertical forces and couples applied at the extremities, that the moment of bending shall disappear at the points corresponding to the piers.

The actual case is complicated by the conditions relating to the two free surfaces at the ends and to the upward pressure of the piers, which will introduce terms depending on inverse powers of the distance from the points where the pressure is applied. These inverse powers of a distance would occur also in an exact solution of the cases in which weight is applied at a point of the beam.

If any one can work out the *exact* solutions, he will have performed a mathematical feat, but I do not think he will have added anything to our practical knowledge of the forces in a beam not near the ends or the points

---

(20) Airy, 'On the strains in the interior of beams': 60–3.

where pressures are applied. For all such points the formulæ obtained in this paper are quite satisfactory and as far as I know they are new.

I must also remark that the supposition made at page 9 about horizontal pressures and the position of the neutral line,[21] are not required, for if we assume $F = (ax^2 + bx + c)y^2 + (ex^2 + fx + g)y^3$ [22] we can determine *all* the constants from the following conditions at the surfaces.

$\frac{d^2F}{dx\,dy} = 0$ 1st when $y = 0$ 2nd when $y = s$ 3rd when $x = r$

$\frac{d^2F}{dx^2} - y = 0$ 1st when $y = 0$ 2nd when $y = s$

$\frac{d^2F}{dy^2} = 0$ when $x = r$.

The result is the same as that given in the paper.[23] I think therefore that this assumption may be dispensed with, and if some notice were taken of the fact that the beam is in some slight degree elastic the paper would be more valuable as a part of the Transactions.[24]

JAMES CLERK MAXWELL

(21) See *supra* and note (9). In his response to Maxwell's critique (see note (12)) Airy cited this passage of his paper, italicising a key clause: '..."the usual assumptions, namely, that there is a neutral point in the centre of the depth, that on the upper side of this neutral point the forces are forces of tension, and on the lower side are forces of compression, and that *these forces are proportional to the distances from the neutral point with equal coefficients on both sides*...". (These last words embody the whole ordinary theory of elasticity. They denote that the elastic forces put in play are proportional to the extension or compression of the material....)'.

(22) As in Airy, 'On the strains in the interior of beams': 57.

(23) Airy, 'On the strains in the interior of beams': 58–60.

(24) In contrast to Maxwell, Rankine raised no objections to Airy's paper in finding that the paper was 'theoretically interesting, and practically useful, in the highest degree, and well worthy of being published in the Transactions'. See also Number 206 note (7).

LETTER TO GEORGE GABRIEL STOKES

29 DECEMBER 1862

From the original in the University Library, Cambridge[1]

Glenlair,
Dalbeattie
29 Dec 1862

Dear Stokes

I enclose a report on the Astronomer Royal's paper on Strains in Beams.[2] I am not enough up in the literature of the subject to say whether it is quite new. I have not Lamés Leçons[3] to refer to and there may be something of the kind in the Journal de L'École Polytechnique.

The establishment of the eq^{ns} of equilibrium of stresses is very well done in Rankine especially for forces in one plane.[4]

But I do not believe that any solution can be other than indeterminate unless we assume a law for the *elasticity* of the beam. The simplest law is that it shall be uniformly elastic and by what I must regard as a mathematical accident the solution in the paper nearly coincides with this supposition.

It does not matter what the numerical value of the elasticity is provided it is uniform, but if it is not uniform or if the lamina be of variable thickness then the stiffest parts will support the greatest forces, no matter how small the actual deflexion may be.

There are two pieces of verbal criticism I have not put in the report because sometimes an author by the frequent use of a word establishes for it a peculiar meaning in his own writings.

The first is at p. 10 et passim 'momentum' plural 'momenta' used to signify the tendency of a force or forces to turn a body round a given point.[5]

English mathematicians generally use 'moment' plural 'moments' in this sense and reserve the other for what Newton calls 'Quantity of Motion'.[6]

---

(1) ULC Add. MSS 7656, M 420.

(2) Number 205.

(3) Gabriel Lamé, *Leçons sur la Théorie Mathématique de l'Élasticité des Corps Solides* (Paris, 1852).

(4) W. J. M. Rankine, *A Manual of Applied Mechanics* (London/Glasgow, 1858): 82–112, esp. 95–8.

(5) In the manuscript of his paper 'On the strains in the interior of beams' (Royal Society, PT. 68.3, on f. 10), Airy used the term 'momentum' and the expression 'equation of momenta' in the sense criticised by Maxwell. In the published text of 'On the strains in the interior of beams', *Phil. Trans.*, **153** (1863): 49–79, on 58, Airy corrected his usage to 'moment' and 'equation of moments'.

(6) Isaac Newton, *Principia*, Definition II; 'Quantitas motus'.

The second is a violation of a rule hardly yet established. It is very useful to have clear distinctions between words expressing forces – tensions – pressures – and words expressing their effects – extensions compressions. It is also useful to have some general word to signify the whole class of actions of each kind. Now a solid is said to be *strained* when its parts are no longer in their primitive relative positions. This is called a state of strain and the displacements themselves properly defined may be called strains.

The internal forces whether pressures tensions or shearing forces have been called by Mr Rankine Stresses[7] and I think that this distinction between strains and stresses ought to be encouraged and recognised as much as possible that our mathematical language may be as complete and accurate as is consistent with its being English.

I must also dissent from the statement that the stress-functions are always in positive integral powers of x & y.[8] They are often in negative powers of r.[9]

Yours truly
J. CLERK MAXWELL

---

(7) Rankine, *Applied Mechanics*: 58. This distinction between 'stress' and 'strain' had been proposed by Rankine in his paper 'On axes of elasticity and crystalline forms', *Phil. Trans.*, **146** (1856): 261–85, esp. 262; and subsequently modified by William Thomson, 'Elements of a mathematical theory of elasticity', *ibid.*: 481–98, esp 481. Maxwell had immediately adopted this usage; see Volume I: 489. In his report on Airy's paper (Royal Society, *Referees' Reports*, 5: 1) Rankine did not object to Airy's use of the term 'strain'; see Number 205 note (10).

(8) Airy, 'On the strains in the interior of beams': 56–7.

(9) See Number 205 esp. note (19).

= 207 =

DRAFT PAPER ON THE CONDUCTION OF HEAT IN GASES[1]

circa SPRING 1863[2]

From the original in the University Library, Cambridge[3]

ON THE CONDUCTION OF HEAT IN GASES[4]

In the Philosophical Magazine for January and July 1860 I applied the theory of the motions and collisions of small elastic particles to the explanation of various properties of gases,[5] according to the analogies already pointed out by Daniel Bernoulli[6] and others and more recently by M. Clausius.*[7] That theory supposes that the particles of gases are in rapid motion, that they

* [7]

---

(1) This manuscript paper, written as if intended for publication (see Number 377 para. 12), constitutes Maxwell's considered response to criticisms of his 1860 theory of gases (see note (5)) advanced by Rudolf Clausius, 'Ueber die Wärmeleitung gasförmiger Körper', *Ann. Phys.*, **115** (1862): 1–56, to which he first alludes in a letter to Lewis Campbell of 21 April 1862 (Volume I: 711–12; and see also Volume I: 713–24).

(2) See Number 377, paras, 12 and 14, where Maxwell implies that this paper was written before his experiments in 1865 on the viscosity of gases (see Numbers 244, 245 and 246). He informed Stokes of his intention to undertake these experiments in a letter of 9 June 1863 (Number 212, and see esp. note (11)). It seems plausible to assume that he wrote the present paper before deciding to resort to an experimental test.

(3) ULC Add. MSS 7655, V, f/5. Previously published in *Molecules and Gases*: 339–47; see note (35).

(4) Compare the title of the English translation of Clausius' paper 'Ueber die Wärmeleitung gasförmiger Körper': 'On the conduction of heat by gases', *Phil. Mag.*, ser. 4, **23** (1862): 417–35, 512–34.

(5) J. C. Maxwell, 'Illustrations of the dynamical theory of gases', *Phil. Mag.*, ser. 4, **19** (1860): 19–32; *ibid.*, **20** (1860): 21–37 (= *Scientific Papers*, **1**: 377–409).

(6) Daniel Bernoulli, *Hydrodynamica, sive de Viribus et Motibus Fluidorum Commentarii* (Strasbourg, 1738): 200–2.

(7) Rudolf Clausius, 'Ueber die Art der Bewegung, welche wir Wärme nennen', *Ann. Phys.*, **100** (1857): 353–80; (trans.) 'On the kind of motion which we call heat', *Phil. Mag.*, ser. 4, **14** (1857): 108–27; and Clausius, 'Ueber die mittlere Länge der Wege, welche bei der Molecularbewegung gasförmiger Körper von den einzelnen Molecülen zurückgelegt werden; nebst einigen anderen Bemerkungen über die mechanische Wärmetheorie', *Ann. Phys.*, **105** (1858): 239–58; (trans.) 'On the mean length of the paths described by the separate molecules of gaseous bodies on the occurrence of molecular motion: together with some other remarks upon the mechanical theory of heat', *Phil. Mag.*, ser. 4, **17** (1859): 81–91. For Maxwell's account of work on the 'Kinetic Theory of Gases' see Number 377.

do not act on one another except within a very small distance, but that an exceedingly intense repulsive force comes into action when two particles come within this distance from each other. The particles therefore move in straight lines except when they come within the reach of the repulsive action of other particles which alters their motion with a suddenness like that of the impact of elastic bodies. The path of each particle is thus made up of a succession of straight lines and very sharp curves, and the mode in which the motion of one set of particles influences that of another will depend upon the average length of the straight part of the path as well as on the mass and velocity of the particles.

M. Clausius has recently published an investigation of the particular case of the conduction of heat through a gas†[8] which was very imperfectly treated by me in the paper referred to. He has pointed out several oversights in my calculation.[9] I have reexamined it and found some others the influence of which extends to other parts of my investigation.§[10] I shall therefore state here so much of my former results as will make the requisite corrections intelligible, and I shall retain the methods used in my former paper except when obliged to compare them with those of M. Clausius.

1   In my former paper I investigated the results of the collision of two elastic spheres and found that the velocity of each after the collision is resolvable into two parts, one of which is equal to the velocity of the centre of gravity of the two spheres before impact, and in the same

† Pogg Annalen Jan 1862[8]   § Prop XXI[10]

---

(8) Clausius, 'Ueber die Wärmeleitung gasförmiger Körper'.

(9) Maxwell had erred, as Clausius pointed out, in that he had disregarded the additional kinetic energy associated with motion in the direction of the temperature gradient within the gas, and assumed an isotropic distribution function; see 'Illustrations of the dynamical theory of gases. Part II. On the process of diffusion of two or more kinds of moving particles among one another', *Phil. Mag.*, ser. 4, **20** (1860): 21–33 (= *Scientific Papers*, **1**: 392–405). Clausius commented ('Ueber die Wärmeleitung gasförmiger Körper': 13n): 'Maxwell hat in seiner oben erwähnten Abhandlung (*Phil. Mag.*, Vol. XX) bei der Bestimmung der Wärmeleitung den Umstand, dass die von einer Schicht ausgesandten Molecüle einen Ueberschuss an positiver Bewegungsgrösse haben, nicht berücksichtigt, sondern hat in seinen Rechnungen stillschweigend vorausgesetzt, dass die Molecüle nach allen Richtungen in gleicher Weise ausgesandt werden.' For Clausius' further criticism of Maxwell's treatment of the conduction of heat in gases see note (39). Clausius also drew attention to two oversights in his estimate of the ratio of the conductivities of air and copper; see 'Ueber die Wärmeleitung gasförmiger Körper': 54n, and Number 377 para. (11) and note (22).

(10) Prop. XXI of 'Illustrations of the dynamical theory of gases. Part II': 31–3 (= *Scientific Papers*, **1**: 403–5): 'To find the amount of energy which crosses unit of area in unit of time when the velocity of agitation is greater on one side than on the other'.

direction while the other is equal to the relative velocity of the sphere with respect to the centre of gravity and may, with equal probability be in any direction.

2 If a great many particles are in motion in the same vessel they will not all have the same velocity, but the average number of particles whose velocity lies within the limits v and $v+dv$ will be

$$N \frac{4}{\alpha^3 \sqrt{\pi}} v^2 e^{-\frac{v^2}{\alpha^2}} dv \qquad (1)$$

where N is the whole number of particles, and α a constant depending on the velocity. The velocities range through all possible values but more particles have a velocity $= \alpha$ than any other given velocity. The mean values of the different powers of v are found by integration to be

$$\frac{1}{v} = \frac{2}{\alpha \sqrt{\pi}}, \quad v = \frac{2\alpha}{\sqrt{\pi}}, \quad v^2 = \frac{3}{2}\alpha^2 \quad v^3 = \frac{4\alpha^3}{\sqrt{\pi}}. \qquad (2)$$

Whenever we have to take the mean values of any power of v we must use the value here given, and not that got by raising the mean value of v to the given power.

3 The motion of the particles after a sufficient number of collisions will be compounded of a velocity V in a given direction, the same for all the particles, and a velocity v which may be in any direction and of which the values are distributed according to the law of eq^n (1). We shall call V the motion of translation and v the motion of agitation.[11]

4 If the velocities of agitation of two systems are distributed according to the law of eq^n (1) then the relative velocities of the particles, one in each system will be distributed according to the same law, but the mean relative velocity of agitation will be the square root of the sum of the squares of the mean velocities of agitation in the two systems.*[12]

*Note. In his original investigation of the length of path described by a particle M. Clausius has assumed the velocities of all the particles in each system to be equal, and in a communication to the Philosophical Magazine he has shown that on that supposition if v_1 and v_2 be the velocities in each system the mean relative velocity is not $\sqrt{v_1^2 + v_2^2}$ but $v_1 + \frac{1}{3}\frac{v_2^2}{v_1}$ where v_1 is the

---

(11) Maxwell, 'Illustrations of the dynamical theory of gases. Part I. On the motions and collisions of perfectly elastic spheres', *Phil. Mag.*, ser. 4, **19** (1860): 19–32, esp. 23–4 (= *Scientific Papers*, **1**: 381–2).

(12) See Maxwell's letter to Stokes of 30 May 1859 (Volume 1: 606–11).

greater of the two velocities. If however the velocities in each system follow the law of eq^n (1) then the mean relative velocity is $\sqrt{v_1^2+v_2^2}$.[13]

By the same method of demonstration it may be shown that if any quantity u is a linear function of several independent quantities $x\,y\,z$ of the form
$$u = ax + by + cz \qquad (3)$$
then if $x\,y\,z$ are distributed according to the law of eq^n (1), u will also be distributed according to that law and the mean values of u, x, y & z will be connected by the equation
$$u^2 = a^2x^2 + b^2y^2 + c^2z^2. \qquad (4)$$

5   The pressure of a gas is one third of the density multiplied by the mean of the square of the velocity.[14] Now if T be the absolute temperature[15] and $p_0\,\rho_0$ the pressure and density when $T = T_0$ then we know by experiment that
$$p = \frac{p_0 \rho T}{\rho_0 T_0} \text{[16]}$$
whence we find $\overline{v^2} = 3\dfrac{p_0}{\rho_0 T_0}T$

or the velocity varies as the square root of the temperature.

6   When particles of different kinds are allowed to communicate their motion of agitation to each other the average *vis viva*[17] of the particles

---

(13) Clausius expressed the velocity of the gas molecules as an average velocity, while Maxwell introduced a statistical distribution function. Clausius had attempted to justify his method in a paper 'On the dynamical theory of gases', *Phil. Mag.*, ser. 4, **19** (1860): 434–6. Clausius' unconvincing objection to Maxwell's mathematical method in 'Illustrations of the dynamical theory of gases. Part I' drew no response from Maxwell: see his comments in Numbers 284 and 377; and W. D. Niven's note in *Scientific Papers*, **1**: 387.

(14) Maxwell, 'Illustrations of the dynamical theory of gases. Part I': 30 (= *Scientific Papers*, **1**: 389). See note (37) and Volume I: 607n.

(15) See William Thomson, 'On an absolute thermometric scale founded on Carnot's theory of the motive power of heat, and calculated from Regnault's observations', *Proc. Camb. Phil. Soc.*, **1** (1848): 66–71 (= *Math. & Phys. Papers*, **1**: 100–6); and Thomson, 'On the dynamical theory of heat. Part V. Thermo-electric currents', *Trans. Roy. Soc. Edinb.*, **21** (1854): 123–71, esp. 125 (= *Math. & Phys. Papers*, **1**: 235), where he states that 'the absolute values of two temperatures are to one another in the proportion of the heat taken in to the heat rejected in a perfect thermodynamic engine working with a source and refrigerator at the higher and lower of the temperatures respectively'.

(16) See W. J. M. Rankine, *A Manual of the Steam Engine and other Prime Movers* (London/Glasgow, 1859): 228.

(17) The term *vis viva* was still generally used, its usage becoming obsolete after Thomson and Tait introduced the term 'kinetic energy' in their *Treatise on Natural Philosophy* (Oxford, 1867): 195. For an account of energy terms see Volume I: 549–51n.

tends to become the same in both sets of particles, or if M_1 and M_2 are the masses of an atom in the two systems then when there is equilibrium of temperature
$$M_1 v_1^2 = M_2 v_2^2$$

or
$$\frac{M_1}{M_2} = \frac{v_2^2}{v_1^2} = \frac{p_2 \rho_1}{p_1 \rho_2}$$

so that when the pressures and temperatures of two gases are the same the atomic weights are proportional to the densities.[18]

7 By considering the effect of the collisions of bodies of any form not spherical it appears that the vis viva of rotation tends to become equal to that of translation so that the whole energy in unit of volume is not $\frac{1}{2}\rho v^2$ as in the case of perfect spheres, but ρv^2.[19] In a medium consisting partly of perfect spheres and partly of other bodies the energy will be $\frac{1}{2}\beta \rho v^2$ where
$$\beta = 1 + q$$

where q is the ratio of the mass of the non-spherical particles to the whole mass.[20]

If γ is the ratio of the specific heat under constant pressure to that under constant volume
$$\gamma = 1 + \frac{2}{3\beta}.$$

If the particles are all spherical with their centres of figure and mass coincident then $q = 0$, $\beta = 1$ and $\gamma = 1\frac{2}{3} = 1.\dot{6}$.

If none of the particles fulfil these conditions then $q = 1$ $\beta = 2$ $\gamma = 1\frac{1}{3} = 1.\dot{3}$.

These are the two extreme cases.

In the case of air $\gamma = 1.408$[21] $\beta = 1.634$ $q = .634$ $1 - q = .366$
so that according to the theory we are treating of we must suppose .634 of the weight of air to consist of non spherical particles and .366 of its

---

(18) Maxwell, 'Illustrations of the dynamical theory of gases. Part I': 30 (= *Scientific Papers*, **1**: 389–90).

(19) On the equipartition theorem of the distribution of kinetic energy among the translational and rotational motions of the particles, see Maxwell, 'Illustrations of the dynamical theory of gases. Part III. On the collision of perfectly elastic bodies of any form', *Phil. Mag.*, ser. 4, **20** (1860): 33–7 (= *Scientific Papers*, **1**: 405–9).

(20) β is 'the ratio of the whole *vis viva* to the *vis viva* of translation'; Maxwell, 'Illustrations of the dynamical theory of gases. Part III': 36 (= *Scientific Papers*, **1**: 409). See Clausius, 'Ueber die Art der Bewegung welche wir Wärme nennen': 377–80.

(21) The accepted contemporary value. See Rankine, *Manual of the Steam Engine*: 319–20. For discussion of this value see Volume I: 608–9n.

weight to consist of perfectly spherical particles having their centres of gravity at their centres.

In the case of Oxygen Hydrogen and Nitrogen the proportions must be supposed nearly the same as in air, but in Carbonic Acid we must suppose the proportion of spherical particles to be smaller.

In the case of Steam, if we admit the value of γ given at p. 320 of 'Rankine on the Steam Engine' is correct[22] we find

$$\gamma = 1.304 \quad \beta = 2.19 \quad q = 1.19 \quad 1-q = -.19$$

that is, we must suppose a negative quantity of spherical particles to exist, or in other words our theory fails to explain how the value of γ can be so low as 1.304.[23]

8   We come now to those properties of gases which depend on the distance which a particle travels between successive collisions. The distance depends on the number of particles in unit of volume and on the distance of the centres of two particles at the moment of collision.

If l_1 be the *mean* length of path of a particle of a gas whose density is ρ_1, mixed with other gases whose densities in the mixture are ρ_2 &c

$$\frac{1}{l_1} = A\rho_1 + B\rho_2 + \&c$$

where $$A = \sqrt{2}\frac{\pi s_1^2}{M_1}, \quad B = \sqrt{1+\frac{v_2^2}{v_1^2}}\frac{\pi s'^2}{M_2}\&c$$

where s_1 is the distance of centres at collision for two particles of the first kind and s' the same for a collision between one of the first and one of the second M_1 & M_2 the masses of particles of each kind and v_1 v_2 the velocities of agitation.

9   The actual length of the path described by a particle between successive collisions is not always the same, but the values of the actual paths are distributed according to the following law, as M. Clausius has shown in his former paper.*[24]

Let l be the mean length of path, then the proportion of the whole particles whose path exceeds nl is e^{-n}.[25]

* Phil. Mag. Feb. 1859[24]

---

(22) Rankine, *Manual of the Steam Engine*: 320.
(23) Compare Maxwell's comments in 'Illustrations of the dynamical theory of gases. Part III': 37 (= *Scientific Papers*, **1**: 409); and in his paper presented to the British Association in 1860 (Volume I: 659–60).   (24) Clausius, 'On the mean length of the paths': 85–7.
(25) Maxwell, 'Illustrations of the dynamical theory of gases. Part I': 27–8 (= *Scientific Papers*, **1**: 386–7).

10 The actual value of the length of path depends on the diameter of the particles and on the number in unit of volume, neither of which quantities are known, but if the internal friction of gases arises from the intermingling of particles from different layers of the moving gas then there will be a relation between l and the coefficient of internal friction, which may be determined by experiments on oscillating bodies[26] and on the passage of gases through long tubes.[27] I have shown that if μ is the tangential force on unit of area when the velocity parallel to that area increases by unity for every unit of length normal to the area

$$\mu = \tfrac{1}{3}\rho l v = \tfrac{1}{3} A v$$

since $\rho l = A$. This shows that μ is proportional to the square root of the absolute temperature, and independent of the density.[28]

From the value of μ given by Professor Stokes†[29] it appears that for air under the ordinary conditions, μ[30] $= \frac{1}{400,000}$ inch nearly.[31]

11 I now come to the question which I neglected to consider in my former paper. When the density and temperature of a gas or the composition of a system of mixed gases vary from one place to another, what is the proportion of particles, which, starting from one given place, arrive at another given place without a collision.

Let us suppose the gas to be a mixture of gases whose densities are ρ_1 ρ_2 &c, their velocities of agitation v_1 v_2 &c all these quantities being functions of x. Let s_1 be the distance of centres for collision between two particles of the first kind, s' for a particle of the first with one of the second.

Let λ_1 be the mean length of path which a particle of the first kind

† [29]

---

(26) O. E. Meyer, 'Ueber die Reibung der Flüssigkeiten', *Ann. Phys.*, **113** (1861): 55–86, 193–228, 383–425. See Maxwell's letter to Campbell of 21 April 1862 (see note (1)).

(27) Thomas Graham, 'A short account of experimental researches on the diffusion of gases through each other, and their separation by mechanical means', *Quarterly Journal of Science*, **28** (1829): 74–83. See Maxwell's letters to Stokes of 30 May 1859 and to Thomas Graham of 1 May 1865 (Number 248).

(28) Maxwell, 'Illustrations of the dynamical theory of gases. Part I': 32 (= *Scientific Papers*, **1**: 391); and see his letter to Stokes of 30 May 1859 (Volume I: 610).

(29) George Gabriel Stokes, 'On the effect of the internal friction of fluids on the motion of pendulums', *Trans. Camb. Phil. Soc.*, **9** part 2 (1851); [8]–[106], esp. 16–17. See Maxwell's letters to Stokes of 7 September 1858 and 30 May 1859 (Volume I: 597–8, 606–11).

(30) Read: *l*.

(31) On this value see Maxwell's discussion in his paper presented to the British Association in 1860 (see note (23)).

having a velocity v' differing slightly from v_1 would have if projected in a system for which $\rho_1\ \rho_2\ v_1\ v_2$ are constant. We find by Prop IX[32]

$$\frac{1}{\lambda_1} = \pi s_1^2 \mathcal{N}_1 \sqrt{1+\frac{v_1^2}{v'^2}} + \pi s'^2 \mathcal{N}_2 \sqrt{1+\frac{v_2^2}{v'^2}}.$$

Putting $v_1 = v' + dv$ we get

$$\frac{1}{\lambda_1} = \sqrt{2}\,\pi s_1^2 \mathcal{N}_1 \left(1+\frac{1}{2}\frac{dv}{v_1}\right) + \pi s'^2 \mathcal{N}_2 \sqrt{1+\frac{v_2^2}{v_1^2}} \left(1+\frac{v^2}{v_1^2+v_2^2}\frac{dv}{v_1}\right)$$

or
$$\frac{1}{\lambda_1} = A\rho_1 \left(1+\frac{1}{2}\frac{dv}{v_1}\right) + B\rho_2 \left(1+\frac{v_2^2}{v_1^2+v_2^2}\frac{dv}{v_1}\right).$$

λ_1 is a function of x, and when $v' = v_1$, $\lambda_1 = l_1$.

If r be measured in any direction and if particles are projected with velocity v' in this direction, then if u represent the number of particles wh: arrive at distance r, the proportion of these which will be stopped in the succeeding portion dr will be $\dfrac{dr}{\lambda_1}$ or in symbols

$$du = u\frac{dr}{\lambda_1}$$

or
$$u = \mathcal{N} e^{-\int_0^r \frac{dr}{\lambda_1}}$$

if $\mathcal{N}$ is the whole number projected and u the number which reach a distance r. Since r must be small because it is the path of a particle we may write $r = n\Lambda$, where $\Lambda = \frac{1}{2}(l_1 + \lambda_1)$ and then

$$u = \mathcal{N} e^{-n}.$$

In all cases therefore, in which the properties of the gas vary from place to place, the number of particles which start from one place and pass through another, depends on the quantity Λ which is a mean distance between l_1 the length of path of the particles at the place where they started, and λ their length of path if they had been projected with their actual velocity at the other place.

By overlooking the differences between $l_1\ \lambda_1\ \&\ \Lambda$, I have gone wrong

---

(32) Maxwell, 'Illustrations of the dynamical theory of gases. Part I': 26–7 (= *Scientific Papers*, **1**: 385–6); for two sets of particles 'to find the number of pairs which approach within a distance s in unit of time.' See also Prop. XI, 'In a mixture of particles of two different kinds, to find the mean free path of each particle.' Maxwell obtains $\dfrac{1}{l_1} = \sqrt{2}\pi s_1^2 \mathcal{N}_1 + \pi \sqrt{1+\dfrac{v_2^2}{v_1^2}}\,s'^2 \mathcal{N}_2$ where l_1 is the mean distance for a particle of the first kind; see 'Illustrations of the dynamical theory of gases. Part I': 28–9 (= *Scientific Papers*, **1**: 387–8).

in Props XIV & XVI of my former paper. I must therefore repeat the calculations of those propositions making the requisite corrections.

12 Prop XIV (corrected) In a system of particles whose density, velocity &c are functions of x, to find the quantity of matter transferred across the plane of yz due to the motion of agitation alone.[33]

If there is a motion of translation we must suppose the plane of yz to move with the same velocity so as to reduce the relative motion of translation to zero.

Let N = number of particles in unit of volume
M = mass of each particle
v = velocity of agitation at distance x
l = mean path of particle at distance x
v_0 = velocity of agitation at origin
λ = mean path of particle with velocity v among the particles at origin
$\Lambda = \tfrac{1}{2}(l+\lambda)$
q = quantity of matter transferred across unit of area in unit time.

Take a stratum whose thickness is dx and distance from origin x the area being unity. The number of collisions taking place in this stratum is

$$N\frac{v}{l}dx.$$

These particles will move in all directions with velocity v till they strike other particles and their lengths of path will be different in different directions, because the properties of the system are different in different places. We have only however to ascertain what proportion of these particles pass through the plane yz and we have shown that this depends only on the value of Λ.

We thus find for the number of particles projected from the stratum in unit of time whose paths are between $n\Lambda$ and $(n+dn)\Lambda$ and which pass through the plane yz in a positive direction

$$\frac{Nv(x\mp n\Lambda)}{2nl\Lambda}e^{-n}\,dx\,dn$$

where x must be between $\pm n\Lambda$ and the upper or lower sign is to be taken according to x is positive or negative.

---

(33) Maxwell, 'Illustrations of the dynamical theory of gases. Part II': 22 (= *Scientific Papers*, **1**: 393). There is a preliminary draft of the revise of this proposition in ULC Add. MSS 7655, V, c/45a.

We find by multiplying by M and integrating with respect to x from $x = -n\Lambda$ to $x = +n\Lambda$ and with respect to n from 0 to ∞

$$q = -\frac{1}{3}\frac{d}{dx}\left(\rho v \frac{\Lambda^2}{l}\right).$$

Since Λ is a mean between l & λ and these three quantities differ by very small quantities we may write

$$q = -\frac{1}{3}\frac{d}{dx}(\rho v \lambda)$$

as the most convenient expression for q. In differentiating λ we must remember that in the value of λ, ρ_1 ρ_2 v_1 v_2 are the values at the origin and therefore are to be regarded as constant, and that v' is the velocity at x, so that $v' = v_1 + \frac{dv_1}{dx}x$ and $dv = -\frac{dv_1}{dx}x$.

We find
$$\frac{d\lambda_1}{dx} = l_1^2 \frac{1}{v_1}\frac{dv_1}{dx}\left(\frac{1}{2}A\rho_1 + \frac{v_2^2}{v_1^2+v_2^2}B\rho_2\right)$$

and $q = -\frac{1}{3}\rho_1 v_1 l_1 \left\{\frac{1}{\rho_1}\frac{d\rho_1}{dx} + \frac{1}{v_1}\frac{dv_1}{dx}\left(1 + \frac{1}{2}Al_1\rho_1 + \frac{v_1^2}{v_1^2+v_2^2}Bl_1\rho_2\right)\right\}$

which is the value of q for two mixed gases. For one gas, the expression becomes

$$q = -\frac{1}{3}\rho_1 v_1 l_1 \left(\frac{1}{\rho}\frac{d\rho_1}{dx} + \frac{3}{2}\frac{1}{v_1}\frac{dv_1}{dx}\right).$$

This is the value to be employed in treating of the conduction of heat ⌊where $\rho = MN$ is the density v the mean velocity of agitation and l the mean length of path.

This result differs from that formerly obtained[34] as l does not come under the sign of differentiation.⌋[35]

13 Let us now apply similar corrections to Prop XVI.

---

(34) See note (35).
(35) These appended remarks are written on the verso of f. 5 of 'On the conduction of heat in gases'. Garber, Brush and Everitt, *Molecules and Gases*: 347, place these remarks at the end of the paper. But compare the conclusion of Prop. XIV of 'Illustrations of the dynamical theory of gases. Part II': 23 (= *Scientific Papers*, **1**: 394): 'We thus find for the quantity of matter transferred across unit of area by the motion of agitation in unit of time, $q = -\frac{1}{3}\frac{d}{dx}(\rho v l)$, where $\rho = MN$ is the density, v the mean velocity of agitation and l the mean length of path.'

Prop XVI (Corrected) To find the resultant dynamical effect of all the collisions which take place in a given stratum.[36]

We have to find the resultant momentum of all the particles which enter the stratum and strike there in unit of time.

Using the same symbols we have to find the momentum of particles which starting from a stratum dx lodge in a stratum whose thickness is α at the origin.

The number of particles projected from dx is as before

$$N \frac{v}{l} dx.$$

The proportion of these whose directions make an angle with x whose cosine lies between μ & $\mu + d\mu$ is

$$\frac{1}{2} d\mu.$$

The proportion of these which reach a distance $r = n\Lambda = \frac{1}{\mu} x$ is

$$e^{-n}.$$

The proportion of these which strike in the stratum α, that is between r and $r+dr$ where $\mu dr = \alpha$ is

$$\frac{\alpha}{\mu \lambda}.$$

The velocity of these particles resolved along the axes of x is $-v\mu$ and the resolved momentum is $-Mv\mu$.

Multiplying all these numbers together and remembering that $\frac{d\mu}{dn} = -\frac{x}{n^2 \Lambda}$, we get for X the whole momentum

$$\alpha \rho X = \int_0^\alpha \int_{-n\Lambda}^{+n\Lambda} \frac{1}{2} \frac{\rho v^2 \alpha}{l\lambda \Lambda n^2} x e^{-n} \, dx \, dn$$

$$= \frac{1}{3} \frac{d}{dx}\left(\frac{\rho v^2 \Lambda^2}{l\lambda}\right) \alpha$$

and since Λ is a mean between l & λ this may be reduced to

$$\rho X = \frac{1}{3} \frac{d}{dx}(\rho v^2) = \frac{dp}{dx} \quad \text{by Prop XI.}^{[37]}$$

---

(36) Maxwell, 'Illustrations of the dynamical theory of gases. Part II': 23 (= *Scientific Papers*, **1**: 394).

(37) Read: Prop. XII of 'Illustrations of the dynamical theory of gases. Part I': 30

This result is the same as that which I obtained before, but the method of procedure is now rendered strict.

14 In applying these results to the case of the conduction of heat through a stratum of air from a hot surface to a cold one[38] we must introduce the conditions that the transfer shall be of heat only and not of matter, and that every intermediate slice of air shall be in equilibrium. In my former paper I paid little attention to this subject as I had no experimental data to compare with the theory, but the errors of principle into which I fell are worth correcting in order to compare the results of my method of calculation with those obtained by M. Clausius.[39]

The whole quantity of matter transferred across unit of area in unit of time is $Q = q + \rho V$ where q has the value given in Prop XIV and V is the velocity of translation. When there is no transfer of matter, $Q = 0$.

The resultant force of the collisions per unit of volume is

$$-\frac{dp}{dx}.$$

When there is no resultant force, p must be constant.

The quantity of energy in each particle depends partly on the velocity of its centre of gravity and partly on its velocity of rotation about that centre. As these velocities tend towards a constant ratio, we can assume that the energy of a particle is $\frac{1}{2}\beta M v^2$.[40]

The amount of energy which is transferred across unit of area in unit of time depends partly on the motion of translation, and partly on that of agitation. That depending on the motion of translation is $\frac{1}{2}\beta V \rho v^2$, and that depending on the motion of agitation may be found by the method of Prop XIV by substituting the energy instead of the mass of each

---

(= *Scientific Papers*, **1**: 389), where Maxwell obtains the result $p = \frac{1}{3}MNv^2$ for the pressure on unit area, where $MN = \rho$.

(38) Compare Prop. XXI of 'Illustrations of the dynamical theory of gases. Part II': 31–3 (= *Scientific Papers*, **1**: 403–5); see note (10).

(39) In his paper 'Ueber die Wärmeleitung gasförmiger Körper': 47–8n Clausius pointed out that Maxwell had derived his expression for the conduction of heat in gases (see note (41)) from his expression for the quantity of matter transferred by the motion of agitation of a gas (see note (35)); and that Maxwell therefore implied that a flow of heat is accompanied by and is partly the result of the motion of the gas molecules. Clausius comments: 'Sie steht also mit der Voraussetzung, welche wir machen müssen, wenn wir von Wärmeleitung sprechen, im Widerspruche, denn unter Wärmeleitung versteht man eine Fortbewegung der Wärme *ohne Fortbewegung der Masse*.'

(40) See note (20).

particle. The whole energy transferred being called E we find

$$E = \frac{1}{2}\beta V \rho v^2 - \frac{1}{3}\frac{d}{dx}\left(\frac{1}{2}\beta\rho v^3 \lambda\right)$$

with the conditions

$$p = \text{constant} = \frac{1}{3}\rho v^2.$$

$$Q = V\rho - \frac{1}{3}\frac{d}{dx}(\rho v \lambda) = 0.$$

We find

$$E = -\frac{1}{12}\beta\rho l \frac{1}{v}\frac{dv}{dx}(v^2 \cdot v + 3v^3)^{(41)}$$

where the mean values of v, v^2 and v^3 must be taken as shown in section 2 so that $v^2 \cdot v + 3v^3 = 5v^2 \cdot v$.

If q is the quantity of heat transferred in unit of time measured in ordinary units, $E = Jgq^{(42)}$ where J is the mechanical equivalent of heat.$^{(43)}$ If T be the absolute temperature

$$\frac{1}{v}\frac{dv}{dx} = \frac{1}{2}\frac{1}{T}\frac{dT}{dx}{}^{(44)}$$

$$\rho v^2 = 3p$$

$$v = \sqrt{\frac{8p_0}{\pi\rho_0}\frac{T}{T_0}}.\;{}^{(45)}$$

---

(41) See '(12) Prop. XIV (corrected)' above. Compare Prop. XXI of 'Illustrations of the dynamical theory of gases. Part II': 32 (= *Scientific Papers*, 1: 404) where he obtains the result, criticised by Clausius (see note (39)) $E = -\frac{1}{2}\frac{\beta v^2}{A}\frac{dv}{dx}$, where $A = \frac{1}{l\rho}$.

(42) g is the acceleration due to gravity.

(43) Following William Thomson, 'On the dynamical theory of heat, with numerical results deduced from Mr Joule's equivalent of a thermal unit, and M. Regnault's observations on steam', *Trans. Roy. Soc. Edinb.*, 20 (1851): 261–88, esp. 269 (= *Math. & Phys. Papers*, 1: 186); '*J* denote[s] the mechanical equivalent of a unit of heat'. Compare also Rankine, *Manual of the Steam Engine*: 299; 'The quantity above stated, 772 foot-pounds for each British thermal unit, is commonly called "*Joule's equivalent*", and denoted by the symbol *J*, in honour of Mr. Joule, who was the first to determine its value *exactly*. His... best set of experiments, from which the accepted value 772 is deduced, may be consulted in the *Philosophical Transactions* for 1850.'

(44) Maxwell equates the velocity gradient with the temperature gradient; see also Rankine, *Manual of the Steam Engine*: 258.

(45) See paras. (2), (5) above.

If l_0 be the value of l where $\rho = \rho_0$, then $l = l_0 \dfrac{\rho_0}{\rho}$ and E becomes

$$Jgq = -\frac{5}{4}\sqrt{\frac{2}{\pi}}\,\beta\, l_0 p_0^{\frac{3}{2}}\, T_0^{-\frac{3}{2}} \rho_0^{-\frac{1}{2}}\, T^{\frac{1}{2}} \frac{dT}{dx}.^{(46)}$$

---

(46) Compare Maxwell, 'Illustrations of the dynamical theory of gases. Part II': 32, where he obtains the expression $Jgq = -\dfrac{3}{4}\beta p l v \dfrac{1}{T}\dfrac{dT}{dx}$ (there is a misprint in *Scientific Papers*, **1**: 404).

=208=
LETTER TO JOHN WILLIAM CUNNINGHAM
24 MARCH 1863
From the original in the King's College London Archives[1]

8 Palace Gardens Terrace
24 March 1863

Dear Sir

I am in receipt of your letter of the 23rd. I think it is very right that Mr Smalleys remuneration should be increased,[2] and I am quite willing to agree to the arrangements for that purpose as stated in your letter.

I remain
Yours truly
J. Clerk Maxwell

J. W. Cunningham Esqre
Secretary of Kings College
London

Turn Over[3]

---

(1) King's College London Archives, KA/IC/M 71.

(2) On his appointment on 11 October 1861 (see Number 204 note (3)) Smalley's salary as Lecturer in Natural Philosophy had been fixed at a fee of 7s. per pupil per term, this sum to be deducted from the Professor's salary (King's College London Archives, King's College Council Vol. I, minute 42).

(3) The *verso* is blank.

= 209 =

LETTER TO GEORGE BIDDELL AIRY

14 MAY 1863

From the original in the Royal Greenwich Observatory Archive[1]

8 Palace Gardens Terrace
W
1863 May 14

Dear Sir

Mr G. R. Smalley has for two sessions given lectures on Mechanics to one division of the Department of Applied Sciences while I have lectured the men in the other division on the same subject, and have examined both divisions.

I believe Mr Smalley to possess the scientific knowledge and the habits of accuracy which would fit him for the work of an Observatory.

He has already had some experience as an observer at the Cape, and he is now desirous to obtain the situation which is vacant in the Observatory at Sydney.

From what I know of Mr Smalley during my intercourse with him at King's College, I consider that he would be steady, accurate and skilful in Observatory work.[2]

I remain
Yours truly
J. CLERK MAXWELL

The Astronomer Royal

---

(1) Royal Greenwich Observatory Archive, ULC, Airy Papers 6/148, 318R–V.
(2) Smalley's resignation was accepted at a meeting of the King's College Council on 21 July 1863, on his appointment as Astronomer Royal for New South Wales (King's College London Archives, King's College Council Vol. I, minute 267).

LETTER TO WILLIAM THOMSON

29 MAY 1863

From the original in the University Library, Cambridge[1]

8 Palace Gardens Terrace
W
1863 May 29

Dear Thomson

Can you dine with us on Tuesday 9th June?

On Wednesday 27th we made three determinations which I have now reduced. I give you the details of the 1st so that you may see our present method.[2]

---

(1) ULC Add. MSS 7342, M 101. First published in Larmor, 'Origins': 734–6.

(2) Maxwell here begins to report measurements of electrical resistance in electromagnetic absolute units which he undertook with Balfour Stewart and Fleeming Jenkin, 'according to the method devised by Professor W. Thomson', as stated in the 'Report of the Committee appointed by the British Association on standards of electrical resistance', *Report of the Thirty-third Meeting of the British Association for the Advancement of Science; held at Newcastle-upon-Tyne in August and September 1863* (London, 1864): 111–76, on 111. See the 'Description of an experimental measurement of electrical resistance, made at King's College' (by Maxwell, Balfour Stewart and Fleeming Jenkin), *ibid.*: 163–76. The apparatus and method is described in the following terms: 'Professor W. Thomson has designed an apparatus by which the resistance of a coil can be determined in electromagnetic measure by the observation of the constant deflection of a magnet, and his arrangement has been adopted for the experiments made by the Committee.... For convenience of description, the apparatus with which the experiments were made may be divided into five parts: 1°, the driving gear; 2°, the revolving coil; 3°, the governor; 4°, the scale, with its telescope, by which the deflections of the magnet were observed; 5°, the electric balance, by which the resistance of the copper coil was compared with a German-silver arbitrary standard.... The apparatus consisted of two circular coils of copper wire, about one foot in diameter, placed side by side, and connected in series; these coils revolved round a vertical axis, and were driven by a belt from a hand-winch, fitted with Huyghens' gear to produce a sensibly constant driving-power. A small magnet, with a mirror attached, was hung in the centre of the two coils, and the deflections of this magnet were read by a telescope from the reflection of a scale in the mirror. A frictional governor controlled the speed of the revolving coil.... By calculation it can be shown that when the coil revolves round a vertical axis... $R = L^2 V/k^2 \tan d$, an equation from which the earth's magnetic force and the moment of the suspended magnet have been eliminated, and by which the absolute resistance (R) can be calculated in terms of the length, L, the velocity, V, the radius, k, and the deflection, d. The resistance thus calculated is expressed in electromagnetic absolute units, because [this] equation... is a simple consequence of... fundamental equations in the electromagnetic system. The essence of Professor Thomson's method consists in substituting, by aid of the laws of electromagnetic induction, the measurement of a velocity and a deflection for the more complex and therefore less accurate measurements of work and force, required in the simple fundamental equations.' (*ibid.*: 163–4, 118–19). The

(A) Determination of zero. Coil rotating + no current. 40 observations of extremities of oscillations

Mean of 1st ten (millimeters)	949.56
2nd—	950.55
3rd—	950.73
4th—	950.52
Mean	950.34

(B) Connexion made. Coil rotating + and 80 oscillations taken

Mean reading of 1st ten	1237.38
2nd	8.33
&c	9.65
	9.86
	8.25
	8.40
	9.35
	7.80
Mean Scale reading.	1238.6275

Time of 3000 revolutions

0 to 3000	530.0
300 3300	530.0
600 3600	530.0
900 3900	530.0
Time of 100 rev. $T =$	17.67[3]

(C) Circuit broken   rotation + zero reading again

	951.30
	50.87
	50.00
After exp. Mean	950.723
Mean zero before and after	950.504

---

apparatus is described in the 'Report': 163–8, and in a series of drawings, Plate VI, *ibid.*: facing 176. See also I. B. Hopley, 'Maxwell's work on electrical resistance. I. The determination of the absolute unit of resistance', *Annals of Science*, **13** (1857): 265–72.

(3) 'The speed of the coil was determined by observing on a chronometer the instant at which a small gong was struck by a detent released once in every hundred revolutions'; see 'Report': 120, and number 216, esp. note (5).

Mean reading due to current	1238.627
deflexion = δ_1	288.123
Time of 100 revolutions = T_1	17.67
Product $T_1\delta_1 =$	5091.13

The second exp. went wrong in the spinning.
The third experiment

	zero	957.00
negative rotation	scale reading	668.936
deflexion negative		288.064
Time of 100 revolutions		17.6284
Product $T\delta$		5078.11

Fourth Exp.	rotation + Scale	1247.11
	zero	957.00
	deflexion	290.11
	Time of 100 rev^{ns}	17.57
	Product $T\delta$	5097.1

Jenkin has the coils which he equated to the spinning coil between these exp^s.[4]

There was a change of zero which we must try to avoid, but I know when it took place.

Now for the measure of resistance[5]

length of wire	303.403 meters
number of turns	308
Distance of scale from mirror	3000 millimeters

---

(4) The 'resistance of the copper coil was compared with a German-silver arbitrary standard'; see 'Report': 164 and note (2). See also Number 214 notes (14) and (18).

(5) In the published 'Report' Maxwell (see 'Report': 163) wrote out an account of the 'Mathematical theory of the experiment' ('Report': 168–71), deriving an expression for the value of the resistance of the rotating copper coil (in electromagnetic units):

$$R = \frac{200\pi^2 Dnl \sin^3\alpha}{T\delta}\{1 + \text{corrections}\},$$

where D is the distance of the scale from the mirror, n the number of windings of the coil, l the length of wire in metres, α the angle subtended at the axis by the radius of the coil, T the time of 100 revolutions of the coil in seconds, and δ the scale-reading deflection in mm.

(equal to a certain wooden rod which I shall measure again)
α = angle subtended by radius of coil at magnet 83° 11′
$\sin^3 \alpha = .978912$.

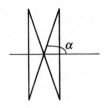

Figure 210,1

Corrections for thickness &c of coil .9996116[6]

$$R[=]\frac{200\pi^2 \times 3000 \times 303.403 \times 308 \times .978912 \times .9996116}{T\delta}\text{[7]}$$

+ correction.

Correction for induction of magnet at centre	+.00720
for torsion of fibre	−.00135
Proportional correction	+.00583.
Correction for reduction of tan 2ϕ to tan ϕ	$= 1.000 \frac{\delta^2}{4D^2}$ [8]
for induction of coil on itself	$= -.7331 \frac{\delta^2}{4D^2}$ [9]
total	$0.2669 \frac{\delta^2}{4D^2}$

Final formula for R

$$R = \frac{544648,000,000}{T\delta} + 4037 \frac{\delta}{T}.\text{[10]}$$

I have not divided out as I have no time.[11]
Here are former values of $T\delta$ on a colder day
5176
5105.

---

(6) The published 'Report' included 'an elaborate analysis of the corrections required ...made by Professor Maxwell' ('Report': 120); and see 'Report': 171–6.
(7) See note (5).
(8) ϕ is the angle between the axis of the magnet and the magnetic meridian, and $\tan 2\phi = \delta/D$; see 'Report': 170, 172, and note (5).
(9) Compare 'Report': 172.
(10) Compare the corrected value in the published 'Report': 173.
(11) But see Number 211.

Jenkin cannot come on Wednesday but I think Thursday will do for an experiment as Stewart, Jenkin & I can repeat what we have done and if you are engaged Thursday it does not so much matter as you could do us more good by advice when we are not spinning than when we are spinning. If you can come here[12] on the 9th I will ask Jenkin & Stewart.

Yours truly
J. C. MAXWELL

(12) The experiments were made at King's College, London; see 'Report': 116, and Numbers 213 and 216.

LETTER TO WILLIAM THOMSON

JUNE 1863[1]

From the original in the University Library, Glasgow[2]

Dear Thomson

We had a spin yesterday with the following results.

Time (mean of series)	Scale readings	Time of 100 revolutions	
$1^h\ 36^m$	1016.40	∞ unknown no connexion	Zero
$1^h\ 48^m$	1306.09	17.3296	+
$2^h\ 40^m\ 50^s$	730.565	17.4625	−
3 21.30	1339.02	15.6715	+
$3.\ 35^m$	1020.325	no connexion	Zero
Values of $T\delta$[3]			
from	1st & 2nd	5020.21	
	2 3	5005.86	
	3 4	5025.41	
	4 5	4994.43	

These are not good but if you observe 1st and 5th observations the zero has changed owing to variation of terrestrial magnetism.[4] I have not got the variations at each instant from Stewart[5] yet but if we suppose that there was

---

(1) See Number 213.

(2) Glasgow University Library, Kelvin Papers, M 13.

(3) See Number 210 esp. note (5).

(4) In the published 'Report of the Committee... on standards of electrical resistance', *Report of the Thirty-third Meeting of the British Association* (London, 1864): 171, Maxwell (see Number 210 note (6)) noted that: 'since the direction of the earth's magnetic action is continually varying, we must find the difference of *declination* between the times of the two readings, and calculate what would have been the undisturbed reading of the scale at the time when the deviation was observed.'

(5) In the published 'Report': 171, Maxwell explained that: 'In our experiments this correction was made by comparison with the photographic registers of magnetic declination made at Kew at the same time that our experiments were going on.' Balfour Stewart was Director of the Kew Observatory.

an increase of 3.925 in 2 hours and that the changes at intermediate times were in proportion to the time then we get corrections which being applied give our four values.

	5011.7
The last is doubtful owing to	5015.2
not knowing the mean time of	5017.1
zero reading exactly.	5004.5

So you see our principal desideratum is a knowledge of the variation of declination for when it is roughly applied it takes away most of the discrepancies. Stewart can give the Kew observations of corresponding times, for better corrections.[6]

By a new observation of the power of the small magnet

$$R = \frac{54512}{T\delta} +$$

$$= 108665000 + 64000$$

$$= 108729000 \frac{\text{meter}}{\text{second}} \quad [7] \quad 4^{\text{th}} \text{ June.}$$

Value of R on 27th May 107,365,000.[8] The difference arises from change of temperature as will be shown by Jenkins observations and coils.[9]

The temperature of the coil increases by spinning owing to the induced currents.

If horizontal terrestrial force = 3.8 British and we go at 300 turns in 50 seconds I find that in 5000 turns (which is about the number in each series) the electrical work done by overcoming resistance is about 7.3 footpounds or about $\frac{1}{100}$ of British thermal unit. I do not know the weight of the coil or the capacity of copper but it all comes out easy now.

Jenkin can now compare numerically the resistance on different days[10] so we shall be able to work the observations into each other to get a mean.

If you come a little before 7 on Wednesday I shall have the mixture of colours in action.[11]

Yours truly
J. C. MAXWELL

---

(6) See notes (4) and (5), and 'Report': 175.

(7) On the dimensions of resistance in electromagnetic units as $[LT^{-1}]$ see J. Clerk Maxwell and Fleeming Jenkin, 'On the elementary relations between electrical measurements' in the 'Report': 130–63, esp. 145, 159.

(8) See Number 210, where Maxwell reports measurements made on 27 May 1863.

(9) See Number 210 esp. note (4).   (10) See Number 210 note (4).

(11) See Number 202.

LETTER TO GEORGE GABRIEL STOKES

9 JUNE 1863

From the original in the University Library, Cambridge[1]

8 Palace Gardens Terrace
9 June 1863

Dear Stokes

I have received your letter and that of the Astronomer Royal.[2] Perhaps I ought to have explained more distinctly what I meant by the conditions arising from elasticity.[3]

There are three separate subjects of investigation in the theory of Elastic Solids.

1st Theory of Internal Forces or Stresses their resolution and composition and the conditions of equilibrium of an element.

2nd Theory of Displacements or Strains their resolution and composition and the equation of continuity (if required).

3rd Theory of Elasticity or the relations between systems of stresses and systems of strains in particular substances.[4]

Mr Airys conclusions are all deducible from the conditions of equilibrium of the *Forces* or *Stresses*[5] for although he has introduced into his calculation considerations arising from the observed uniformly varying strain and stress between the top & bottom of the beam (see top of p 3 of his letter and his paper art 15)[6] yet I have shown that on his own principles these assumptions

---

(1) ULC Add. MSS 7656, M 421.

(2) Airy's letter is his letter to Stokes of 22 February 1863 (Royal Society, *Referees' Reports*, 5: 4; see Number 205 notes (12) and (21)). In a letter to Stokes of 27 February 1863 (copy in Royal Greenwich Observatory Archive, ULC, Airy Papers 6/392, 130R–131V) Airy wrote: 'Pray send my letter for Prof. Maxwell's reading, if you think there is nothing in it at which he can take the slightest umbrage.' In his reply dated 18 March 1863 (Airy Papers 6/392, 131A–132A) Stokes told Airy that 'I have not yet written to Prof.^{r} Maxwell about your paper, because there was no hurry about it'.

(3) In his report (Number 205) on Airy's paper 'On the strains in the interior of beams', *Phil. Trans.*, **153** (1863): 49–79.

(4) On Maxwell's distinction, following Rankine and William Thomson, between 'stress' and 'strain' see Number 206, esp. note (7).

(5) See Numbers 205 and 206.

(6) See Number 205 note (21) for the passages in Airy's letter to Stokes, and in the paper 'On the strains in the interior of beams', to which Maxwell refers. Article (15) here referred to was subsequently re-numbered (16) in the manuscript of Airy's paper (Royal Society, PT. 68.3, on f. 9), a new §12 as in the printed text being inserted; see Airy, 'On the strains in the interior of beams': 55, 58.

are not required, for the results may be got from the conditions near the end of my report namely that the pressure all over the surface is zero. Now we know this without any theory of elasticity and any application of elastic principles which tells us no more than this may in a mathematical paper be treated as an episode an illustration or instructive consideration but not a necessary part of the investigation ⟨just as many mechanical experiments help us to see the truth of principles which we can establish otherwise⟩.

What I meant by the conditions arising from the elasticity of the beam may perhaps be more accurately described as 'Conditions arising from the beam having been once an unstrained solid free from stress'.

That is, the stresses must be accounted for by displacements of an elastic solid from a state in which there were no forces in action.

I think what you and the author intend is that I should state the result of the above assumption instead of that of the paper.[7] The mode of getting complete solutions I have only partially worked out. It depends on expanding the applied forces in Fouriers series the terms are of the form $A \sin(nx+b)e^{\pm ny}$. I shall send you the note or appendix when I can write it I hope before Thursday.[8]

I have not been out of town but have been busy with the standard of Electric resistance. We have now got no errors comparable with those produced by the change of magnetic declination during the experiment. These we shall shortly be able to eliminate by comparison with the photographic records at Kew.[9]

I have been studying oscillations of magnets by aid of mirrors[10] and I hope to apply the principle to the determination of gaseous friction by means of a disc oscillating in a gas and determining the log. decrement of oscillation and the time of oscillation.[11]

Yours truly
J. CLERK MAXWELL

---

(7) In his letter to Stokes of 22 February 1863 (see note (2)) Airy concluded with the suggestion: 'If Professor Maxwell on further consideration should see reason for making other remarks, I shall be delighted to see them in the form of Appendix to the paper, if approved by the President and Council of the Royal Society.'

(8) Airy's paper as published does not contain an appendix by Maxwell. The paper had reached revise proofs by June 1863 (see Airy Papers 6/392, 145R).

(9) See Number 211 esp. notes (4) and (5).

(10) Suggested by the method used in the apparatus for measuring electrical resistance: see Number 210 note (2).

(11) See Numbers 244, 245, 246 and 252. A sheet of data among Maxwell's manuscripts (ULC Add. MSS 7655, V, f/4) records experiments on gas viscosity dated '6 Nov 1863'.

213

LETTER TO JOHN WILLIAM CUNNINGHAM

27 JUNE 1863

From the original in the King's College London Archives[1]

8 Palace Gardens Terrace
W
27 June 1863

Dear Sir

We have now completed the first series of experiments[2] in the room down stairs. We may however require to repeat them in October. Can we have the stone &c left there till then? and can Mr Jenkin be allowed to go there occasionally during the vacation to work by himself? If you have any communication to make to him address

   Fleeming Jenkin Esqre
   6 Duke Street
   Adelphi W.C.

I shall be abroad till the end of July after which at Glenlair, Dalbeattie NB.

We did not find it necessary to make any experiments at night. We expect to be able to deduce excellent results from those made in the day time.

I remain
Yours truly
J. CLERK MAXWELL

J. W. Cunningham Esqre

---

(1) King's College London Archives, KA/IC/M 71.
(2) The British Association experiments on standards of electrical resistance were carried out at King's College: see Numbers 210 note (12), 214 esp. note (6), and 216.

214

LETTER TO WILLIAM THOMSON

31 JULY 1863

From the original in the University Library, Glasgow[1]

Address till 1st October   Glenlair
(Not known in Wigtonshire)   Dalbeattie
                                                                                1863 July 31

Dear Thomson

I cannot tell you much about the action of the tides on the earth.[2] I have the old calculation at London somewhere. Date probably 1853. I have never printed on that subject. See however papers by Daniel Vaughan in Phil Mag 1862.[3] I know no old papers about it. People were always incredulous and told you that there was no such thing on account of Thales and his eclipse.[4] But the whole effect possible would not do any harm to any eclipse so recent as Thales.

Jenkin & I have finished up the 1st set of exp. We measured everything with a box wood meter of Becker's.[5] The wire was gently uncoiled and laid in a groove between two planks of the Museum floor 50 feet at a time and so measured straight but not stretched. Jenkin managed by this wrinkle to straighten the wire.[6]

I have been in Germany for a month and having borrowed from the schoolmaster Log. Tables I worked out the self-induction of the coil with accuracy.[7] For experiments on self-induction kicks with the galvanometer we must have a needle for which the 'deadening' due to all causes is small and of which the time of oscill^n is long enough to take good observations of the

---

(1) Glasgow University Library, Kelvin Papers, M 14. Previously published in A. T. Fuller, 'James Clerk Maxwell's Glasgow manuscripts: extracts relating to control and stability', *International Journal of Control*, **43** (1986): 1595–7.

(2) See Thomson's paper 'On the rigidity of the earth', *Phil. Trans.*, **153** (1863): 573–82 (= *Math. & Phys. Papers,* **3**: 312–36), and his letters to Stokes of 19 April 1862 and 8 July 1862 (ULC Add. MSS 7656, K 137, K 138; printed in Wilson, *Stokes–Kelvin Correspondence*, **1**: 292–3, 295).

(3) Daniel Vaughan, 'On the form of satellites revolving at small distances from their primaries', *Phil. Mag.*, ser. 4, **20** (1860): 409–18; Vaughan, 'Static and dynamic stability in the secondary systems', *ibid.*, **22** (1861): 489–97.

(4) On the story of Thales' alleged prediction of a solar eclipse see O. Neugebauer, *The Exact Sciences in Antiquity* (Providence, $_2$1957): 142–3.

(5) Carl Ludwig Christian Becker, of Elliott Bros. (Boase).

(6) Compare the 'Report of the Committee... on standards of electrical resistance', *Report of the Thirty-third Meeting of the British Association* (London, 1864): 111–76, esp. 120, on the measurement of the length of the copper wire in the Museum of King's College.

(7) See Number 210, esp. note (9).

ends of each swing. If the observer were to have command of the make & break key I think very good numerical results might be got by exp.

I have now got the whole theory of the inductive coefficient of one circle placed near and parallel to another, the distance between the circles being small compared with the radii.[8]

I take the electrotonic coeffts F, G, H[9] and express the equations of no electric current[10]

$$\frac{d^2F}{dx^2}+\frac{d^2F}{dy^2}+\frac{d^2F}{dz^2}=0 \quad \&c$$

first in cylindrical coordinates and then in annular coordinates (that is distance along a ring, distance from it, and angle between that distance and radius of ring).

In the case of a circular current let N be the electrotonic 'force' parallel to the ring at dist r from the ring[11]

$$\frac{d^2N}{dr^2}+\frac{1}{r}\frac{dN}{dr}+\frac{1}{r^2}\frac{d^2N}{d\theta^2}+\frac{1}{a+r\cos\theta}\left(\frac{dN}{dr}\cos\theta-\frac{dN}{d\theta}\sin\frac{\theta}{r}\right)-\frac{N}{(a+r\cos\theta)^2}=0.\text{[12]}$$

By this eq^n and by the principle that the inductive coeff of A on B is equal to that of B on A I get

$$N=\log\frac{r}{8a}\left\{1-\frac{1}{2}\frac{r\cos\theta}{a}+\frac{3}{16}\frac{r^2}{a^2}(1+2\cos^2\theta)-\frac{1}{32}\frac{r^3\cos\theta}{a^3}(9+5\cos^2\theta)+\&c\right\}$$
$$+2-\frac{1}{2}\frac{r\cos\theta}{a}+\frac{1}{32}\frac{r^2}{a^2}(11+6\cos^2\theta)-\frac{1}{32}\frac{r^3\cos\theta}{a^3}\left(\frac{39}{2}-\frac{5}{3}\cos^2\theta\right)\&c.$$

The inductive potential between two wires whose distance is r and radii a and $a+r\cos\theta$ respectively is

$$-2\pi a\gamma\gamma'N$$

where $\gamma\gamma'$ are the currents and N the quantity found above.

---

(8) Compare 'Part VII. Calculation of the coefficients of electromagnetic induction' of Maxwell's paper 'A dynamical theory of the electromagnetic field', *Phil. Trans.*, **155** (1865): 459–512, esp. 506–12 (= *Scientific Papers*, **1**: 589–97).

(9) On Maxwell's development of Faraday's concept of the electro-tonic state see his papers 'On Faraday's lines of force', *Trans. Camb. Phil. Soc.*, **10** (1856): 27–83, esp. 63–7, and 'On physical lines of force. Part II', *Phil. Mag.*, ser. 4, **21** (1861): 281–91, 338–48, esp. 289–91, 338–42 (= *Scientific Papers*, **1**: 203–9, 475–82). See Volume I: 371–5, 406–9, 688).

(10) Compare Maxwell, 'A dynamical theory of the electromagnetic field': 506 (= *Scientific Papers*, **1**: 589).

(11) Compare Maxwell, 'A dynamical theory of the electromagnetic field': 507–8 (= *Scientific Papers*, **1**: 591–3).

(12) a is the radius of the coil, θ the angle between r and the plane of the coil.

By integration I find the coefft of
  A on B and B on A to be   104153.295 meters
  A on A and B on B   293521.736
Correction for want of homogeneity
and for return currents in wire   +75.5

                    Total   397750 meters
By experiment June 16   398500 meters.⁽¹³⁾

I do not think much of the experiment as we could not determine well the time of oscillation owing to rapid diminution of swing.

Here are the results of the last 3 days after we got good scales and cleared away iron.

Figure 214,1. Section of coil.

They are corrected for variation of magnetic declinations for change of resistance observed directly and for scale errors.

T = time of 100 revolutions
δ = deflexion in millimeters
R = resistance Jenkins German silver[14] being unity.[15]
$T\delta R$ should be const.[16]

	$T\delta R$
June 16	5046.18
19	5075.77
23	5037.98
Mean	5053.32[17]

Resistance of Jenkins German Silver

$$R = 107620116 \frac{\text{meters}}{\text{second}}^{(18)}$$

---

(13) These are the values recorded in the 'Report of the Committee... on standards of electrical resistance': 172.

(14) German silver: an alloy of nickel, copper and zinc; see Henry Watts, *A Dictionary of Chemistry*, 5 vols. (London, 1863–9), **2**: 51.   (15) See Number 210 esp. note (4).

(16) See the values for $T\delta$ reported in Numbers 210 and 211.

(17) These are the values recorded in the 'Report': 175.

(18) See the 'Report': 176; for the 'coil of German silver, marked June 4th... we find as the result of the experiments for the resistance of "June 4" in absolute measure 107620116 metres per second. Knowing the absolute resistance of "June 4" we may construct coils of given resistance by known measure'.

I think we might do better still.

Have you written any description of your Governor with a spring?[19] I have been doing the theory of Jenkins friction gov.[20] and what I suppose to be yours. They have both a diff^1 eq^n of 4th order, reducible to 3rd by integration. Of the 3 solutions one is of the form e^{-nt} and the other two, $e^{\pm n't}\cos mt$. The condition is that n' in the last expression shall be negative. In Jenkins gov this must be got by putting a fan on the axle of the screw. In yours, by impeding by some kind of fluid friction the *radial* motion of the bob. I have a plan with mercury. Jenkins is the easiest to fulfil conditions. Yours is independent of the coefft of friction. Both yours and mine depend on a spring.[21]

Yours truly J.C.M.

(19) For further discussion see Maxwell's letter to William Thomson of 11 September 1863 (Number 219).

(20) The governor used in the experiments on standards of electrical resistance; see 'Report': 120, 166; and Number 219 esp. note (8).

(21) The governors Maxwell labels T and TJ, respectively, in his letter to Thomson of 11 September 1863; see Number 219 notes (7) and (9).

215
LETTER TO JOHN WILLIAM CUNNINGHAM
10 AUGUST 1863
From the original in the King's College London Archives[1]

Glenlair
Dalbeattie
1863 Aug 10

Dear Sir

I enclose £10 for Kings College Hospital.

I shall be here till the end of the vacation. I think that is 2nd October.

Yours truly
J. Clerk Maxwell

J. W. Cunningham Esqre
King's College
London WC.

---

(1) King's College London Archives, KA/IC/M 71.

216

LETTER TO ROBERT DUNDAS CAY[1]

21 AUGUST 1863

From the original in the Library of Peterhouse, Cambridge[2]

Glenlair
21 August 1863

Dear Uncle

I enclose Receipt for £5..2. We are very glad to hear of Charlies[3] success. It is very well to read at this time but he must keep himself cool in January. How are Aunt Jane & Uncle Albert? Johnnie was in good spirits when we saw him last. We have just been dining the Presbytery of Kircudbright who ordained Mr Sturrock minister of Corsock yesterday.[4] The Corsock district is now a parish quoad sacra and the congregation fills the church. I am finishing a report on electrical measurements for the British Asses.[5] I do not mean to go to Newcastle but the only place where the report would be intelligible at present is in the basement story of Kings College where all our instruments are set up.

We are to have four men to work there together in autumn, one man (the Secretary) to turn the driving wheel, another (the Astronomer) to take the time of a bell ringing every 100 turns[6] another (myself) to look at a scale through a telescope and a fourth to look at another scale through another telescope. We have to go on turning steadily taking times and viewing scales for $\frac{1}{2}$ hour then stop & reverse and so on.

Your aff^t nephew
J. CLERK MAXWELL

---

(1) Maxwell's uncle; see Volume I: 682.
(2) Peterhouse, Maxwell MSS (23).
(3) Charles Hope Cay: see Number 240.
(4) Rev. Geo. Sturrock, *Corsock Parish Church: Its Rise and Progress &c* (Castle-Douglas, 1899). See also *Life of Maxwell*: 329 on the endowment of the church.
(5) 'Report of the Committee...on standards of electrical resistance', *Report of the Thirty-third Meeting of the British Association for the Advancement of Science; held at Newcastle-upon-Tyne in August and September 1863* (London, 1864): 111–76. See Numbers 210, 211 and 214.
(6) See Number 210 note (3) and 'Report': 120; 'Mr. Balfour Stewart's skill in this kind of observation enabled...great accuracy' to be achieved.

217

LETTER TO GEORGE PHILLIPS BOND[1]

25 AUGUST 1863

From the original in the Harvard University Archives[2]

Glenlair House
Dalbeattie
Scotland
1863 Aug 25

Dear Sir

When your letter[3] arrived I had just gone abroad, and my letters were not forwarded to me so that I was not aware of your kindness in sending me such valuable books.[4] I hope that my being out of town has not put either you or Mr Parker[5] to inconvenience. I have asked Mr Parker if he has not already sent them to my house, to keep them till I return to London in October.

I shall study what you say about Saturn in your letter[6] when I see your

---

(1) See notes (2) and (7).

(2) Bond MSS UAV. 630.6, Harvard University Archives, Pusey Library, Harvard University. Published in part in Edward S. Holden, *Memorials of William Cranch Bond, Director of the Harvard College Observatory 1840–1859, and of his Son George Phillips Bond, Director of the Harvard College Observatory 1859–1865* (San Francisco/New York City, 1897): 203–6.

(3) G. P. Bond to Maxwell, 9 July 1863 (holograph copy in Bond MSS UAV. 630.6). The letter is addressed from the 'Observatory of Harvard College, Cambridge Mass.'

(4) On Bond's acquaintance with Maxwell (whom he had met in May 1863) see note (7). In his letter of 9 July 1863 Bond wrote: 'I shall have the pleasure of forwarding to you, shortly, through Henry Tooke Parker Esq. 3 Ladbroke Gardens, Notting Hill, London a package containing: Annals of the Astronomical Observatory of Harvard College Vol. I (Parts I–II)/Vol. II Part I/III/IV Part I/ Observatory Reports for 1862 & 1863 and a collection of Memoirs and shorter articles. / By some accident your name was not inserted in its proper place on our list for distribution, & I am sorry on this account not to be able to furnish you with a full collection of our publications of many of which we have no copies remaining.'

(5) See note (4).

(6) Bond had written: 'Of one very remarkable fact, however, I am perfectly convinced. It is that during the time of the so-called disappearance of the ring, the bright protuberances seen upon the edge, like little satellites, have no sensible motion of rotation about the ball. / Among other curious subjects, the peculiar configuration of the shadow of the ball on the ring, & its visibility on *both* sides of the ball at the same time, are particularly noticeable. / Perhaps the suddenness of the illumination of the ring as its reappearance in Sept. 1848, may throw some light on the nature of the surface of the ring, as to its reflective quality, when it is considered at what a very small angle of elevation the sun was then shining upon it. Between the 4th & 13th of Sept. the breadth of the ring did not exceed 0".25; still the amount of light reflected was such as to make it visible in a telescope of only 3in aperture. / I have never seen upon the ring any object by which the time of its rotation could be inferred. The protuberances at the "disappearance" are sufficiently prominent, *but they do not move*. I am aware that Sir William Herschel has derived a

drawings and observations.⁽⁷⁾ I have no doubt that the time is coming when we shall know more about the heavenly bodies than that they attract each other from a distance.

In Saturns Rings we certainly have a very wonderful object to examine and when we come to understand it we shall certainly know more mechanics than we do now.

Your observations of comets' tails⁽⁸⁾ go far to render them legitimate subjects of speculation and I think that when we have mastered the theory of these tails we shall know more about what the heavens are made of.⁽⁹⁾

I think the heavenly spaces are by no means empty since, as Thomson has

---

time of rotation from them, but after considering all the data which he has collected, the telescopes which he used, & all the circumstances of the observations, I cannot think that the evidence is sufficient to outweigh the numerous observations made with our great refractor under very favourable circumstances. The latter, moreover, agree as to the main question, the immobility of the bright points, Schröters observations at Lilienthal, which were numerous & were made with large telescopes.' On William Herschel's observation of the period of rotation of Saturn's ring, see his paper 'On the satellites of the planet Saturn, and the rotation of its ring on an axis', *Phil. Trans.*, **80** (1790): 427–95, esp. 479; and see volume I: 443n. See also J. H. Schröter, 'Nachricht von merkwürdigen Beobachtungen über den Ring des Saturns', *Astronomisches Jahrbuch* (1806): 159–64.

(7) See W. C. Bond, *Observations of the Planet Saturn, made with the Twenty-three Foot Equatorial, at the Observatory of Harvard College, 1847–1857* (Cambridge, Mass., 1857), Volume II, Part I of *Annals of the Astronomical Observatory of Harvard College*; see note (4). In 1850 Bond had observed the dark 'obscure ring' interior to the two bright rings of Saturn; see G. P. Bond, 'Inner ring of Saturn', *Monthly Notices of the Royal Astronomical Society*, **11** (1851): 20–7. In *On the Stability of the Motion of Saturn's Rings* (Cambridge 1859): 3–4n (= *Scientific Papers*, **1**: 294n) Maxwell referred to Bond's paper 'On the rings of Saturn', *Astronomical Journal*, **2** (1851): 5–8, 9–10. See also his letter to William Thomson of 1 August 1857 (Volume I: 527–31) for allusions to Bond's papers on the rings of Saturn. Bond had visited London in May 1863; in his 'Diary' he recorded an entry on Tuesday 5 May 1863: 'I went this morning to Palace Garden Terrace for Professor Maxwell, and found him at home. At the Royal Society, Saturday evening, I saw his apparatus to illustrate the motions of a ring of thirty-six satellites about Saturn. He does not think the constitution of Satellites conforms with the aspect of the ring. He has discussed the subject of the ring being a disintegrated solid. He states that the loss of force by friction and heat would not be appreciable to observation, supposing there were perpetual collisions. So loss by friction of a fluid would be inappreciable. He doubts if a ring of satellites would satisfy the observed aspect. / He referred to the aspect of the moon at full having the rim brightest, as probably an indication of a rough surface of large blocks – not fine sand.' (Holden, *Memorials*: 129). Maxwell described his model illustrating the movements of the satellites constituting the rings of Saturn in his letter to William Thomson of 30 January 1858 (Volume I: 578–9 and Plate VII).

(8) George P. Bond, 'An account of Donati's comet of 1850', *Edinburgh New Philosophical Journal*, **10** (1859): 60–84; and G. P. Bond, *Account of the Great Comet of 1858* (Cambridge, Mass., 1862), Volume III of *Annals of the Astronomical Observatory of Harvard College* (see note (4)).

(9) See Number 309.

shown,[10] a cubic mile of sunlight, even at the earths distance is worth mechanically 12,050 foot-pounds and a cubic foot of space near the sun can contain energy equal to .0038 foot-pound *at least*.

This is under ordinary circumstances and gives an estimate of the amount of strain which the medium has been for ages subjected to without in any way giving way.

But we have no reason to believe that if the suns heat were increased 1000 fold, the medium would be unable to transmit it, or would break down under the forces applied.

We have therefore no knowledge of the ultimate *strength* of the heavenly medium but it is well able to do all that is required of it, whether we give it nothing to do but to transmit light & heat or whether we make it the machinery of magnetism and electricity also and at last assign gravitation itself to its power.[11]

If we could understand how the presence of a dense body could produce a linear pressure radiating out in straight lines from the body and keep up this kind of pressure continually, then gravitation would be explained on mechanical principles and the attraction of two bodies would be the consequence of the repulsive action of the lines of pressure in the medium.

For instance in the case of a body at a distance from the Sun the equation to the lines of force w^d be

$$P\cos\theta + r^2 \sin^2\theta = C$$

where r is the distance from P and θ the angle which r makes with PS.

There are two sets of lines separated by the surface of revolution whose eq^n is got by making $C = P$

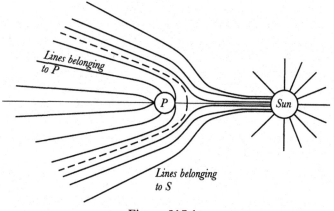

Figure 217,1

$$r^2 = \frac{a^2}{(1+\cos\theta)}.$$

---

(10) William Thomson, 'Note on the possible density of the luminiferous medium and on the mechanical value of a cubic mile of sunlight', *Trans. Roy. Soc. Edinb.*, **21** (1854): 57–61 (= *Math. & Phys. Papers*, **2**: 28–33).

(11) An issue discussed by Maxwell in his paper 'A dynamical theory of the electromagnetic field', *Phil. Trans.*, **155** (1865): 459–512, esp. 492–3 (= *Scientific Papers*, **1**: 570–1); see Number 238.

This surface has the general shape of a paraboloid of rev^n but suggests the appearance of a comets tail being more like a catenary than a parabola near the head.

Is there anything about a comet to render its lines of force visible? and not those of a planet which are stronger.

I think that visible lines of gravitating force are extremely improbable, but I never saw anything so like them as some tails of comets.[12]

What Herschel says about the repulsive action of the Sun[13] leaves unexplained the fact that the motion of the nucleus is that of a body gravitating toward the Sun with a force neither more nor less than that of ordinary matter.

If there were at any time matter in the comet which was not gravitating, or not gravitating to the same extent as earthly matter, then the path of the comet would be less curved to the sun than if it were made of ordinary matter, and therefore calculations depending upon the common value of the Suns attractive power would not give the true path of comets.

I have nothing yet to send you,[14] but we are making a report on Electrical Measurements for the Brit. Ass.[15] which I will send you when I get copies, and if you will inform me of any electrical men in America I will bring forward their claims to have copies of the standard coil of electrical Resistance.

We have hopes of producing coils next winter the resistance of which is known to within a small fraction in electromagnetic units. Such coils may be employed in measuring electromotive forces, in determining the mechanical equivalent of Heat and in other researches.

The present measures of resistance in absolute units vary by 6 or 7 per cent but I think we are already safe within $\frac{1}{2}$ per cent and I see how to make determinations quite as exact as we can determine the size of our coil in meters.[16]

In the course of our work we have had to obtain a constant velocity of rotation. This was secured by means of a governor invented by Mr Fleeming Jenkin, but we propose to make a new governor combining the principles of

---

(12) Compare Maxwell's comments in his letter to Faraday of 9 November 1857 (Volume I: 550).

(13) In his lecture 'On comets', *Good Words* (1863): 476–82, 549–57, esp. 553 (= J. F. W. Herschel, *Familiar Lectures on Scientific Subjects* (London, 1867): 90–141, esp. 128–30), where he refers to Bond's observations of comets' tails (see note (8)). See also Number 309.

(14) In response to Bond's request, in his letter of 9 July 1863, for 'any publications which you can in future add to those which you had the kindness to give me when in London'.

(15) See Number 210 note (2).   (16) See Number 214 esp. note (6).

Prof. W. Thomson and Mr Jenkin and we hope to get results comparable with clockwork.[17] I have been studying the mathematical principles of governors and I have been able to detect the sources of irregularities in the motion and, I hope, to correct them.[18] We mean to expose the new governor to severe tests by sudden variations of driving power, and if we find it answer I hope it will be taken into consideration in devising moving power for large equatoreals. The dynamics of governors is exceedingly interesting on account of the number of conditions which may be introduced by various arrangements of the machinery, and the different and sometimes opposite effects of these on the stability of the motion.

I am exceedingly obliged to you for your kindness in sending the books. I hope to be able to say so again when I have read the part about Saturn. I think the visibility of the ring under oblique sunshine shows that its surface is very rough, the roughness being not like that of paper or sandstone but like that of a wilderness of sharp rocks so that we being on the same side as the sun see nearly every spot of sunshine while most of the shadows are hid by their respective objects.

Aragos test of the solidity of a heavenly body by polarized light[19] supposes the solid body to be as smooth as a rough bar of iron if not actually polished whereas the smoothest part of our earth is a paved street and even the sea is generally too rough to polarize much light.

With much Respect
Yours truly
J. CLERK MAXWELL

Prof. G. P. Bond

---

(17) See Maxwell's letter to William Thomson of 11 September 1863 (Number 219, esp. notes (7), (8) and (9)).

(18) See Number 219.

(19) Maxwell may have had in mind Arago's discussion in his *Popular Astronomy*, (trans.) W. H. Smyth and R. Grant, 2 vols. (London, 1855–8), **1**: 418. See also Herschel, 'On comets': 555.

A body is placed at F under the attraction of a very distant body S. The curve separating the lines of force which belong to F from those which belong to S has the equation $r^2 = \dfrac{a^2}{1+\cos\theta}$.

Construction. Draw the dotted lines at distance $\dfrac{a}{2}$ from the axis. Draw with any radius and centre F a circle AQP and make $QP = AQ$. P is a point on curve. There are two asymptotes at distance a on each side of the axis. When S is not at an infinite distance these meet in the line FS.

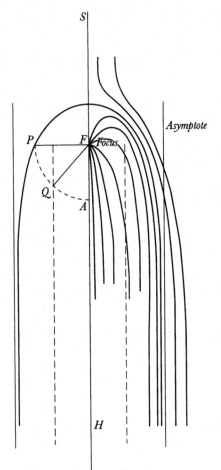

Figure 217,2

= 218 =

FROM A LETTER TO FLEEMING JENKIN[1]

27 AUGUST 1863

From Campbell and Garnett, *Life of Maxwell*[2]

27 Aug. 1863

To compare electromagnetic with electrostatic units:—[3]

1st, Weber's method – Find the capacity of a condenser in electrostatic measure (meters).[4]

Determine its potential when charged, and measure the charge of discharge through a galvanometer.

2d, Thomson's – Find the electromotive force of a battery by electromagnetic methods, and then weigh the attraction of two surfaces connected with the two poles.[5]

3d, (Not tried, but talked of by Jenkin). – Find the resistance of a very bad conductor in both systems –

(1) By comparison with (4th June),[6]

(2) By the log. decrement of charge per second.

All the methods require a properly graduated series of steps. The 1st and 2d determine V, a velocity = 310,740,000 meters per second.[7]

---

(1) According to Lewis Campbell's account (*Life of Maxwell*: 317), a 'mass of correspondence, containing numerous suggestions made by Maxwell from day to day in 1863–4, has been preserved by Professor Jenkin'. The correspondence is no longer extant.

(2) *Life of Maxwell*: 336–7.

(3) Compare the discussion of the 'Experimental determination of the ratio, v, between electromagnetic and electrostatic measures of quantity' in the paper by J. Clerk Maxwell and Fleeming Jenkin, 'On the elementary relations between electrical measurements', included in the 'Report of the Committee... on standards of electrical resistance', *Report of the Thirty-third Meeting of the British Association* (London, 1864): 111–76, esp. 130–63, on 153–4 (reprinted, with corrections, in *Phil. Mag.*, ser. 4, **29** (1865): 436–60, 507–25, esp. 515–16).

(4) R. Kohlrausch and W. Weber, 'Elektrodynamische Maassbestimmungen insbesondere Zurückführung der Stromintensitätsmessungen auf mechanisches Maass', *Abhandlungen der Königlichen Sächsischen Gesellschaft der Wissenschaften*, (*math.-phys. Klasse*), **3** (1857): 219–92; W. Weber and R. Kohlrausch, 'Ueber die Elektricitätsmenge, welche bei galvanischen Strömen durch den Querschnitt der Kette fliesst', *Ann. Phys.*, **99** (1856): 10–25.

(5) William Thomson, 'Measurement of the electrostatic force produced by a Daniell's battery', *Proc. Roy. Soc.*, **10** (1860): 319–26 (= *Electrostatics and Magnetism*: 238–46).

(6) The German-silver arbitrary standard used in the experiments on electrical resistance; see Number 210, esp. note (4) and Number 214 note (18); and see 'Report': 174–6.

(7) Compare J. C. Maxwell, 'On physical lines of force. Part III', *Phil. Mag.*, ser. 4, **23** (1862): 12–24, esp. 21–2 (= *Scientific Papers*, **1**: 498–500); and his letters of 19 October 1861 to Michael Faraday and of 10 December 1861 to William Thomson (Volume I: 683–9, 692–8);

Letter to Fleeming Jenkin, 27 August 1863

The 3d method determines V^2.

The first method requires a condenser of large capacity, and the measurement of this capacity and that of the discharge by a galvanometer.

I think this method looks the best; but I would use a much larger condenser than Weber, and determine its capacity by more steps.

The chief difficulty of Thomson's method is the measurement of a very small force and a very small distance. I think these difficulties may be overcome by making the force act on a comparatively stiff spring and magnifying optically the deflection.

On the third method we require a very large condenser indeed, also a series of resistances in steps between 4th June and that of the insulating substance of the condenser, and a galvanometer (or electrometer) to measure discharge (or tension).

'From the determination by Kohlrausch and Weber of the numerical relation...I have determined the velocity of propagation of transverse vibrations' (Volume I: 685).

219

LETTER TO WILLIAM THOMSON

11 SEPTEMBER 1863

From the original in the University Library, Glasgow[1]

Glenlair
Dalbeattie
1863 Sept 11

Dear Thomson

I have been working at the theory of the induction of currents on themselves[2] and have ascertained 1st what happens when a cylindrical conductor begins to conduct, 2nd when it has currents in it of the form $\sin nt$. The different shells of the cylinder have different currents at first and there is therefore a want of 'solidarity' about the electricity. Let $\frac{1}{2}L\gamma^2$ be the intrinsic energy of the current γ in a conductor of length l[3] calculated on the supposition that γ is uniform then in all cases of variable currents we must make $L' = L - \frac{1}{4}l$[4]
that is, the want of solidarity diminishes the 'mass' of the electricity by $\frac{1}{4}l$ just as any looseness in a thing diminishes its mass for instantaneous effects though not for prolonged ones.

I have also got the theory of circular coils of various sections and their values of L and the experimental determination of $\dfrac{L}{R}$ whence either L or R might be found.[5]

Do you know any publication on this subject.

---

(1) Glasgow University Library, Kelvin Papers, M 15. Previously published in A. T. Fuller, 'James Clerk Maxwell's Glasgow manuscripts: extracts relating to control and stability', *International Journal of Control*, **43** (1986): 1593–612, on 1597–600.

(2) Compare J. Clerk Maxwell, 'A dynamical theory of the electromagnetic field', *Phil. Trans.*, **155** (1865): 459–512, esp. 508–12 (= *Scientific Papers*, **1**: 592–7). See also Maxwell's letter to Thomson of 31 July 1863 (Number 214).

(3) L is the 'coefficient of self-induction'; see 'A dynamical theory of the electromagnetic field': 508 (= *Scientific Papers*, **1**: 592).

(4) See Number 239 §8; and compare 'A dynamical theory of the electromagnetic field': 511 (= *Scientific Papers*, **1**: 595–6), where he writes $\frac{1}{4}\mu l$, where μ is the 'coefficient of magnetic induction for the substance of the wire'.

(5) R is the resistance of the wire.

Governors[6]

I have been working at the conditions of steady motion for your governor (T)[7] for Jenkins (J)[8] for yours & J's in series TJ,[9] for T & J independent on

---

(6) The term was conventional; see John Robison, *A System of Mechanical Philosophy*, 4 vols. (Edinburgh, 1822), **2**: 152–9; and Henry Moseley, *The Mechanical Principles of Engineering and Architecture* (London, 1843): 390–4. Maxwell's discussion in this letter was preliminary to his paper 'On governors', *Proc. Roy. Soc.*, **16** (1868): 270–83 (= *Scientific Papers*, **2**: 105–20).

(7) Maxwell's drawing of Thomson's governor (Fig. 219, 1) is in accordance with his account of Thomson's device in his paper 'On governors': 273 (= *Scientific Papers*, **2**: 107), where he notes that 'the force restraining the centrifugal piece is that of a spring acting between a point of the centrifugal piece and a fixed point at a considerable distance, and the break is a friction-break worked by the reaction of the springs on the fixed point'. This governor differs in construction and mode of operation from the device described by Thomson in his paper 'On a new form of centrifugal governor', *Transactions of the Institution of Engineers and Shipbuilders in Scotland*, **12** (1868): 67–71; see Fuller, 'Maxwell's Glasgow manuscripts': 1604–5. The leaf spring mechanism (see Fig. 219, 1) is described by Fleeming Jenkin in a letter to Thomson of 8 August 1860 (Kelvin Papers J 38, Glasgow University Library).

(8) In the 1863 'Report of the Committee... on standards of electrical resistance' in the *Report of the Thirty-third Meeting of the British Association for the Advancement of Science* (London, 1864): 120, reference is made to a 'frictional governor of novel form, designed by Mr Jenkin for another purpose, and lent for the experiments'. This governor has been confused with the governor which Maxwell labels TJ. In his list of 'instruments belonging to the Committee of the British Association on Electric Standards' (*Cambridge University Reporter* (27 April, 1875): 354) Maxwell listed both 'Jenkin's governor with contact-breaker' and 'Thomson and Jenkin's governor' (on which see note (9)). For a reconstruction of Jenkin's governor see Fuller, 'Maxwell's Glasgow manuscripts': 1605–6; and see note (18).

(9) In his letter of 31 July 1863 (Number 214) Maxwell refers to this governor as 'mine'; and he labels the corresponding equation (M) *infra*. In 'On governors': 279 (= *Scientific Papers*, **2**: 115) he terms this the 'compound governor', stating that it had 'been constructed and used'. This may be the governor preserved in the Cavendish Laboratory, Cambridge, which is reproduced in Plate I and in I. B. Hopley, 'Maxwell's work on electrical resistance. I. The determination of the absolute unit of resistance', *Annals of Science*, **13** (1957): 265–72, Plate 13. This governor is presumably the instrument which Maxwell described in 1875 as 'Thomson and Jenkin's governor' (see note (8)); it incorporates the principles described for the governor TJ and for the 'compound governor' described in 'On governors', and thus embodies Maxwell's own development of Jenkin's governor. It incorporates a spring-loaded rod (now missing from the instrument, but shown in Plate I) which opposes the centrifugal force of the rotating fly-weights, in a manner similar to the spring in Thomson's governor (see note (7)). The governor in the Cavendish Laboratory is discussed by Fuller, 'Maxwell's Glasgow manuscripts': 1606–8, who reconstructs its mode of operation. This governor also incorporates a damper, apparently unlike Jenkin's governor as constructed in 1863 (see *infra* and note (18)). In the 1863 'Report of the Committee... on standards of electrical resistance': 120, 166, it is stated that 'better results are expected with a larger governor, made specially for the apparatus, on the joint plans of Professor Thomson and Mr Jenkin'; and that 'an improved governor on the same principle will be

the same axle T+J and for Siemens S.⁽¹⁰⁾ T & J have eqⁿˢ of 3ʳᵈ order T+J & S 4ᵗʰ and TJ of the 5ᵗʰ order.⁽¹¹⁾ Here is TJ in which T is employed to turn the loose wheel of J and lay on friction so.⁽¹²⁾

Let angle described by main axle	$= \omega t + \theta$
Moment of inertia of main axle	$= M$
Power of damper or centrifugal friction break	$= X$
Driving power	$= L$
Angle described by loose Jenkin wheel	$= \psi$
Moment of inertia	$= C$
Power of damper to J	$= Y$
Power of Js friction beak⁽¹³⁾	$= \mathcal{J}.$
Angle between Thomsons centrifugal piece & axes	$= \alpha + \phi$
A' = difference of mom. inert.	$A = A' \sin 2\alpha\omega$
B = mom about axis of suspension	
T = power of Ts friction break⁽¹⁴⁾ then	

(M) $\quad M\dfrac{d^2\theta}{dt^2} + X\dfrac{d\theta}{dt} + A\dfrac{d\phi}{dt} + T\phi + \mathcal{J}\psi = L$

(J) $\quad M\dfrac{d^2\psi}{dt^2} + Y\dfrac{d\psi}{dt} = T\phi$

(T) $\quad B\dfrac{d^2\phi}{dt^2} = A\dfrac{d\theta}{dt}$ ⁽¹⁵⁾ when properly adjusted as to spring power.

By T it appears that whenever the centrifugal piece is in equilibrium the machine is not only at the right velocity but in the right place, so that the

---

adopted in further experiments, in describing which an account of its construction will be given'. These experiments were carried out in the following year (see Number 222), but no mention of this governor (presumably the governor here denoted TJ by Maxwell) is made in the 'Description of a further experimental measurement of electrical resistance made at King's College', in the *Report of the Thirty-fourth Meeting of the British Association* (London, 1865): 350–1.

(10) The governor described by C. W. Siemens, 'On an improved governor for steam engines', *Proceedings of the Institution of Mechanical Engineers* (1853): 75–83, Plates 17 and 18.

(11) See Maxwell, 'On governors': 276, 278–9 (= *Scientific Papers*, **2**: 111, 114–15).

(12) In Maxwell's governor (TJ) a spring, employed as in Thomson's governor (see notes (7) and (9)), controls the fly-weights (of Jenkin's governor) which on rotation turn a horizontal wheel connected to a friction brake.

(13) See note (12).   (14) See note (7).

(15) Compare Maxwell, 'On governors': 278, equations (13) (= *Scientific Papers*, **2**: 115), where a term for friction is added to the equation corresponding to (T).

Plate I. The 'compound' governor (constructed after 1863) preserved in the Cavendish Laboratory, that Maxwell described as 'Thomson and Jenkin's governor'. This device incorporates Maxwell's modification (the spring-loaded rod, suggested by the spring opposing centrifugal force in Thomson's governor) of Jenkin's governor (Number 219).

effect of an increase of driving power is to produce oscillations after which clock error and rate are both as before.

Let $$\frac{Y}{C}=e \quad \frac{X}{M}=f \quad \frac{AT}{BM}=g \quad \frac{A^2}{BM}=h \quad \frac{J}{C}=j$$

then if θ is of the form $P_1 e^{x_1 t} + P_2 e^{x_2 t}$ &c

$$x^5 + (e+f)x^4 + efx^3 + (g+he)x^2 + gex + gj = 0.^{(16)}$$

The roots of this eq^n are in this case of the form

$$a, \ b \pm \sqrt{-1}\,c, \ b' \pm \sqrt{-1}\,c'.$$

If either $a\ b$ or b' is positive there will be destructive oscillations. Can you find the conditions of their being all negative?[17] Here are two necessary conditions

$$(e+f)ef > (g+he)$$
$$(e+f)e > j.$$

Here g is the power of Thomson j of Jenkin
 $f =$ damper of main axle e of Jenkin.
The 1st condition gives the necessary power of f
the 2nd ———————— of e.

f is got either by a simple centrif. friction break like the Edin^h Equatoreals clock or Jenkins without the screw part, or by some loose wheels fitting with various degrees of friction on the main axis.

e is got by making Jenkins scale pan go up & down in water or better by letting a wire from the bottom of it dip into Canada Balsam or Tar.[18] Can you tell me if there is any other condition than these two of $a\ b\ b'$ being $-^{ve}$?

---

(16) Compare Maxwell, 'On governors': 279, equation (16) (= *Scientific Papers*, **2**: 115).

(17) In his paper 'On governors' Maxwell linearises the equations of motion, which he reduces to a characteristic polynomial; the coefficients of this characteristic equation determine whether the governor is stable. He notes that this 'is mathematically equivalent to the condition that all the possible roots and the possible parts of the impossible roots, of a certain equation shall be negative'; 'On governors': 271 (= *Scientific Papers*, **2**: 106). This mathematical technique is the condition first introduced in his essay *On the Stability of the Motion of Saturn's Rings* (Cambridge, 1859): 10–11 (= *Scientific Papers*, **1**: 301–2), and see Volume I: 450–1. In his review of *Saturn's Rings* the Astronomer Royal, George Biddell Airy, 'commend[ed] these propositions to the study of the reader, as an interesting example of a beautiful method, applied with great skill to the solution of the difficult problems which follow'; G. B. Airy, 'On the stability of the motion of Saturn's rings', *Monthly Notices of the Royal Astronomical Society*, **19** (1859): 297–304, on 300.

(18) In 'On governors': 275 (= *Scientific Papers*, **2**: 111) Maxwell describes Jenkin's governor as having a damper: 'a weight is made to hang in a viscous liquid'. This was presumably a modification to Jenkin's governor as constructed in 1863.

This machine (TJ) is easily turned into T by clamping the loose wheels.[19] I think with a good spring T is an excellent time keeper. Spring short and not near the cent. piece but kept as near the axis as may be connected to C by a thin wire so that when AB is vertical $SC \perp CO$ and tension $= 0$.[20]

By keeping AB as free as possible and making the velocity considerable and the working angle of $AB = 45°$ you get very quick action and increased stability with the same power of dampers.

I send a photograph and shall be much obliged for one of you if you have some still. I shall be here till the 30th Sept. after which in London.

Yours truly
J. Clerk Maxwell

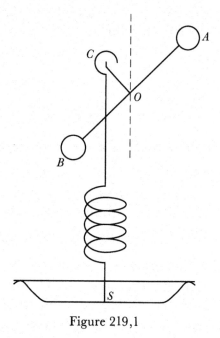

Figure 219,1

---

(19) The horizontal wheel of Jenkin's governor (see note (12)) had a loose fit on the vertical axle.

(20) See note (7). The lower end of the spring S is attached to a horizontal leaf spring.

REPORT ON A PAPER BY CHARLES CHAMBERS[1] ON THE MAGNETIC ACTION OF THE SUN

LATE OCTOBER 1863[2]

From the original in the Library of the Royal Society, London[3]

REPORT ON Mr C. CHAMBERS PAPER ON THE NATURE OF THE SUNS MAGNETIC ACTION UPON THE EARTH[4]

The author first shows (after Poisson)[5] that the three components of terrestrial magnetism due to the Sun's action as a magnet on the earth and the soft iron &c in it are linear functions of the components of the suns direct magnetic action.

From this it follows that the part of the disturbance due to the suns action as a magnet ought to be a harmonic variation whose period is one solar day, and that terms having periods of $\frac{1}{2}$ $\frac{1}{3}$ &c of a day are not due to the action of the Sun as a magnet.

On comparison with observation it appears that there are considerable variations dependent on the Suns hour angle but that those portions whose period is a fraction of a day are very considerable with respect to the term whose period is one day.

Hence the effect of the sun not due to action as a magnet is large compared to his effect as a magnet.[6]

Further it appears that on account of the Suns rotation the mean diurnal variation taken over a considerable time will be the same as if the sun were magnetized in the direction of his axis. Hence a law of the variations

---

(1) Charles Chambers was an assistant at Kew Observatory from 1856–63.

(2) In a letter to Stokes of 29 October 1863 (ULC Add. MSS 7656, RS 419; printed in Wilson, *Stokes–Kelvin Correspondence*, 1: 308), William Thomson wrote: 'Hearing from Maxwell that it was to him, not me, that it had been intended to send Chambers' paper I have given it to him. / I received it at the Royal Institution last June, with a note from you, so I suppose I was one of the referees, and I therefore leave a report for you upon it'. According to the Royal Society's *Register of Papers Received* Chambers' paper was approved for publication on 29 October 1863.

(3) Royal Society, *Referees' Reports*, 5: 48.

(4) Charles Chambers, 'On the nature of the sun's magnetic action upon the earth', *Phil. Trans.*, 153 (1863): 503–16. The paper was received by the Royal Society on 30 April 1863, and read on 21 May 1863; see the abstract in *Proc. Roy. Soc.*, 12 (1863): 567.

(5) S. D. Poisson, 'Second mémoire sur la théorie du magnétisme', *Mémoires de l'Académie Royale des Sciences de l'Institut de France*, 5 (1826): 488–533, esp. 533.

(6) Compare Maxwell's similar remark (referring to Chambers) in the *Treatise*, 2: 125 (§471).

depending on the position of the earth with respect to the points where the plane of the suns equator cuts the ecliptic.

The numbers deduced from this rule do not correspond with the actual variations as is shown by observations at different places.

Hence the suns action as a magnet is very small compared with his action on the magnetism of the earth in other ways e.g. (1) by heating it (2) by attracting it (3) by directing its course through space (4) by producing internal pressures in its substance.

The manner in which the results of observation are compared with the results of the hypothesis of the Sun's being a magnet is very clear and well conceived and I consider that the paper would be valuable as an addition to the Societies Transactions.[7]

J. CLERK MAXWELL

---

(7) In a brief report dated 28 October 1863 (Royal Society, *Referees' Reports*, **5**: 47) William Thomson also recommended publication, adding: 'I have long had strong reason for forming the same conclusion as that to which Mʳ Chambers has been led by a thorough examination of the results of observation. I add a short note (accompanying this report) which if approved by the Council, might be printed at the end of the paper.' Thomson's supplementary 'Note', affirming 'that no effect of the sun's action as a magnet is sensible at the earth', was printed as an addendum to Chambers' paper, in *Phil. Trans.*, **153** (1863): 515–16.

MANUSCRIPT ON THE EQUILIBRIUM AND STIFFNESS OF A FRAME[1]

circa JANUARY 1864[2]

From the original in the University Library, Cambridge[3]

TRIANGULAR ARCHED BRIDGE[a][b]

This is a stiff unstrained frame before it is loaded. When loaded, it is strained first by the load and the upward pressure at the springs, and second by the horizontal thrust of the springs.

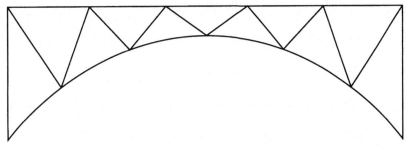

Figure 221,1

If the load is given it is easy to calculate the stress on each piece supposing the supporting forces at the springs vertical (as in a roof).

This may be done either by drawing a diagram or by arithmetical calculation.

Let p be the stress on one of the pieces on this supposition when the load is unity.

Next find the stress on each piece due to a tension unity between the spring

---

(a) {Endorsed} From Prof. Maxwell 26 January 1864 / Triangular Arched Bridge.

(b) {Headed} Diagram in office[4] / yield 1^{in} in 150^{ft} – this gives E / take e from Clark on Britannia Bridge[5] load unity.

(1) Compare Maxwell's paper 'On the calculation of the equilibrium and stiffness of frames', *Phil. Mag.*, ser. 4, **27** (1864): 294–9 (= *Scientific Papers*, **1**: 598–604).

(2) See the endorsement *infra*.

(3) ULC Add. MSS 7655, V, g/5.

(4) The manuscript may well have been written for Maxwell's cousin William Dyce Cay (son of Robert Cay), who was an engineer engaged in bridge-building: see Number 229, and Volume I: 410, 480, 575.

(5) Edwin Clark, *The Britannia and Conway Tubular Bridges*, 2 vols. (London, 1850).

of the arch. Let q be the stress on that piece for which the former stress was found.

Finally find the stress on each piece due to a single load equal to unity placed on a given joint A and let that on the selected piece be r (the supporting forces at the springs being vertical).

Then for a load L distributed as in the first case combined with a horizontal thrust H between the springs the stress on a piece is

$$pL + qH.$$

If e be the number of pounds weight required to produce unit elongation in the piece[6] then the actual elongation

$$= \frac{1}{e}(pL + qH).$$

The elongation of the line joining the springs due to the elongation of this piece only, the others remaining of invariable length, is by the principle of work[7]

$$\frac{1}{e}(pqL + q^2H).$$

Hence if we call the sum of all quantities of this kind with respect to each piece of the frame

$$\sum \left\{ \frac{1}{e}(pqL + q^2H) \right\}$$

this will be the total elongation of the line joining the springs.

Let the springs be connected by a tie beam whose elasticity is E[8]

then
$$\frac{1}{E}H + \sum \frac{1}{e} pqL + \sum \frac{1}{e} q^2 H = 0$$

or
$$H = -L \frac{\sum \left(\frac{1}{e} pq \right)}{\sum \left(\frac{1}{e} q^2 \right) + \frac{1}{e}}.$$ [9]

---

(6) e is the 'elasticity' of a piece, 'the force required to produce extension-unity'; $\frac{1}{e}$ 'the extension produced in a piece by tension-unity', is its 'extensibility'; compare 'On the calculation of the equilibrium and stiffness of frames': 295 (= *Scientific Papers*, **1**: 599–600).

(7) In his paper 'On the calculation of the equilibrium and stiffness of frames': 294 (= *Scientific Papers*, **1**: 598) Maxwell states: 'The method is derived from the principle of Conservation of Energy, and is referred to in Lamé's *Leçons sur l'Elasticité*, Leçon 7me, as Clapeyron's Theorem; but I have not yet seen any detailed application of it.' See Gabriel Lamé, *Leçons sur la Théorie Mathématique de l'Élasticité des Corps Solides* (Paris, 1852): 80–3.

(8) See note (6).

(9) Compare 'On the calculation of the equilibrium and stiffness of frames': 297 (= *Scientific Papers*, **1**: 601).

This gives us the tension of the tie beam in terms of L. If we make $E = \infty$ the springs become fixed. The elongation of the tie beam is

$$\frac{1}{E}H = -L\frac{\sum\left(\frac{1}{e}pq\right)}{\sum\left(\frac{1}{e}q^2\right)+1}.$$

If we put $E = 0$ we get the spread of the springs if there were no tie beam and they rested on a smooth horizontal plane.

To find the deflexion at the joint A due to the elongation (l) of the selected piece, the rest being rigid.

If the stress on A is 1 that on the piece is r therefore if the deflexion of A is d and the elongation of the piece l

$$d = rl$$

In the present case

$$d = \frac{1}{e}(rpL + rqH).$$

Hence the total deflexion at A is

$$L\sum\left(\frac{1}{e}rp\right) + H\sum\left(\frac{1}{e}rq\right)$$

or

$$D = L\left\{\sum\left(\frac{1}{e}rp - \frac{\sum\left(\frac{1}{e}pq\right)\sum\left(\frac{1}{e}rq\right)}{\sum\left(\frac{1}{e}q^2\right)+\frac{1}{E}}\right)\right\}. \quad (10)$$

This is the deflexion of any joint A due to the imposition of a load L in a given manner, $p\,q\,r$ are the stresses on a piece of elasticity e due to unity of the given load, unity of tension of tie beam and unity of load at A respectively and $\sum$ implies that all quantities of the kind are to be added. The tie beam whose elasticity is E is not included in the summation.

Note – the value of D is symmetrical with respect to p and r. Hence the deflexion produced at A by a load L at B is equal to the deflexion produced at B by L placed at A.

It will be best to make a table of the values of q once for all and two other tables one of x (the stress on each piece due to unity of vertical thrust on the left spring) and another of y (the same due to unit vertical thrust on the right spring). Then if the load divides the space in the ratio of n to $1-n$, p will lie $(1-n)x$ for the pieces to the left of the load and ny for those on the right.

---

(10) See note (9).

FROM A LETTER TO KATHERINE MARY CLERK MAXWELL

28 JANUARY 1864

From Campbell and Garnett, *Life of Maxwell*.[1]

We are going to have a spin with Balfour Stewart tomorrow.[2] I hope we shall have no accidents, for it puts off time so when anything works wrong, and we cannot at first find out the reason, or when a string breaks, and the whole spin has to begin again....However, we hope to bring out our standards by September,[3] and Becker[4] makes them up excellently.

---

(1) *Life of Maxwell*: 316.
(2) Further experiments on standards of electrical resistance: see Numbers 210, 211 and 214, and note (3).
(3) See the 'Description of a further experimental measurement of electrical resistance made at King's College' (by Maxwell, Balfour Stewart, Fleeming Jenkin and Charles Hockin), in the 'Report of the Committee on standards of electrical resistance', *Report of the Thirty-fourth Meeting of the British Association for the Advancement of Science; held at Bath in September 1864* (London, 1865): 345–67, esp. 350–1.
(4) See Number 214 note (5).

REPORT ON A PAPER BY WILLIAM JOHN MACQUORN RANKINE ON FLUID MOTION

LATE FEBRUARY 1864[1]

From the original in the Library of the Royal Society, London[2]

REPORT ON Dr RANKINE'S PAPER 'ON PLANE WATER-LINES'[3]

This paper is partly theoretical and partly practical. The theoretical part discusses two kinds of lines of fluid motion.[4] The practical part shows how certain of these lines may be adapted to the drawing of the waterlines of ships.

The theoretical definition of a Plane Waterline is 'a curve which a particle of liquid describes in flowing past a solid body[5] when such flow takes place in plane layers'.[6]

The general theory of such lines is in many respects simpler than that of waterlines in general.[7] The velocity of the fluid at any point is given by the equations $u = \dfrac{dU}{dy}$ $v = -\dfrac{dU}{dx}$ which of themselves satisfy the equation of continuity. The equation of a waterline is then $U = \text{const.}$[8]

---

(1) According to the Royal Society's *Register of Papers Received* Rankine's paper was referred to Maxwell on 18 February 1864, and approved for publication on 17 March 1864; and see note (15).

(2) Royal Society, *Referees' Reports*, **5**: 216.

(3) W. J. M. Rankine, 'On plane water-lines in two dimensions', *Phil. Trans.*, **154** (1864): 369–91. The paper was received by the Royal Society on 28 July 1863, and read on 26 November 1863; see the abstract in *Proc. Roy. Soc.*, **13** (1863): 15–17.

(4) By 'lines of fluid motion', which Rankine terms 'water-lines', Maxwell here denotes the lines traced by the paths of particles in a current of fluid, curves which Rankine subsequently termed 'stream-lines'. See Number 337, esp. note (4). For cases of steady motion, with which Rankine's paper is concerned, the paths of particles (stream lines) coincide with lines drawn to indicate the direction of fluid motion. See Number 337, esp. notes (5) and (6); and Horace Lamb, *A Treatise on the Mathematical Theory of the Motion of Fluids* (Cambridge, 1879): 21–2.

(5) See note (4).

(6) Rankine, 'On plane water-lines in two dimensions': 369.

(7) Maxwell's statement of the theory of stream lines in the case of motion in two dimensions, x and y, follows Rankine, 'On plane water-lines in two dimensions': 370. He had himself given a similar exposition in a manuscript 'On the steady motion of an incompressible fluid...', dated 9 May 1855 (Volume I: 295, 297).

(8) U is the stream function.

The rotation of a fluid element is represented by

$$\frac{d^2U}{dx^2}+\frac{d^2U}{dy^2}=\chi$$

and since as has been shown by Stokes (lectures &c?)[9] and recently by Helmholtz (Crelle 1859)[10] this rotation remains constant for the same particles of a perfect fluid during their motion the condition of motion is $\chi =$ function of U.

In the present paper χ is always equal to 0.[11]

This is equivalent to $udx+vdy=d\phi$[12] and then, as has been shown by W. Thomson Cam & Dub Math Journal III p 286[13] the systems of curves defined by $U=$ const and $\phi=$ const. are reciprocal that is if either is a system of water lines the other is a system of velocity function-curves.

(In the theory of Heat these would be lines of flow of heat and isothermals and in magnetism or electricity they would be lines of force and equipotential lines.)[14]

The waterlines here discussed are those due to the motion of an infinite sheet of water the distant parts of which move with uniform velocity C while the parts near the solid are disturbed in their course by having to flow past it.

It is manifest that the introduction of a solid of any form would generate a system of plane water lines of which the solid itself would be one. Physically considered it would be the first water line, but mathematically considered it would be one of a series any one of which might be substituted for the solid, and would produce the remaining waterlines.

---

(9) On reviewing Rankine's paper (see note (15)) William Thomson appended the comment 'This very remarkable result due to Stokes?' to the MS of Rankine's paper (Royal Society, PT. 70.7, f. 6). See G. G. Stokes, 'On the steady motion of incompressible fluids', *Trans. Camb. Phil. Soc.*, **7** (1842): 439–53, esp. 441–6 (= *Papers*, **1**: 1–16).

(10) H. Helmholtz, 'Über Integrale der hydrodynamischen Gleichungen, welche den Wirbelbewegungen entsprechen', *Journal für die reine und angewandte Mathematik*, **55** (1858): 25–55, esp. 33–7.

(11) The condition of irrotational motion of an incompressible fluid in two dimensions; see Volume I: 311, and Stokes, 'On the steady motion of incompressible fluids': 441.

(12) The function ϕ is the velocity potential; for Maxwell's use of this term (following Helmholtz) see Number 254. On the equation see Stokes, 'On the steady motion of incompressible fluids': 439–41.

(13) [William Thomson,] 'Note on orthogonal isothermal surfaces', *Camb. Math. J.*, **3** (1843): 286–8 (= *Math. & Phys. Papers*, **1**: 22–4).

(14) The argument is basic to Maxwell's paper 'On Faraday's lines of force', *Trans. Camb. Phil. Soc.*, **10** (1856): 27–83 (= *Scientific Papers*, **1**: 155–229). There he also makes reference to Thomson's paper on orthogonal surfaces; see Volume I: 361.

The cases considered by the author are those in which the lines are produced by a circular cylinder or by an oval of a peculiar form.

In both cases the mathematical expressions indicate a system of lines within as well as without the primitive curve, which do not belong to this question.

As I think these particular cases and the graphical method employed by the author[15] can be more easily explained in a physical way than by reference to the equations in the memoir I shall do so, observing that the author has already given several examples of such treatment in cases where it is not so easy to apply it as in the present case.

It follows from the nature of plane water lines that if two systems of water lines be drawn, so that the constant in each series increases by equal intervals, a third system of lines may be drawn diagonally through these and this system will also be a system of water-lines.

1 The waterlines corresponding to a uniform rectilinear flow form a system of parallel lines at equal intervals.
2 The waterlines corresponding to a flow outwards from a centre form a system of lines radiating from a point at equal angles.
3 The waterlines corresponding to a flow outwards from one focus and inwards towards another may be got by combining the two cases graphically. The result, however is more simply got by drawing a system of circles through the two points so that the tangents at those points shall be a series of lines at equal angles.
4 When the two points coincide, these circles become a system of circles all touching at the same point and having their radii in harmonic series.
5 By combining (1) & (4) we get the 'Cyclogenous Neoids'.[16]
6 By combining (1) and (3) we get the 'Oogenous Neoids'.[17]

---

(15) See Plate VIII Figs. 1 and 2 in *Phil. Trans.*, **154** (1864) for Rankine's figures. In a letter to Stokes of 17 February 1864, reporting on Rankine's paper (Royal Society, *Referees' Reports*, **5**: 214; in Wilson, *Stokes–Kelvin Correspondence*, **1**: 317–19), William Thomson remarked that 'Maxwell I believe was the first to use the diagonal method of drawing, for lines of force & I think should be referred to'. In a brief supplementary note, published as an 'Appendix' to his paper 'On plane water-lines in two dimensions': 390, Rankine responded by citing Maxwell's method of constructing lines of force; see Volume I: 627–8, and the *Treatise*, **1**: 147–9 (§123), and Maxwell's paper 'On a method of drawing the theoretical forms of Faraday's lines of force without calculation', *Report of the Twenty-sixth Meeting of the British Association for the Advancement of Science* (London, 1857), part 2: 12 (= *Scientific Papers*, **1**: 241).

(16) Rankine, 'On plane water-lines in two dimensions': 373; '*Cyclogenous Neoids*, that is, *ship-shape curves generated from a circle*'.

(17) Rankine, 'On plane water-lines in two dimensions': 373; water-line curves generated from '*Ovals, or Oögenous Neoïds*'.

7 By combining (1) and (2) we get the 'Parabologenous Neoids'[18] or the system of lines seen when a carriage wheel rolls behind a vertical railing.

8 By combining a sufficient number of cases of (2) with (1) we may get waterlines of any form and there will be one closed curve among them provided as much water flows out of one set of points as flows in at another.

Which of all these systems of waterlines including all forms whatever is best for shipbuilding must be decided by considering which gives the smoothest and simplest motion to the water beyond the vessel, and is least liable to generate waves and so waste energy.

On examining the waterlines of the Oogenous kind it appears that those near the centre have three points of minimum velocity (where they are furthest apart), and two points of maximum velocity (where they are closest together), but that those at a distance have two points of minimum and one of maximum velocity.

On the limiting waterline where the two maxima and one minimum coalesce there will be at that point a position of most uniform velocity and that waterline may be considered as the waterline of least variation of velocity. The author therefore selects it as the best waterline for practice.[19]

(It is impossible to have a system of waterlines of absolutely uniform velocity, for in that case both the water lines and their orthogonal system of curves must be equidistant, whence it follows by geometry that both systems must be straight lines.)

The waterlines finally selected are the portions of these lines of most uniform flow up to the point of minimum velocity. Such waterlines may be of any degree of bluffness or sharpness and the author shows that the discontinuity at the extremities does not interfere much with the ships motion.

Of course the external waterlines of such a ship will differ in some degree from the 'Oogenous Neoids' of this paper, but unless the water is thrown into eddies and waves the effect on the ships motion will be inconsiderable.[20]

---

(18) Rankine, 'On plane water-lines in two dimensions': 377.

(19) Rankine, 'On plane water-lines in two dimensions': 380, 388; termed the 'water-lines of smoothest gliding, or *Lissoneoïds*'. In his letter to Stokes of 17 February 1864 (note (15)) Thomson emphasised Rankine's discussion of the 'trajectories of minimum & of max^m velocity of water relative to solid...the "lissenoid" core is very remarkable'.

(20) In his letter to Stokes of 17 February 1864 Thomson declared: 'But the application is not, as the author supposes, even approximate for a real ship. His statements on this subject would require *very decided correction* but this would leave the main substance of the paper untouched. / A much closer approx^n to real ship water lines would be had by taking a solid of revolution moving through a liquid instead of a case in which the motion is entirely in parallel planes.'

The author has also investigated the effect of the friction of the water against the surface of the ship, and has shown how to reduce to a mathematical form the problem of the waterline of least frictional resistance.

The friction here considered is that of the water against the solid side of the vessel and is assumed proportional to the square of the velocity of sliding. The work done against friction divided by the distance described by the vessel in the same time, gives the resistance to the motion.

This friction differs from the internal friction of the fluid the effects of which are proportional to the velocity simply.

The effect of the variations of velocity in producing inequalities of level near the vessel are investigated. These inequalities may become the origin of waves, which may dissipate the energy of the vessel over the ocean. This part of the paper appears from its bearing upon the resistance to be worthy of more extended investigation.

The paper as a whole is an instance of mathematical principles applied with skill to a practical subject which is beset with very great and necessary difficulties and I consider it worthy of a place in the Transactions.

= 224 =

DRAFTS ON THE THEORY OF SATURN'S RINGS
1864[1]
From the originals in the University Library, Cambridge[2]

[1]   MATHEMATICAL THEORY OF SATURNS RINGS

We assume the Rings to consist of independent portions of solid matter of small dimensions compared with the thickness of the rings (100 miles or less) revolving about Saturn in orbits very nearly circular, the differences of the actual motion from that of a satellite in a circular orbit in the plane of the ring being small quantities of the first order. Let S be the Mass of Saturn r the distance from his centre then the linear velocity of the supposed satellite at distance r would be $\sqrt{S\frac{1}{r}}$ in the positive direction at right angles to r, and the actual motion of a particle may be resolved into velocities

u in the direction of r, away from Saturn $= \dfrac{dr}{dt}$

$\sqrt{S\dfrac{1}{r}}+v$ in the positive direction around Saturn $= r\dfrac{d\theta}{dt}$

w normal to the plane of reference $= \dfrac{dz}{dt}$.

Let z be the actual distance of the particle from the plane of reference.

First, for the motion in the plane of reference we have as usual[3]

$$\frac{1}{r} = \frac{S}{h^2}(1+e\cos(\theta-\alpha)),$$

$$\frac{1}{r^2}\frac{dr}{dt} = \frac{S}{h^2}e\sin(\theta-\alpha)\frac{d\theta}{dt},$$

$$h = r^2\frac{d\theta}{dt}.$$

---

(1) In his letter to G. B. Airy of 16 October 1872 (Number 424) Maxwell indicated that these drafts were written 'about the year 1864'.

(2) ULC Add. MSS 7655, V, a/7. Previously published (in different sequence) in S. G. Brush, C. W. F. Everitt and E. Garber, *Maxwell on Saturn's Rings* (Cambridge, Mass./London, 1983): 169–81, 183–9. See also A. T. Fuller, 'James Clerk Maxwell's Cambridge manuscripts: extracts relating to control and stability – IV', *International Journal of Control*, **39** (1984): 619–56. Brush, Everitt and Garber include a preliminary worksheet (on which see note (23)) and some supplementary notes, not reproduced here; see *Maxwell on Saturn's Rings*: 181–3, 190–4.

(3) The equation in polar coordinates for an ellipse of eccentricity e.

Whence
$$u = \frac{S}{h}e\sin(\theta-\alpha) \quad v = \frac{1}{2}\frac{S}{h}e\cos(\theta-\alpha).$$

Let u_0 and v_0 be the values of u & v when $\theta = 0$
$$u = u_0 \cos\theta + 2v_0 \sin\theta$$
$$v = v_0 \cos\theta - \tfrac{1}{2}u_0 \sin\theta.$$

In these expressions v is the tangential velocity relative to that in a circle at the distance from the centre at which the particle is *at that instant* so that while $\sqrt{\dfrac{S}{r}}$ represents the average tangential velocity v represents the additional velocity due to agitation.

Let us suppose that R is the total mass of the ring contained within the radius r so that R is a function of r which is zero when r is less than the inner radius of the ring and equal to the whole ring when r is greater than the outer radius of the ring.

Then the quantity of matter in unit of area of the ring will be
$$\frac{1}{2\pi r}\frac{dR}{dr}.$$

The attraction of the ring on a particle at its surface, normal to the ring will be
$$\frac{1}{r}\frac{dR}{dr}$$

and if the particles of the ring be supposed uniformly scattered within a stratum whose thickness $= Z$ on either side of the plane of reference the attraction on a particle within it will be
$$\frac{1}{r}\frac{dR}{dr}\frac{z}{Z} \quad \text{towards the plane of reference.}$$

The equation of motion in z will therefore be
$$\frac{d^2z}{dt^2} = -\left(\frac{S}{r^3} + \frac{1}{rZ}\frac{dR}{dr}\right)z$$

whence if we make
$$1 + \frac{r^2}{SZ}\frac{dR}{dr} = n^2\mu^2 \quad \text{and} \quad n = \sqrt{\frac{S}{r^3}} = \frac{d\theta}{dt}$$

we shall have
$$z = z_0 \cos\mu\theta + \frac{w_0}{n\mu}\sin\mu\theta$$
$$w = w_0 \cos\mu\theta - z_0 n\mu \sin\mu\theta.$$

z, the distance from the plane of reference and w the velocity perpendicular to that plane are connected together by the following equation which we obtain by eliminating θ from the two equations above

$$z^2 n^2 \mu^2 + w^2 = z_0^2 n^2 \mu^2 + w_0^2.$$

If z^2 represents the mean square of the distance of all the particles from the plane of reference and w^2 the mean square of the agitation normal to it it will be seen that in the case in which the mean thickness of the ring does not alter the value of w^2 will also be constant, that is, for the case of stability

$$z^2 = z_0^2 \quad \text{and} \quad w^2 = w_0^2.$$

[2]   [THE STABILITY OF SATURN'S RINGS]

The existence of a thin flat and circular system of rings, surrounding, yet nowhere touching the planet Saturn has been known for 200 years but we have as yet little knowledge of their structure and little foundation for coming to a decision whether we may expect them to continue in their present state for a long time, or whether their total or partial destruction is likely to be witnessed by living astronomers.

Considerable changes have certainly taken place in their appearance as seen by successive astronomers[4] but we know that the earlier observers had more imperfect telescopes than those which are now directed to Saturn so that the evidence requires very careful examination before we can conclude in favour of an actual change of form or a development of new features.[5]

Mathematicians, however, while they accept the results of observation as to the changeableness or permanence of an astronomical phenomenon, are not at liberty to accept them as ultimate facts from which the future phases of the motion may be deduced by the principle of continuity. They cannot regard Saturns Rings as the result of some undiscovered law of generation and development prevailing among a class of planets. They must either explain on mechanical principles how they have continued to exist so long and whether they are subject to decay, or they must confess that a gap has

---

(4) Otto Struve had claimed that the rings had changed in form during the two centuries following their first observation; see Otto Struve, 'Sur les dimensions des anneaux de Saturne', *Mémoires de l'Académie Impériale des Sciences de Saint-Pétersbourg*, ser. 6, **5** (1853): 439–75, esp. 473 (= *Recueil de Mémoires présentés à l'Académie des Sciences par les Astronomes de Poulkova*, **1** (1853): 349–85, esp. 383).

(5) A question considered by Maxwell in his essay *On the Stability of the Motion of Saturn's Rings* (Cambridge, 1859): esp. 67–8 (= *Scientific Papers*, **1**: 373–4), where he made reference to Struve's paper.

been discovered in celestial mechanics which may be perceived by the telescope but cannot be stopped up by the calculus.[6]

We must suppose the Rings to consist of matter in some of the states known to us and to be acted on by gravitation. Laplace was the first to show that a solid uniform ring is necessarily unstable and must fall on the body of the planet.[7] I have shown that a single thin ring loaded at one point of its circumference with a mass rather more than $4\frac{1}{2}$ times its own weight *might* permanently revolve about a central body. The adjustment of weight however must be very accurate it must not be less than .8159 or greater than .8279 of the whole.[8] The magnitude of such a weight would render it impossible to escape observation and the delicacy of adjustment would soon be impaired by the immense forces called into play tending to break or bend the ring – forces under which the strongest materials known to us would behave like sand or wax.

The hypothesis of a ring forming a solid mass is therefore untenable. That of the coexistence of many such rings has still less mechanical possibility. We are therefore obliged to regard the rings as consisting of matter the parts of which are not rigidly connected.

I have shown that it is possible for a ring consisting of a single row of unconnected particles to revolve permanently about the planet under certain conditions and that many such rings may revolve concentrically about the planet but that their mutual perturbations will gradually increase till some of them are thrown into a state of confusion.

The conclusion at which I arrived in my former paper was – 'that the only system of rings which can exist is one composed of an indefinite number of unconnected particles revolving round the planet with different velocities according to their respective distances. These particles may be arranged in a series of narrow rings, or they may move through each other irregularly. In the first case the destruction of the system will be very slow; in the second case it will be more rapid, but there may be a tendency towards an arrangement in narrow rings which may retard the process'.[9]

I was then of the opinion that 'When we come to deal with collisions among bodies of unknown number size and shape we can no longer trace the mathematical laws of their motion with any distinctness' (§(32)).[10] I

---

(6) Compare *Saturn's Rings*: 1 (= *Scientific Papers*, **1**: 290–1).

(7) P. S. de Laplace, *Traité de Mécanique Céleste*, 5 vols. (Paris, An VII [1799]–1825), **2**: 155–66; see *Saturn's Rings*: 2–4 (= *Scientific Papers*, **1**: 292–4), and Volume I: 440–2.

(8) Maxwell, *Saturn's Rings*: 15–16 (= *Scientific Papers*, **1**: 307–8); and see Volume I: 564.

(9) Maxwell, *Saturn's Rings*: 67 (= *Scientific Papers*, **1**: 373).

(10) Maxwell, *Saturn's Rings*: 53 (= *Scientific Papers*, **1**: 354). Compare his remark in his letter

propose now to take up the question at this point and to endeavour to throw some light on the theory of a confused assemblage of jostling masses whirling round a large central body.

I shall not enter into the theory of the *formation* of a ring (see papers by Mr Daniel Vaughan[11]). I shall suppose the rings already existing and find the conditions of their stability and the rate of their decay. In my former paper I restricted myself to cases in which no collisions take place and in which the mutual gravitation of the planet and the particles is the only force in action. It appears however that in this case that particles of each ring must be at a certain distance apart and each ring of particles must be at a considerable distance from the next so that even at the immense distance from which we view them we should see the discontinuity of their structure by their almost perfect transparency and the feebleness of their illumination. Whatever, therefore may be the condition of the dark inner rings, the outer rings are too substantial to have a constitution of this kind. The particles composing them must be so near together that they influence each other far more by collisions and jostling than by the attraction of gravitation. The individual masses, even if large compared with meteoric stones or even mountains are probably so small compared with planets that the effect of the mutual gravitation of two of them on the velocity or path of either may be entirely neglected. We have therefore to consider the motions of an immense number of small bodies occupying a space in the form of a flat ring or rings of which the thickness is less than a thousandth of the diameter and whirling round a planet in the centre with velocities nearly corresponding to their respective distances.

Collisions will occur between these bodies and after collision each body will be projected with a velocity which will carry it into some other part of the cloud of particles, where it will meet with other particles moving with a velocity different from its own. Another collision will thus occur and in this way the jostling of the particles once begun will be carried on throughout the

---

to William Thomson of 14 November 1857: 'The general case of a fortuitous concourse of atoms each having its own orbit & excentricity is a subject above my powers at present' (Volume I: 555).

(11) Maxwell is alluding to a series of papers by the American astronomer Daniel Vaughan: 'On the form of satellites revolving at small distances from their primaries', *Phil. Mag.*, ser. 4, **20** (1860): 409–18; 'On the stability of satellites in small orbits, and the theory of Saturn's rings', *ibid.*, **21** (1861): 263–74; 'On phenomena which may be traced to the presence of a medium pervading all space', *ibid.*, **21** (1861): 507–15; and 'Static and dynamic stability in the secondary systems', *ibid.*, **22** (1861): 489–97. In his paper 'On phenomena which may be traced to the presence of a medium pervading all space': 508 Vaughan had discussed Maxwell's conclusions in the essay on *Saturn's Rings*; see Brush, Everitt and Garber, *Maxwell on Saturn's Rings*: 23.

system and kept up on account of the different velocities of the different parts of the system so as to produce a continual loss of energy and a decay in the motion of the rings.

The principles by which problems of this kind can be treated were first discussed by Prof^r Clausius in a paper 'on the nature of the motion which we call heat',*[12] and were applied to several cases in gaseous physics by myself in a paper on the Motions and Collisions of Perfectly Elastic Spheres.†[13] Professor Clausius‡ has since pointed out some mistakes in the latter parts of this paper[14] in his paper on the conduction of Heat in Gases.[15] I hope to be able to complete a correct investigation of diffusion and conduction of heat in gases and to establish the distribution of velocities among the particles in all cases,[16] but at present I must confine my attention to the effects of the collisions of rough imperfectly elastic bodies, in which case the complete theory is much more difficult and we must be satisfied with certain approximations. This is less to be regretted as we do not know the coefficient of elasticity for the collisions of the pieces of Saturns Rings and therefore we can expect only approximate numerical results.

We compare the motion of any particle at any instant with that which it would have if it revolved uniformly about the central body at that distance. We find that it differs from it by a small quantity which may be resolved into three components, a radial component (x) and a tangential component (y) and a component normal to the orbit (z). These components constitute the *velocity of agitation* of the particle as distinguished from the velocity of the ring at that point which is that corresponding to a circular orbit. If we trace this velocity of agitation for a single particle we find that it moves among the different concentric rings as if it described an ellipse in the same time as the time of revolution but in the opposite direction the major axis being in the direction of the radius vector and equal to twice the minor. It also oscillates

*
†
‡

---

(12) Rudolf Clausius, 'On the kind of motion which we call heat', *Phil. Mag.*, ser. 4, **14** (1857): 108–27; trans. from 'Ueber die Art der Bewegung welche wir Wärme nennen', *Ann. Phys.*, **100** (1857): 353–80.

(13) J. C. Maxwell, 'Illustrations of the dynamical theory of gases. Part I. On the motions and collisions of perfectly elastic spheres', *Phil. Mag.*, ser. 4, **19** (1860): 19–32 (= *Scientific Papers*, 1: 377–91). See Volume I: 606–11.

(14) See Number 207.

(15) Rudolf Clausius, 'On the conduction of heat by gases', *Phil. Mag.*, ser. 4, **23** (1862): 417–35, 512–34; see Number 207 note (1). (16) See Number 263.

perpendicularly to the plane of the ring in a period rather less than that of revolution.

This is what would take place if the particle did not meet with any other particle in its course, but we know that other particles exist and can easily calculate the chance of its not being struck for a given time. In this way we can deduce an equation connecting the velocity of agitation of particles at the instant of their projection with that which they have when they suffer their next collision. On account of the difference of mean motion of the different concentric rings the motion of agitation among the particles when they meet is greater than that with which each was originally projected in the ring from which it came so that if the particles were perfectly elastic the motion of agitation would increase continually till the rings were dispersed in a cloud. But if the particles are inelastic the velocities after collision are generally less than before it, and thus the increase in the motion of agitation due to the interpenetration of particles belonging to different rings, and the decay of the motion of agitation due to the imperfect elasticity of the striking particles, may produce a kind of equilibrium or steadiness of motion in certain cases, while in other cases the motion of agitation will continually increase or diminish, till some change is effected in the arrangement of the system.

In studying the nature of the motion of agitation we shall find that it does not consist of a system of disturbances in the motion distributed alike in all directions but that the directions and velocities are distributed differently in different directions. The measure of the agitation in a given direction which we shall adopt is found by multiplying half the mass of each particle by the square of the motion of agitation resolved in that direction. This we shall call the Energy of Agitation in that direction. It appears that the energy of agitation is greatest in one direction, least in a direction at right angles to this and of intermediate value in a direction normal to the plane of these two directions, and that its value in any other direction is found by the same rules as are used to determine 'moments of inertia' and other mathematical quantities having an arrangement similar to that of the diameters of an ellipsoid. The sum of the energies in three rectangular directions is always equal to the total energy of agitation and the absolute energy is equal to the total energy of agitation together with the total energy due to the motion of the particles in mass.

We have next to examine the effect of collisions on the distribution of the agitation. We find that the total energy of agitation is diminished in the ratio of p to 1 where p has a value depending on the elasticity and on the nature of the bodies. The difference of the energy of agitation in any two of the principal axes is also diminished in the ratio of q to 1. The investigation of the values of p and q must be attended to separately.

[3]   [ON THE MOTION AND COLLISION OF PARTICLES]

To find the relations between the velocities and rotations of two bodies of any form before and after impact.

I have considered the case of the collisions of perfectly elastic bodies of any form in a paper on the Dynamical Theory of Gases, (Philosophical Magazine July 1860)[17] and have shown that the average vis viva of translation of every particle tends to become equal after many such collisions, and that the vis viva of rotation of each particle about each of its principal axes is equal and that the whole vis viva of rotation of each particle is equal to its vis viva of translation.[18] The equality of the vis viva of particles of different sizes leads to an explanation of Gay Lussacs law of atomic volumes of gases[19] and the relation between the vis viva of translation and rotation leads to the result that Bernoullis hypothesis[20] in its simplest form will not explain the relation between the specific heat of air at constant pressure and at constant volume.[21]

When the particles are not perfectly elastic, the motion of agitation cannot be kept up without some external cause and the investigation of the question becomes much more complicated than in the case where the motion of agitation if the particles are confined within an elastic vessel is self sustaining and capable of attaining a constant state. The external cause which sustains the motion of agitation in the case of Saturn's rings is the different velocities of contiguous portions of the rings and the energy which is lost by collision is made up by a supply drawn partly from the energy of motion of the rings round Saturn and partly from the potential energy of their gravitation towards him. As this source of energy is gradually diminished the form of the rings is gradually altered.

As we cannot investigate the effects of the collisions of inelastic bodies so easily as when the elasticity is perfect and as our only object is to obtain approximate numerical values for p & q we shall simplify the calculations by the following assumptions.

1st That the principal moments of inertia of each body are equal and represented by $M_1 k_1^2$ and $M_2 k_2^2$.

---

(17) J. C. Maxwell, 'Illustrations of the dynamical theory of gases. Part III. On the collision of perfectly elastic bodies of any form', *Phil. Mag.*, ser. 4, **20** (1860): 33–7 (= *Scientific Papers*, **1**: 405–9).
(18) On the equipartition theorem see Number 207 para. 7.
(19) Viz. 'Avogadro's hypothesis': see Number 259 §4, esp. notes (13) and (14).
(20) On Daniel Bernoulli and the kinetic theory of gases see Numbers 257, 263 and 377.
(21) See Number 207 para. 7.

2nd   That the points of the two bodies at which the impact takes place are at distances $a_1\ a_2$ from their respective centres of gravity.

3rd   That at a certain stage of the collision these two points are at rest relatively to each other on account of the action of the 'impulse of compression' which we may call R.

4th   That the whole impulsive force acting between the two bodies consists of the impulse of compression R, and the impulse of restitution R' and that these two forces act in the same direction and are in the ratio of 1 to e where e is the coefficient of elasticity of impact for the two bodies.

It is this part of our assumption which is most precarious. It supposes that there is no slipping between the bodies and that the value of e is the same for normal and for oblique impact. It is probable that the tangential impulse, when much smaller than the normal is independent of it but when the normal impulse is small the tangential impulse will have a maximum value equal to the normal impulse multiplied by a coefficient of impulsive friction.

In an investigation like the present in which we know so little about the bodies in motion it would not be advisable to begin by the introduction of complicated conditions arising from laws of friction and collision which at best are empirical.

We therefore begin with two rough spherical masses M_1 & M_2 whose radii are a_1 and a_2 and radii of gyration k_1 & k_2. Let the direction cosines of the line drawn from M_1 and M_2 at collision be l, m, n.

Let the velocities of the centres of gravity resolved along the axes of $x\ y\ z$ be

$u_1\ v_1\ w_1$ and $u_2\ v_2\ w_2$ before impact
$\bar{u}_1\ \bar{v}_1\ \bar{w}_1$ and $\bar{u}_2\ \bar{v}_2\ \bar{w}_2$ at great compression
$u'_1\ v'_1\ w'_1$ and $u'_2\ v'_2\ w'_2$ after restitution.

Let the angular velocities of rotation about the axes $x\ y\ z$ be denoted according to the same system of accentuation and suffixes by

$$p\ q\ r.^{(22)}$$

Let the components of the impulse of compression be

$$X\ Y\ Z$$

and those of the impulse of restitution according to our hypothesis

$$eX\ eY\ \&\ eZ,$$

those of the whole impulse will be

$$(1+e)X\quad (1+e)Y\quad \&\quad (1+e)Z.$$

---

(22) p and q are here used differently from usage *supra*; see *infra* where Maxwell uses p' and q' for p and q as used in §2.

The equations of motion are now easily written down, but as their number is great we may confine ourselves to those relating to the axis of x and to the instant of greatest compression.

$$\bar{u}_1 = u_1 + \frac{1}{M_1} X \quad \bar{p}_1 = p_1 + \frac{a_1}{M_1 k_1^2}(mZ - nY)$$

$$\bar{u}_2 = u_2 - \frac{1}{M_2} X \quad \bar{p}_2 = p_2 + \frac{a_2}{M_2 k_2^2}(mZ - nY).$$

To find the final velocities we must substitute an accent for the bar and multiply the impulse by $(1+e)$.

The velocities of the striking points in the direction of x are

$$u_1 - (mr_1 - nq_1) a_1 \quad \text{and} \quad u_2 + (mr_2 - nq_2) a_2.$$

At the instant of greatest compression these points have no relative motion, or

$$\bar{u}_2 - \bar{u}_1 + m(a_1 \bar{r}_1 + a_2 \bar{r}_2) - n(a_1 \bar{q}_1 + a_2 \bar{q}_2) = 0.$$

Substituting the values of these velocities we find

$$\left(\frac{1}{M_1} + \frac{1}{M_2}\right) X + \left(\frac{a_1^2}{M_1 k_1^2} + \frac{a_2^2}{M_2 k_2^2}\right)((m^2 + n^2) X - lmY - nlZ)$$
$$= u_2 - u_1 + m(a_1 r_1 + a_2 r_2) - n(a_1 q_1 + a_2 q_2)$$

with two other equations related to y & z as this is to x. Multiplying the first by $\left(\frac{1}{M_1} + \frac{1}{M_2} + l^2\left(\frac{a_1^2}{M_1 k_1^2} + \frac{a_2^2}{M_2 k_2^2}\right)\right)$ the second by $lm\left(\frac{a_1^2}{M_1 k_1^2} + \frac{a_2^2}{M_2 k_2^2}\right)$ and the third by $nl\left(\frac{a_1^2}{M_1 k_1^2} + \frac{a_2^2}{M_2 k_2^2}\right)$ and adding we obtain the value of X

$$X = \frac{1}{\frac{a_1^2 + k_1^2}{M_1 k_1^2} + \frac{a_2^2 + k_2^2}{M_2 k_2^2}} \left\{ u_2 - u_1 + \frac{\frac{a_1^2}{M_1 k_1^2} + \frac{a_2^2}{M_2 k_2^2}}{\frac{1}{M_1} + \frac{1}{M_2}} l\{l(u_2 - u_1) + m(v_2 - v_1) + n(w_2 - w_1)\} + m(a_1 r_1 + a_2 r_2) - n(a_1 q_1 + a_2 q_2) \right\}.$$

In the same way we find

$$mZ - nY = \frac{1}{\frac{a_1^2 + k_1^2}{M_1 k_1^2} + \frac{a_2^2 + k_2^2}{M_2 k_2^2}} \{m(w_2 - w_1) - n(v_2 - v_1)$$
$$- (m^2 + n^2)(a_1 p_1 + a_2 p_2) + lm(a_1 q_1 + a_2 q_2) + ln(a_1 r_1 + a_2 r_2)\}.$$

If we write $\dfrac{a_1^2+k_1^2}{M_1 k_1^2}+\dfrac{a_2^2+k_2^2}{M_2 k_2^2}=\dfrac{2}{A}$ and $\dfrac{\dfrac{a_1^2}{M_1 k_1^2}+\dfrac{a_2^2}{M_2 k_2^2}}{\dfrac{1}{M_1}+\dfrac{1}{M_2}}=B$

in these expressions and substitute them in the equations for the final velocities

$$u_1' = u_1 + \frac{1+e}{M_1}X \quad p_1' = p_1 + \frac{(1+e)a_1}{M_1 k_1^2}(mZ - nY)$$

$$(23)\; u_1' = u_1 + \frac{1+e}{M_1}\frac{A}{2}\{u_2 - u_1 + Bl(l(u_2-u_1)+m(v_2-v_1)+n(w_2-w_1))$$

$$+ m(a_1 r_1 + a_2 r_2) - n(a_1 q_1 + a_2 q_2)\}$$

$$p_1' = p_1 + \frac{(1+e)a\,A}{M_1 k_1^2}\frac{A}{2}\{m(w_2-w_1) - n(v_2-v_1) - (m^2+n^2)(a_1 p_1 + a_2 p_2)$$

$$+ lm(a_1 q_1 + a_2 q_2) + ln(a_1 r_1 + a_2 r_2)\}.$$

The other ten equations for the components of velocity and rotation may be easily written down from these

We have next to determine the relations between the energy of agitation before and after impact. For this purpose we suppose the coordinate axes to be taken so as to coincide with the principal axes of agitation. We then square the equations for u_1' and p_1' remembering that all terms containing products of different components of the velocities will disappear on summation, so that in obtaining mean values we retain only those terms containing squares of velocities. The following equations are therefore true of the mean squares of the quantities

$$u_1'^2 = u_1^2 - \frac{1+e}{M_1}A\{1+Bl^2\}u_1^2 + \frac{(1+e)^2 A^2}{4M_1^2}\{(1+2Bl^2+B^2l^4)(u_1^2+u_2^2)$$

$$+ B^2 l^2 m^2 (v_2^2+v_1^2) + B^2 l^2 n^2 (w_1^2+w_2^2) + m^2(a_1^2 r_1^2 + a_2^2 r_2^2) + n^2(a_1^2 q_1^2 + a_2^2 q_2^2)\}$$

$$p_1'^2 = p_1^2 - \frac{(1+e)a_1^2}{M_1 k_1^2}A(m^2+n^2)p_1^2 + \frac{(1+e)^2 A^2 a_1^2}{4 M_1^2 k_1^4}\{m^2(w_1^2+w_2^2)$$

$$+ n^2(v_1^2+v_2^2) + (m^4+2m^2n^2+n^4)(a_1^2 p_1^2+a_2^2 p_2^2)$$

$$+ l^2 m^2 (a_1^2 q_1^2 + a_2^2 q_2^2) + l^2 n^2 (a_1^2 r_1^2 + a_2^2 r_2^2)\}.$$

Now $l\,m\,n$, the direction cosines of the line of centres at impact are independent of the velocities and by integrating over the surface of a sphere we find that

---

(23) Brush, Everitt and Garber, *Maxwell on Saturn's Rings*: 181–3 print a preliminary draft of the following paragraphs, concluding at '... $l^2 m^2$ is $\frac{1}{15}$'. There is another draft folio in ULC Add. MSS 7655, V, c/45a.

the mean value of the square of a cosine such as l^2 is $\frac{1}{3}$, that of the fourth power as l^4 is $\frac{1}{5}$ and that of the square of a product as $l^2 m^2$ is $\frac{1}{15}$.[24] The equations may therefore be written

$$u_1'^2 = u_1^2 - \frac{(1+e)A}{M_1}\left(1 + \frac{1}{3}B\right)u_1^2 + \frac{(1+e)^2 A^2}{4 M_1^2}\left\{\left(1 + \frac{2}{3}B + \frac{1}{5}B^2\right)(u_1^2 + u_2^2)\right.$$

$$\left. + \frac{1}{15} B^2 (v_1^2 + v_2^2 + w_1^2 + w_2^2) + \frac{1}{3}(a_1^2 r_1^2 + a_2^2 r_2^2 + a_1^2 q_1^2 + a_2^2 q_2^2)\right\}$$

$$p_1'^2 = p_1^2 - \frac{2}{3}\frac{(1+e)A a_1^2}{M_1 k_1^2} p_1^2 + \frac{(1+e)^2 A^2 a_1^2}{4 M_1^2 k_1^2}\left\{\frac{1}{3}(v_1^2 + v_2^2 + w_1^2 + w_2^2)\right.$$

$$\left. + \frac{8}{15}(a_1^2 p_1^2 + a_2^2 p_2^2) + \frac{1}{15}(a_1^2 q_1^2 + a_2^2 q_2^2 + a_1^2 r_1^2 + a_2^2 r_2^2)\right\}$$

with ten other equations which may be written down from symmetry.

When, as in the case of Saturns rings, the motion of agitation is sustained by a cause which affects the motions of translation without directly altering the velocity of rotation the energy of rotation must be sustained by the energy of translation and we must have $p_1'^2 = p_1^2$. The second equation then becomes

$$M_1 k_1^2 p_1^2 = \frac{(1+e)A}{8}\left\{v_1^2 + v_2^2 + w_1^2 + w_2^2 + \frac{8}{5}(a_1^2 p_1^2 + a_2^2 p_2^2)\right.$$

$$\left. + \frac{1}{5}(a_1^2 q_1^2 + a_2^2 q_2^2 + a_1^2 r_1^2 + a_2^2 r_2^2)\right\}.$$

Since the right hand side of this expression would remain the same if the suffixes were exchanged, we must have

$$M_1 k_1^2 p_1^2 = M_2 k_2^2 p_2^2 = P \quad \text{suppose}$$

or the energy of rotation about the axis of x is the same for large & small particles.

Let
$$\frac{a_1^2}{M_1 k_1^2} + \frac{a_2^2}{M_2 k_2^2} = 2C$$

then if we write $Mk^2 q^2 = Q$ and $Mk^2 r^2 = R$ we find

$$P = \frac{(1+e)A}{8}\left\{v_1^2 + v_2^2 + w_1^2 + w_2^2 + \frac{2}{5}C(8P + Q + R)\right\}.$$

If we write down the two similar equations and add, we shall have

$$P + Q + R = \frac{(1+e)A}{4}\{u_1^2 + v_1^2 + w_1^2 + u_2^2 + v_2^2 + w_2^2 + 2C(P + Q + R)\}$$

---

(24) Maxwell's values are discussed and confirmed by Fuller, 'James Clerk Maxwell's Cambridge manuscripts': 652–4.

writing V_1^2 & V_2^2 for the squares of the resultant velocities
$$2(P+Q+R)(2-(1+e)AC) = (1+e)A(V_1^2+V_2^2).$$
When $e = 1$ this expression becomes
$$= k_1^2(p_1^2+q_1^2+r_1^2) + k_2^2(p_2^2+q_2^2+r_2^2) = V_1^2+V_2^2.$$
When $e = 0$ it becomes
$$= \frac{2}{A}(P+Q+R) = V_1^2+V_2^2. \quad (25)$$

Subtracting the equation for Q from that for P we get
$$(P-Q)\left(\frac{2}{A} - \frac{7}{10}(1+e)C\right) = \frac{1+e}{4}(v_1^2+v_2^2-(u_1^2+u_2^2)).$$

Returning to the equation for $u_1'^2$ and adding the two similar equations
$$V_1'^2 = V_1^2 - \frac{(1+e)A}{M_1}\left(1+\frac{1}{3}B\right)V_1^2 + \frac{(1+e)^2A^2}{4M_1^2}\left(1+\frac{2}{3}B+\frac{1}{3}B^2\right)(V_1^2+V_2^2)$$
$$+ \frac{(1+e)^3A^3C}{6M_1^2(2-(1+e)AC)}(V_1^2+V_2^2)$$

which gives the value of $V_1'^2$ in terms of V_1^2 and V_2^2. As we do not know the relation between V_1^2 & V_2^2 we shall begin with the case of equal masses and $V_1^2 = V_2^2$. Then we have $A = \frac{Mk^2}{a^2+k^2}$ $B = \frac{a^2}{k^2}$ $C = \frac{a^2}{Mk^2}$ and if we make $V'^2 = p'V^2$ we find
$$p' = 1 - \frac{(1+e)(a^2+3k^2)}{3(a^2+k^2)} + \frac{(1+e)^2(a^4+2a^2k^2+3k^4)}{6(a^2+k^2)^2}$$
$$+ \frac{(1+e)^3a^2k^4}{3(a^2+k^2)^2((1-e)a^2+2k^2)}$$

p' is the ratio of the whole energy after collision to the whole energy before collision on an average of all possible cases.[26]

In the same way we get by subtracting v'^2 from u'^2 and putting
$$u'^2 - v'^2 = q'(u^2-v^2)$$
$$q' = 1 - \frac{(1+e)(a^2+3k^2)}{3(a^2+k^2)} + \frac{(1+e)^2(\frac{2}{5}a^4+2a^2k^2+3k^4)}{6(a^2+k^2)^2}$$
$$+ \frac{(1+e)^3a^2k^4}{6(a^2+k^2)^2(4(a^2+k^2)-\frac{7}{5}a^2(1+e))}.$$

---

(25) Read: $\frac{2}{A}(2-AC)(P+Q+R) = V_1^2+V_2^2$.

(26) p' and q' here denote p and q as used in §2 *supra*.

When $e = 1$ we find $p' = 1$ or the energy is the same before & after impact. When $e = 0$ and $k^2 = \frac{2}{5}a^2$ as in a solid sphere,

$$p' = \frac{1803}{2646} = \frac{601}{882} \quad \frac{1}{p'} = 1.467$$

$$q' = \frac{1837}{3087} \quad \frac{1}{q'} = 1.681.^{(27)}$$

[4]   [ON COLLISION PROBABILITIES]

To find an expression for the number of particles which are struck in unit of time and for the proportion of these which describe an angle θ round the central body before being struck again.

Let x be the number of particles which describe an angle θ without being struck – then while they are describing the additional angle $d\theta$, a number of these will be struck depending on x on the distribution of other particles and on $d\theta$ which may be expressed by

$$-dx = \frac{x}{\lambda} d\theta$$

whence

$$x = Ce^{-\frac{\theta}{\lambda}}.$$

Let $N =$ the whole number of particles then the number struck in unit of time will be $\dfrac{N\,d\theta}{\lambda\,dt}$

and the number of these which reach a distance θ without being struck will be $x = \dfrac{N\,d\theta}{\lambda\,dt} e^{-\frac{\theta}{\lambda}}$

and the number of these which will be struck between θ and $\theta + d\theta$ will be

$$-dx = \frac{N\,d\theta}{\lambda^2\,dt} e^{-\frac{\theta}{\lambda}} \quad^{(28)}$$

---

(27) There are slips in Maxwell's arithmetic:

$$p' = \frac{1813}{2646} = \frac{37}{54}, \quad \frac{1}{p'} = 1.459$$

$$q' = \frac{1921}{3087}, \quad \frac{1}{q'} = 1.607.$$

(28) Read: $-dx = \dfrac{N\,d\theta}{\lambda^2\,dt} e^{-\frac{\theta}{\lambda}} d\theta.$

λ is the mean value of the angle described by a particle between successive collisions.

[5] [ON THE ENERGIES OF THE PARTICLES]

To find expressions for the integrals of $\frac{1}{2}Mu^2$ $\frac{1}{2}Mv^2$ $\frac{1}{2}Mw^2$ $\frac{1}{2}Mz^2$ and Muv in terms of the energies of agitation along the principal axes and the inclination of these axes to the radius vector.

Let a be the sum and b the difference of the energies of agitation in the principal axes in the plane of the orbit and let α be the angle between the radius vector and the greater axis measured in the direction of rotation. Let c be the energy in the normal direction. Then by the ordinary investigation of moments of inertia, internal pressures &c &c,

$$\frac{1}{2}\sum Mu^2 = \frac{1}{2}a + \frac{1}{2}b\cos 2\alpha$$

$$\frac{1}{2}\sum Mv^2 = \frac{1}{2}a - \frac{1}{2}b\cos 2\alpha$$

$$\frac{1}{2}\sum Mw^2 = c$$

$$\sum Muv = \frac{1}{2}b\sin 2\alpha.$$

[6] [ON PARTICLE COLLISIONS]

To find the relation between the nature of the agitation of the particles just after being struck and just before the next collision.

The values of u^2 v^2 w^2 & uv are connected by the following equations

$$u^2 = u_0^2 \cos^2\theta + 4v_0^2 \sin^2\theta + 4u_0 v_0 \sin\theta\cos\theta \tag{1}$$

$$v^2 = v_0^2 \cos^2\theta + \frac{1}{4}u_0^2 \sin^2\theta - u_0 v_0 \sin\theta\cos\theta \tag{2}$$

$$w^2 = w_0^2 \cos^2\mu\theta + n^2\mu^2 z_0^2 \sin^2\mu\theta - 2n\mu z_0 w_0 \sin\mu\theta\cos\mu\theta \tag{3}$$

$$z^2 = z_0^2 \cos^2\mu\theta + \frac{1}{n^2\mu^2} w_0^2 \sin^2\mu\theta + \frac{2}{n\mu} z_0 w_0 \sin\mu\theta\cos\mu\theta \tag{4}$$

$$uv = \left(2v_0 - \frac{1}{2}u_0\right)^{(29)} \sin\theta\cos\theta + u_0 v_0 (\cos^2\theta - \sin^2\theta) \tag{5}$$

$$wz = \left(\frac{w_0^2}{n\mu} - z_0^2 n\mu\right) \sin\mu\theta\cos\mu\theta + z_0 w_0 (\cos^2\mu\theta - \sin^2\mu\theta). \tag{6}$$

---

(29) Read: $(2v_0^2 - \frac{1}{2}u_0^2)$.

From these we obtain
$$u^2 + 4v^2 = u_0^2 + 4v_0^2$$
$$w^2 = n^2\mu^2 z^2 = w_0^2 + n^2\mu^2 z_0^2$$
which are independent of θ.

In order to get the energy of the agitation of the particles projected in unit of time we must multiply the left side of each equation by $\dfrac{\frac{1}{2}NM}{\lambda}\dfrac{d\theta}{dt}$ and the right hand side by $\dfrac{\frac{1}{2}NM}{\lambda^2}\dfrac{d\theta}{dt}e^{-\frac{\theta}{\lambda}}d\theta$ and integrate from $\theta = 0$ to $\theta = \infty$. It will be sufficient to multiply the right side by $\dfrac{1}{\lambda}e^{-\frac{\theta}{\lambda}}d\theta$ and integrate remembering that

$$\int_0^\infty \sin m\theta\, e^{-\frac{\theta}{\lambda}}d\theta = \frac{\lambda^2 m}{1+\lambda^2 m^2} \quad \text{and} \quad \int_0^\infty \cos m\theta\, e^{-\frac{\theta}{\lambda}}d\theta = \frac{\lambda}{1+\lambda^2 m^2}.$$

We thus get from the equations (1), (2) &c the following

1. $(4\lambda^2 + 1)u^2 = (2\lambda^2 + 1)u_0^2 + 8\lambda^2 v_0^2 + 4\lambda u_0 v_0$
2. $(4\lambda^2 + 1)v^2 = (2\lambda^2 + 1)v_0^2 + \dfrac{1}{2}\lambda^2 u_0^2 - \lambda u_0 v_0$
3. $(4\mu^2\lambda^2 + 1)w^2 = (2\mu^2\lambda^2 + 1)w_0^2 + 2\mu^4\lambda^2 n^2 z_0^2 - 2\mu^2\lambda n w_0 z_0$
4. $(4\mu^2\lambda^2 + 1)z^2 = (2\mu^2\lambda^2 + 1)z_0^2 + 2\dfrac{\lambda^2}{n^2}w_0^2 + 2\dfrac{\lambda}{n}w_0 z_0$
5. $(4\lambda^2 + 1)uv = \left(2v_0^2 - \dfrac{1}{2}u_0^2\right)\lambda + u_0 v_0$
6. $(4\mu^2\lambda^2 + 1)wz = \left(\dfrac{w_0^2}{n\mu} - z_0^2 n\mu\right)\mu\lambda + w_0 z_0.$

From (4) and (6) we find that if $z^2 = z_0^2$, $wz = 0$ and since the equations must be true independent of the value of λ, $w_0 z_0 = 0$ whence we find by (4) that $w^2 = w_0^2 = n^2\mu^2 z^2$.

[7]

To express these relations in terms of $a\ b\ c$ & α.[30]

Let these quantities be written $a_0\ b_0\ c_0$ & α_0 when they refer to the particles when first projected. We have two equations independent of λ

$$5a - 3b\cos 2\alpha = 5a_0 - 3b_0\cos 2\alpha_0$$
$$c = c_0 = n^2\mu^2 z^2.$$

---

(30) The quantities a, b, c here denote half mean square values.

(1)−(2) gives $(4\lambda^2+1) 2b \cos 2\alpha = \frac{15}{2}\lambda^2 a_0 + \left(2-\frac{9}{2}\lambda^2\right) b_0 \cos 2\alpha_0$
$\qquad\qquad\qquad + 5\lambda b_0 \sin 2\alpha_0$

(5) $\qquad (4\lambda^2+1) b \sin 2\alpha = \frac{3}{2}\lambda a_0 - \frac{5}{2}\lambda b_0 \cos 2\alpha_0 + b_0 \sin 2\alpha_0$

whence $\qquad (2\cos 2\alpha - 5\lambda \sin 2\alpha) b = 2b_0 \cos 2\alpha_0.$

[8] [STEADY STATE CONDITIONS]

To find the values of $a_0\ b_0\ c_0\ \alpha_0$ and λ when the motion of agitation is exactly sustained.

Let us suppose that the result of the collision, on an average of all possible cases is to reduce the total energy of agitation in the ratio of p to 1 and to reduce the *difference* of energy in any two principal axes in the ratio of q to 1 while the direction of these principal axes remains unchanged. We shall calculate the numerical values of p and q by a separate investigation. We then have

$$a+c = p(a_0+c_0)$$
$$b = qb_0$$
$$\tfrac{1}{2}a - c = q\left(\tfrac{1}{2}a_0 - c_0\right)$$

whence
$$a = \tfrac{1}{3}\{2p(a_0+c_0) + q(a_0-2c_0)\}$$
$$b = qb_0$$
$$c = \tfrac{1}{3}\{p(a_0+c_0) - q(a_0-2c_0)\}.$$

Substituting these values of $a\ b\ c$ and omitting the suffixes, remembering that $a\ b\ c$ now refer to the velocities at projection only[31]

$$5\{(2p+q-3) a + 2(p-q) c\} = 9(q-1) b \cos 2\alpha$$
$$(p+2q) c = (3+q-p) a$$
$$\{(4\lambda^2+1) q - 1\} b \sin 2\alpha + \frac{5}{2}\lambda b \cos 2\alpha = \frac{3}{2}\lambda a$$
$$2(q-1) \cos 2\alpha = 5\lambda \sin 2\alpha.$$

---

(31) Errors here enter the algebra; see Fuller, 'Maxwell's Cambridge manuscripts': 645–7.

Whence we find
$$a = 3\lambda(q-1)(p+2q)h$$
$$c = 3\lambda(q-1)(3+q-p)h$$
$$b\sin 2\alpha = 2(q-1)\{p(3q+1)-4q\}h$$
$$b\cos 2\alpha = 5\lambda\{p(3q+1)-4q\}h$$

where h is a quantity not yet determined. We also find the following equations in λ^2 p & q

$$\{\lambda^2(16q^2-16q+25)+4(q-1)^2\}(p(3q+1)-4q) = 9\lambda^2(q-1)(p+2q).$$

$$\lambda^2 = 4(q-1)^2$$
$$\times \frac{(3q+1)p-4q}{(64q^2+18q)(q-1)+100q-\{(3q+1)16q(q-1)+25(3q+1)-9(q-1)\}p}$$
$$= 2(q-1)^2 \frac{(3q+1)p-4q}{32q^3-23q^2+41q-\{24q^3-16q^2+25q+17\}p}.$$

225

LETTER TO HERMANN HELMHOLTZ[1]

12 APRIL 1864

From the original in the Akademie-Archiv, Berlin[2]

Dear Sir

I have been a long time getting my instrument for mixing colours[3] put right but it is now ready.

Can you come and take lunch with us on Saturday[4] about half past one o Clock and then we can have light to analyze.

Yours truly
J. CLERK MAXWELL

8 Palace Gardens Terrace, W.
1864 April 12

---

(1) On 14 April 1864 Helmholtz read his Croonian Lecture to the Royal Society: see Number 279 note (5).
(2) Nachlass Helmholtz 305 Briefe Maxwell, Akademie-Archiv, Berlin.
(3) See Number 202 esp. note (3).
(4) 16 April 1864.

226

LETTER TO JOHN TYNDALL

20 APRIL 1864

From the original in the Smithsonian Institution Libraries[1]

8 Palace Gardens Terrace
W
1864 Ap 20

Dear Tyndall

It would give me much pleasure to belong to the Philosophical Club.[2] I got your letter at King's College today.

Yours truly
J. CLERK MAXWELL

---

(1) Dibner Library, Smithsonian Institution Libraries, Washington, DC.

(2) Founded in 1847, a group of leading members of the Royal Society: 'The purpose of the Club is to promote as much as possible the scientific objects of the Royal Society, to facilitate intercourse between those Fellows who are actively engaged in cultivating the various branches of Natural Science & who have contributed to its progress; to increase the attendance at the Evening Meetings & to encourage the contribution & the discussion of Papers.'; See 'Objects & Rules of the Philosophical Club' in 'Minute Book, Volume I' (Royal Society, London); and also T. G. Bonney, *Annals of the Philosophical Club of the Royal Society* (London, 1919). Maxwell was elected a member on 25 April 1864; see 'Minute Book, Volume I': 309–10; and Bonney, *Annals of the Philosophical Club*: 57.

= 227 =

PAPER ON THE MOTION OF THE EARTH THROUGH THE ETHER[1]

circa 24 APRIL 1864[2]

From the original in the University Library, Cambridge[3]

ON AN EXPERIMENT TO DETERMINE WHETHER THE MOTION OF THE EARTH INFLUENCES THE REFRACTION OF LIGHT

by J. Clerk Maxwell, F.R.S.

According to an experiment of M Fizeau*[4] the propagation of light in a tube carrying a stream of water takes place with greater velocity in the direction in which the water moves than in the opposite direction. This phenomenon of acceleration and retardation was not observed when air was substituted for water in the tube, and the amount of the effect in the case of water was much smaller than it would have been if the whole motion of the water had been compounded with that of the light.

The explanation given by M. Fizeau is founded on the hypothesis of Fresnel with respect to the constitution of the luminiferous medium within dense bodies, according to which the motion of the body only partially affects the motion of the ether within it so as to make its average velocity $= v(\mu^2 - 1)$, where v is the velocity of the body and μ its index of refraction.[5]

---

(1) The paper was submitted to the Royal Society for publication, but was withdrawn: see note (6) and Maxwell's letter to Stokes of 6 May 1864 (Number 228).

(2) The paper is endorsed 'Rec'd. 26 April 1864'; in the paper itself Maxwell refers to observations recorded on 23 April 1864.

(3) ULC Add. MSS 7655, V, b/15.

(4) Hippolyte Fizeau, 'Sur les hypothèses relatives a l'éther lumineux. Et sur une expérience qui parait démontrer que le mouvement des corps change la vitesse avec laquelle la lumière se propage dans leur intérieur', *Ann. Chim. Phys.*, ser. 3, **57** (1859): 385–404; (trans.) 'On the effect of the motion of a body upon the velocity with which it is traversed by light', *Phil. Mag.*, ser. 4, **19** (1860): 245–58. The paper was presented to the Académie des Sciences on 29 September 1851, and reported in the *Comptes Rendus*, **33** (1851): 349–55. Maxwell had inquired about this report of Fizeau's experiment in a letter to Stokes of 8 May 1857 (Volume I: 503).

(5) [A. J. Fresnel,] 'Lettre de M. Fresnel à M. Arago, sur l'influence du mouvement terrestre dans quelques phénomènes d'optique', *Ann. Chim. Phys.*, **9** (1818): 57–66. In 1810 Arago had carried out an experiment to detect the deviation of stellar light, finding no effect of the earth's motion on the refrangibility of light. See François Arago, 'Mémoire sur la vitesse de la lumière, lu à la première Classe de l'Institut, le 10 décembre 1810', *Comptes Rendus*, **36** (1853): 38–49. Fresnel proposed his hypothesis of partial ether drag in response to Arago's conclusion.

In fact if the density of the ether within the body is μ^2 times that outside it, and if we suppose the ether outside to be undisturbed by the motion of the body, and the motion of the ether inside to be independent of the shape of the body, then this law is a consequence of the law of continuity of the ether. But other modes of motion which would also satisfy the law of continuity would have been the result if our suppositions had been different, as for instance if we had supposed that ether cannot pass the boundary of the body, or that there is a resistance to the motion of the body through it.

Taking the hypothesis in its most simple shape as adopted by M Fizeau, if the velocity of the ether be reckoned with respect to the body itself then if the velocity of the ether outside the body is v that within will be $\dfrac{1}{\mu^2}v$ and in the same direction.

If the direction of propagation of a ray of light makes an angle θ with the direction of motion before incidence, and ϕ within the medium then the index of refraction will become

$$\mu \frac{1+\dfrac{v}{V}\cos\theta}{1+\dfrac{v}{V}\dfrac{1}{\mu}\cos\phi}$$

where μ is the index of refraction for the body at rest, and V is the velocity of Light.

Hence if P is the angle of a prism, D the minimum deviation of light due to the prism when at rest, and ϕ the direction of the ray within the prism when in the position of minimum deviation and δ the displacement due to the motion in circular measure

$$\delta = \frac{v}{V}\cos\phi\frac{\sin(\tfrac{1}{2}P+D)-\sin\tfrac{1}{2}P}{\cos\tfrac{1}{2}(P+D)}.$$

The deviation of the ray is increased by this quantity when the ether moves relatively to the prism in the same direction as the ray.[6]

---

(6) Maxwell ignores the compensating change in the density of the medium (which varies as μ^2; see 'Lettre de M. Fresnel à M. Arago': 62). According to Fresnel's theory the ether and the transparent medium satisfy a continuity equation at their boundary; this has the consequence that the retardation due to the refractive medium is not affected by the motion of the earth. Maxwell acknowledges his error, to which Stokes drew his attention, in his letter to Stokes of 6 May 1864 (Number 228). Stokes had himself established this consequence of Fresnel's theory in 1846 (see Number 228 note (4)). Maxwell gives a revised account of the problem in a letter to William Huggins of 10 June 1867 (Number 271).

If v is the velocity of the earth in its orbit then $\dfrac{v}{V}$ is the coefficient of aberration in circular measure or about $20''\tfrac{1}{2}$. For a prism whose angle is $60°$ and minimum deviation $49°\tfrac{1}{2}$

we find
$$\delta = 17''.17 \cos \phi$$

where ϕ is the angle between the direction of motion and the ray within the prism.

The greatest displacement for one prism is therefore $17''.17$. For two similar prisms it is $31''.28$, and for three $39''.20$. A greater number of prisms would be of no use, as the displacement would diminish when the ray moves oppositely to the ether.

Hence a good spectroscope constructed so firmly that it might be turned round without altering the relative position of its parts and capable of reading to half a minute, might measure the displacement directly.

In the Annales de Chimie et de Physique for Feb. 1860 M Fizeau has described an experiment in which a ray of polarized light was passed through a series of inclined glass plates so as to rotate the plane of polarization.[7] The amount of this rotation depends on the index of refraction of the glass, and therefore may be made to indicate any change in that index. The methods by which disturbing influences were checked, and the effects multiplied are described in the memoir of M Fizeau. His result was that a displacement of the plane of polarization in the direction expected was obtained when the direction of the ray was coincident with or opposed to the Earth's motion and to an amount not discordant with the theory.[8]

It appears to me that it is as easy to measure the deviation of a marked line in the spectrum to one minute as to ascertain the plane of polarization of a ray

---

(7) H. Fizeau, 'Sur une méthode propre a rechercher si l'azimut de polarisation du rayon réfracté est influencé par le mouvement du corps réfringent – essai de cette méthode', *Ann. Chim. Phys.*, ser. 3, **58** (1860): 129–63. The paper was reported in the *Comptes Rendus*, **49** (1859): 717–23; an English summary of this report was appended to the translation of Fizeau's paper on the propagation of light in a tube carrying a stream of water, *Phil. Mag.*, ser. 4, **19** (1860): 258–60.

(8) Fizeau, 'Sur une méthode propre a rechercher si l'azimut de polarisation du rayon réfracté est influencé par le mouvement du corps réfringent': 162; 'Les rotations du plan de polarisation, produites par des piles de glaces inclinées, sont constamment plus grandes lorsque l'appareil est dirigé vers l'ouest, que lorsqu'il est dirigé vers l'est, l'observation étant faite vers le milieu du jour'. Fizeau concluded that the azimuth of the plane of polarisation of a refracted ray is influenced by the motion of the refracting medium, and that the motion of the earth has an effect upon the rotation of the plane of polarisation produced by a series of inclined glass plates. In his letter to Huggins of 10 June 1867 Maxwell questions the validity of Fizeau's observations and conclusions; see note (6).

to several minutes, so that I should prefer the direct method with prisms if it were possible.

But as we may have reason to suspect some mechanical displacement of the telescopes or prisms, or some alteration of temperature of the prisms between the times of observation, I have adopted the following arrangement which appears to me to be free from such sources of error, to afford a more distinct object to observe, and to double the displacement.

If we could send every ray back to the prism in the exact direction in which it emerged, then if there were no motion, it would return on its own path, but if the effect due to motion takes place, the refraction will be diminished on the return ray as much as it is increased in the direct one, so that the ray will no longer return to its starting point but will be displaced to an extent double of its original displacement.

Now by receiving the ray on the object glass of a telescope having a plane mirror at its principal focus to throw the light back, we can cause every ray to return in a direction exactly parallel to that in which it fell on the telescope. This is the arrangement for reflecting light used by M. Fizeau in his experiment on the velocity of light.*[9]

The apparatus I have made use of consists of a spectroscope constructed by Mr Becker.[10] Light is admitted through a tube at right angles to the axis of the first telescope and is reflected towards the object glass by a transparent plate of parallel glass at an angle of 45°. In the tube slides a screen with a vertical slit, in the middle of which is a vertical spider line. This spider line is placed so that its virtual image in the first surface of the glass plate coincides with the crossing of the spider lines of the telescope, and with the principal focus of the object glass.

Hence rays from the vertical spider line emerge from the telescope in parallel pencils. They then fall on the plane faces of the prisms, and after refraction the rays of each colour emerge parallel and fall on the second telescope, which has a mirror at its principal focus, and therefore returns the rays still parallel and in an exactly reverse direction. After returning through the prisms they enter the first telescope, and form an image of the vertical spider line at the cross lines of the first telescope. On looking through the eyepiece the image of the vertical slit and spider line is seen in contact with the crossing of the spider lines in the axis of the telescope.

* Comptes Rendus vol XXIX (1849) p 90[9]

---

(9) H. Fizeau, 'Sur une expérience relative à la vitesse de propagation de la lumière', *Comptes Rendus*, **29** (1849): 90–2. Maxwell had inquired about this paper in his letter to Stokes of 8 May 1857. (10) See Number 214 note (5).

The coincidence of the images depends only on the relative position of the vertical slit, the glass plate and the cross lines, and on the accurate focussing of the telescopes. If the telescopes are moved relatively to each other different coloured rays fall on the mirror and form the image of the slit, but the position of the image as seen through the eye piece remains the same. The colour of the image is the resultant of the mixture of all that portion of the spectrum which falls on the second telescope with its mirror and therefore varies with the position of the prisms and telescopes, but the coincidence of the images of the lines is unaltered by such movement and the dispersion is so exactly compensated by returning the rays through the prisms that the image of the spider line is seen perfectly distinct.

The image of the slit subtends 14′ that of the spider line about 10 [′ so that] a displacement of the spider line could be easily observed. Now on April 23rd the motion of the earth at 11^h 10^m before noon was nearly horizontal and towards a point about 26° South of West. Hence if three prisms are used and placed so that the direction of the ray within the middle prism coincides with that of the earth motion, we shall have an increase of deviation = 39″.2 when the ray moves from West to East and an equal diminution of deviation when it returns. If the ray enters from the west and returns the total displacement will be 78″.4 and by turning the instrument round so as to make the ray enter from the East this displacement will be reversed so that if our hypothesis be correct we should have a difference of position = 156″.8′ or two minutes and a half.

The experiment was tried in full sunlight at the proper time of day in the open air but no displacement could be observed in whatever direction the instrument was turned, provided the telescopes were correctly focussed.

It was also tried at night with candle light. The image was very distinct but no displacement could be detected.

Hence the result of the experiment is decidedly negative to the hypothesis about the motion of the ether in the form stated here.

I hope to repeat the experiment at a different time of year and in more exposed situations.[a][b]

(a) {Maxwell} Note. The distinctness of definition can be shown by candlelight if desired. J.C.M.

(b) {Maxwell} Klinkerfues – Nachrichten v.d. Kön Ges. der Wiss. in Gottingen. Jan 31, 1866.[11]

(11) Wilhelm Klinkerfues, 'Fernere Mittheilungen über den Einfluss der Bewegung der Lichtquelle auf die Brechbarkeit eines Strahls', *Nachrichten von der Königl. Gesellschaft der Wissenschaften und der Georg–August–Universität zu Göttingen* (1866): 33–60. Klinkerfues had maintained 'dass die Bewegung eines Sterns, zerlegt nach der Richtung des Visions-Radius die Brechung des Strahls beeinflusst'; see his paper 'Ueber ein Einfluss der Bewegung der

Lichtquelle und eines brechenden Mediums auf die Richtung des gebrochenen Strahls', *ibid.* (1865): 157–60, 210. Maxwell's appended reference to Klinkerfues' 'Fernere Mittheilungen' probably dates from 1867–8. Compare his critical comment in his letter to William Huggins of 10 June 1867 (Number 271) on the use of an achromatic prism (as in Klinkerfues' experiments) to detect the motion of stars. It is possible that Huggins drew Maxwell's attention to Klinkerfues' paper. See Number 271 note (2) on the circumstances of Maxwell's letter to Huggins. Huggins included Maxwell's letter in his paper 'Further observations on the spectra of some of the stars and nebulae, with an attempt to determine therefrom whether these bodies are moving towards or from the earth...', *Phil. Trans.*, **158** (1868): 529–64, on 532–5; and commented critically, in terms similar to Maxwell's remarks on experiments with an achromatic prism, on Klinkerfues' 'Fernere Mittheilungen': 'as Klinkerfues employs an achromatic prism, it does not seem possible, by his method of observing, to obtain any information of the motion of the stars... [as] the difference of period... would be as far as possible, annulled' (on 531).

LETTER TO GEORGE GABRIEL STOKES

6 MAY 1864

From the original in the University Library, Cambridge[1]

8 Palace Gardens Terrace
London W.
1864 May 6

Dear Stokes

I have your letter and my paper.[2] Fizeau[3] does not lean with confidence on any theory of the dependence of the rotation of the plane of polarization on the velocity-ratio of propagation in the media.

The rotation of course depends on the ratios of *intensity* of rays polarized in different planes and passing through the inclined plate.

You have proved[4] that on Fresnels theory the *direction* of the refracted ray is not affected by the motion of the aether.[5]

---

(1) ULC Add. MSS 7656, M 422. First published in Larmor, *Correspondence*, 2: 23–5.

(2) Number 227. Stokes had clearly criticised Maxwell's assumption, in his paper 'On an experiment to determine whether the Motion of the Earth influences the Refraction of Light', that such an effect was to be anticipated. See Number 227 note (6) and Maxwell's revised discussion of the issue in his letter to William Huggins of 10 June 1867 (Number 271), where he acknowledges that no such effect is to be expected; and see note (5).

(3) H. Fizeau, 'Sur une méthode propre a rechercher si l'azimut de polarisation du rayon refracté est influencé par le mouvement du corps réfringent – essai de cette méthode', *Ann. Chim. Phy.*, ser. 3, **58** (1860): 129–63. See Number 227 note (7).

(4) G. G. Stokes, 'On Fresnel's theory of the aberration of light', *Phil. Mag.*, ser. 3, **28** (1846): 76–81, esp. 81 (= *Papers*, 1: 141–7). Having considered refraction from a vacuum into a refracting medium, Stokes concluded that 'the laws of reflexion and refraction at the surface of a refracting medium will not be affected by the motion of the ether.' He went on to point out that 'the result is the same in the general case of refraction out of one medium to another, and reflexion at the common surface.'

(5) [A. J. Fresnel,] 'Lettre de M. Fresnel à M. Arago, sur l'influence du mouvement terrestre dans quelques phénomènes d'optique', *Ann. Chim. Phys.*, **9** (1818): 57–66. See Number 227 note (5). In 1865 Maxwell drafted a question for the 1866 Cambridge Mathematical Tripos on Stokes' interpretation of Fresnel's ether drag hypothesis: 'If the velocity of light in the luminiferous medium is inversely proportional to the index of refraction of the body through which the light passes, and if the luminiferous medium itself is not fixed in the body, show that the retardation due to a plate of glass interposed between two given points will be independent of the motion of the medium provided that that motion is inversely proportional to the square of the index of refraction and that the square of the ratio of the velocity of the medium to that of light may be neglected. / Hence show that on Fresnels hypothesis about the luminiferous medium in bodies all phenomena of reflexion & refraction will be the same whether the medium is carried along with the earth or does not partake of its motion.' (King's College London Archives, Maxwell Notebook (2), question (45)). See the question as set in *The Cambridge*

Have you$^{(6)}$ or Jamin$^{(7)}$ or anyone else done anything towards the determination of the intensity.

Fizeau rests his calculation on experiments with plates of different indices of refraction.

I am not inclined and I do not think I am able to do the dynamical theory of reflexion and refraction on different hypotheses & unless I see some good in getting it up, I would rather gather the result from men who have gone into the subject.$^{(8)}$

If Fizeau has really found a phenomenon related to the earth's motion in space or rather in the luminiferous medium a great deal may be founded upon it independently of a good optical theory.

I think M. Faye corroborates Fizeaus experiment.$^{(9)}$ If the experiment is good it would be worth the while of an eminent astronomical observer to have the instrument properly mounted and so to work for a year determining frequently the direction and (proportional) velocity of the rush of æther through his observatory and so to have a log book of the earth's motion.

I have been reading Fraunhofer on the spectrum$^{(10)}$ and making estimates of the intensity of the pure colours by bringing each to an equality with my

---

University Calendar for the Year 1866 (Cambridge, 1866): 475 (question (8)): '...Fresnel supposes that when bodies move in the luminiferous medium, the relative motion of the medium with respect to the body is in the same direction within and without the body, but in the proportion of 1 to μ^2: shew that the retardation due to a plate of glass interposed between two given points will be independent of the motion of the earth, if we neglect the square of the ratio of the earth's velocity to that of light.'

(6) Stokes had discussed the rotation of the plane of polarisation of plane-polarised light which has undergone reflection or refraction at the surface of a transparent uncrystallised medium, in his paper 'On the dynamical theory of diffraction', *Trans. Camb. Phil. Soc.*, **9** (1849): 1–62, esp. 47–61 (= *Papers*, **2**: 243–327). He had recently published a paper 'On the intensity of the light reflected from or transmitted through a pile of plates', *Proc. Roy. Soc.*, **11** (1862): 545–57 (= *Papers*, **4**: 145–56).

(7) Jules Jamin had recently published a paper entitled 'Note sur la théorie de la réfléxion et de la réfraction', *Ann. Chim. Phys.*, ser. 3, **59** (1860): 413–26. For Maxwell's discussion of this paper see his draft on the reflection and refraction of light (Number 236) and his letter to Stokes of 15 October 1864 (Number 237). (8) See Numbers 236 and 237.

(9) H. A. Faye, 'Sur les expériences de M. Fizeau consideréees au point de vue du mouvement de translation du système solaire', *Comptes Rendus*, **49** (1859): 870–5. Faye had presented his paper to the Académie des Sciences on 5 December 1859, following Fizeau's paper presented on 14 November 1859; see *Comptes Rendus*, **49** (1859): 717–23.

(10) Joseph Fraunhofer, 'Bestimmung des Brechungs- und Farben-Zerstreuungs-Vermögens verschiedener Glasarten, in bezug auf die Vervollkommnung achromatischer Fernröhre', *Annalen der Physik*, **56** (1817): 264–313. See Maxwell's comment (Volume I: 569) that 'Fraunhofers lines are the land marks of the spectrum'.

standard white light.[11] I used to try this by making an adjustment and then observing, then making another adjustment and so on, and I got very inconsistent results. Now the adjustment is made while I observe and I find the results not very inconsistent not worse I think than Fraunhofer's. Has any one else repeated such measurements. I can do them quickly and mean to get a good many to compare.

Dove believes in the comparison of intensity of light of different colours by his photometer with a photographic print.[12]

I mean to try it with two half-square prisms ◨ joined with Canada Balsam[13] laid on in narrow streaks so that certain portions are transparent and others reflecting.

Yours truly
J. Clerk Maxwell

---

(11) See Volume I: 617, 619–20, 635–6.
(12) H. W. Dove, 'Beschreibung eines Photometers', *Ann. Phys.*, **114** (1861): 145–63; (trans.) 'On a new photometer', *Phil. Mag.*, ser. 4, **25** (1863): 14–27, esp. 24–5.
(13) A transparent gum used for cementing in optical apparatus.

229

LETTER TO ROBERT DUNDAS CAY[1]

12 JULY 1864

From the original in the Library of Peterhouse, Cambridge[2]

Craiglachie
July 12 1864

Dear Uncle

I enclose the receipt of £8..8..4.[3] I called on Willy[4] at his office in London and found him surrounded by Indian bridges.[5] After 16th inst address to Glenlair. I am very busy reducing observations of the electrical experiments at Kings College[6] so that the standard resistance coils may be made up before the British Asses meet.[7]

Your afft nephew
J. CLERK MAXWELL

---

(1) See Number 216.
(2) Maxwell MSS (25), Peterhouse.
(3) See Volume I: 682n.
(4) William Dyce Cay, Robert Cay's son.
(5) See Number 221.
(6) See Number 222 esp. note (3).
(7) See Number 232 note (5).

DRAFT ON THE DETERMINATION OF COEFFICIENTS OF SELF-INDUCTION[1]

circa SUMMER 1864[2]

From the original in the University Library, Cambridge[3]

WHEATSTONES BRIDGE[4] APPLIED TO THE DETERMINATION OF THE INDUCTION OF A CURRENT UPON ITSELF[5]

Let A and B be two points kept at uniform tension by an electrometer and let them be connected by the four conductors AP, PB, AQ, QB and let P and Q be connected by a conductor part of which acts as a galvanometer.

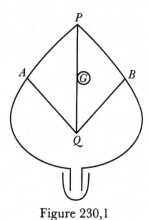

Figure 230,1

If the resistances in the four conductors form the terms of a proportion then after the currents have come to equilibrium there will be no current in PQ but at the first instant of the passage of the current if there be induction of some of the conductors on themselves there may be transient currents in PQ which may produce their effect in giving an impulse to the galvanometer. Let us investigate the conditions of this impulse.

---

(1) A draft of the section 'On the determination of coefficients of induction by the electric balance' in 'A dynamical theory of the electromagnetic field', *Phil. Trans.*, **155** (1865): 459–512, esp. 475–7 (= *Scientific Papers*, **1**: 547–50).

(2) 'A dynamical theory of the electromagnetic field' was completed in October 1864: see Numbers 237, 238 and 239.

(3) ULC Add. MSS 7655, V, f/4.

(4) The term 'Wheatstone's bridge' is used by William Thomson, 'On the measurement of electric resistance', *Proc. Roy. Soc.*, **11** (1861): 313–28, esp. 313n (= *Math. & Phys. Papers*, **5**: 369n). Thomson preferred the term 'Wheatstone's balance' for Wheatstone's 'differential resistance measurer'; see Charles Wheatstone, 'An account of several new instruments and processes for determining the constants of a voltaic current', *Phil. Trans.*, **133** (1843): 303–27, esp. 323–5 and Figs. 5 and 6. See also Maxwell's historical note in the *Treatise*, **2**: 439n.

(5) Compare Maxwell's account of the use of Wheatstone's bridge in the *Treatise*, **1**: 398–408 (§§ 347–52).

	AP	PB	AQ	QB	PQ
Let the five conductors be					
The resistance in each	$r+s$	$r-s$	$r'-s'$	$r'+s'$	R
The coefficient of induction in each	$p+q$	$p-q$	$p'-q'$	$p'+q'$	L
The current at any instant	$x+\tfrac{1}{2}z$	$x-\tfrac{1}{2}z$	$y-\tfrac{1}{2}z$	$y+\tfrac{1}{2}z$	Z.

Let E be the potential at A P at P Q at Q and let that at B be zero.

Then the electromotive force arising from induction is equal to the decrement of current multiplied by the proper coefficient so that we have these five equations

$$(1) \qquad (r+s)\left(x+\frac{1}{2}z\right)+(p+q)\left(\frac{dx}{dt}+\frac{1}{2}\frac{dz}{dt}\right)=E-P$$

$$(2) \qquad (r-s)\left(x-\frac{1}{2}z\right)+(p-q)\left(\frac{dx}{dt}-\frac{1}{2}\frac{dz}{dt}\right)=P$$

$$(3) \qquad (r'-s')\left(y-\frac{1}{2}z\right)+(p'-q')\left(\frac{dy}{dt}-\frac{1}{2}\frac{dz}{dt}\right)=E-Q$$

$$(4) \qquad (r'+s')\left(y+\frac{1}{2}z\right)+(p'+q')\left(\frac{dy}{dt}+\frac{1}{2}\frac{dz}{dt}\right)=Q$$

$$(5) \qquad Rz+L\frac{dz}{dt}=P-Q.$$

By adding $(1)+(2)$ and $(3)+(4)$ and by taking away $(4)-(2)+(5)$ we get the following

$$2rx+2P\frac{dx}{dt}+sz+q\frac{dz}{dt}=E \qquad (6)$$

$$2r'y+2p'\frac{dy}{dt}+s'z+q'\frac{dz}{dt}=E \qquad (7)$$

$$2sx+2q\frac{dx}{dt}+2s'y+2q'\frac{dy}{dt}+(r+r'+2R)z+(p+p'+2L)\frac{dz}{dt}=0. \qquad (8)$$

These being linear simultaneous equations the solution will be a number of terms of the form Ce^{nt} in the value of x y & z with constant terms the values of which are found by simple equations.

FRAGMENT OF A DRAFT OF 'A DYNAMICAL THEORY OF THE ELECTROMAGNETIC FIELD'[1]

circa SUMMER 1864[2]

From the original in the University Library, Cambridge[3]

[GENERAL EQUATIONS OF THE ELECTROMAGNETIC FIELD]

[1] **Specific resistance ρ**[4]

Let ρ be the coefficient of resistance to current electricity of a portion of a substance unity of length and unity of section, the electromotive force P required to maintain a current p is $P = \rho p$ and we shall have the equations of resistance in an isotropic medium

$$P = \rho p \quad Q = \rho q \quad R = \rho v. \tag{11}$$

Electric elasticity k

Let the electromotive force P required to produce an electrical displacement f be kf then k is the coefficient of electric elasticity or resistance to displacement for the given medium. The equations of elasticity in an isotropic medium are therefore

$$P = kf \quad Q = kg \quad R = kh. \tag{12}$$

Electric potential ψ

The electric potential is a kind of pressure arising from the resultant action of all the electromotive forces.

---

(1) *Phil. Trans.*, **155** (1865): 495–512 (= *Scientific Papers*, **1**: 526–97).
(2) See Number 230 note (2).
(3) ULC Add. MSS 7655, V, c/8, f/4. The three folios are consecutive, and are numbered '22', '23' and '24'.
(4) Compare 'A dynamical theory of the electromagnetic field': 484–5 (= *Scientific Papers*, **1**: 559–61).

Equations of Electromotive Force

$$P = \mu\left(\gamma\frac{dy}{dt} - \beta\frac{dz}{dt}\right) - \frac{dF}{dt} - \frac{d\psi}{dx} \\ Q = \mu\left(\alpha\frac{dz}{dt} - \gamma\frac{dx}{dt}\right) - \frac{dG}{dt} - \frac{d\psi}{dy} \\ R = \mu\left(\beta\frac{dx}{dt} - \alpha\frac{dy}{dt}\right) - \frac{dH}{dt} - \frac{d\psi}{dz}.$$ (13)

The first term on the right hand side of each equation is the electromotive force arising from the motion of the conductor in the magnetic field, where μ is the magnetic coefficient of the medium $\alpha\,\beta\,\gamma$ the components of magnetic force, and $\frac{dx}{dt}\,\frac{dy}{dt}\,\frac{dz}{dt}$ the components of the velocity of the conductor.

The second term shows the effect of changes in the position or strength of magnets or currents in the field.

The third term shows the effect of the electric potential which arises from the presence of free electricity.

[2] ### Statical Electricity[5]

Let us now consider the case of a field in which there is no motion or change and no force except that which arises from electric displacement. We have then[6]

$$P = -\frac{d\psi}{dx} = -kf$$

$$Q = -\frac{d\psi}{dy} = -kg$$

$$R = -\frac{d\psi}{dz} = -kh$$

$$e = -\left(\frac{df}{dx} + \frac{dg}{dy} + \frac{dh}{dz}\right) = -\frac{1}{k}\left(\frac{d^2\psi}{dx^2} + \frac{d^2\psi}{dy^2} + \frac{d^2\psi}{dz^2}\right) = -\frac{1}{k}\nabla^2\psi.$$ [7]

---

(5) Compare 'A dynamical theory of the electromagnetic field': 490–2 (= *Scientific Papers*, **1**: 568–9).

(6) Compare the positive sign in equations (12) *supra*. The MS shows Maxwell's hesitancy in here inserting minus signs in the equations for *P, Q, R*. In 'A dynamical theory of the electromagnetic field': 485 (= *Scientific Papers*, **1**: 560) he deletes the minus sign. For discussion see Daniel M. Siegel, *Innovation in Maxwell's Electromagnetic Theory* (Cambridge, 1991): 180–1.

(7) On the use of ∇^2 see Number 239 note (15).

The work done by the electromotive forces in producing the displacement is $\sum \frac{1}{2}(Pf+Qg+Rh)$
$$= \sum \frac{1}{2k}\left(\overline{\frac{d\psi}{dx}}\Big|^2 + \overline{\frac{d\psi}{dy}}\Big|^2 + \overline{\frac{d\psi}{dz}}\Big|^2\right).$$

Now let us suppose two small electrified bodies e_1 and e_2 at a distance $=a$ then the equation $e = -\frac{1}{k}\nabla^2\psi$ can be satisfied by one and only one value of ψ in the space outside the electrified bodies namely
$$\psi = \frac{1}{4\pi}k\left(\frac{e_1}{r_1}+\frac{e_2}{r_2}\right)$$
where r_1 is the distance from e_1 and r_2 the distance from e_2.

The whole work stored up in the dielectric in consequence of the first displacement of the electricity within it is found by integrating by parts and remembering that ψ vanishes at an infinite distance to be $\sum \frac{1}{2k}\psi\nabla^2\psi$ or $\sum \frac{1}{2}\psi e$.

[3] In this case ψ consists of two parts, one depending on e_1 and the other on e_2. Let us call them ψ_1 and ψ_2, then the expression becomes
$$\sum \frac{1}{2}(\psi_1 e_1 + \psi_2 e_2 + \psi_1 e_2 + \psi_2 e_1).$$

Since the values of ψ_1 depend on the distance from e_1 it is manifest that $\psi_1 e_1$ will not alter when the distance between e_1 & e_2 is changed and the same may be said of $\psi_2 e_2$. But
$$\psi_1 e_2 = \frac{1}{4\pi}k\frac{e_1 e_2}{a} \quad \text{and} \quad \psi_2 e_1 = \frac{1}{4\pi}k\frac{e_2 e_1}{a}$$
so that the part of the work stored up in the dielectric which may be altered by varying a is
$$\frac{1}{4\pi}k\frac{e_1 e_2}{a}.$$

If a is increased, this quantity is diminished, that is to say, work is done by the dielectric upon the electrified bodies and this can only be done by urging the bodies asunder.

It appears, therefore that two bodies electrified with quantities of electricity $e_1 e_2$ in electromagnetic measure and at a distance a, repel each other with a force
$$\frac{1}{4\pi}k\frac{e_1 e_2}{a^2}.$$

Now let $\eta_1 \eta_2$ be the quantities $e_1 e_2$ reduced to electrostatic measure and let

E be the number of electrostatic units of electricity in one electromagnetic unit, then this force will be
$$\frac{k}{4\pi E^2}\frac{\eta_1\eta_2}{a^2}$$
but by definition of electrical quantity in electrostatic measure the repulsion of η_1 & η_2 is $\frac{\eta_1\eta_2}{a}$ therefore we have
$$\frac{1}{4\pi}k = E^2.^{(8)}$$

---

(8) Compare Number 239 §4.

FROM A LETTER TO CHARLES HOCKIN[1]

7 SEPTEMBER 1864

From Campbell and Garnett, *Life of Maxwell*[2]

Glenlair
Dalbeattie
September 7 1864

I have been doing several electrical problems. I have got a theory of 'electric absorption', *i.e.* residual charge, etc.,[3] and I very much want determinations of the specific induction, electric resistance, and absorption of good dielectrics, such as glass, shell-lac, gutta-percha, ebonite, sulphur, etc.

I have also cleared the electromagnetic theory of light from all unwarrantable assumption, so that we may safely determine the velocity of light by measuring the attraction between bodies kept at a given difference of potential, the value of which is known in electromagnetic measure.[4]

I hope there will be resistance coils at the British Association.[5]

---

(1) St John's 1859, third wrangler 1863, Fellow 1864–73 (Venn).

(2) *Life of Maxwell*: 340.

(3) See Maxwell's discussion in 'A dynamical theory of the electromagnetic field', *Phil. Trans.*, **155** (1865): 459–512, esp. 494–7 (= *Scientific Papers*, **1**: 573–6).

(4) Maxwell, 'A dynamical theory of the electromagnetic field': 497–505 (= *Scientific Papers*, **1**: 577–88); and Number 235.

(5) On the display of standard resistance coils see the 'Report of the committee on standards of electrical resistance', *Report of the Thirty-fourth Meeting of the British Association; held at Bath in September 1864* (London, 1865): 345–67, esp. 348.

MANUSCRIPT ON THE DETERMINATION OF THE NUMBER OF ELECTROSTATIC UNITS IN ONE ELECTROMAGNETIC UNIT OF ELECTRICITY

circa SEPTEMBER 1864[1]

From the original in the University Library, Cambridge[2]

EXPERIMENT TO DETERMINE THE NUMBER v OF ELECTROSTATIC UNITS IN ONE ELECTROMAGNETIC UNIT OF ELECTRICITY

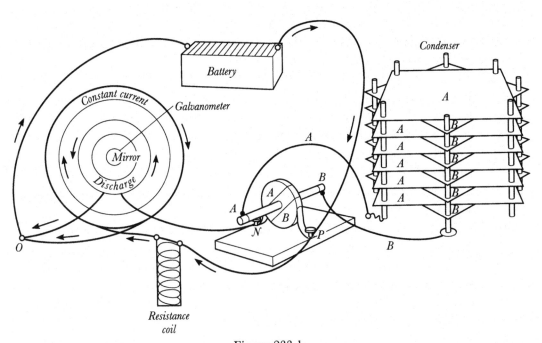

Figure 233,1

---

(1) Compare Maxwell's letter to Thomson of 27 September 1864 (Number 234), where the same experimental arrangement is described. There is no evidence that the experiment was performed.

(2) ULC Add. MSS 7655, V, c/14(ii). Endorsed: 'Experimental Determination of $v = \frac{\text{electrostatic}}{\text{electromagnetic}}$ measure of electricity'. The manuscript is described by I. B. Hopley, 'Maxwell's determination of the number of electrostatic units in one electromagnetic unit of electricity', *Annals of Science*, **15** (1959): 91–108, esp. 99–105.

The method proposed is founded on the comparison of the current produced by the repeated discharges of a condenser of known capacity with that kept up against a known resistance, the electromotive force employed in charging the condenser and in keeping up the current being the same.

The condenser is formed of alternate plates of metal nearly square the set A being nowhere in contact with the set B and each set being fixed on four metal pillars independent of the other set. In this way a powerful condenser may be formed having air as its dielectric and therefore free from 'electric absorption'.[3]

The capacity of this condenser is to be ascertained by dividing its charge with Thomsons Standard Condenser[4] a considerable number of times and finding the ratio of its potential before and after the process.

The capacity of the Standard Condenser being known in Electrostatic measure from its known form and dimensions, that of the large condenser may be determined. Let it be $= c$ meters (little c).

The commutator consists of a revolving disc & axle driven at constant speed $= n$ revolutions per second. The circumference of the disc consists of two nearly semicircular pieces of metal well insulated from each other. Of these one A is connected with the metal ring A and the other B, with the ring B. The rings A & B are kept connected with the plates A & B of the condenser.

The springs P & N press on exactly opposite extremities of the disc. P is always connected with the positive pole of the battery and N with the inner coil of the Galvanometer.

The Galvanometer consists of two separate coils, the inner one of a good many revolutions, the outer one of a smaller number. The magnet and mirror suspended in the centre of the coils should be of considerable mass, and the time of a single swing should be at least 10^s.

When the same current passes through both coils the effect of the inner coil on the magnet is ρ times that of the outer coil.

To determine ρ let a current be divided and sent in opposite directions through the two coils and let resistances be introduced into one of them till there is no effect on the magnet. Then

$$\rho = \frac{\text{resistance of inner coil \& appendages}}{\text{resistance of outer coil}}.$$

In the determination of v, the positive pole of the battery is connected with the spring P and the negative pole with O. P is kept constantly connected with

---

(3) See Faraday, *Electricity*, **1**: 364–7 (paras. 1169 to 1178); and Numbers 232 and 486.

(4) See Number 234 esp. note (2).

O by a resistance coil of great resistance and the outer coil of the galvanometer. Let the resistance from P to O by this course be R.

P is also connected with one set B of the plates of the condenser while the other set A is connected with the spring N and N is connected with O through the inner coil of the galvanometer.

When the commutator is in this position B is charged $+$ & A $-$ with the quantity of electricity corresponding to the difference of potentials between P & O. When the commutator alters the connexions this charge is sent through the galvanometer and the current goes on till an equal and opposite charge is produced so that a double charge goes through the galvanometer at each change of connexions. The speed &c are so arranged that the magnet is not affected. To determine v from the results

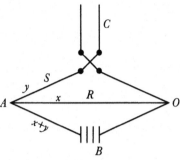

Figure 233,2

Let x = current through resistance coil &c R whose resistance = R
y = current through commutator &c S ——————— S
$x+y$ = ——————— battery, resistance ——————— B
C = capacity of condenser in electromagnetic measure
F = electromotive force of battery
η = difference of potentials of condenser
Y = charge of condenser
K = force on magnet due to unit current in outer coil
H = Earths hor. intensity
T = time of single vibration of magnet
M' = magnetic moment[5]
A = moment of inertia
$L\ M\ N$ coeffts of induction for x & y[6]
A & O potentials at A & O.

---

(5) Maxwell writes M, but to avoid confusion the magnetic moment of the galvanometer needle is here denoted M'.

(6) L and N are the coefficients of induction of the outer and inner galvanometer coils, M the coefficient of mutual induction between them.

Equations of Currents

$$Rx + L\frac{dx}{dt} + M\frac{dy}{dt} = A - O$$

$$Sy + N\frac{dy}{dt} + M\frac{dx}{dt} = A - O + \eta$$

$$B(x+y) = F + O - A$$

$$Y = C\eta$$

$$y = -\frac{dY}{dt}$$

Eliminating A & O

$$(R+B)x + By + L\frac{dx}{dt} + M\frac{dy}{dt} = F$$

$$+Rx - Sy + (L-M)\frac{dx}{dt} + (M-N)\frac{dy}{dt} = -\eta = -\frac{Y}{C}.$$

Let us suppose that the time of contact is sufficient for complete discharge then at first and also at last

$$x = \frac{F}{R+B} \quad y = 0.$$

Since the currents are the same at first and at last the inductive currents due to the coefficients $L\ M\ N$ will each be zero when integrated during the whole time. We may therefore make our calculation, as if quantities were zero.

We find then
$$x = \frac{FS - \frac{Y}{C}B}{(R+B)S + BR}$$

$$\frac{dY}{dt} = \frac{-FR - \frac{Y}{C}(R+B)}{(R+B)S + BR}.$$

Whence
$$Y = -FC\frac{R}{R+B}(1 + Y_0 e^{-\alpha t})$$

where
$$\alpha = \frac{R+B}{C(RS + BS + BR)}.$$

When $t = 0$ the charge on the condenser is $FC\frac{R}{R+B}$ so that we get

$$Y = FC\frac{R}{R+B}(2e^{-\alpha t} - 1) \quad \text{whence} \quad y = 2\alpha FC\frac{R}{R+B}e^{-\alpha t}$$

and
$$x = \frac{F}{(R+B)S+BR}\left(S+\frac{RB}{R+B}(1-2e^{-\alpha t})\right).$$

The equation of motion of the magnet is

$$A\frac{d^2\theta}{dt^2} = -M'H\sin\theta + M'K(x-\rho y)\cos\theta.^{(7)}$$

The oscillations of the magnet are partly free, performed in the time $T = \pi\sqrt{\frac{A}{M'H}}$ and of indeterminate extent and partly forced, performed in the time $\frac{1}{4n}$, and their extent is

$$\theta = \frac{1}{32n}\frac{M'K}{A}\frac{F}{R+B} = \frac{\pi^2}{32nT^2}\tan\beta$$

where β is the deflexion due to constant current.

The mean position of the magnet is determined by the equation $\tan\theta = \frac{K}{H}(x-\rho y)$
where x and y have their mean values. To find these.

Integrate x & y from $t = 0$ to $t = T$ where T is the time of contact.

$$\int x\,dt = \frac{Ft}{R+B} + \frac{2CFRB}{(R+B)^2}(e^{-\alpha t}-1)$$

$$\int y\,dt = 2CF\frac{R}{R+B}(1-e^{-\alpha t})$$

$$\tan\theta = \frac{K}{H}\frac{\int x\,dt - \rho\int y\,dt}{t}$$

$$t = \frac{1}{2n}$$

$$\tan\theta = \frac{K}{H}\frac{F}{R+B}\left\{1-4CRn\rho\left(1-e^{-\alpha T}\right)\left(1-\frac{1}{\rho}\frac{B}{R+B}\right)\right\}$$

an equation to determine the value of C in electromagnetic measure.
R or n should be varied till $\tan\theta$ is nearly zero then

$$C = \frac{1}{4Rn\rho} \quad \text{roughly}$$

the corrections depending on $e^{-\alpha t}$ and $\frac{1}{\rho}\frac{B}{R+B}$ being small.

---

(7) θ is the mean deflection of the galvanometer needle.

In order to read the galvanometer distinctly the forced oscillations ought to be small compared with the deflexion due to the current in x alone. If $T = 10$ seconds and $n = 50$ $\dfrac{\pi^2}{32n\,T^2} = \dfrac{1}{16000}$ nearly which would be sufficiently accurate as these oscillations consist of a series of kicks the apparent mean position will be one third from the extreme end of the oscillation.

To find the correction $e^{-\alpha T}$. Let the ratio of the metallic to the whole circumference of the disc be r, r is not far from 1 and $T = \dfrac{r}{2n}$ also $n = \dfrac{1}{4CR\rho}$ nearly

$$\alpha T = \frac{2(R+B)\,R\rho r}{RS + SB + BR}.$$

If R be great compared with B or S and if ρ be a large number αT will be a large number and the correction $e^{-\alpha T}$ will be negligible.

The most important correction is that depending on $\dfrac{1}{\rho}\dfrac{B}{R+B}$ since it is difficult to ascertain B, the resistance of the battery with much accuracy.

If however $\rho = 100$ and $R = 100B$ the correction is less than $\dfrac{1}{10{,}000}$ and its approximate value may still be ascertained.

If c is 100 in electrostatic measure, it is $\dfrac{100}{v^2}$ in electromagnetic measure and

$$v^2 = \frac{c}{C} = 4cRn\rho\,(1 + \text{corrections}).$$

From Webers experiments $v =$ about $(300{,}000{,}000)$ metres per second.[8]

Hence if $c = 100$ metres $\rho = 100$ $n = 25$ revolutions per second R should be about 90,000,000,000 metres per second or about 900 times the standard resistance coil of 1863.[9]

---

(8) Weber's experiments gave a value of 310,740,000 meters per second; see Number 218 esp. notes (4) and (7).

(9) The value of the resistance of the coils was recorded in the 1863 'Report of the Committee...on standards of electrical resistance'; see Number 214, esp. note (18). No standards based on the 1863 determination were officially issued, but some coils were made; see the 'Report of the Committee on standards of electrical resistance', *Report of the Thirty-fourth Meeting of the British Association* (London, 1865): 345–67, esp. 345.

then
$$v^2 = 4cRn\rho \frac{\left(1 - \frac{1}{\rho}\frac{B}{R+B}\right)\left(1 - e^{-\alpha T}\right)}{1 - \frac{\tan\theta}{\tan\beta}}$$

c = electrostatic capacity, θ = mean galv^r reading
β = reading due to current through R.

LETTER TO WILLIAM THOMSON

27 SEPTEMBER 1864

From the original in the University Library, Glasgow[1]

Glenlair
Dalbeattie
Sept 27 1864

Dear Thomson

Is your Standard Condenser in actual existence? that is to say a plate of air which will have a known capacity of so many feet or meters capable of measurement to about $\frac{1}{10}$ per cent.[2]

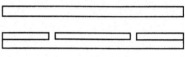

Figure 234,1

If so I should like to get hold of it to measure the capacity of an air battery I propose to make.[3]

Two sets of square metal plates are fixed each to four vertical pillars at the corners and arranged so that the one set are interleaved with the other set but nowhere in contact. The whole to be firmly fixed on an insulating plate so that the distances of the plates cannot change, and enclosed in a dry atmosphere.

Thus we may with plates 9 or 10 inches square easily and safely get a capacity of 2 meters per plate,

$$\frac{\frac{1}{25}}{4\pi \times \frac{1}{1000}} = \frac{1000}{100\pi}.$$

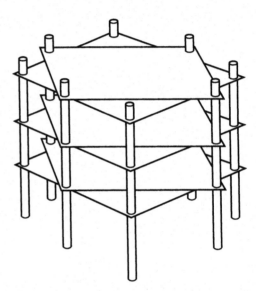

Figure 234,2

Let the capacity of say 50 plates be 100 meters and let it be well measured by comparison with your standard condenser, by charging the condenser say

---

(1) Glasgow University Library, Kelvin Papers, M 16.

(2) See Maxwell, *Treatise*, **1**: 283–5 (§228) and Fig. 20 (corresponding to Figure 234, 1), an 'arrangement, due to Sir W. Thomson, which we may call the Guard-ring arrangement, by means of which the quantity of electricity on an insulated disk may be exactly determined in terms of its potential'.

(3) See Number 233.

100 times and always discharging it every time and finding the loss of potential by your electrometer.

Now let A, B be two conducting parts of the rim of a revolving disc insulated from each other and let A be connected permanently with one set of plates & B with the other. Also let P & N be connected with the electrodes of a battery (voltaic). Then B will be charged $+$ & $A-$.

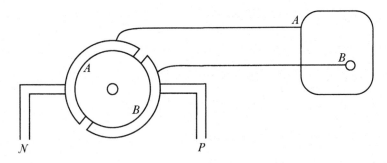

Figure 234,3

But when A & B are reversed this charge will be let off and a new and equal reverse charge established so that at every reversal a double charge is sent through $P\,N$ and by reversing often a continuous effect on the galvan^r may be produced.

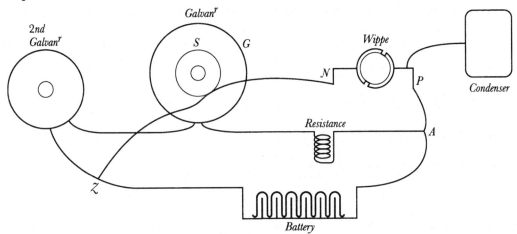

Figure 234,4

Now let the battery current be divided at A and part sent by way of P to condenser thence to N thence to a sensitive galvan^r S and to Z.

The other part through a resistance coil an outer coil of the galvan^r G and a second galv^r still less sensitive.

S and G run in opposite directions and act on the same needle. S is ρ times more sensitive than G the 2nd galv^r is σ times less sensitive than G that is if a current 1 passed through S & a current ρ through G the needle would be at rest, and if 1 passed through G and σ thro the 2nd galv^r the effects w^d be equal.

Now let the Wippe[4] go round n times per second and let the resistance be so arranged that the 1st galv^r is very little affected, and its mean deflexion is θ while that of the 2nd is β

we get the value of v or $\dfrac{\text{electrostatic}}{\text{electromagnetic}}$ measure of electricity by the formula

$$v^2 = 4c\,Rn\rho \frac{\left(1-\dfrac{1}{\rho}\dfrac{B}{R+B}\right)\left(1-e^{-\alpha T}\right)}{1-\dfrac{1}{\sigma}\dfrac{\tan\theta}{\tan\beta}}.$$ [5] (a)

Here

c = capacity of condenser electrostatic measure
R = resistance from A to Z through resistance coil &c
n = no of revolutions per second of commutator
ρ = ratio of currents giving equal effects in the two coils of the 1st galvan^r
σ = ratio of the 2nd coil of d^o to the 2nd galvan^r

(a) {Thomson}
V, R resist^{ce} electrost
r——— [electro] m[agnetic]
$Q = \mu$ = flowing, electrost.
$\dfrac{V}{R} = Q;\quad \dfrac{r}{R} = r\dfrac{Q}{V}$

resist^{ce} of wippe = $\dfrac{1}{nc}$ electrostatic
———— coils = R ———— magn^c
$v = 1000 \times 10^6$ feet   192 000 miles

$v^2 = \rho nc\,R$ Let $R = 10^{12}\ \substack{\text{feet}\\\text{metres}}\!\!/\text{sec}$

$v^2 \div R = \dfrac{v}{1000} = 10^6$ feet

$n \times c \times e =$ for^y in electrost meas.
$\dfrac{Vv}{R} =$ ————mag. "
    $= v^{-1}q$
$n \times c \times R = v^2$

(4) Commutator (see the *Treatise*, 2: 375 (§775)).   (5) See Number 233.

θ = mean deflexion of 1st galvan^r
β = ——————— 2nd ———————
B = resistance of battery from Z to A

$$\alpha T = \frac{2(R+B)R\rho r}{RS+SB+BR}^{(6)}$$

where S is resistance from A to Z through condenser &c & r = ratio of metallic part of the disc to the whole. αT is very large. If $c = 100$ & $n = 25$ & $\rho = 100$ R should be about 900 of the unit coils of 1863 which would do very well.[7] I think we might get this done this year by diligence.

Yours truly
J. CLERK MAXWELL

---

(6) T is the time of an oscillation of the galvanometer needle.
(7) See Number 233 (note (9)).

235

LETTER TO WILLIAM THOMSON
15 OCTOBER 1864
From the original in the University Library, Glasgow[1]

8 Palace Gardens Terrace W
1864 Oct 15

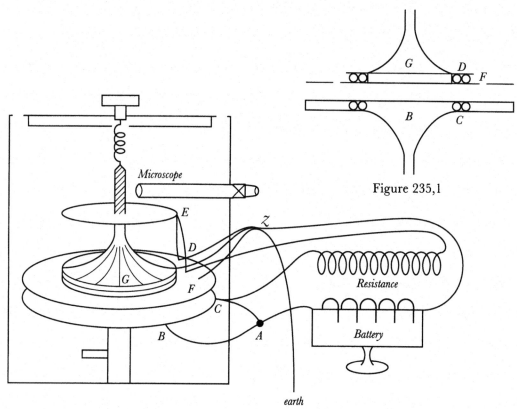

Figure 235,1

Figure 235,2

Dear Thomson

Here is a plan to weigh an electrostatic attraction against an electromagnetic repulsion directly,[2] so as to require no standard except a

---

(1) Glasgow University Library, Kelvin Papers, M 17.

(2) The experimental arrangement which Maxwell devised at this time established the principle of the method employed in his paper 'On a method of making a direct comparison of electrostatic with electromagnetic force; with a note on the electromagnetic theory of light', *Phil. Trans.*, **158** (1868): 643–57, esp. 643–52 (= *Scientific Papers*, **2**: 125–36). See Number 289.

resistance coil[3] and some proportional measures of dimensions in any scale you please.

The electrostatic attraction of two discs kept at a constant potential is balanced[4] against the electromagnetic repulsion of two coils of wire through which a current is urged by the same electromotive force which keeps up the difference of potential.

G Fig. [235,]1 is an aluminium disc strengthened by ribs behind the surface plane &c potential always zero.

F is a ring surrounding it the lower surface being in the same plane with *G*.

D is a coil of insulated wire, from 5 to ten turns as close as possible to the upper surface of *G*.

E is an equal coil a good bit above *D* wound in the opposite direction to avoid the effects of terrestrial magnetism.[5]

B is a large disc as big as the ring with a coil *C* just under its surface like *D* and opposite to *D*.[6]

B and *C* move vertically by a micrometer screw.

G D and *E* are hung up by a spring and adjusted to be in the plane of *F* and certain marks on the stem are observed with a microscope.

The electrode *A* of a battery is connected

1st with the disc *B*

2nd with the following series Coil *C*, Resistance coil, Coil *E* Coil *D* to electrode *Z* of battery.

Z is connected with the hanging disc *G* the ring *F* the box of the instrument and the Earth.

Turn on the current and observe the stem with the microscope. If it is pulled down screw the disc *B* down & vice versa till turning on the current produces no effect.

Then immediately measure the resistance between *A* and *Z* by comparison with a standard coil, and at your leisure measure the distance from *B* to *G*.

---

(3) 'The ratio of the electromagnetic unit to the electrostatic unit is...that of a certain distance to a certain time...this ratio is a *velocity*...The electromagnetic value of the resistance of a conductor is also a quantity of the nature of a velocity [see Number 211 note (7)], and therefore we may express the ratio of the two electrical units in terms of the resistance of a known standard coil; and this expression will be independent of the magnitude of our standards of length, time, and mass'; Maxwell, 'On a method of making a direct comparison of electrostatic with electromagnetic force': 643–4 (= *Scientific Papers*, **2**: 126). On the ratio of electrical units see the Introduction and the *Treatise*, **2**: 241–4 (§§625–8).

(4) In the 1868 experiments the comparison was made using a torsion balance. For a description of the torsion balance see Number 243.

(5) See Maxwell, 'On a method of making a direct comparison of electrostatic with electromagnetic force': 646 (= *Scientific Papers*, **2**: 130).

(6) The current passes through the coils in opposite directions so as to produce a repulsion.

Do this with various resistances in circuit.

The electrostatic attraction is $\dfrac{1}{2}\dfrac{F^2}{4\pi v^2}\dfrac{\pi a^2}{d^2}$ [7]

where
F = electromotive force from A to Z
a = radius of disc
d = distance of discs.

The electromagnetic repulsion is

$$4\pi \frac{F^2}{R^2}\frac{a'}{d'}n^2 \text{ [8]} + \text{corrections which I can make}^{[9]}$$

where
R = resistance from A to Z
a' = effective radius of coils C and D less than a
n = number of windings in each
d' = distance between them = $d+$const.

$$v = \frac{1}{\sqrt{32\pi}}\frac{a}{d}\sqrt{\frac{d'}{a'}}\frac{1}{n}R \quad \text{for 1}^{\text{st}}\text{ approx}^{\text{n}[10]}$$

If $\dfrac{a}{d} = 10$, 100 Daniels[11] would give ⟨400 grain W⟩ ⟨1250 grammes weight⟩.

---

(7) F is the difference of potential between the two discs in electromagnetic measure, v is the ratio of electrical units; see Maxwell, 'On a method of making a direct comparison of electrostatic with electromagnetic force': 645 (= *Scientific Papers*, **2**: 128). On electrostatic attraction between plane surfaces see William Thomson, 'On the mathematical theory of electricity in equilibrium. I. On the elementary laws of statical electricity', *Camb. & Dubl. Math. J.*, **1** (1845): 75–95, esp. 78 (= *Electrostatics and Magnetism*: 15–37).

(8) The repulsive force depends on the ratio of the diameter of the coils to their distance. Maxwell writes this relation in slightly different form in 'On a method of making a direct comparison of electrostatic with electromagnetic force': 645 (= *Scientific Papers*, **2**: 128).

(9) In his paper 'On a method of making a direct comparison of electrostatic with electromagnetic force': 646 (= *Scientific Papers*, **2**: 128–9) Maxwell explained that the correction factor would 'take into account the fact that the section of each coil is of sensible area.' Making the depth of the coil equal to the breadth of the section, from the differential equation of the potential of two coils given in his paper 'A dynamical theory of the electromagnetic field', *Phil. Trans.*, **155** (1865): 459–512, on 508 (= *Scientific Papers*, **1**: 591), he obtains a correction factor of the form $(1-\alpha'^2/12a'^2)$, where α' is the depth of the coil.

(10) Compare the expression in 'On a method of making a direct comparison of electrostatic with electromagnetic force': 649 (= *Scientific Papers*, **2**: 133). The only quantities to be determined in absolute measure are the resistances (see note (3)).

(11) The electric battery (with zinc and copper electrodes) invented by John Frederic Daniell; see his papers 'On voltaic combinations', *Phil. Trans.*, **126** (1836): 107–24; 'Additional observations on voltaic combinations', *ibid.*: 125–9; and 'Further observations on voltaic combinations', *ibid.*, **127** (1837): 141–60.

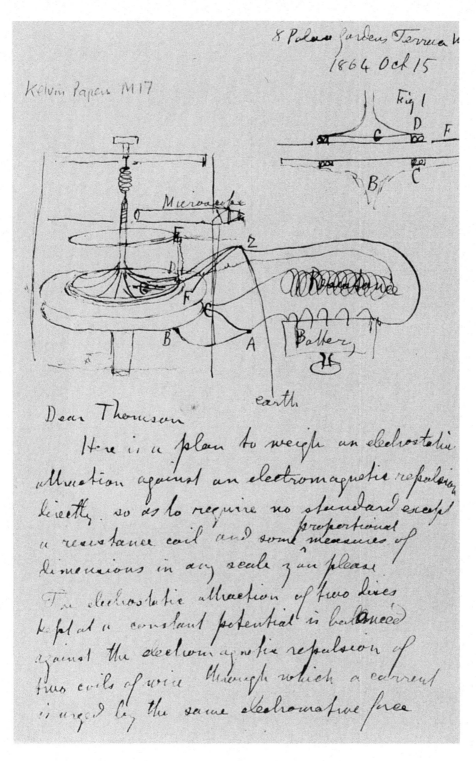

Plate II. A suggested experiment (1864) to establish the ratio of electrostatic and electromagnetic units of electricity, from a letter to William Thomson (Number 235).

The absolute attraction is about

$$\frac{1}{80}N^2\frac{a^2}{d^2} \text{ in grammes or } \frac{1}{800}N^2\frac{a^2}{d^2} \text{ gr wt}^{(12)}$$

where N is the number of Daniels employed so it could be easily got up to a good value.

Can you tell me about the absolute dimensions for the discs and rings for the electrostatic department after your experience of such things.[13] I can get the repulsion of the coils of wire as correct as I please to any no. of terms.

I have just got your letter of the 14th and mean to work out your calculations when I have digested my dinner. Meanwhile your little magnet and mirror might do as a test of immobility of the suspended disc if it were not for electromagnetic action of the coils.

Do you think of doing the Cavendish exp^t.[14] I have been some time devising a plan for doing it in a vacuum tube like a T upside down in a cellar in the country.

The Joulian Exp$^{t(15)}$

Is not ☿[16] a good thing to find J.[17]

Get an iron or steel tube 12 to 20 feet long and $\frac{1}{2}$ or $\frac{3}{4}$ inch internal diam^r.

Put a cistern for mercury at the top and screw on at the bottom a plug of cane through which the mercury is squeezed. Just above the cane have a ring shaped cistern of mercury to test the temperature there (or stick a thermometer into the tube if you can). Let the mercury come out of the cane into another cistern and try the temperature there too. The

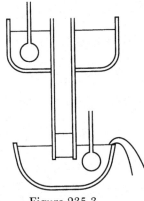

Figure 235,3

---

(12) Grain weight (1/7000 lb.).   (13) See Number 289 note (11).

(14) Possibly Cavendish's experimental demonstration of the law of electrostatic force; see *The Electrical Researches of The Honourable Henry Cavendish, F.R.S.*, ed. J. Clerk Maxwell (Cambridge, 1879): 104–12. Maxwell subsequently repeated the experiments at the Cavendish Laboratory 'in a somewhat different manner', *ibid.*: 417–18. Thomson had long been familiar with Cavendish's unpublished MSS (see Number 435).

(15) To determine the mechanical equivalent of heat, as determined by James Prescott Joule: see Number 207 note (43). Compare Maxwell's account of this proposed experiment in his letter to P. G. Tait of 23 December 1867 (Number 278).   (16) Mercury.

(17) The mechanical equivalent of heat: see Number 207 note (43).

difference will be that due to the column $h = \dfrac{h}{772}.32 \times 13.5$ [18] $= .56$ degree Fah per foot.

Cover the whole tube well with wool &c measure with the same thermometer the temperature at the top and bottom and at the outflow through the porous cane and keep it going for a long time till all is steady. Having got J for your mercury in feet get for water by finding sp. heat of your mercury and its sp gravity by the best methods.

This only requires plenty ☿ and not any great height and no row of wheels noise or shaking.

I shall go through your wippe plan[19] when I am free from post considerations.[20]

The tendency in my rotatory theory of magnetism[21] was towards the to me inconceivable and ∴ no doubt to the misty[22] though why you put a c after the y I cannot see why. Perhaps the eminent London scavengers Messrs Cleavers and Mist might find a weapon to combat the tendency.

I can find the velocity of transmission of electromagnetic disturbances indepᵗ of any hypothesis now & and it is $= v$ and the disturbances must be transverse to the direction of propagation or there is no propagation thereof.[23]

One result is that if the resistance of gold is exactly the same for small electromotive force as for great gold leaf $\frac{1}{282000}$ inch thick ought to transmit 10^{-300} of the incident light. I find it very difficult to estimate the amount of light transmitted on account of the holes in the gold leaf, but I think it is between $\frac{1}{400}$ and $\frac{1}{900}$ when light from green glass is used.[24]

---

(18) $J = 772$ foot pounds per British thermal unit (see Number 207 note (43)); specific gravity of mercury = 13.5 (see Number 278 note (19)); acceleration due to gravity = 32 ft/sec².

(19) See Number 234 note (4); and see Number 241 and Maxwell's letter to Thomson of 25 February 1865 (Number 242).

(20) An early indication of Maxwell's intention to resign his post of Professor of Natural Philosophy at King's College, London. According to the minutes of King's College Council Maxwell's resignation was recorded on 10 February 1865: 'The Principal laid before the Council a letter of J. C. Maxwell Esq. resigning his office of Professor of Natural Philosophy, but expressing his readiness to continue his work until the appointment of his successor.' (King's College London Archives, King's College Council Vol. I, minute 410).

(21) The theory of molecular vortices advanced by Maxwell in 'On physical lines of force', *Phil. Mag.*, ser. 4, **21** (1861): 161–75, 281–91, 338–48; *ibid.*, **23** (1862): 12–24, 85–95 (= *Scientific Papers*, **1**: 451–513).

(22) Compare Maxwell's comment in his letter to P. G. Tait of 23 December 1867 (Number 278).

(23) Maxwell, 'A dynamical theory of the electromagnetic field': 497–505 (= *Scientific Papers*, **1**: 577–88). (24) Compare Number 239 §7.

Any way nobody could see 10^{-300} times the light of a candle.

Hockin is going to measure the resistance of a bit of gold leaf to compare.[25]

I hope to spread some leaf smooth by means of a wrinkle of Faraday's[26] and get the proportion of light better.

So the connexion between transparency and resistance is not complete at least for gold leaf.[27]

Yours truly
J. CLERK MAXWELL

(25) See Number 239 note (17).

(26) Faraday had described a technique for stretching leaves of gold film – by laying the leaves on dampened glass before stretching them – in his 1857 Bakerian Lecture. See Michael Faraday, 'Experimental relations of gold (and other metals) to light', *Phil. Trans.*, **147** (1857): 145–82, esp. 147 (= Faraday, *Experimental Researches in Chemistry and Physics* (London, 1859): 391–443). Maxwell acknowledged receipt of this paper in a letter to Faraday of 9 November 1857 (Volume I: 548).

(27) See Maxwell's discussion of the 'relation between electric resistance and transparency' in 'A dynamical theory of the electromagnetic field': 504–5 (= *Scientific Papers*, **1**: 586–7). He found that the opacity of a body is greater, the greater its conductivity, but that 'gold, silver, and platinum are good conductors, and yet when reduced to sufficiently thin plates they allow light to pass through them.... This result cannot be reconciled with the electromagnetic theory of light'. Compare the *Treatise*, **2**: 394–5 (§§ 798–800). See Number 239 § 7.

NOTES ON THE EXPLANATION OF THE REFLECTION AND REFRACTION OF LIGHT BY THE ELECTROMAGNETIC THEORY OF LIGHT

OCTOBER 1864[1]

From the original in the University Library, Cambridge[2]

[ON THE REFLECTION AND REFRACTION OF LIGHT][3]

[Three waves of amplitude 1, A, B: incident, reflected and refracted waves]

Equation of [conservation of] energy[4]

$$(1 - A^2) k \sin i \cos i = k' B^2 \sin r \cos r\ ^{(5)}$$

[where i and r are the angles of incidence and refraction]

---

(1) See Maxwell's letter to Stokes of 15 October 1864 (Number 237).

(2) ULC Add. MSS 7655, V, b/12.

(3) Maxwell's argument is based on the treatment of the reflection and refraction of light by Jules Jamin, 'Note sur la théorie de la réflexion et de la réfraction', *Ann. Chim. Phys.*, ser. 3, **59** (1860): 413–26; as he explains in his letter to Stokes of 15 October 1864. In this paper Jamin begins by discussing the solutions which had been obtained by Fresnel, MacCullagh and Neumann. See A. J. Fresnel, 'Mémoire sur la loi des modifications que la réflexion imprime à la lumière polarisée', *Mémoires de l'Académie Royale des Sciences de l'Institut de France*, **11** (1832): 393–433; James MacCullagh, 'On the laws of crystalline reflexion', *Phil. Mag.*, ser. 3, **10** (1837): 42–5; MacCullagh, 'On the laws of crystalline reflexion and refraction', *Transactions of the Royal Irish Academy*, **18** (1837): 31–74; and Franz Neumann, 'Theoretische Untersuchung der Gesetze, nach welchen das Licht an der Grenze zweier vollkommen durchsichtigen Medien reflectirt und gebrochen wird', *Mathematische Abhandlungen der Königlichen Akademie der Wissenschaften zu Berlin*, Aus dem Jahre 1835 (Berlin, 1837): 1–160. These papers propose hypothetical boundary conditions which determine the oscillation of the ether at the interface between two media. For the alternative boundary conditions proposed by Fresnel, and by MacCullagh and Neumann, see note (9) and Number 237 notes (4) and (7). These boundary conditions impose constraints on the continuity of the media at their interface: for Maxwell's comments on their validity see Number 237.

(4) The law of the conservation of *vis viva* is assumed by Fresnel, MacCullagh and Neumann. See Fresnel, 'Mémoire sur la loi...': 400, and MacCullagh, 'On the laws of crystalline reflexion': 43.

(5) Compare Jamin, 'Note sur la théorie de la réflexion et de la réfraction': 421, equation (α):

$(1 - a^2) = b^2 \dfrac{\sin r \cos r}{\sin i \cos i} \dfrac{d'}{d}$, where d' and d are the densities of the ether in the two media. Jamin obtains this equation on the supposition (with MacCullagh and Neumann) that $d = d'$; see his 'Note...': 415, and Number 237 note (5). Maxwell interpolates a relation between the density of the ether and his coefficient of 'electric elasticity' k; see note (6).

[where amplitudes] 1 *A* *B* [are] displacements
[and *k* and *k'* are coefficients of electric elasticity in the two media]

[so] *k*   *kA*   *k'B* [are electric] forces.⁽⁶⁾

[The equation for the propagation of an electromagnetic wave is]

$$v^2 = \frac{k}{4\pi\mu} \quad (7)$$

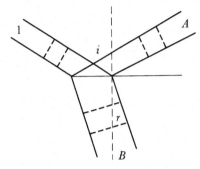

Figure 236,1

[where μ is the coefficient of magnetic induction]⁽⁸⁾

$$\begin{aligned}
\text{displacement} &= 1 \\
\text{mag force} &= 4\pi v \\
\text{e m f} &= 4\pi\mu v^2 = k \\
\text{mag induction} &= 4\pi\mu v = \frac{k}{v}
\end{aligned}$$

[Boundary conditions]⁽⁹⁾

---

(6) To establish an electromagnetic theory of optical reflection and refraction Maxwell seeks to integrate results drawn from his electromagnetic theory of light into Jamin's expressions for the oscillation of the ether at the interface between two media. He equates the displacements in the ether with the 'electric displacement' in the electromagnetic medium. He introduces equations (*E*), the 'Equations of electric elasticity', from his paper 'A dynamical theory of the electromagnetic field', *Phil. Trans.*, **155** (1865): 459–512, esp. 485 (= *Scientific Papers*, **1**: 560). For isotropic substances *k* is 'the ratio of the electromotive force to the electric displacement'. See Number 231, equations (12).

(7) From equation (71) of Maxwell's 'A dynamical theory of the electromagnetic field': 498 (= *Scientific Papers*, **1**: 579); *v* is the velocity of propagation of magnetic disturbances transmitted through the electromagnetic field.

(8) See Maxwell, 'A dynamical theory of the electromagnetic field': 480 (= *Scientific Papers*, **1**: 556); 'μ is a quantity depending on the nature of the medium, its temperature, the amount of magnetization already produced' (for an isotropic medium).

(9) Jamin considers two boundary conditions, as assumed by Fresnel and by MacCullagh and Neumann. Fresnel assumed that the components of the oscillation parallel to the interface are continuous across the interface; and then considered two cases, for oscillations parallel to the plane of incidence and oscillations parallel to the interface. See Fresnel, 'Mémoire sur la loi des modifications que la réflexion imprime…': 394–402; and Jamin, 'Note sur la théorie de la réflexion et de la réfraction': 415, where he observes that '[Fresnel] à considérer deux cas: 1° celui où les vibrations sont normales au plan d'incidence et parallèles à la surface; 2° celui où elles sont dans le plan d'incidence.' These two cases are considered by Maxwell. MacCullagh and Neumann however supposed that 'the vibrations are equivalent at the common surface of two

I Displacements in plane of incidence

	[displacements]	1	a	b
e m f		k	ka	$k'b$
mag ind[uction]		$\dfrac{k}{v}$	$\dfrac{k}{v}a$	$\dfrac{k'}{v'}b$
mag force		$4\pi v$	$4\pi va$	$4\pi v'b$

[where k, k' and v, v' are the coefficients of electric elasticity and the velocities of wave propagation in the two media]

[Equations for]

    normal displacement $(1-a)\sin i = b\sin r$ [10]

    tangential mag force? $(1+a)v = bv'$. [11]

II Displacements perp to plane of incidence

                               1   a b

[Equations for]

    normal mag ind[uction] $(1-a)\dfrac{k}{v}\sin i = b\dfrac{k'}{v'}\sin r$

                       or $(1-a)\mu = b\mu'$

    tangential e m f $(1+a)k = bk'$

[To obtain a and b]

If $\mu = \mu'$ [then] $k \propto v^2$

and [writing conservation of energy equation as]

$$(1-A^2)\sin r \cos i = B^2 \sin i \cos r \quad (12)$$

normal displacement $(1-a)\sin i = b\sin r$

[assume Snell's law as] $v\sin i = v'\sin r$ [13]

$$\left[\text{and substitute } \frac{k}{k'} = \left(\frac{v}{v'}\right)^2 = \left(\frac{\sin r}{\sin i}\right)^2\right]$$

---

media'; MacCullagh, 'On the laws of crystalline reflexion': 43. This is the boundary condition favoured by Jamin, but questioned by Maxwell: see Number 237 esp. note (4).

(10) The expression obtained by Jamin, 'Note sur la théorie de la réflexion et de la réfraction': 420, for an oscillation normal to the interface.

(11) Compare Jamin, 'Note sur la théorie de la réflexion et de la réfraction': 415; and Fresnel, 'Mémoire sur la loi...': 401, for an oscillation parallel to the interface.

(12) The equation for the conservation of *vis viva* obtained by Fresnel, 'Mémoire sur la loi...': 400, equation (A), on the supposition that the densities of the ether in the two media are different, the ratio of densities d'/d being equal to $\sin^2 i/\sin^2 r$. See Fresnel, 'Mémoire sur la loi...': 398, and Jamin, 'Note sur la théorie de la réflexion et de la réfraction': 415, esp. equation (1); and see also note (5).

(13) Read: $v/v' = \sin i/\sin r$; see Jamin, 'Note sur la théorie de la réflexion et de la réfraction': 414. The expressions obtained below are therefore incorrect.

[tangential magnetic force] $\dfrac{(1+a)\sin r \cos i}{\sin i} = b\dfrac{\sin i \cos r}{\sin r}$

$$(1-a)\dfrac{\sin i}{\sin r} = \dfrac{(1+a)\sin^2 r \cos i}{\sin^2 i \cos r}.$$

If $k = k'$ [then] $\mu \propto \dfrac{1}{v^2}$

and [conservation of energy equation]
$$(1-A'^2)\sin i \cos i = B'^2 \sin r \cos r^{(14)}$$
[for displacements] $\parallel \quad 1-a'$.

---

(14) The equation for the conservation of *vis viva* obtained by Jamin on the supposition that the density of the ether is the same in both media; see note (5).

LETTER TO GEORGE GABRIEL STOKES

15 OCTOBER 1864

From the original in the University Library, Cambridge[1]

8 Palace Gardens Terrace
1864 Oct 15

Dear Stokes

I have been reading Jamins Note on the Theory of Reflexion & Refraction Ann de Ch 1860 pt. 1 p 413.[2]

I am not yet able to satisfy myself about the conditions to be fulfilled at the surface except of course the condition of conservation of energy.[3]

Jamin insists on the equality of the motion both horizontal & vertical in the two media.[4] I do not see the necessity for equality of motion but I think action and reaction must be equal between the media provided the media pure and simple vibrate and nothing along with them.

If the gross matter in each medium does not vibrate or has a different phase and amplitude from the ether then there will be 6 relations between the 4 quantities – Two portions of ether & two kinds of gross matter.

Have you written anything about the rival theories of reflexion? or can you tell me of any thing you agree with or eminently differ from on that subject. I think you once told me that the subject was a stiff one to the best skilled in undulations.

Jamin deduces (p 422) from his conditions of equality of motion in the two

---

(1) ULC Add. MSS 7656, M 423. First published in Larmor, *Correspondence*, **2**: 25–6.

(2) Jules Jamin, 'Note sur la théorie de la réflexion et de la réfraction', *Ann. Chim. Phys.*, ser. 3, **59** (1860): 413–26.

(3) See Maxwell's draft on an electromagnetic theory of optical reflection and refraction (Number 236).

(4) On Jamin's boundary condition see his 'Note sur la théorie de la réflexion et de la réfraction': 419–21; 'je vais faire en admettant comme Neumann et MacCullagh que les composantes horizontales et verticales sont égales au-dessus et au-dessous de la surface de séparation des deux milieux.' Jamin is alluding to papers by James MacCullagh, 'On the laws of crystalline reflexion and refraction', *Transactions of the Royal Irish Academy*, **18** (1837): 31–74, and by Franz Neumann, 'Theoretische Untersuchung der Gesetze, nach welchen das Licht an der Grenze zweier vollkommen durchsichtigen Medien reflectirt und gebrochen wird', *Mathematische Abhandlungen der Königlichen Akademie der Wissenschaften zu Berlin*, Aus dem Jahre 1835 (Berlin, 1837): 1–160. MacCullagh proposed four fundamental hypotheses, including the boundary condition: 'The vibrations in two contiguous media are equivalent; that is, the resultant of the incident and reflected vibrations is the same, both in length and direction, as the resultant of the refracted vibrations' (see MacCullagh, 'On the laws of crystalline reflexion and refraction': 34).

media for vibrations in the plane of incidence that the density of the medium is the same in all substances.⁽⁵⁾

That is to say he gets this by pure mathematics without any experiment.

Or according to him no such vibrations could exist in the media unless they were of equal density.

This I think simply disproves his original assumption of the equality of the displacements in the two media.

In fact the equality of displacements combined with the equality of energy involves the equality of density.

Therefore the general theory, which ought to be able to explain the case of media of unequal density⁽⁶⁾ (even if there were none such) must not assume equality of displacements, of contiguous particles on each side of the surface.⁽⁷⁾

I suppose if two media of different density were glued hard together and large vibrations sent through them they would be separated at their common surface.

But there is nothing in the surface of separation of two media analogous to this gluing together that I can detect.

I have now got materials for calculating the velocity of transmission of a magnetic disturbance through air founded on experimental evidence without

---

(5) Jamin, 'Note sur la théorie de la réflexion et de la réfraction': 422. He obtains the equation $(1-a^2) = b^2 \dfrac{\sin r \cos r}{\sin i \cos i}$ (where 1, a, b are the amplitudes of incident, reflected, and refracted rays, and i and r the angles of incidence and refraction), and concludes: 'en comparant cette dernière équation à celle des forces vives, il faut admettre que $d' = d$, c'est-à-dire que la densité de l'éther est la même dans tous les corps.' This equation is Jamin's equation (α) (see his 'Note...': 415, 417, 421), 'l'équation des forces vives' obtained 'on supposait, comme MacCullagh et Neumann, que $d = d'$'; and see Number 236 note (5). MacCullagh and Neumann had supposed that the density of the ether is the same in all media; see MacCullagh, 'On the laws of crystalline reflexion and refraction': 34, and Neumann, 'Theoretische Untersuchung der Gesetze...': 8.

(6) As supposed by A. J. Fresnel, 'Mémoire sur la loi des modifications que la réflexion imprime à la lumière polarisée', *Mémoires de l'Académie Royale des Sciences de l'Institut de France*, **11** (1832): 393–433, esp. 395–400; and see Number 236 note (12).

(7) Jamin had concluded that Fresnel's solution (based on the boundary condition that the components of the oscillation parallel to the interface are continuous across the interface, and the hypothesis that the densities of the two media are unequal) 'entraîne implicitement entre les composantes verticales des vibrations une relation qu'il est difficile d'admettre, tandis qu'en supposant avec Neumann et MacCullagh que la densité de l'éther est constante dans tous les corps' (Jamin, 'Note sur la théorie de la réflexion et de la réfraction': 420). For this reason Jamin had adopted the boundary condition and the assumption of equal density in the two media as proposed by MacCullagh and Neumann; see notes (4) and (5), and Number 236 note (9).

any hypothesis about the structure of the medium or any mechanical explanation of electricity or magnetism.[8]

The result is that only transverse disturbances can be propagated and that the velocity is that found by Weber and Kohlrausch[9] which is nearly that of light.[10] This is the velocity with which such slow disturbances as we can make would be propagated. If the same law holds for rapid ones then there is no difference between polarized light and rapid electromagnetic disturbances in one plane.[11]

I have written out so much of the theory as does not involve the conditions at bounding surfaces and will send it to the R.S. in a week.[12]

I am trying to understand the conditions at a surface for reflexion and refraction but they may not be the same for the period of vibration of light and for experiments made at leisure.[13]

We are devising methods to determine this velocity $= \dfrac{\text{electromagnetic}}{\text{electrostatic}}$ unit of electricity.[14] Thomson is going to weigh an electromotive force.[15] Jenkin & I are going to measure the capacity of a conductor both ways[16] and I have a plan of direct equilibrium between an electromagnetic repulsion and electrostatic attraction.[17]

Yours truly
J. C. MAXWELL

---

(8) Hence differing from the physical model employed in Maxwell's paper 'On physical lines of force. Part III. The theory of molecular vortices applied to statical electricity', *Phil. Mag.*, ser. 4, **23** (1862): 12–24 (= *Scientific Papers*, **1**: 489–502). See Maxwell's letters to Faraday and William Thomson of 19 October and 10 December 1861 (Volume I: 683–9, 692–8).

(9) Rudolf Kohlrausch and Wilhelm Weber, 'Elektrodynamische Maassbestimmungen insbesondere Zurückführung der Stromintensitätsmessungen auf mechanisches Maass', *Abhandlungen der Königlichen Sächsischen Gesellschaft der Wissenschaften, math.-phys. Klasse*, **3** (1857): 219–92, esp. 260. See Number 238.

(10) See Maxwell, 'On physical lines of force. Part III': 22 (= *Scientific Papers*, **1**: 500); and 'A dynamical theory of the electromagnetic field', *Phil. Trans.*, **155** (1865): 459–512, esp. 499 (= *Scientific Papers*, **1**: 580).

(11) See Maxwell, 'A dynamical theory of the electromagnetic field': 501–3 (= *Scientific Papers*, **1**: 583–6); and compare Maxwell, *Treatise*, **2**: 392–4 (§§ 794–7).

(12) See Numbers 238 and 239. (13) See Number 236.
(14) See Number 235 note (3).
(15) See the 'Report of the Committee on standards of electrical resistance', *Report of the Thirty-ninth Meeting of the British Association* (London, 1870): 434–8, on 434–6.
(16) See Numbers 233 and 234. (17) See Numbers 235 and 289.

ABSTRACT OF PAPER 'A DYNAMICAL THEORY OF THE ELECTROMAGNETIC FIELD'

[27 OCTOBER 1864][1]

From the *Proceedings of the Royal Society*[2]

A DYNAMICAL THEORY OF THE ELECTROMAGNETIC FIELD[3]

By Professor J. Clerk Maxwell, F.R.S.

Received October 27, 1864

(Abstract)

The proposed Theory seeks for the origin of electromagnetic effects in the medium surrounding the electric or magnetic bodies, and assumes that they act on each other not immediately at a distance, but through the intervention of this medium.

The existence of the medium is assumed as probable, since the investigations of Optics have led philosophers to believe that in such a medium the propagation of light takes place.

The properties attributed to the medium in order to explain the propagation of light are –

1st. That the motion of one part communicates motion to the parts in its neighbourhood.

2nd. That this communication is not instantaneous but progressive, and depends on the elasticity of the medium as compared with its density.

The kind of motion attributed to the medium when transmitting light is that called transverse vibration.

An elastic medium capable of such motions must be also capable of a vast variety of other motions, and its elasticity may be called into play in other ways, some of which may be discoverable by their effects.

One phenomenon which seems to indicate the existence of other motions than those of light in the medium, is that discovered by Faraday, in which the plane of polarization of a ray of light is caused to rotate by the action of

---

(1) The date the paper was received by the Royal Society. The paper was read on 8 December 1864: see note (2). (2) *Proc. Roy. Soc.*, **13** (1864): 531–6.

(3) Published in *Phil. Trans.*, **155** (1865): 459–512 (= *Scientific Papers*, **1**: 526–97). Reporting on the paper in a letter to Stokes of 15 March 1865 (Royal Society, *Referees' Reports*, **5**: 137), William Thomson declared that the paper was 'most decidedly suitable for publication in the Transactions'.

magnetic force.[4] Professor W. Thomson*[5] has shown that this phenomenon cannot be explained without admitting that there is motion of the luminiferous medium in the neighbourhood of magnets and currents.[6]

The phenomena of electromotive force seem also to indicate the elasticity or tenacity of the medium. When the state of the field is being altered by the introduction or motion of currents or magnets, every part of the field experiences a force, which, if the medium in that part of the field is a conductor, produces a current. If the medium is an electrolyte, and the electromotive force is strong enough, the components of the electrolyte are separated in spite of their chemical affinity, and carried in opposite directions. If the medium is a dielectric, all its parts are put into a state of electric polarization, a state in which the opposite sides of every such part are oppositely electrified, and this to an extent proportioned to the intensity of the electromotive force which causes the polarization. If the intensity of this polarization is increased beyond a certain limit, the electric tenacity of the medium gives way, and there is a spark or 'disruptive discharge'.

Thus the action of electromotive force on a dielectric produces an electric displacement within it, and in this way stores up energy which will reappear when the dielectric is relieved from this state of constraint.

A dynamical theory of the Electromagnetic Field must therefore assume that, wherever magnetic effects occur, there is matter in motion, and that, wherever electromotive force is exerted, there is a medium in a state of constraint; so that the medium must be regarded as the recipient of two kinds of energy – the actual energy of the magnetic motion, and the potential energy of the electric displacement.[7] According to this theory we look for the explanation of electric and magnetic phenomena to the mutual actions between the medium and the electrified or magnetic bodies, and not to any direct action between those bodies themselves.

* Proceedings of the Royal Society June 1856 and June 1861.

---

(4) Michael Faraday, 'Experimental researches in electricity. Nineteenth series. On the magnetization of light and the illumination of magnetic lines of force', *Phil. Trans.*, **136** (1846): 1–20 (= *Electricity*, **3**: 1–26).

(5) William Thomson, 'Dynamical illustrations of the magnetic and the heliocoidal rotatory effects of transparent bodies on polarized light', *Proc. Roy. Soc.*, **8** (1856): 150–8; and Thomson, 'On the measurement of electric resistance', *ibid.*, **11** (1861): 313–28, esp. 327n (= *Math. & Phys. Papers*, **5**: 383n).

(6) On Maxwell's theory of the rotation of molecular vortices see Volume I: 692–5.

(7) The terms 'actual energy' and 'potential energy' were introduced by W. J. M. Rankine, 'On the general law of the transformation of energy', *Phil. Mag.*, ser. 4, **5** (1853): 106–17, esp. 106.

In the case of an electric current flowing in a circuit A, we know that the magnetic action at every point of the field depends on its position relative to A, and is proportional to the strength of the current. If there is another circuit B in the field, the magnetic effects due to B are simply added to those due to A, according to the well-known law of composition of forces, velocities, &c. According to our theory, the motion of every part of the medium depends partly on the strength of the current in A, and partly on that in B, and when these are given the whole is determined. The mechanical conditions therefore are those of a system of bodies connected with two driving-points A and B, in which we may determine the relation between the motions of A and B, and the forces acting on them, by purely dynamical principles. It is shown that in this case we may find two quantities, namely, the 'reduced momentum' of the system referred to A and to B, each of which is a linear function of the velocities of A and B. The effect of the force on A is to increase the momentum of the system referred to A, and the effect of the force on B is to increase the momentum referred to B. The simplest mechanical example is that of a rod acted on by two forces perpendicular to its direction at A and at B.[8] Then any change of velocity of A will produce a force at B, unless A and B are mutually centres of suspension and oscillation.

Assuming that the motion of every part of the electromagnetic field is determined by the values of the currents in A and B, it is shown –

1st. That any variation in the strength of A will produce an electromotive force in B.

2nd. That any alteration in the relative position of A and B will produce an electromotive force in B.

3rd. That if currents are maintained in A and B, there will be a mechanical force tending to alter their position relative to each other.

4th. That these electromotive and mechanical forces depend on the value of a single function M, which may be deduced from the form and relative position of A and B, and is of one dimension in space; that is to say, it is a certain number of feet or metres.

The existence of electromotive forces between the circuits A and B was first deduced from the fact of electromagnetic attraction, by Professor Helmholtz*[9] and Professor W. Thomson†[10] by the principle of the Con-

---

* Conservation of Force. Berlin, 1847: translated in Taylor's Scientific Memoirs, Feb. 1853, p. 114.[9]

† Reports of British Association, 1848. Phil. Mag. Dec. 1851.[10]

---

(8) See Number 239 §1.

(9) Hermann Helmholtz, *Über die Erhaltung der Kraft, eine physikalische Abhandlung* (Berlin, 1847); (trans.) 'On the conservation of force', in *Scientific Memoirs, Natural Philosophy*, ed. J. Tyndall and W. Francis (London, 1853): 114–62, esp. 156–8.

(10) William Thomson, 'On the theory of electro-magnetic induction', *Report of the Eighteenth*

servation of Energy.[11] Here the electromagnetic attractions, as well as the forces of induction, are deduced from the fact that every current when established in a circuit has a certain persistency or momentum – that is, it requires the continued action of an unresisted electromotive force in order to alter its value, and that this 'momentum' depends, as in various mechanical problems, on the value of other currents as well as itself. This momentum is what Faraday has called the Electrotonic State of the circuit.[12]

It may be shown from these results, that at every point in the field there is a certain direction possessing the following properties –[13]

A conductor moved in that direction experiences no electromotive force.

A conductor carrying a current experiences a force in a direction perpendicular to this line and to itself.

A circuit of small area carrying a current tends to place itself with its plane perpendicular to this direction.

A system of lines drawn so as everywhere to coincide with the direction having these properties is a system of lines of magnetic force; and if the lines in any one part of their course are so distributed that the number of lines enclosed by any closed curve is proportional to the 'electric momentum' of the field referred to that curve, then the electromagnetic phenomena may be thus stated –

The electric momentum of any closed curve whatever is measured by the number of lines of force which pass through it.

If this number is altered, either by motion of the curve, or motion of the inducing current, or variation in its strength, an electromotive force acts round the curve and is measured by the decrease of the number of lines passing through it in unit of time.

If the curve itself carries a current, then mechanical forces act on it tending to increase the number of lines passing through it, and the work done by these forces is measured by the increase of the number of lines multiplied by the strength of the current.

Meeting of the British Association for the Advancement of Science; held at Swansea in August 1848 (London, 1849), part 2: 9–10 (= *Math. & Phys. Papers*, **1**: 91–2); and Thomson, 'Applications of the principle of mechanical effect to the measurement of electro-motive forces, and of galvanic resistances, in absolute units', *Phil. Mag.*, ser. 4, **2** (1851): 551–62 (= *Math. & Phys. Papers*, **1**: 490–502). (11) See Volume I: 259.

(12) See Faraday, *Electricity*, **1**: 16 (§60), **3**: 420 (§3269). See Number 214 note (9).

(13) For the discussion of lines of force in the electromagnetic field, which follows, compare 'Part II. On Faraday's electro-tonic state' of Maxwell's 'On Faraday's lines of force', *Trans. Camb. Phil. Soc.*, **10** (1856): 27–83 (= *Scientific Papers*, **1**: 155–229). See especially the 'summary of the theory of the electro-tonic state', in 'On Faraday's lines of force': 65–7 (= *Scientific Papers*, **1**: 205–9); and the abstract of the paper (Volume I: 371–5).

A method is then given by which the coefficient of self-induction of any circuit can be determined by means of Wheatstone's electric balance.[14]

The next part of the paper is devoted to the mathematical expression of the electromagnetic quantities referred to each point in the field, and to the establishment of the general equations of the electromagnetic field, which express the relations among these quantities.

The quantities which enter into these equations are – Electric currents by conduction, electric displacements, and Total Currents; Magnetic forces, Electromotive forces, and Electromagnetic Momenta. Each of these quantities being a directed quantity, has three components; and besides these we have two others, the Free Electricity and the Electric Potential, making twenty quantities in all.

There are twenty equations between these quantities, namely Equations of Total Currents, of Magnetic Force, of Electric Currents, of Electromotive Force, of Electric Elasticity, and of Electric Resistance, making six sets of three equations, together with one equation of Free Electricity, and another of Electric Continuity.

These equations are founded on the facts of the induction of currents as investigated by Faraday,[15] Felici,[16] &c., on the action of currents on a magnet as discovered by Oersted,[17] and on the polarization of dielectrics by electromotive force as discovered by Faraday[18] and mathematically developed by Mossotti.[19]

An expression is then found for the intrinsic energy of any part of the field, depending partly on its magnetic, and partly on its electric polarization.

From this the laws of the forces acting between magnetic poles and between electrified bodies are deduced, and it is shown that the state of constraint due

---

(14) See Number 230, esp. note (4).

(15) Michael Faraday, 'Experimental researches in electricity. First series. On the induction of electric currents...', *Phil. Trans.*, **122** (1832): 125–62 (= *Electricity*, **1**: 1–41); Faraday, 'Experimental researches in electricity. Ninth series. On the influence, by induction of an electric current on itself: and on the inductive action of electric currents generally', *Phil. Trans.*, **125** (1835): 41–56 (= *Electricity*, **1**: 322–43).

(16) Riccardo Felici, 'Mémoire sur l'induction électrodynamique', *Ann. Chim. Phys.*, ser. 3, **34** (1852): 64–77.

(17) H. C. Oersted, *Experimenta circum Effectum Conflictus Electrici in Acum Magneticam* (Copenhagen, 1820).

(18) Michael Faraday, 'Experimental researches in electricity. Eleventh series. On induction', *Phil. Trans.*, **128** (1838): 1–40, 79–81 (= *Electricity*, **1**: 360–416).

(19) O. F. Mossotti, 'Discussione analitica sull' influenza che l'azione di un mezzo dielettrico ha sulla distribuzione dell' elettricità alla superfizie di più corpi elettrici disemminati in esso', *Memorie di Matematica e di Fisica della Società Italiana delle Scienze* (Modena), **24** (1850): 49–74.

to the polarization of the field is such as to act on the bodies according to the well-known experimental laws.

It is also shown in a note that, if we look for the explanation of the force of gravitation in the action of a surrounding medium, the constitution of the medium must be such that, when far from the presence of gross matter, it has immense intrinsic energy, part of which is removed from it wherever we find the signs of gravitating force. This result does not encourage us to look in this direction for the explanation of the force of gravity.[20]

The relation which subsists between the electromagnetic and the electrostatic system of units is then investigated, and shown to depend upon what we have called the Electric Elasticity of the medium in which the experiments are made (i.e. common air). Other media, as glass, shellac, and sulphur have different powers as dielectrics; and some of them exhibit the phenomena of electric absorption and residual discharge.

It is then shown how a compound condenser of different materials may be constructed which shall exhibit these phenomena, and it is proved that the result will be the same though the different substances were so intimately intermingled that the want of uniformity could not be detected.

The general equations are then applied to the foundation of the Electromagnetic Theory of Light.

Faraday, in his 'Thoughts on Ray Vibrations'*,[21] has described the effect of the sudden movement of a magnetic or electric body, and the propagation of the disturbance through the field, and has stated his opinion that such a disturbance must be entirely transverse to the direction of propagation. In 1846 there were no data to calculate the mathematical laws of such propagation, or to determine the velocity.

The equations of this paper, however, show that transverse disturbances, and transverse disturbances only, will be propagated through the field, and that the number which expresses the velocity of propagation must be the same as that which expresses the number of electrostatic units of electricity in one electromagnetic unit, the standards of space and time being the same.

The first of these results agrees, as is well known, with the undulatory

---

* Phil. Mag. 1846. Experimental Researches, vol. iii. p. 447.[21]

---

(20) Compare Maxwell's discussion of gravity in his letters to Faraday of 9 November 1857 (Volume I: 550), to George Phillips Bond of 25 August 1863 (Number 217), and to William Huggins of 13 October 1868 (Number 309).

(21) Michael Faraday, 'Thoughts on ray-vibrations', *Phil. Mag.*, ser. 3, **28** (1846): 345–50 (= *Electricity*, **3**: 447–52). On Faraday's statement, in his letter to Maxwell of 25 March 1857 (*Life of Maxwell*: 519–20), of his intention to 'make some experiments on the time of magnetic action' see Volume I: 686n.

theory of light as deduced from optical experiments. The second may be judged of by a comparison of the electromagnetical experiments of Weber and Kohlrausch[22] with the velocity of light as determined by astronomers in the heavenly spaces, and by M. Foucault in the air of his laboratory.

Electrostatic units in an electro-magnetic unit	310,740,000 metres per second.[23]
Velocity of light as found by M. Fizeau	314,858,000.[24]
Velocity of light by M. Foucault	298,000,000.[25]
Velocity of light deduced from aberration	308,000,000.[26]

At the outset of the paper, the dynamical theory of the electromagnetic field borrowed from the undulatory theory of light the use of its luminiferous medium. It now restores the medium, after having tested its powers of transmitting undulations, and the character of those undulations, and certifies that the vibrations are transverse, and that the velocity is that of light. With regard to normal vibrations, the electromagnetic theory does not allow of their transmission.

What, then, is light according to the electromagnetic theory? It consists of alternate and opposite rapidly recurring transverse magnetic disturbances, accompanied with electric displacements, the direction of the electric displacement being at right angles to the magnetic disturbance, and both at right angles to the direction of the ray.

The theory does not attempt to give a mechanical explanation of the nature of magnetic disturbance or of electric displacement, it only asserts the identity of these phenomena, as observed at our leisure in magnetic and electric experiments, with what occurs in the rapid vibrations of light, in a portion of time inconceivably minute.

This paper is already too long to follow out the application of the electromagnetic theory to the different phenomena already explained by the

---

(22) Rudolf Kohlrausch and W. Weber, 'Elektrodynamische Maassbestimmungen insbesondere Zurückführung der Stromintensitätsmessungen auf mechanisches Maass', *Abhandlungen der Königlichen Sächsischen Gesellschaft der Wissenschaften, math.-phys. Klasse*, **3** (1857): 219–92 (= *Wilhelm Weber's Werke*, 6 vols. (Berlin, 1892–4), **3**: 609–76).

(23) Kohlrausch and Weber, 'Elektrodynamische Maassbestimmungen': 260. See Volume I: 685, 695; and Number 218 note (7).

(24) Hippolyte Fizeau, 'Sur une expérience relative à la vitesse de propagation de la lumière', *Comptes Rendus*, **29** (1849): 90–2.

(25) Léon Foucault, 'Détermination expérimentale de la vitesse de la lumière; parallaxe du soleil', *Comptes Rendus*, **55** (1862): 501–3, esp. 502.

(26) Foucault, 'Détermination expérimentale de la vitesse de la lumière': 502.

undulatory theory. It discloses a relation between the inductive capacity of a dielectric and its index of refraction. The theory of double refraction in crystals is expressed very simply in terms of the electromagnetic theory. The non-existence of normal vibrations and the ordinary refraction of rays polarized in a principal plane are shown to be capable of explanation; but the verification of the theory is difficult at present, for want of accurate data concerning the dielectric capacity of crystals in different directions.

The propagation of vibrations in a conducting medium is then considered, and it is shown that the light is absorbed at a rate depending on the conducting-power of the medium. This result is so far confirmed by the opacity of all good conductors, but the transparency of electrolytes shows that in certain cases vibrations of short period and amplitude are not absorbed as those of long period would be.

The transparency of thin leaves of gold, silver, and platinum cannot be explained without some such hypothesis.[27]

The actual value of the maximum electromotive force which is called into play during the vibrations of strong sunlight is calculated from Pouillet's data,[28] and found to be about 60,000,000, or about 600 Daniell's cells per metre.[29]

The maximum magnetic force during such vibrations is .193, or about $\frac{1}{10}$ of the horizontal magnetic force at London.

Methods are then given for applying the general equations to the calculation of the coefficient of mutual induction of two circuits, and in particular of two circles the distance of whose circumferences is small compared with the radius of either.

The coefficient of self-induction of a coil of rectangular section is found and applied to the case of the coil used by the Committee of the British Association on Electrical Standards. The results of calculation are compared with the value deduced from a comparison of experiments in which this coefficient enters as a correction, and also with the results of direct experiments with the electric balance.

---

(27) See Number 239 §7.

(28) C. S. M. Pouillet, 'Mémoire sur la chaleur solaire, sur les pouvoirs rayonnants et absorbants de l'air atmosphérique, et sur la température de l'espace', *Comptes Rendus*, **7** (1838): 24–65; (trans.) 'Memoir on the solar heat, on the radiating and absorbing powers of the atmospheric air, and on the temperature of space', in *Scientific Memoirs*, ed. R. Taylor, **4** (London, 1846): 44–90, esp. 79. See William Thomson, 'On the mechanical energies of the solar system', *Trans. Roy. Soc. Edinb.*, **21** (1854): 63–80, esp. 66 (= *Maths. & Phys. Papers*, **2**: 6), where Thomson uses Pouillet's data to calculate the energy of sunlight at the earth's surface.

(29) On Daniell's cell see Number 235 note (11).

CANCELLED PASSAGES IN THE MANUSCRIPT AND PROOFS OF 'A DYNAMICAL THEORY OF THE ELECTROMAGNETIC FIELD'[1]

OCTOBER 1864[2]

From the originals in the Libraries of the Royal Society, London and The Johns Hopkins University[3]

[1. Passage deleted in the manuscript from §23 on the 'Mutual action of two currents':][4]

As a dynamical illustration suppose two horses harnessed to a carriage by the intervention of a lever so that each horse pulls at its own arm of the lever while the lever is attached to the carriage by its fulcrum. Then if one horse increases its speed the immediate effect will be to produce a tension in the traces of the other horse tending to pull him back.

[2. Passage deleted in the manuscript from §34 on the 'Mechanical action between conductors', concerning the explication of the relations between electric currents 'by mechanical reasoning':][5]

[...] all such considerations and confine myself to the solution of problems on the mutual action of currents, the experimental determination of coefficients of induction, and the calculation of these coefficients from the known form of the circuit.

---

(1) J. Clerk Maxwell, 'A dynamical theory of the electromagnetic field', *Phil. Trans.*, **155** (1865): 459–512 (= *Scientific Papers*, **1**: 526–97).

(2) The paper was received by the Royal Society on 27 October 1864: see Number 238. The proofs are dated 10 August 1865.

(3) The MS is in Royal Society, PT. 72.7. The proofs are in the Stokes Collection, Electromagnetism volume 1, QC 760 E3, Eisenhower Library, The Johns Hopkins University, Baltimore.

(4) See 'A dynamical theory of the electromagnetic field': 467 (= *Scientific Papers*, **1**: 537).

(5) See 'A dynamical theory of the electromagnetic field': 471 (= *Scientific Papers*, **1**: 542).

[3. Passage deleted in the manuscript from §55, on 'Electrical displacements (f, g, h)':][6]

Electrical quantity (e)

Let e represent the quantity of free electricity in unit of volume (either positive or negative) then the equation of continuity[7] is

$$e + \frac{df}{dx} + \frac{dg}{dy} + \frac{dh}{dz} = 0.$$

[4. Passage deleted in the manuscript from §81, on the 'Measurement of electrostatic effects':][8]

The quantity E which denotes the number of electrostatic units of electricity which are contained in the electromagnetic unit in Webers system of electrical measurements is a velocity which as determined by Weber and Kohlrausch[9] is

310 740 kilometers per second

195 647 miles per second.[10]

This quantity determines according to our theory what we have called k the electric elasticity of the medium, by the equation

$$k = 4\pi E^2.\text{[11]}$$

As the value of E is of great importance in electrical science the Committee of the British Association on Electric Standards are making arrangements for a new determination of it.[12]

---

(6) See 'A dynamical theory of the electromagnetic field': 480 (= *Scientific Papers*, **1**: 554). The passage is transferred (in revised form) to §68 of the paper; see 'A dynamical theory of the electromagnetic field': 485 (= *Scientific Papers*, **1**: 561).

(7) This equation is termed, in §68 of the paper, the 'equation of free electricity'; on the significance of the sign in the equation for e, see Daniel M. Siegel, *Innovation in Maxwell's Electromagnetic Theory* (Cambridge, 1991): 149–50.

(8) See 'A dynamical theory of the electromagnetic field': 492 (= *Scientific Papers*, **1**: 570).

(9) See Number 238 notes (22) and (23).

(10) In 'On physical lines of force. Part III. The theory of molecular vortices applied to statical electricity', *Phil. Mag.*, ser. 4, **23** (1862): 12–24, esp. 22 (= *Scientific Papers*, **1**: 499–500) Maxwell gives 193,088 miles per second as the equivalent of Kohlrausch and Weber's metric value, and calculates Fizeau's value of the velocity of light as 195,647 miles per second. See Volume I: 695.

(11) See 'A dynamical theory of the electromagnetic field': 491 (= *Scientific Papers*, **1**: 569); and Number 231.

(12) See Number 237 esp. notes (15) to (17).

[5. Final paragraph in §99 on the propagation of transverse vibrations, which was amended in proof:][13]

Hence J is either zero or it continually increases or diminishes with the time, if e remains constant, which no physical quantity can do. Hence J is zero and the only disturbance propagated is that indicated by F', G', H'[14] which is wholly transversal.

[An additional passage on the verso of the manuscript is cancelled in pencil:]

Differentiating these three equations with respect to x y & z respectively and adding we find that the first terms destroy each other leaving

$$\frac{d^2 J}{dt^2} + \frac{d}{dt}\nabla^2 \psi = 0.\text{[15]}$$

[6. Passage deleted in the manuscript at end of §102 on the 'Propagation of electromagnetic disturbances in a crystallised medium':][16]

[...] and that (as in the case of an isotropic medium) the terms including ψ have nothing to do with the result.

---

(13) See 'A dynamical theory of the electromagnetic field': 500 (= *Scientific Papers*, **1**: 582) for Maxwell's revision: 'Since the medium is a perfect insulator, e, the free electricity is immoveable, and therefore dJ/dt is a function of x, y, z, and the value of J is either constant or zero, or uniformly increasing or diminishing with the time; so that no disturbance depending on J can be propagated as a wave.' Here $J = dF/dx + dG/dy + dH/dz$, where F, G, H are the components of the electro-tonic state (electromagnetic momentum); see 'A dynamical theory of the electromagnetic field': 497 (= *Scientific Papers*, **1**: 578). His concern here is to obtain a condition for the propagation of transverse electromagnetic waves. The question of transverse and longitudinal vibrations in dynamical theories of the optical ether had been recently discussed by G. G. Stokes, 'Report on double refraction', *Report of the Thirty-second Meeting of the British Association* (London, 1863): 253–82 (= *Papers*, **4**: 157–202). Compare the alternative form of the argument presented in the *Treatise*, **2**: 385 (§783).

(14) Maxwell wrote $F' = F - d\chi/dt, \ldots$ and $\nabla^2 \chi = J$; see 'A dynamical theory of the electromagnetic field': 500 (= *Scientific Papers*, **1**: 581).

(15) Maxwell writes $\nabla^2 = d^2/dx^2 + d^2/dy^2 + d^2/dz^2$; see 'A dynamical theory of the electromagnetic field': 497 (= *Scientific Papers*, **1**: 578). For this usage see William Thomson, 'Dynamical problems regarding elastic spheroidal shells and spheroids of incompressible liquid', *Phil. Trans.*, **153** (1863): 583–616, esp. 583 (= *Math. & Phys. Papers*, **3**: 351–94). ψ is the electric potential.

(16) See 'A dynamical theory of the electromagnetic field': 501 (= *Scientific Papers*, **1**: 583).

[7. Part of the final paragraph of §107 on transparent solid bodies, which was amended in proof:][17]

[...] experiment, the amount of light which passes through a thickness of $\frac{1}{282000}$ inch would be only 10^{-300} of the incident light, a totally imperceptible quantity. I find that between $\frac{1}{500}$ and $\frac{1}{900}$ of green light gets through such gold leaf.

[8. Following §115 on the determination of the coefficient of self-induction of a coil of wire (L), a passage on the verso of the manuscript is cancelled in pencil:][18]

Hence the total counter current in each element

$$\frac{1}{\rho}(T_\infty - T_0) - \frac{\mu\pi}{\rho^2} P r^2.{}^{(19)}$$

Integrating over the section of the wire from $r = 0$ to $r = r$

$$\frac{1}{\rho}(T_\infty - T_0)\pi r^2 + \frac{\mu\pi}{\rho^2}\frac{P\pi r^4}{2}$$

or since $\dfrac{P}{\rho} = p$ and if C be the total current $C = \pi r^2 p$ the second term becomes

$$\frac{1}{2}\frac{\mu\pi}{\rho} C r^2.$$

Now if p instead of being variable from the centre to the circumference of the wire had been uniform at every instant throughout the section the second term would have been

$$\frac{3}{4}\frac{\mu\pi}{\rho} C r^2.$$

Now the counter current is $\dfrac{L}{R}C.$

---

(17) See 'A dynamical theory of the electromagnetic field': 504–5 (= *Scientific Papers*, **1**: 587) for the revision: '[...] make experiments, the amount of light which passes through a piece of gold-leaf, of which the resistance was determined by Mr. C. Hockin, would be only 10^{-50} of the incident light, a totally imperceptible quality. I find that between 1/500 and 1/1000 of green light gets through such gold-leaf'. See Number 235 esp. note (27).

(18) See 'A dynamical theory of the electromagnetic field': 510–11 (= *Scientific Papers*, **1**: 595–6).

(19) P is the electromotive force in a cylindrical wire of specific resistance ρ, μ is the coefficient of magnetic induction, T is a function of the time, and r is the distance from the axis of the cylinder.

Hence the correction to be applied on account of the current being variable is

$$-\frac{1}{4} \text{ per unit length.}^{(20)}$$

(20) Compare Maxwell's letter to Thomson of 11 September 1863 (Number 219, esp. note (4)).

240

FROM A LETTER TO CHARLES HOPE CAY[1]

5 JANUARY 1865

From Campbell and Garnett, *Life of Maxwell*[2]

Glenlair
5 January 1865

The Manse of Corsock is now finished;[3] it is near the river, not far from the deep pool where we used to bathe.

I set Prof. W. Thomson a prop. which I had been working with for a long time. He sent me 18 pages of letter of suggestions about it, none of which would work; but on Jan 3, in the railway from Largs, he got the way to it, which is all right; so we are jolly, having stormed the citadel, when we only hoped to sap it by approximations.[4]

The prop. was to draw a set of lines like this so that the ultimate reticulations shall all be squares.[5]

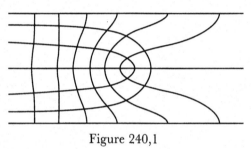

Figure 240,1

The solution is exact, but rather stiff. Now I have a disc A hung by a wire D, between two discs B, C, the interval being occupied by air, hydrogen, carbonic acid, etc., the friction of which gradually brings A to rest. In order to calculate the thickdom or viscosity of the gas, I require to solve the problem above mentioned, which is now done, and I have the apparatus now ready to begin.[6] We are also intent on electrical measurements, and are getting up apparatus, and have made sets of wires of alloy of platinum and silver, which

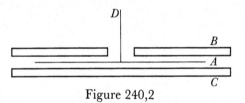

Figure 240,2

---

(1) Maxwell's cousin (son of Robert Cay), Caius 1860, 6th wrangler 1864, Fellow 1865-9 (Venn); see *Life of Maxwell*: 315, 324, 343-4.

(2) *Life of Maxwell*: 341-2; abridged.   (3) See Number 216 esp. note (3).

(4) See also Number 303. The problem arose in the mathematical theory of Maxwell's experiments on gas viscosity; see Maxwell, 'On the viscosity or internal friction of air and other gases', *Phil. Trans.* **156** (1866): 249-68, esp. 261-2 (= *Scientific Papers*, **2**: 16-17).

(5) Compare Fig. 9 of 'On the viscosity or internal friction of air and other gases': Plate XXI (= *Scientific Papers*, **2**: Plate IX).   (6) See Numbers 244, 245 and 246.

are to be sent all abroad as standards of resistance.[7] I have also a paper afloat, with an electromagnetic theory of light, which, till I am convinced to the contrary, I hold to be great guns.[8]

Spice[9] is becoming first-rate: she is the principal patient under the ophthalmoscope,[10] and turns her eyes at command, so as to show the tapetum, the optic nerve, or any required part. Dr. Bowman, the great oculist,[11] came to see the sight, and when we were out of town he came again and brought Donders of Utrecht[12] with him to visit Spice.

---

(7) See the 'Report of the Committee on standards of electrical resistance', *Report of the Thirty-fifth Meeting of the British Association...in September 1865* (London, 1866): 308–13.

(8) See Numbers 238 and 239.

(9) A dog.

(10) On Maxwell's construction of an ophthalmoscope, based on the instrument devised by Helmholtz, and his use of it in 1854–5 to study dogs' eyes, see Volume I: 250, 304, 308, 315.

(11) William Bowman, Surgeon to the Royal London Ophthalmic Hospital, 'among the first to become expert' in the use of the ophthalmoscope (*DNB*): see *Proc. Roy. Soc.*, **52** (1893): i–vii.

(12) Franciscus Cornelis Donders; see Bowman's obituary notice in *Proc. Roy. Soc.*, **49** (1891): vii–xxiv.

NOTES ON THE DETERMINATION OF THE NUMBER OF ELECTROSTATIC UNITS IN ONE ELECTROMAGNETIC UNIT OF ELECTRICITY

circa FEBRUARY 1865[1]

From the original in the University Library, Cambridge[2]

[1] DETERMINATION OF v BY WIPPE[3]

B = resistance of Battery
Electromotive force of d° = F.
P, Q, R resistance coils,
G = resistance of galvanometer.
$KHLM$ potentials of these points
C = capacity of condenser.

Exterior of condenser always connected with H, Interior alternately with K & L.

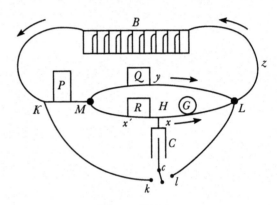

Figure 241,1

1st   When C is in equilibrium let x be the current through G then

$$M-L = (R+G)\,x = Q\,y$$

$$K-M = P(x+y) = P\left(1+\frac{R+G}{Q}\right)x$$

$$\therefore K-L = \left(P+R+G+\frac{P}{Q}(R+G)\right)x.$$

2nd   When c after touching k leaves it and goes to l it discharges through lL a quantity of electricity $= C(K-L)$ which returns to H in various ways.
1st   direct through G 2nd through Q and R 3rd through B, P and R.
Hence the discharge through G

$$= X_1 = -C(K-L)\left\{1-\frac{(B+P)\,G+GQ}{(B+P+R)\,Q+(B+P)\,(R+G)+GQ}\right\}.$$

---

(1) See Maxwell's letters to William Thomson of 15 October 1864 and 25 February 1865 (Numbers 235 and 242).   (2) ULC Add. MSS 7655, V, c/14 (iii).

(3) Commutator (see Number 234 note (4)). This MS is discussed and reproduced in facsimile by I. B. Hopley, 'Maxwell's determination of the number of electrostatic units in one electromagnetic unit of electricity', *Annals of Science*, **15** (1959): 91–108, esp. 105–8.

3rd When c after touching l leaves it and goes to k it discharges through kK a quantity of electricity $= -C(K-L)$ which returns to H.

1st by P and R,   2nd by $P\ Q$ & G 3rd by B and G.

The discharge through G is

$$X_2 = C(K-L)\left\{\frac{R(P+B)+Q(P+R)}{(P+B)R+Q(P+R+B+G)+B(R+G)}\right\}.^{(4)}$$

The total discharge through G when c makes a double oscillation is X_1+X_2. If this takes place in time t and if the total current in $G = \xi^{(5)}$

$$\xi = x\left\{1-\frac{C}{t}\left\{P+(R+G)\left(1+\frac{P}{Q}\right)\right\}\right\}\left\{1-\frac{(P+Q+B)G}{(P+B)(R+G)+Q(P+R+G+B)}\right.$$
$$\left.-\frac{R(P+B)+Q(P+R)}{(P+B)R+B(R+G)+Q(P+R+B+Q)}^{(6)}\right\}.$$

[2]   THOMSONS PLAN. DOUBLE WIPPE.[7]

e and f go simultaneously to right and left when connected to

h & l difference of potentials

$$H-L = -GX$$

λ & k

$$L-M = \left(\frac{(G+R)(P+Q)+P}{Q}\right)x$$

1st   motion left to right. Quantity discharged $= C(H-L-\overline{L-K})$

$$= -C\left(2G+R+(G+R)\frac{P}{Q}+P\right)x.$$

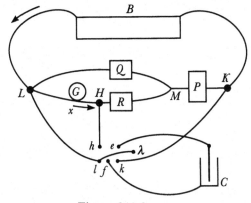

Figure 241,2

The discharge is from L to K through three conductors $G+R+P$, $Q+P$ and B.

---

(4) The denominator should read: $Q(P+R+B+Q)+(B+P)(R+G)$.

(5) From the galvanometer reading C may be determined in electromagnetic units. From a determination of C in electrostatic units the value of v may be obtained.

(6) The denominator should read: $Q(P+R+B+Q)+(B+P)(R+G)$.

(7) See Number 242.

The proportion through G is $\dfrac{1}{1+\dfrac{G+R}{Q}+\dfrac{P}{B}\dfrac{Q+G+R}{Q}}$

$= \dfrac{BQ}{(B+P)(Q+G+R)+Q(G+R)}.$

2nd motion right to left. Discharge $= C(L-K-\overline{H-L})$

$= C\left(2G+R+P+(G+R)\dfrac{P}{Q}\right)x.$

This discharge is from H to L.

Proportion through $G = 1 - \dfrac{G}{G+R+\dfrac{(P+B)Q}{P+B+Q}}$

Total discharge through G in a complete double vibration

$-C\left(2G+R+P+(G+R)\dfrac{P}{Q}\right)x\left\{1-\dfrac{G(P+B+Q)}{(G+R)(P+B+Q)+(P+B)Q}\right.$

$\left.+\dfrac{BQ}{(B+P)(Q+G+R)+Q(G+P)}\right\}$

$= -Cx\left(2G+P+R+(G+R)\dfrac{P}{Q}\right)\left\{1+\dfrac{B(Q-G)-G(P+Q)}{B(Q+G+R)+(P+Q)(G+R)+PQ}\right\}.$

The condition of B disappearing is $\dfrac{G-Q}{Q+G+R} = \dfrac{G(P+Q)}{(P+Q)(G+R)+PQ}$

whence $P(Q+G+R)+Q(2G+R) = 0$.

This cannot be fulfilled but by making P much greater than Q R or G its effect is insignificant.

Let $G:Q:R:P::1:10:10:100$ the fraction becomes

$$1 - \dfrac{110+9B}{110\times 11+1100+21B}.$$

242

LETTER TO WILLIAM THOMSON

25 FEBRUARY 1865

From the original in the University Library, Glasgow[1]

8 Palace Gardens Terrace
1865 Feb 25

Dear Thomson

I have been considering the comparison of capacities of condensers by means of an electro*scope* instead of an electro*meter*. (Of course a delicate electrometer is an electroscope too.)[2] I have devised an instrument for exchanging electricity in various forms, and I want to know if you have either a plan or an actual machine before I set it to be made.

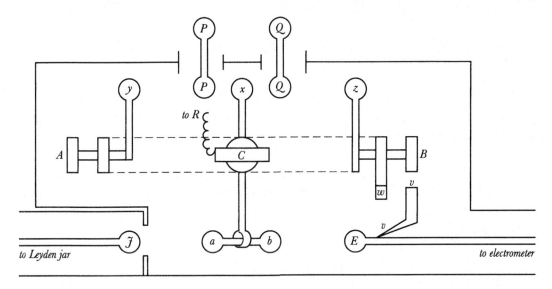

Figure 242,1. Handle is in front. R is below P connected with C. S is below Q a knob on the box.

J Leyden jar E electrometer Electrodes
$PQRS$ the four conductors of 2 condensers all at the back of the box.
ABC a sector centred at the bottom & working between 2 stops about $\frac{5}{8}$ inch plug.

---

(1) Glasgow University Library, Kelvin Papers, M 18.
(2) Compare Maxwell's comments in the *Treatise*, **1**: 262–3 (§214); and see William Thomson, 'Report on electrometers and electrostatic measurements', in 'Report of the committee on standards of electrical resistance', *Report of the Thirty-seventh Meeting of the British Association* (London, 1868): 489–512, esp. 489 (= *Electrostatics and Magnetism*: 260–86).

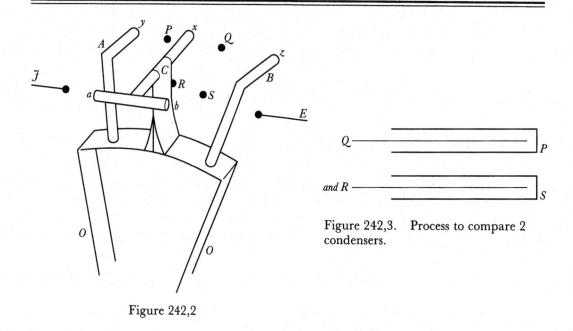

Figure 242,3. Process to compare 2 condensers.

Figure 242,2

It carries the T shaped metal $x\,a\,b$ on the vulcanite arm C which has a slight spring also Ay and Bz metal springs connected with the ground.

R is always connected to x and S to ground

v is a crank which touches E and keeps it to earth till wanted.

1st Put sector hard up to left. z touches Q and x touches P and a is twisted round till it touches J.

This makes $P = R = J$, $Q = S = 0$.

2nd Move to right slightly. a leaves J but x and z still touch P and Q.

$$P = R \text{ insulated} \quad Q = S = 0.$$

3 More to right x and z leave P and Q

$$P\,Q \text{ and } R \text{ all separately insulated.}$$

4 More to right y touches P and

$$P = 0.$$

5 More to right x touches Q and connects R & Q W lifts v from x

$$R = Q, \quad P = 0 \quad S = 0, \quad E \text{ insulated.}$$

6 Hard up to right b touches E and discharges $R + Q$ to electrometer.

$$R = Q = E \quad P = 0, \quad S = 0.$$

If $E = 0$ then the capacities are equal of R+electrode x, a, b and Q+electrode Q.

So much for the comparison of equal condensers. I think you said you had a machine for it if not I will get one made.

I think your disc is about 4 inches diameter in the condenser with micrometer screw.[3]

The micrometer will act well in measuring distances from $\frac{1}{4}$ to $\frac{1}{2}$ inch or for capacities from 4 to 2 inches. If the diameter of each plate of the great condenser is 8 inches and distance about $\frac{1}{20}$ inch the capacity of each pair of surfaces will be 80 inches or for 2 pair 160 inches.

I would therefore make a set of condensers equal respectively to 2, 4, 8, 16, 32, 64, 128, inches, roughly estimated thus.

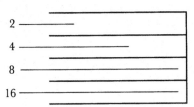

Figure 242,4

These are all to consist of brass plates in a brass vessel insulated by small discs or pillars of vulcanite or glass. The first two can be measured directly by the micrometrical condenser. The others by combining the micrometer condenser with the smaller condensers of the series.

The great condenser is to consist of a series each of which = 160 inches or thereby and can be measured separately in this way. 25 pairs would give about 100 metres capacity which is a very good quantity for the exp^t.

I wrote you a plan of the wippe exp^t about January which I now see to be all wrong because of the double discharge. I now see we must use a double wippe, if the discharge is to go through the same wire as the constant current. So we must either have double wippe or double galvanometer coil as I

---

(3) Thomson's guard-ring modification to the attracted disc electrometer (see Number 289 note (11)), which Maxwell employed in his measurement of the ratio of electromagnetic and electrostatic units: see his letter to Thomson of 15 October 1864 (Number 235); and his drawing of the torsion balance for the experiment, dated 1 March 1865 (Number 243).

proposed at first.⁽⁴⁾ The latter is the simplest mechanically but the former I most approve.

Jenkin has done nothing towards the electro dynamometer for you & Joule as yet.⁽⁵⁾ We have the experimental coil still in existence and accurately measured.⁽⁶⁾ Now you want a more compact and sensitive instrument than our proposed great one so I think we should make the instrument on a smallish scale, say great coils 4 inches radius small coils about 1 inch radius and determine their true coefficients by galvanometric comparison with the King's College Coils – thus.

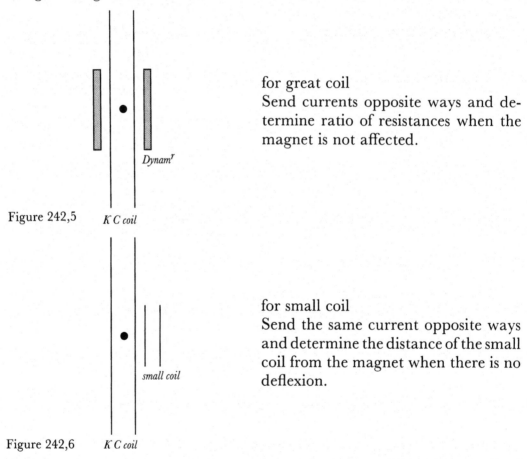

for great coil
Send currents opposite ways and determine ratio of resistances when the magnet is not affected.

Figure 242,5   K C coil

for small coil
Send the same current opposite ways and determine the distance of the small coil from the magnet when there is no deflexion.

Figure 242,6   K C coil

---

(4) See Number 241, and the experimental arrangement described by Maxwell in his letter to Thomson of 27 September 1864 (Number 234).

(5) See the 'Report of the committee on standards of electrical resistance', *Report of the Thirty-seventh Meeting of the British Association*: 479; and J. P. Joule, 'Determination of the dynamical equivalent of heat from the thermal effects of electric currents', *ibid.*: 512. See also the *Treatise*, 2: 332–3 (§726).

(6) The experimental coils used in the British Association measurements of electrical resistance (at King's College, London) in 1863 and 1864: see Numbers 210 note (2) and 222 note (3).

I am reading Webers expts with Dynam^r⁽⁷⁾ and will have a little more experience presently. Gassiot⁽⁸⁾ has a dynam^r of Webers construction wh: is at present with Robinson, Armagh.⁽⁹⁾ Gassiot has also 2000 cells of sulphate of mercury⁽¹⁰⁾ which are doing very well and Matthiessen is to make him a tellurium resistance and measure it.⁽¹¹⁾

Gassiot says he will be delighted to let you measure his electromotive force by electrometer or dynam^r.

How do you get on with your electrometer balance?⁽¹²⁾ If you can work it with the dynamometer well and good, otherwise I am game to construct a special electrometer and dynamometer combined in which the electric attraction of 2 discs is balanced by the electromagnetic repulsion of two coils.

AA' suspended discs at potential 0
BB' fixed large discs at potential F
aa' rings surrounding AA' at 0
coils in A and B' +^{ve} A' and B −^{ve}
∴ no terrestrial directive action⁽¹³⁾

$$R = \text{resistance} \quad \text{current} = \frac{F}{R}$$

R to be altered till there is no deflexion for a certain distance AB or $A'B'$ or these distances are to be altered R remaining.

---

(7) Wilhelm Weber, 'Elektrodynamische Maassbestimmungen', *Ann. Phys.*, **73** (1848): 193–240, figs. facing 336; (trans.) 'On the measurement of electrodynamic forces', *Scientific Memoirs*, ed. R. Taylor, **5** (London, 1852): 489–529. Weber gave a full account of his experiments with the electrodynamometer in his 'Elektrodynamische Maassbestimmungen, über ein allgemeines Grundgesetz der elektrischen Wirkung', *Abhandlungen der Königlichen Sächsischen Gesellschaft der Wissenschaften* (1846): 211–378 (= *Wilhelm Weber's Werke*, 6 vols. (Berlin, 1892–4), **3**: 25–214). See Maxwell's account in the *Treatise*, **2**: 328–9 (§725).

(8) John Peter Gassiot, a researcher in electricity; see his 'A description of an extensive series of the water battery', *Phil. Trans.*, **134** (1844): 39–52.

(9) See Number 198 note (3).

(10) Compare the battery of Gassiot's used by Maxwell in his 1868 determination of the ratio of electrical units: see Number 289.

(11) Augustus Matthiessen: see Number 245. See A. Matthiessen and M. von Bose, 'On the influence of temperature on the electric conducting power of metals', *Phil. Trans.*, **152** (1862): 1–27, on 20–2.

(12) See Thomson's account of attracted disc electrometers in his 'Report on electrometers and electrostatic measurements', *Report of the Thirty-seventh Meeting of the British Association*: 497–509.

(13) Compare Number 243 note (2).

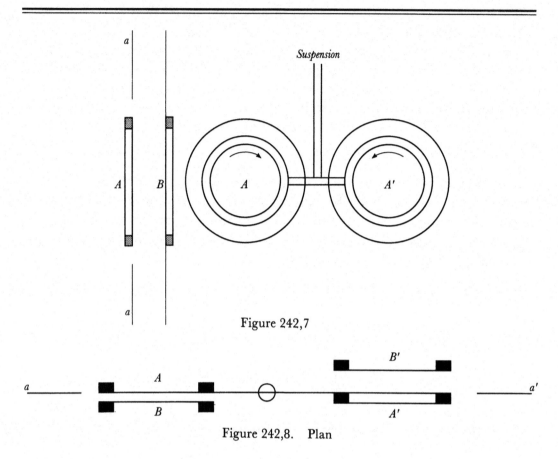

Figure 242,7

Figure 242,8. Plan

Optical devices to ascertain the position of A & A' at once during experiments.

I have had what Sharpey[14] calls an implosion of my gas apparatus due to external pressure.[15] It is now remade stronger and will be ready soon.

I hope the Peelers[16] will have more distinct views in future as to the nature of their duties, and the necessity of concocting evidence with a view to its being compared with that of persons not belonging to the force.

I remain
Yours truly
J. CLERK MAXWELL

---

(14) See Number 197 note (1).   (15) See also Number 244.
(16) Officers of the Metropolitan Police established by Sir Robert Peel, as Home Secretary, in 1829.

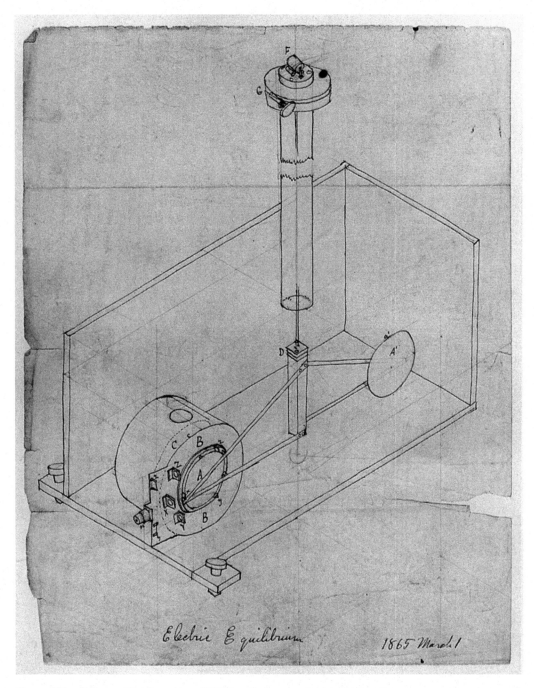

Plate III. Maxwell's drawing (1865) of the torsion balance for an experiment on the determination of the ratio of the electrostatic to the electromagnetic unit of electricity (Number 243).

=243=

TORSION BALANCE TO COMPARE AN ELECTROSTATIC ATTRACTION WITH AN ELECTROMAGNETIC REPULSION

1 MARCH 1865

From the original in the University Library, Cambridge[1]

ELECTRIC EQUILIBRIUM[2] 1865 MARCH 1

---

(1) ULC Add. MSS 7655, V, c/14 (i), Previously published by I. B. Hopley in *Annals of Science*, **15** (1959): plate facing 104 (see Number 241 note (3)).

(2) Plate III. The torsion balance for Maxwell's experiment on the determination of the ratio of the electrostatic and electromagnetic units of electricity, by observing the equilibrium between the electrostatic attraction of two discs and the electromagnetic repulsion of two coils. See his letter to William Thomson of 15 October 1864 (Number 235 esp. note (3)); and his paper 'On a method of making a direct comparison of electrostatic with electromagnetic force', *Phil. Trans.*, **158** (1868): 643–57, esp. 643–52 (= *Scientific Papers*, **2**: 125–36), and see Number 289. One of the discs, with one of the coils at its back (compare Figure 235, 1), is attached to one arm of the torsion balance, while the larger fixed disc, with its coil, could be moved to various distances from the suspended disc by a micrometer screw. A counterpoise disc and coil, which is traversed by the same current in the opposite direction, is attached to the other arm of the torsion balance, to eliminate the effect of terrestrial magnetism. The torsion balance consists of a light brass frame suspended by a copper wire from a torsion head which is supported by a hollow pillar. The balance was made by Carl Becker (see Number 289). The suspended disc was fitted with a guard-ring: see Number 289 esp. note (11). See Plate XI.

244
LETTER TO PETER GUTHRIE TAIT
7 MARCH 1865
From the original in the University Library, Cambridge[1]

8 Palace Gardens Terrace
London W.
1865 March 7

Dear Tait[2]

The true origin of Electrical Resistance as expressed in B.A. units is Fleeming Jenkin Esqre 6 Duke Street Adelphi W.C. Price £2..10 in a box.[3]

I was happy to see that the 1st instalment of B. Stewart & Tait was in the R S Proceedings.[4] I suppose the wooden disc is either at Edinburgh or at Kew at a given time and that you have not yet imparted to it the velocity so frequently referred to in books on Elementary Dynamics which at the end of time t would cause it to be in Edin^h & Kew at once.

Does any one write quaternions but Sir W. Hamilton[5] & you?[6]

I heard him greatly slanged by a mathematical clergyman unknown to me, along with Plucker & Jacobi.[7] We were to see an end of all that school of mathematics very soon.

---

(1) ULC Add. MSS 7655, I, b/3.

(2) On 4 March 1865 Tait had written to Stokes (ULC Add. MSS 7656, T 56) inquiring: 'Can you tell me anything about Clerk Maxwell? He used to be a regular correspondent – but several late letters of mine are unanswered, and I see his Chair advertised as vacant.' See Number 235 note (20).

(3) See Fleeming Jenkin, 'Electric standard', *Phil. Mag.*, ser. 4, **29** (March 1865): 248, and also the 'Report of the committee on standards of electrical resistance', *Report of the Thirty-fifth Meeting of the British Association...held in September 1865* (London, 1866): 308–13, on the copies of standard coils made available for sale.

(4) Balfour Stewart and P. G. Tait's 'Preliminary note on the radiation from a revolving disc' was read at a meeting of the Royal Society on 23 February 1865; see *Proc. Roy. Soc.*, **14** (1865): 90.

(5) William Rowan Hamilton, *Lectures on Quaternions* (Dublin, 1853).

(6) See P. G. Tait, 'Quaternion investigations connected with electrodynamics and magnetism', *Quarterly Journal of Pure and Applied Mathematics*, **3** (1860): 331–42; 'Quaternion investigation of the potential of a closed circuit', *ibid.*, **4** (1861): 143–4; 'Formulae connected with small continuous displacements of the particles of a medium', *Proc. Roy. Soc. Edinb.*, **4** (1862): 617–23; and 'Note on a quaternion transformation', *Proc. Roy. Soc. Edinb.*, **5** (1863): 115–19.

(7) Julius Plücker and Carl Gustav Jacobi. The incident very likely occurred at a meeting of the Royal Society on 2 February 1865, when Plücker read his paper 'On a new geometry of space', *Proc. Roy. Soc.*, **14** (1865): 53–8.

Where can one obtain the most rapid approx^{ns} to the areas of spherical ellipses whose major axes are nearly $= \pi$.[8]

I made an erroneous estimate by rule of thumb as to the strength of a glass plate $\frac{1}{2}$ inch thick in consequence of which when exposed to a pressure of $\frac{3}{4}$ atmosphere it succumbed with a stunning implosion and sent me a month back with regard to the friction of gases and exhibited beautiful specimens of radial cracks in this style.

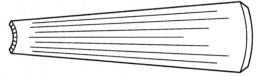

Figure 244,1

Thick ribbed brass now takes the place of glass and if the glass receiver goes it will only smash itself.

Yours truly
J. CLERK MAXWELL

Find the sum of

$$\frac{3}{4}(1-x) + \frac{3.5.7}{4.4.8}(1-x)^3 + \frac{3.5.7.9.11}{4.4.8.8.12}(1-x)^5$$
$$+ \frac{3.5.7.9.11.13.15}{4.4.8.8.12.12.16}(1-x)^7 + \&c$$

in decent terms of x a small quantity. It ought to come out convergently because I have solved the identical problem otherwise where x is small but as it stands it is not agreeable to me to engage it.[9]

---

(8) For a calculation in Maxwell's paper 'On the viscosity or internal friction of air and other gases', *Phil. Trans.* **156** (1866): 249–68, on 261–2 (= *Scientific Papers*, **2**: 16–17).

(9) A preliminary attempt to calculate the decrement in amplitude of the vibrating discs, in the experiments on the viscosity of gases. Maxwell soon abandoned this method: see Number 245 esp. note (4).

245

LETTER TO PETER GUTHRIE TAIT

3 APRIL 1865

From the original in the University Library, Cambridge[1]

8 Palace Gardens Terrace W
1865 April 3

Dear Tait

My results about friction of gases are now in a fair way towards existence. I got into swinging order on the 21st and have done something every day since but I have been occupied lately with the measurement of my dimensions and the determination of moments of inertia which are not yet reduced to numbers. I can promise you nothing about friction of ether but the machine goes like a clock or better and if there is anything appreciable say $\frac{1}{2}$ per cent I think it will find it. I have had nothing but undried air as yet but I have only to provide other innocent gases and my machine will do for them.

In 1860 I gave out that the coeff^t of friction in air is independent of density Phil Mag Jan^y.[2] Behold the results of the first days experiments the exhaustion was not carried far that day because I had not proved my apparatus then.

21 March
3 discs oscillating between 4 fixed ones
distance .186 inch between moving &
fixed 45 °F. Time 71.5 seconds

Figure 245,1

Barometer[3]	Log decrement of arc[4]
29.9	.02780
16.51	.02746
12.21	.02783
29.7	.02769

---

(1) ULC Add. MSS 7655, I, b/3A.

(2) J. C. Maxwell, 'Illustrations of the dynamical theory of gases. Part I. On the motions and collisions of perfectly elastic bodies', *Phil. Mag.*, ser. 4, **19** (1860): 19–32, on 32 (= *Scientific Papers*, **1**: 391). See also Number 207 §10 and Volume I: 610.

(3) Barometric pressure in inches.

(4) On Maxwell's calculation of the mean logarithmic decrement in amplitude of the vibrating discs, see 'On the viscosity or internal friction of air and other gases', *Phil. Trans.*, **156** (1866): 249–68, on 252–3 (= *Scientific Papers*, **2**: 5–6).

In case you should say this resistance is independent of the air here is the log dec. when the three discs are in contact and 1 inch of air between them & the fixed.

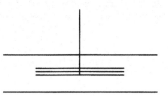

Figure 245,2

Barometer	Log dec
29.9	.00603
13.5	.00596
1.03	.00516

Here the difference partly depends on the influence of mass of air 1 inch thick & is greater when dense.

After Thursday I mean to go ahead with the exp^{ts} as I now know my distances to .001 inch. Never mind my series[5] I have forgotten it and have got my results a different way.[6]

I have not tried the disc with currents but if you have a spheroid polar semiaxis b equatorial ditto a made of stuff of resistance ρ per unit of volume spinning with velocity ω in a field of mag. intensity I about an axis inclined α to the mag. force in an insulating medium the work done against electromagnetic forces and converted into heat is

$$I^2 \sin^2 \alpha \, \omega^2 \cdot \frac{4\pi}{3} \frac{a^2 b}{\rho} \cdot \frac{2}{5} \frac{a^2 b^2}{(a+b)^2}. \quad (7)$$

You may get ρ by exp^t or from Jenkins table of Resistance Units, see Matthiessens copper $\frac{1}{16}$ inch wire 1 mile long, British Ass^n 1862.[8]

N.B. This does not include the action of the induced currents in inducing other currents in the disc.

Yours truly
J. C. MAXWELL

P. G. Tait Esqre

---

(5) See Number 244. (6) See note (4).

(7) In their paper 'On the heating of a disc by rapid rotation', *Proc. Roy. Soc.*, **14** (1865): 339–43, on 342 (read 15 June 1865), Balfour Stewart and Tait comment on the cause of heating of the disc: 'it is not due to revolution under the earth's magnetic force, for Professor Maxwell has kindly calculated the effect due to this cause under the conditions of the experiment, and he finds it infinitesimally small.'

(8) Read: 1864. See the value of ρ obtained by Augustus Matthiessen, recorded in the table of units of resistance, in the 'Report of the committee on standards of electrical resistance', *Report of the Thirty-fourth Meeting of the British Association...in September 1864* (London, 1865): 345–67, table facing 349 on 'Approximate relative values of various units of electrical resistance.'

LETTER TO WILLIAM THOMSON

17 AND 18 APRIL 1865

From the original in the University Library, Cambridge[1]

8 Palace Gardens Terrace
London W
1865 Ap 17

Dear Thomson

You told me some time ago you wanted to hear about the friction of gases. I have only got results very lately but the apparatus is in full swing now and I expect to get on as fast as I can prepare gases and heat mix & measure them.

The apparatus is 3 discs swinging about a vertical axis between 4 fixed ones all glass. Time of double vibration 71.6 seconds diameter of swinging discs 10.562 inches. Thickness of air = .425 at present. All distances measured to .001 inch by a gauge I have tested, except the distance from fixed to moving disc which is got optically so as to make the moving disc at equal distances from the fixed ones wh: makes the error of the 2nd order.[2]

The first result is that the coefficient of friction μ is independent of the density of the gas, temperature being the same.[3]

μ = dyn measure of tangential pressure on one square inch due to its moving at 1 inch per second at 1 inch from a fixed plane.

The dimensions of μ are $\dfrac{\frac{\text{Force}}{\text{area}}}{\frac{\text{velocity}}{\text{distance}}} = \dfrac{\frac{ML}{L^2T^2}}{\frac{L}{TL}}$

or $\dfrac{M}{LT}$.[4]

Therefore if μ is in grain inch second measure multiply by 12 to bring it to feet and divide by 7000 to bring it to pounds.

Stokes worked in inches and made μ = .00417.[5] I find at present for air μ = .00406 but I shall be better when I have reduced more obs^{ns}.[6]

I suppose Carbonic Acid μ = .0033
and Hydrogen μ = .0018
(all at about 60° in grain–inch, second) both much less than air.

---

(1) ULC Add. MSS 7655, II, 22A.
(2) On Thomson's interest in the experiment see Number 252 note (3).
(3) See Number 245 esp. note (2).
(4) On Maxwell's dimensional notation see the Introduction: 8.
(5) See Number 252.   (6) Compare the values given in Numbers 249 and 252.

Hydrogen 14.88 inches + Air 14.14 inches $\mu = .0036$ so that air is more powerful than hydrogen in determining the μ of a mixture.

All the gases are dried with sulphuric acid but I do not find much difference for ordinary air & dry air. I think μ is greatest for dry air. Here is the comparison for pressures.

Barometer	Therm.	Log dec for 5 swings	
30.07	63°	.0810	
9.7	68.5	.0810	dry air
1.6	69	.0814	
30.1	62°	.08062	
12.76	61	.0810	
7.86	61	.08025	

I expected a result for hot air today but it was dark before I got everything ready and temperature constant.

I expect μ to vary as $\sqrt{\text{absolute temperature}}$.[7]

April 18. I find μ for air at 115° Fah^r = .00465 the change is much greater than $\sqrt{T}$ gives but I mean to try steam next before the end of the week. The increase with temperature is quite plain.[8]

Measurement of v by equilibrium[9]

The advantage of equilibrating electrostatic attraction with electromagnetic repulsion derived from the same source, instead of balancing each separately by weights or springs is that the forces are applied simultaneously to a body already in equil^m and you have no trouble about unstable eq^m when you have eq^m at all, and the instability may be just overcome by the elasticity of the suspension.

Hockin[10] is working at the galvanometer. I mean to make out the

---

(7) As predicted by Maxwell in 'Illustrations of the dynamical theory of gases. Part I. On the motions and collisions of perfectly elastic spheres', *Phil. Mag.*, ser. 4, **19** (1860): 19–32, esp. 30–2 (= *Scientific Papers*, **1**: 389–91); and see also Number 207.

(8) Maxwell ultimately concluded that the viscosity is nearly a linear function of the absolute temperature (see Number 252).

(9) See Maxwell's letter to Thomson of 15 October 1864 (Number 235).

(10) Charles Hockin: see Number 232 note (1).

corrections in summer, ie the series for the potentials, but at present I am busy with μ.

I suppose you will be here in May.

Yours truly
J. Clerk Maxwell

=247=

LETTER TO ROBERT DUNDAS CAY

28 APRIL 1865

From the original in the library of Peterhouse, Cambridge[1]

8 Palace Gardens Terrace W
1865 Ap 28

Dear Uncle

I enclose receipt of £47..9..4.[2] I met Willy[3] in a high state of preservation in Hyde Park. He told me of the flitting. At present I am measuring the stiffness of various gases, air is very stiff to work carbonic acid less so and Hydrogen very smooth indeed. Hot air is stiffer than cold. I have got it all in grains on the square foot now.

Your aff^t nephew
J. CLERK MAXWELL

---

(1) Maxwell MSS (26), Peterhouse.
(2) See Volume I: 682n.
(3) William Dyce Cay; see Number 221 note (4).

248

LETTER TO THOMAS GRAHAM[1]

1 MAY 1865

From the original in the University Library, Cambridge[2]

8 Palace Gardens Terrace
London W
1865 May 1

Dear Sir

I have now got a few results to compare with your experiments on the transpiration of gases[3] but I find that my method of observation is more exact than some of my data derived from measurements so that at present I have taken the apparatus down to measure everything and so get results worthy of the trouble.

I have tried air at pressures from 30 inches to 0.7 inches and from 42° to 158° Fah.[4]

The friction is the same for all densities, but increases with the temperature, apparently in the same proportion as the air expands.[5] I expected it would be as the square root of the absolute temperature but I think I am wrong.[6]

These results agree with yours.[7]

I have also tried hydrogen and carbonic acid and find the velocity for hydrogen about 2.16 of that for air a little more than yours but my results are not fully reduced yet.[8] Carbonic acid is also a good deal smoother than air.

Mixtures of air and hydrogen are more like air than like hydrogen a little air making it very rough. Damp air does not differ very much from dry.[9]

---

(1) Maxwell had been familiar with Graham's work on gases since 1859: see Volume I: 609, 615, 660, 706.

(2) ULC Add. MSS 7655, II, 23. Previously published in *Molecules and Gases*: 351–2.

(3) Thomas Graham's experiments on the passage of gases through a tube: 'On the motion of gases', *Phil. Trans.*, **136** (1846): 573–632; and 'On the motion of gases. Part II', *Phil. Trans.*, **139** (1849): 349–401.

(4) Compare J. C. Maxwell, 'On the viscosity or internal friction of air and other gases', *Phil. Trans.*, **156** (1866): 249–68, esp. 256–7 (= *Scientific Papers*, **2**: 10–11).

(5) Maxwell, 'On the viscosity or internal friction of air and other gases': 256 (= *Scientific Papers*, **2**: 10); and see Number 252.

(6) See Number 246.

(7) Graham concluded that the transpiration times for air at different pressures were 'highly uniform', and for other gases varied only slightly; and he observed a relation between transpiration times and the temperature of the gas. See Graham, 'On the motion of gases. Part II': 356–61.

(8) Compare the value which Maxwell gives in 'On the viscosity or internal friction of air and other gases' (Number 252).

(9) See Number 252.

Have you got any more results about the transpiration velocity of mixed gases, especially hydrogen & oxygen or Ether vapour & oxygen. I see you have determined the transpiration of equal volumes of H & O.[10] If you have also that of 2 volumes H & 1 volume O it would serve as a test for the theory.

I think the absolute value of the friction of a few gases may be best determined by my method but the comparison of gases and the effects of mixture can be best done by transpiration through tubes by your method.

Has any one but you made such experiments on gases, of course Poisueille[11] & others[12] have tried liquids.

Have you any remaining copy of your paper on Transpiration in the Phil Trans.[13] I have your papers on Molecular Mobility &c[14] & Liquid Diffusion[15] and on Gaseous Diffusion[16] too and I should like to put them all together if you have a copy of the Transpiration to spare.

I suppose the hydrogen particles must either be much bigger than the oxygen ones or else they must act on one another at a greater distance, though they are 16 times less in mass.

Yours truly
J. CLERK MAXWELL

The Master of the Mint

---

(10) But see Graham's results reported in 'On the motion of gases': 627.

(11) J. L. M. Poiseuille, 'Récherches expérimentales sur le mouvement des liquides dans les tubes de très petits diamètres, *Mémoires Présentés par Divers Savants à l'Académie Royale de l'Institut de France*, **9** (1846): 433–544.

(12) The 'Rapport fait à l'Académie des Sciences, le 26 décembre 1842, au nom d'une Commission composée de MM. Arago, Babinet, Piobert, Regnault rapporteur, sur un Mémoire de M. le docteur Poiseuille, ayant pour titre: Recherches expérimentales sur le mouvement des liquides dans les tubes de très-petits diamètres', *Ann. Chim. Phys.*, ser. 3, **7** (1843): 50–74, esp. 50, cited by Graham in 'On the motion of gases. Part II': 350n, refers to earlier work on the flow of liquids in tubes of small diameter, notably by P. S. Girard, 'Mémoire sur le mouvement des fluides dans les tubes capillaires et l'influence de la température sur ce mouvement', *Mémoires de la Classe des Sciences Mathématiques et Physiques de l'Institut de France. Années 1813, 1814, 1815* (1818): 249–380.

(13) See note (3).

(14) Thomas Graham, 'On the molecular mobility of gases', *Phil. Trans.*, **153** (1863): 385–405.

(15) Thomas Graham, 'Liquid diffusion applied to analysis', *Phil. Trans.*, **151** (1861): 183–224. See also Graham, 'On the diffusion of liquids', *ibid.*, **140** (1850): 1–46, 805–36; *ibid.*, **141** (1851): 483–94.

(16) Thomas Graham, 'On the law of the diffusion of gases', *Trans. Roy. Soc. Edinb.*, **12** (1834): 222–58.

=249=

LETTER TO PETER GUTHRIE TAIT

17 JUNE 1865

From the original in the University Library, Cambridge[1]

Craiglachie
Errol
1865 June 17

Dear Tait

23 is founded on fact,[2] the problem like others about that date was anon.[3] but was legitimized in the Q J of M. March 1858 at the end of a theory of Opt Ins^{ts}.[4]

I am reducing friction of air to numerical values, but I get on slowly by reason of great heat and no logarithms at hand. However in foot, grain, second measure

$$\mu = 0.0925$$

for air at 60.6.[5]

μ is independent of pressure and proportional to absolute temperature not to square root thereof.[6] Hydrogen about $\frac{1}{2}$ air.

The value above given is nearly double what Stokes deduces from pendulum exp^{ts} but agrees with Grahams exp^{ts} on transpiration.[7]

---

(1) ULC Add. MSS 7655, I, b/4. Previously published in *Molecules and Gases*: 352–3.

(2) Tait had sent Maxwell proof sheets of §24 (§23 in the proof) of his paper 'On the application of Hamilton's characteristic function to special cases of constraint', *Trans. Roy. Soc. Edinb.*, **24** (1865): 147–66, esp. 163–4 (ULC Add. MSS 7655, I, a/1). Drawing an analogy between the brachistochrone (the path of swiftest descent) and the path of a light ray in a heterogeneous refracting medium, Tait refers to: 'The following due I believe to Maxwell. If the path of a medium be such a function of the distance from a given point that the path of any one ray is a circle, the path of every other ray is a circle; and all rays diverging from any one point converge accurately in another.' He refers to a paper in *Camb. & Dubl. Math. J.*, **9** (1854): 9, and appends on the proof: 'Report, O Maxwell! whether the underwritten accusation §23 be printed in fact – or no. Excuse speed. If it be printed say are you content with the form thereof. Y^{rs} P.G.T.' See also Number 380.

(3) Proposed and solved by Maxwell (see Number 421). See *Camb. & Dubl. Math. J.*, **8** (1853): 188; and [J. C. Maxwell,] 'Solutions to problems', *ibid.*, **9** (1854): 7–11, esp. 9–11 (= *Scientific Papers*, **1**: 76–9). See Volume I: 232–5.

(4) J. C. Maxwell, 'On the general laws of optical instruments', *Quarterly Journal of Pure and Applied Mathematics*, **2** (1858): 232–46, esp. 246 (= *Scientific Papers*, **1**: 284–5).

(5) Compare the value given in Maxwell's letter to William Thomson of 17 April 1865 (Number 246), and that in 'On the viscosity or internal friction of air and other gases' (Number 252).

(6) See Numbers 246 and 252. (7) See Number 252.

To reduce to French or other measure divide by $\dfrac{\text{Foot}}{\text{grain second}}$ and multiply by the corresponding foreign measures.

Yours truly
J. C. MAXWELL

250
FROM A LETTER TO HENRY RICHMOND DROOP[1]
19 JULY 1865
From Campbell and Garnett, *Life of Maxwell*[2]

Glenlair
Dalbeattie
19 July 1865

There are so many different forms in which Societies may be cast, that I should like very much to hear something of what those who have been thinking about it propose as the plan of it.

There is the association for publishing each other's productions; for delivering lectures for the good of the public and the support of the Society; for keeping a reading room or club, frequented by men of a particular turn; for dining together once a month, etc.

I suppose W——'s object is to increase the happiness of men in London who cultivate physical sciences, by their meeting together to read papers and discuss them, the publication of these papers being only one, and not the chief end of the Society, which fulfils its main purpose in the act of meeting and enjoying itself.

The Royal Society of Edinburgh used to be a very sociable body, but it had several advantages. Most of the fellows lived within a mile of the Society's rooms. They did not need to disturb their dinner arrangements in order to attend.

Many of them were good speakers as well as sensible men, whose mode of considering a subject was worth hearing, even if not correct.

The subjects were not limited to mathematics and physics, but included geology, physiology, and occasionally antiquities and even literary subjects. Biography of deceased fellows is still a subject of papers. Now those who cultivate the mathematical and physical sciences are sometimes unable to discuss a paper, because they would require to keep it some days by them to form an opinion on it, and physical men can get up a much better discussion about armour plates or the theory of glaciers than about the conduction of heat or capillary attraction.

The only man I know who can make everything the subject of discussion is Dr. Tyndall.[3] Secure his attendance and that of somebody to differ from him, and you are all right for a meeting.

If we can take the field with a plan in our head, I dare say we could find a good many men who would co-operate.

---

(1) See Volume I: 557, 703–6. (2) *Life of Maxwell*: 342–3. (3) See Number 226.

Letter to Henry Richmond Droop, 19 July 1865

We ride every day, sometimes both morning and evening, and so we consume the roads. I have made 68 problems, all stiff ones, not counting riders.[4]

I am now getting the general equations for the motion of a gas considered as an assemblage of molecules flying about with great velocity. I find they must repel as inverse fifth power of distance.[5]

---

(4) For the Cambridge Mathematical Tripos in 1866: see Numbers 228 note (5) and 253: Appendix I.

(5) See Number 263.

LETTER TO LEWIS CAMPBELL
21 NOVEMBER 1865
From the original in the University Library, St Andrews[1]

8 Palace Gardens Terrace
London W
1865 Nov 21

Dear Lewis[2]

Trinity College Cambridge is said to favour duplicity and multiplicity in its elections to fellowships.[3]

No College however can be consistent in this for occasionally they must prefer a single man who will be of use to a man who is merely free from ignorance on all the curriculum.

If a man can do *good* Greek & Latin either prose or verse there is no doubt it will be a great lift to him at Trinity and it will be of advantage to himself too. But if he can only grind up bad verses, he will suffer more for this than for none at all. Bad mathematics do no man any harm (with examiners) but bad classics do.[4] Thompson (Greek Prof^r)[5] said before I went in that if they elected me they never had let through such bad classics. I am confident however that if I had done any they would have kept me waiting a while.[6]

If young Forbes[7] likes Logic he can get it in good style where he is whatever heresies he may imbibe along with it concerning the necessity of being known.

This kind of thing gets on very well at Trinity, better than at any other College.

But I have not myself the faculty of the learned tongues so that I cannot judge of the deficiencies of a man who cannot make verses in them and no one can tell whether young Forbes verses (when made) are likely to be good

---

(1) St Andrews University Library, Forbes MSS 1865/161.

(2) Lewis Campbell had been appointed Professor of Greek at St Andrews in 1863, where James David Forbes (on whose son's behalf this letter was written: see note (7)) was Principal of the United College of St Salvator and St Leonard.

(3) Candidates for fellowships at Trinity College, Cambridge were required to be examined in classics, mathematics and metaphysics. See Charles Astor Bristed, *Five Years in an English University*, 2 vols. (New York, 1852), **1**: 386–96.

(4) For a similar judgment see Bristed, *Five Years in an English University*, **1**: 388.

(5) William Hepworth Thompson, Trinity 1828, Regius Professor of Greek 1853, Master 1866 (Venn).

(6) On Maxwell's failure to gain a fellowship at Trinity in October 1854, and his success the following year, see Volume I: 12, 280n, 327.

(7) George Forbes, Christ's 1867, from St Andrews University (Venn).

without seeing him and knowing whether verse making is prevalent in the company which he moves in.

Your aft friend
J. Clerk Maxwell

ABSTRACT OF PAPER 'ON THE VISCOSITY OR INTERNAL FRICTION OF AIR AND OTHER GASES'

[23 NOVEMBER 1865][1]

From the *Proceedings of the Royal Society*[2]

FEBRUARY 8, 1866.

Lieut.-General Sabine, President, in the Chair.

The Bakerian Lecture was delivered by James Clerk Maxwell, M.A., F.R.S., 'On the Viscosity or Internal Friction of Air and other Gases.'[3] **The following is an abstract.**

All bodies which are capable of having their form indefinitely altered, and which resist the change of form with a force depending on the rate of deformation, may be called Viscous Bodies. Taking tar or treacle as an instance in which both the change of form and the resistance opposed to it are easily observed, we may pass in one direction through the series of soft solids up to the materials commonly supposed to be most unyielding, such as glass and steel, and in the other direction through the series of liquids of various degrees of mobility to the gases, of which oxygen is the most viscous, and hydrogen the least.

The viscosity of elastic solids has been investigated by M. F. Kohl-

---

(1) The date the paper was received by the Royal Society. The paper was read on 8 February 1866: see note (2).

(2) *Proc. Roy. Soc.*, **15** (1866): 14–17.

(3) Published in *Phil. Trans.*, **156** (1866): 249–68 (= *Scientific Papers*, **2**: 1–25). There is a referee's report by William Thomson: see his letter to Stokes of 11 April 1866 (Royal Society, *Referees' Reports*, **6**: 178; printed in Wilson, *Stokes–Kelvin Correspondence*, **1**: 324–5). Thomson declared that: 'The evidence it contains as to the accuracy of the results in absolute measure is very satisfactory.... The plan he adopts is quite the same as one I had long contemplated, and intended applying myself, for liquids (except that I intended to have only one vibrating disc).' Thomson had outlined an experiment on the viscosity of liquids, using a vibrating disc, in a letter to Stokes of 10 March 1862 (ULC Add. MSS 7656, K 133; see *Stokes–Kelvin Correspondence*, **1**: 288–9). At the time, Stokes had been investigating Graham's results on the transpiration of gases, concluding in favour of Maxwell's result that gas viscosity is independent of density; see Stokes to Thomson 22 February and 25 February 1862 (*Stokes–Kelvin Correspondence*, **1**: 283–7). Maxwell mentioned Stokes' conclusion in a letter to H. R. Droop of 28 January 1862 (Volume I: 706).

Plate IV. Maxwell's apparatus (1865) to determine the viscosity of gases as a function of pressure and temperature (Number 252).

rausch*[4] and Professor W. Thomson†[5] that of gases by Professor Stokes‡,[6] M. O. E. Meyer§,[7] and Mr. Graham∥.[8]

The author has investigated the laws of viscosity in air by causing three horizontal glass disks, 10.56 inches diameter, to perform rotatory oscillations about a vertical axis by means of the elasticity of a steel suspension wire about 4 feet long. The period of a complete oscillation was 72 seconds, and the maximum velocity of the edge of the disks was about $\frac{1}{12}$ inch per second.

The three disks were placed at known intervals on the vertical axis, and four larger fixed disks were so adjusted above and below them and in the intervals between them, that strata of air of known thickness were intercepted between the surfaces of the moving disks and the fixed disks. During the oscillations of the moveable disks, the viscosity of the air in these six strata caused a gradual diminution of the amplitude of oscillation, which was measured by means of the reflexion of a circular scale in a mirror attached to the axis.

The whole apparatus was enclosed in an air-tight case, so that the air might be exhausted or exchanged for another gas, or heated by a current of steam round the receiver. The observed diminution in the arc of oscillation is in part due to the viscosity of the suspending wire. To eliminate the effect of the wire from that of the air, the arrangement of the disks was altered, and the three disks, placed in contact, were made to oscillate midway between two fixed glass disks, at distances sometimes of 1 inch, and sometimes of .5 inch.

From these experiments on two strata of air, combined with three sets of experiments on six strata of thicknesses .683, .425, and .1847 inches respectively, the value of the coefficient of viscosity or internal friction was determined.

Let two infinite planes be separated by a stratum of air whose thickness is unity. Let one of these planes be fixed, while the other moves in its own plane

* Pogg. Ann. cxix. (1863).[4]
† Proceedings of the Royal Society, May 18, 1865.[5]
‡ Cambridge Philosophical Transactions, 1850.[6]
§ Pogg. Ann. cxiii. (1861).[7]
∥ Phil. Trans. 1846 & 1849.[8]

(4) F. W. G. Kohlrausch, 'Ueber die elastische Nachwirkung bei der Torsion', *Ann. Phys.*, **119** (1863): 337–68.

(5) William Thomson, 'On the elasticity and viscosity of metals', *Proc. Roy. Soc.*, **14** (1865): 289–97.

(6) G. G. Stokes, 'On the effect of the internal friction of fluids on the motion of pendulums', *Trans. Camb. Phil. Soc.*, **9**, part 2 (1851): [8]–[106] (= *Papers*, **3**: 1–136).

(7) O. E. Meyer, 'Ueber die Reibung der Flüssigkeiten', *Ann. Phys.*, **113** (1861): 55–86, 193–238, 383–425.

(8) Thomas Graham, 'On the motion of gases', *Phil. Trans.*, **136** (1846): 573–632; 'On the motion of gases. Part II', *ibid.*, **139** (1849): 349–401.

with a uniform velocity unity; then, if the air in immediate contact with either plane has the same velocity as the plane, every unit of surface of either plane will experience a tangential force μ, where μ is the coefficient of viscosity of the air between the planes.

The force μ is understood to be measured by the velocity which it would communicate in unit of time to unit of mass.

If L, M, T be the units of length, mass, and time, then the dimensions of μ are $L^{-1} M T^{-1}$.

In the actual experiment, the motion of the surfaces is rotatory instead of rectilinear, oscillatory instead of uniform, and the surfaces are bounded instead of infinite. These considerations introduce certain complications into the theory, which are separately considered.

The conclusions which are drawn from the experiments agree, as far as they go, with those of Mr. Graham on the Transpiration of Gases*.[9] They are as follows.

1. The coefficient of viscosity is independent of the density, the temperature being constant. No deviation from this law is observed between the atmospheric density and that corresponding to a pressure of half an inch of mercury.

This remarkable result was shown by the author in 1860†[10] to be a consequence of the Dynamical Theory of Gases. It agrees with the conclusions of Mr. Graham, deduced from experiments on the transpiration of gases through capillary tubes.[11] The considerable thickness of the strata of air in the present experiments shows that the property of air, to be equally viscous at all densities, is quite independent of any molecular action between its particles and those of solid surfaces, such as those of the capillary tubes employed by Graham.

2. The coefficient of viscosity increases with the temperature, and is proportional to $1 + \alpha\theta$, where θ is the temperature and α is the coefficient of expansion per degree for air.

This result cannot be considered so well established as the former, owing to the difficulty of maintaining a high temperature constant in so large an

---

* Phil. Trans. 1846.[9] † Phil. Mag. Jan. 1860.[10]

---

(9) Graham, 'On the motion of gases'. See Maxwell's letter to Graham of 1 May 1865 (Number 248).

(10) J. C. Maxwell, 'Illustrations of the dynamical theory of gases. Part I. On the motions and collisions of perfectly elastic spheres', *Phil. Mag.*, ser. 4, **19** (1860): 19–32, esp. 32 (= *Scientific Papers*, **1**: 391).

(11) Graham, 'On the motion of gases. Part II': 361. See Number 248 note (7).

apparatus, and measuring it without interfering with the motion. Experiments, in which the temperature ranged from 50° to 185° F, agreed with the theory to within 0.8 per cent, so that it is exceedingly probable that this is the true relation to the temperature.

The experiments of Graham led him to this conclusion also.[12]

3. The coefficient of viscosity of hydrogen is much less than that of air. I have never succeeded in filling my apparatus with perfectly pure hydrogen, for air leaks into the vacuum during the admission of so large a quantity of hydrogen as is required to fill it. The ratio of the viscosity of my hydrogen to that of air was .5156. That obtained by Graham was .4855.

4. The ratio for carbonic acid was found to be .859. Graham makes it .807.[13] It is probable that the comparative results of Graham are more exact than those of this paper, owing to the difficulty of introducing so large a volume of gas without letting in any air during the time of filling the receiver. I find also that a very small proportion of air causes a considerable increase in the viscosity of hydrogen. This result also agrees with those of Mr. Graham.[14]

5. Forty experiments on dry air were investigated to determine whether any slipping takes place between the glass and the air in immediate contact with it.

The result was, that if there were any slipping, it is of exceedingly small amount; and that the evidence in favour of the indicated amount being real is very precarious.

The results of the hypothesis, that there is no slipping, agree decidedly better with the experiments.

6. The actual value of the coefficient of viscosity of dry air was determined, from forty experiments of five different kinds, to be

$$\mu = .0000149\,(461° + \theta),$$

where the inch, the grain, and the second are the units, and the temperature is on Fahrenheit's scale.

At 62° this gives $\mu = .007802$.

---

(12) Graham, 'On the motion of gases. Part II': 356. See Number 248 note (7).

(13) In 'On the motion of gases. Part II': 364, Graham gives the transpiration times of equal volumes of hydrogen, oxygen, air and carbon dioxide under the same pressure. Taking the transpiration time of oxygen as 1, he gives those for hydrogen as 0.4375, and carbon dioxide as 0.7272, while that for air is 0.9010. Maxwell reduces Graham's values to ratios of hydrogen and carbon dioxide to air.

(14) Graham, 'On the motion of gases': 622–3, 628 and Plate XXXV facing 634.

Professor Stokes, from the experiments of Baily on pendulums,[15] has found[16]

$$\sqrt{\frac{\mu}{\rho}} = .116,$$

which, with the average temperature and density of air, would give

$$\mu = .00417,$$

a much smaller value than that here found.

If the value of μ is expressed in feet instead of inches, so as to be uniform with the British measures of magnetic and electric phenomena, as recorded at the observatories,

$$\mu = .000179\,(461 + \theta)$$
$$= .08826 \text{ at } 32°.$$

In metre-gramme-second measure and Centigrade temperature,

$$\mu = .01878\,(1 + .00366\,\theta).$$

M. O. E. Meyer (Pogg. Ann. cxiii. (1861) p. 383)[17] makes μ at 18 °C = .000360 in centimetres, cubic centimetres of water, and seconds as units, or in metrical units,

$$\mu = .0360.$$

According to the experiments here described, μ at 18 °C = .02.

M. Meyer's value is therefore nearly twice as great as that of this paper, while that of Professor Stokes is only half as great.

In M. Meyer's experiments, which were with one disk at a time in an open space of air, the influence of the air near the edge of the disk is very considerable; but M. Meyer (Crelle, 59;[18] Pogg. cxiii. 76)[19] seems to have arrived at the conclusion that the additional effect of the air at the edge is proportional to the thickness of the disk. If the additional force near the edge is underestimated, the resulting value of the viscosity will be in excess.

7. Each of the forty experiments on dry air was calculated from the concluded values of the viscosity of the air and of the wire, and the result compared with the observed result. In this way the error of mean square of

---

(15) Francis Baily, 'On the correction of a pendulum for the reduction to a vacuum: together with remarks on some anomalies observed in pendulum experiments', *Phil. Trans.*, **122** (1832): 399–492.

(16) Stokes, 'On the effect of the internal friction of fluids on the motion of pendulums': 65. See Volume I: 597–8, 606–11.

(17) Meyer, 'Ueber die Reibung der Flüssigkeiten', *Ann. Phys.*, **113** (1861): 383.

(18) O. E. Meyer, 'Ueber die Reibung der Flüssigkeiten', *Journal für die reine und angewandte Mathematik*, **59** (1861): 229–303 (on the mathematical theory of viscosity).

(19) Meyer, 'Ueber die Reibung der Flüssigkeiten', *Ann. Phys.*, **113** (1861): 76.

each observation was determined, and from this the 'probable error' of μ was found to be .036 per cent of its value. These experiments, it must be remembered, were made with five different arrangements of the disks, at pressures ranging from 0.5 inch to 30 inches, and at temperatures from 51° to 74 °F; so that their agreement does not arise from a mere repetition of the same conditions, but from an agreement between the properties of air and the theory made use of in the calculations.

NOTES ON JAMES THOMSON'S VORTEX TURBINE[1]

circa LATE 1865[2]

From the original in the University Library, Cambridge[3]

VORTEX WHEEL – FIRST APPROXIMATION[4]

radius of wheel at entrance $= a$ at exit $= b$
angle of waves $= \alpha$ $= \beta$
inner angle of guide blades γ
depth of wheel c angular velocity ω moment of twisting R
Volume of water per second V effective head H
density of water ρ gravity $= g$
radius at any point r

then

$$\text{radial velocity} = \frac{V}{2\pi c}\frac{1}{r} \quad \text{Let } \frac{V}{2\pi c} \text{ be put} = k \tag{1}$$

1st to find R. The angular velocity of the water as it leaves the guide blades is $\frac{k}{r^2}\tan\gamma$. Hence the angular momentum of the water which enters per second is $V\rho k \tan\gamma$.

---

(1) James Thomson, 'On the vortex water-wheel', *Report of the Twenty-second Meeting of the British Association for the Advancement of Science* (London, 1853): 317–22. For Maxwell's likely sources see also notes (4) and (14).

(2) This is conjectural; the manuscript may well have relation to Maxwell's question on the stability of vortex motion in the Mathematical Tripos 1866: see Appendix I *infra*.

(3) ULC Add. MSS 7655, V, e/19.

(4) In James Thomson's water turbine water is directed by exterior guide blades and injected at the circumference, impinging on vanes which curve from radial to nearly tangential, and is ejected from near the centre. Water is injected at the same speed as the wheel: if the wheel slows, the inflow is greater, increasing the torque. The wheel tends to maintain equilibrium in response to fluctuations of inflow. See W. J. M. Rankine, *A Manual of Applied Mechanics* (London/Glasgow, 1858): 596–7, on 'James Thomson's vortex water-wheel'. I am indebted to a personal communication (September 1990) from A. T. Fuller.

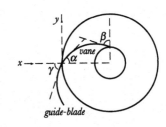

Figure 253,1

The angular velocity of the water which leaves the wheel is $\frac{k}{r^2}\tan\beta - \omega^{(5)}$

so that the angular momentum of the issuing water per second is $V\rho(k\tan\beta - b^2\omega).^{(6)}$

The difference of these angular momenta must be necessarily by pressure friction impact or otherwise communicated to the wheel.

Hence $R = V\rho(k(\tan\gamma - \tan\beta) + b^2\omega).^{(7)}$ \hfill (2)

The useful work per second is
$$R\omega = V\rho(k\omega(\tan\gamma - \tan\beta) - b^2\omega^2) \tag{3}$$

The applied work per second is
$$W = V\rho gH \tag{4}$$

∴ the efficiency is

$$E = \frac{1}{gH}(k\omega(\tan\gamma - \tan\beta) + b^2\omega^2)^{(8)} \tag{5}$$

2nd To find the difference of pressures at entry & exit of the wheel p_1 & p_2.

Energy per cubic foot at entry =
$\frac{\rho}{2}\left\{k^2\frac{\sec^2\alpha}{a^2} + 2k\omega\tan\alpha + \omega^2 a^2\right\} + p_1.$

Work done by pressure in wheel (no impact) =
$\rho\{k\omega(\tan\alpha - \tan\beta) + (a^2 - b^2)\omega^2\}.$

Energy at exit = $\frac{\rho}{2}\left\{k^2\frac{\sec^2\beta}{b^2} + 2k\omega\tan\beta + \omega^2 b^2\right\} + p_2.$

Hence $p_1 - p_2 = \frac{\rho}{2}\left\{k^2\left(\frac{\sec^2\beta}{b^2} - \frac{\sec^2\alpha}{a^2}\right) + \omega^2(a^2 - b^2)\right\}.$ \hfill (6)

3rd to find the pressure p_1.

$$p_1 = \rho gH - \frac{\rho}{2}k^2\frac{\sec^2\gamma}{a^2} \quad \& \quad p_2 = 0$$

Hence $\quad 2gH = k^2\left\{\frac{\sec^2\gamma - \sec^2\alpha}{a^2} + \frac{\sec^2\beta}{b^2}\right\} + \omega^2(a^2 - b^2).$ \hfill (7)

---

(5) Read: $+\omega$. \hfill (6) Read: $+b^2\omega$.
(7) Read: $-b^2\omega$. \hfill (8) Read: $-b^2\omega^2$.

Diff^t (2)$^{(9)}$
$$dR = \left(2V\rho \frac{1}{2\pi c}(\tan\gamma - \tan\beta) + \rho b^2 \omega\right)dV + V\rho b^2 d\omega.$$

Diff^t (7)
$$0 = \frac{1}{4\pi^2 c^2} VdV\left(\frac{\sec^2\gamma - \sec^2\alpha}{a^2} + \frac{\sec^2\beta}{b^2}\right) + \omega d\omega(a^2 - b^2).$$

Now let the standard values of the quantities be got thus

$$\frac{V}{2\pi c}\tan\beta = b^2\omega^{(10)}$$

$$\frac{V}{2\pi c}(\tan\gamma - \tan\alpha) = a^2\omega^{(11)} \quad \& \text{ let } \alpha = 0^{(12)}$$

then
$$R = V\rho a^2 \omega$$

$$2gH = 2a^2\omega^2 + \left[\frac{V}{2\pi c}\right]^2 \frac{1}{b^2}$$

$$E = \frac{a^2\omega^2}{a^2\omega^2 + \frac{1}{2}\left[\frac{V}{2\pi c}\right]^2 \frac{1}{b^2}}. \qquad (13)$$

$$\frac{dV}{d\omega} = -\frac{V}{\omega}\frac{a^2 - b^2}{a^2 + b^2}$$

$$\frac{dR}{d\omega} = -2V\rho a^2 \frac{a^2 - 2b^2}{a^2 + b^2}$$

$$\frac{dV}{dR} = -\frac{1}{2\rho a^2 \omega}\frac{a^2 - b^2}{a^2 - 2b^2}.$$

$$\frac{d}{d\omega}(R\omega) = V\rho a^2 \omega^2 \frac{4b^2 - a^2}{a^2 + b^2}$$

$$\frac{d}{dV}(R\omega) = \rho a^2 \omega^3 \frac{4b^2 - a^2}{b^2 - a^2}.$$

---

(9) To calculate sensitivity of torque.
(10) Assuming the angular velocity of the water emerging from the wheel is zero.
(11) Assuming that the angular velocity of the water on passing from the guide blade into the wheel is constant.
(12) As assumed by Thomson.
(13) In obtaining the results *infra* Maxwell assumes that the efficiency E is approximately unity: hence $V/2\pi c \ll ab\omega$. There are algebraic errors in Maxwell's equations, and in the values given in his table.

	Thomson	Fontaine parallel	Outward Fourneyron[14]
	$a = 2b$	$a = b$	$2a = b$
$\dfrac{dV}{d\omega} =$	$-\dfrac{3}{5}\dfrac{V}{\omega}$	0	$+\dfrac{3}{5}\dfrac{V}{\omega}$
$\dfrac{dR}{d\omega} =$	$-\dfrac{4}{5}V\rho a^2$	$+V\rho a^2$	$+\dfrac{14}{5}V\rho a^2$
$\dfrac{dV}{dR} =$	$\dfrac{3}{4}\dfrac{1}{\rho a^2 \omega}$	0	$+\dfrac{3}{14}\dfrac{1}{\rho a^2 \omega}$

From this it appears that when $a = 2b$ $\dfrac{dV}{d\omega}$ is $-^{ve}$ or the faster the speed the less the flow of water. When $2a = b$ the greater the speed the greater the flow. When the speed increases the resistance that can be overcome diminishes in Thomson and increases in the others. Hence Thomson is stable.

APPENDIX I: ON THE STABILITY OF VORTEX MOTION

circa LATE 1865[15]

From the original in the King's College London Archives[16]

[DRAFT QUESTION FOR THE MATHEMATICAL TRIPOS][17]

A mass M of fluid is running round a circular groove or channel of radius a with velocity u. An equal mass is running round another channel of radius b with velocity v.

---

(14) See Rankine's description of 'Thomson's turbine, or vortex wheel...[an] inward flow turbine', 'Fontaine's...parallel flow turbine', and 'Fourneyron's...outward flow turbine', in his *A Manual of the Steam Engine* (London/Glasgow, 1859): 201–10.

(15) See note (2) and Appendix II *infra*.

(16) King's College London Archives, Maxwell Notebook (2), question (101).

(17) Maxwell had been appointed a moderator for the Mathematical Tripos in 1866; see *The Cambridge University Calendar for the Year 1866* (Cambridge, 1866): 448. For the question as set in the Tripos see *Calendar for 1866*: 473. For a solution to the question see A. T. Fuller, 'Maxwell's Cambridge manuscripts: extracts relating to control and stability – VI', *International Journal of Control*, **43** (1986): 1135–68, esp. 1152–3.

The one channel is made to expand and the other to contract till their radii are exchanged show that the work expended in effecting the change is

$$-\frac{1}{2}\left(\frac{u^2}{b^2}-\frac{v^2}{a^2}\right)(a^2-b^2)\,M.$$

Hence show that the motion of a fluid in a circular whirlpool will be stable or unstable according as the areas described by particles in equal times increase or diminish from centre to circumference.

APPENDIX II: LETTER TO ROBERT DUNDAS CAY
8 december 1865
From the original in the Library of Peterhouse, Cambridge[18]

8 Palace Gardens Terrace
W
1865 Dec 8

Dear Uncle

I enclose the receipt you sent me. We are glad to hear Uncle John is better and hope it will do Aunt Jane good. We should be much obliged to you for your carte de visite as we have not one of you.

The Cambridge questions are nearly all printed now but they have all to be cross questioned yet.

Your aff^t nephew
J. Clerk Maxwell

---

(18) Maxwell MSS (27), Peterhouse.

=254=

MANUSCRIPT FRAGMENTS ON THE STABILITY OF FLUID MOTION

circa 1865[1]

From the originals in the University Library, Cambridge[2]

[1] ON THE CONDITION OF STABILITY OF THE STEADY MOTION OF AN INCOMPRESSIBLE FLUID[3]

The question as to the stability of any state implies the possibility of such a state. We must therefore treat of the necessary conditions of steady motion as well as of the method of distinguishing whether this motion if slightly disturbed will be restored to its original state or completely altered in character.

The ordinary hydrodynamical equations are of the form

$$\frac{dp}{dx} = -\rho\left(X - \frac{du}{dt} - u\frac{du}{dx} - v\frac{du}{dy} - w\frac{du}{dz}\right)^{[4]}$$

where p is the pressure, ρ the density X the force in x acting on the element due to external causes $u\ v\ w$ the resolved velocities.

---

(1) This manuscript may have been written in connection with a question Maxwell set for the Cambridge Mathematical Tripos in 1866. See *The Cambridge University Calendar for the Year 1866* (Cambridge, 1866): 478; 'If the motion of an incompressible homogeneous fluid under the action of such forces as occur in nature we put

$$\alpha = \frac{dv}{dz} - \frac{dw}{dy}, \beta = \frac{dw}{dz} - \frac{du}{dz}, \gamma = \frac{du}{dy} - \frac{dv}{dx}$$

shew that

$$\frac{d\alpha}{dt} + u\frac{d\alpha}{dx} + v\frac{d\alpha}{dy} + w\frac{d\alpha}{dz} = \alpha\frac{du}{dx} + \beta\frac{du}{dy} + \gamma\frac{du}{dz}.$$

P, Q are adjacent particles of the fluid, such that at a given instant the projections on the axes of x, y, z of the line joining them are proportional to α, β, γ respectively: shew that, during the subsequent motion of the fluid, the projections of the line joining P and Q will remain proportional to α, β, γ.' See Numbers 275 and 294 on setting the 'Helmholtz dogma' on fluid vortices; and see Hermann Helmholtz, 'Über Integrale der hydrodynamischen Gleichungen, welche den Wirbelbewegungen entsprechen', *Journal für die reine und angewandte Mathematik*, **55** (1858): 25–55, esp. 31–5 for the source of the question.

(2) ULC Add. MSS 7655, V, c/5, 8.

(3) Compare the documents published in Volume I: 295–9, 507n.

(4) See S. D. Poisson, *Traité de Mécanique*, 2 vols. (Paris, 1833), **2**: 669; G. G. Stokes, 'On the theories of the internal friction of fluids in motion, and of the equilibrium and motion of elastic solids', *Trans. Camb. Phil. Soc.*, **8** (1845): 287–319, esp. 296–7 (= *Papers*, **1**: 75–129); Helmholtz, 'Über Integrale der hydrodynamischen Gleichungen': 28.

Let
$$\alpha = \frac{dw}{dy} - \frac{dv}{dz}$$
$$\beta = \frac{du}{dz} - \frac{dw}{dx}$$
$$\gamma = \frac{dv}{dx} - \frac{du}{dy}$$

be the velocities of rotation of an element of the fluid about the three directions of x y & z. If the motion of the fluid is regulated by a velocity potential[5] α β & γ will disappear.

If we have also $X = \dfrac{dV}{dx}$ $Y = \dfrac{dV}{dy}$ $Z = \dfrac{dV}{dz}$ and ρ constant

$$\frac{dp}{dx} = -\rho \left\{ \frac{dV}{dx} - \frac{1}{2}\frac{d}{dx}(u^2+v^2+w^2) - \frac{du}{dt} + v\gamma - w\beta \right\}$$

or if we put $\tfrac{1}{2}\rho(u^2+v^2+w^2) - \rho V - p = G$[6] ⟨(the dynamic head)⟩[7]

$$\frac{dG}{dx} = \rho\left\{-\frac{du}{dt} + v\gamma - w\beta\right\}.$$

In a steady motion $\dfrac{du}{dt} = 0$,[8] therefore the condition of steady motion is given by the following equations

$$\frac{dG}{dx} = \rho(v\gamma - w\beta)$$
$$\frac{dG}{dy} = \rho(w\alpha - u\gamma) \qquad [(1)]$$
$$\frac{dG}{dz} = \rho(u\beta - v\alpha).$$

---

(5) Helmholtz's term 'Geschwindigkeitspotential'; see his 'Über Integrale der hydrodynamischen Gleichungen': 25.

(6) The Bernoulli equation. See G. G. Stokes, 'On the steady motion of incompressible fluids', *Trans. Camb. Phil. Soc.*, **7** (1842): 439–53, esp. 439 (= *Papers*, **1**: 1–16).

(7) See W. J. M. Rankine, *A Manual of Applied Mechanics* (London/Glasgow, 1858): 568; 'The quotient p/ρ is what is called the *height, or head due to the pressure*...as the vertical ordinate z is measured *positively downwards* from a datum horizontal plane...$p - \rho z$ is the difference between the intensity of the actual pressure at...[a] particle and the pressure due to its depth below the datum horizontal plane; and $p/\rho - z = h$ is the *height* or *head due to that difference of intensity*, being what will be termed the *dynamic head.*'

(8) Compare Stokes, 'On the steady motion of incompressible fluids': 449.

[2] From these equations it appears that the system of surfaces $G = $ constant is such that the directions of motion of the fluid elements and their axes of rotation lie in these surfaces.

Let $F = $ const be the equation to another system of surfaces of fluid motion so arranged that by the intersection with the surfaces (G) they form tubes of fluid motion, through each of which unit of fluid passes in unit of time, then

$$u = \frac{dF}{dy}\frac{dG}{dz} - \frac{dF}{dz}\frac{dG}{dy}$$

$$v = \frac{dF}{dz}\frac{dG}{dx} - \frac{dF}{dx}\frac{dG}{dz}$$

$$w = \frac{dF}{dx}\frac{dG}{dy} - \frac{dF}{dy}\frac{dG}{dx}.$$

Let $H = $ const be the equation to a third system of surfaces so drawn that by their intersection with the surfaces (G) they form unit eddy tubes (Helmholtz's Wirbelfäden)[9] such that the direction of the tube at any point corresponds to the axis of rotation and its section multiplied by the velocity of rotation is unity.

Then
$$\alpha = \frac{dH}{dz}\frac{dG}{dy} - \frac{dH}{dy}\frac{dG}{dz}$$

$$\beta = \frac{dH}{dx}\frac{dG}{dz} - \frac{dH}{dz}\frac{dG}{dx}$$

$$\gamma = \frac{dH}{dy}\frac{dG}{dx} - \frac{dH}{dx}\frac{dG}{dy}$$

and equations [(1)] will become

$$\frac{dG}{dx} = \rho \frac{dG}{dx} \left\{ \frac{dF}{dx} \cdot \frac{dG}{dy}\frac{dH}{dz} + \frac{dG}{dx} \cdot \frac{dH}{dy}\frac{dF}{dz} \right.$$
$$\left. + \frac{dH}{dx} \cdot \frac{dF}{dy}\frac{dG}{dz} - \frac{dF}{dz} \cdot \frac{dG}{dy}\frac{dH}{dx} - \frac{dG}{dz} \cdot \frac{dH}{dy}\frac{dF}{dx} - \frac{dH}{dz} \cdot \frac{dF}{dy}\frac{dG}{dx} \right\}.$$

---

(9) Helmholtz, 'Über Integrale der hydrodynamischen Gleichungen': 26. Rendered as 'vortex-filaments' by P. G. Tait in his translation of Helmholtz's 'On the integrals of the hydrodynamical equations, which express vortex motion', *Phil. Mag.*, ser. 4, **33** (1867): 485–512, on 486.

Let us put

$$K = \frac{dF}{dx}\frac{dG}{dy}\frac{dH}{dz} + \frac{dG}{dx}\frac{dH}{dy}\frac{dF}{dz} + \frac{dH}{dx}\frac{dF}{dy}\frac{dG}{dz}$$

$$- \frac{dF}{dz}\frac{dG}{dy}\frac{dH}{dx} - \frac{dG}{dz}\frac{dH}{dy}\frac{dF}{dx} - \frac{dH}{dz}\frac{dF}{dy}\frac{dG}{dx}$$

$$= u\frac{dH}{dx} + v\frac{dH}{dy} + w\frac{dH}{dz}$$

$$= \alpha\frac{dF}{dx} + \beta\frac{dF}{dy} + \gamma\frac{dF}{dz}.$$

REPORT ON A PAPER BY JOHN TYNDALL ON CALORESCENCE

1 JANUARY 1866

From the original in the Library of the Royal Society, London[1]

REPORT ON PROF[r] TYNDALLS PAPER ON CALORESCENCE[2]

This paper gives an account of experiments on invisible radiant heat and shows that rays which are not capable of exciting in us the sense of sight may, by heating a body, cause the body to emit luminous rays.[3]

The progress of knowledge of the distribution of heat in the spectrum is first

---

(1) Royal Society, *Referees' Reports*, **6**: 292.

(2) John Tyndall, 'On calorescence', *Phil. Trans.*, **156** (1866): 1–24. The paper was received by the Royal Society on 20 October 1865, and read on 23 November 1865; see the abstract in *Proc. Roy. Soc.*, **14** (1865): 476.

(3) See note (8). Tyndall introduced the term 'calorescence' for this phenomenon of infra-red radiation, to 'express this transmutation of heat-rays into others of higher refrangibility...the invisible being rendered visible.' He observed that it 'harmonizes well with the term "fluorescence" introduced by Professor Stokes', and he noted the phrase 'transmutation of rays' introduced by James Challis; see 'On calorescence': 17. See G. G. Stokes, 'On the change of refrangibility of light', *Phil. Trans.*, **142** (1852): 463–562, on 479n (= *Papers*, **3**: 267–409); and James Challis, 'On the transmutation of rays', *Phil. Mag.*, ser. 4, **12** (1856): 521–6. Tyndall's investigation of the phenomenon arose in the course of his work on the absorption and radiation of heat in the 1860s (see Number 258). See especially his paper 'Contributions to molecular physics', *Phil. Trans.*, **154** (1864): 327–64, esp. 360–2, where he suggests the possibility of calorescence. The speculation, though not the discovery of the phenomenon, had already been made by C. K. Akin, leading to public confrontation between the two men, prior to Tyndall's presentation of his paper 'On calorescence' to the Royal Society. See John Tyndall, 'On luminous and obscure radiation', *Phil. Mag.*, ser. 4, **28** (1864): 329–41; C. K. Akin, 'Note on ray-transmutation', *ibid.*: 554–60; Akin, 'On calcescence', *Phil. Mag.*, **29** (1865): 28–43; Tyndall, 'On the history of negative fluorescence', *ibid.*: 44–55; Akin, 'Further statements concerning the history of calcescence', *ibid.*: 136–51; Tyndall, 'On the history of calorescence', *ibid.*: 218–31; Tyndall, 'On combustion by invisible rays', *ibid.*: 241–4. Tyndall conceded Akin's priority in speculation, but not of discovery and investigation. In his report on Tyndall's paper (Royal Society, *Referees' Reports*, **6**: 293), dated 18 January 1866, Stokes emphasised the experimental basis of Tyndall's work, at the commencement of his report: 'There can be no question, I think, as to the propriety of printing this paper in the Philosophical Transactions. It contains the experimental answer to the question Is it possible to render a body luminous simply by concentration upon it rays of solely invisible heat? The affirmative answer, besides solving the theoretical problem, renders it possible to make experiments on these invisible rays by a ready and direct method, and is connected collaterally with various questions of high interest.'

considered, and the experiments of Sir J. Herschel[4] and Prof[r] Müller[5] on the heat of the Solar spectrum are compared with those of the author on the spectrum of the Electric Lamp.

If we had good methods of splitting up a ray into its spectrum and selecting any given portion corresponding to wave lengths between known limits, the determination of the heating effect of all such portions would furnish the most complete quantitative knowledge of the nature of the light. For if the ray is entirely consumed in heating a body, the quantity of heat produced in a second is a measure in known terms of the energy of the ray, and though the luminous properties of rays of different wave-lengths are in very different ratios to their heating powers, this ratio must be fixed for each determinate wave length.

Hence a determination of the distribution of heat in the spectrum of a given kind of light, combined with a previous knowledge of the relation of the heat to the other properties of each ray as a function of its wave-length, would lead to a complete knowledge of the properties of the given beam of light, whether chromatic or chemical.

Every step, therefore, which is made in the knowledge of the distribution of heat in a spectrum, is a step towards a complete knowledge, not of its heat alone, but of its other properties. In the paper, the heat radiated by the carbon points of the electric lamp is examined. As the temperature rises, the radiation, which was at first confined to the invisible part of the spectrum, extends into the visible part, but the invisible part of the radiation continues to increase in intensity, so that the temperature of the source the heating power of the invisible rays and the brightness of the luminous rays all increase together indefinitely as far as we can carry our observations.

The author in p. 3 expresses this by saying that 'the luminous and non luminous emissions augment together, the *maximum* of brightness of the visible rays coinciding with the maximum calorific power of the invisible ones'.[6] I

---

(4) In 'On calorescence': 7 Tyndall does refer to John Herschel's experiments on thermal effects of solar radiation; see J. F. W. Herschel, 'On the chemical action of the rays of the solar spectrum on preparations of silver and other substances, both metallic and non-metallic, and on some photographic processes', *Phil. Trans.*, **130** (1840): 1–59, esp. 52–9. But the work on the distribution of heat in the solar spectrum, which Maxwell here alludes to, was due to William Herschel, and it is this work which Tyndall reviews in the introduction to 'On calorescence': 1–2; see William Herschel, 'Experiments on the solar spectrum, and on the terrestrial rays that occasion heat', *Phil. Trans.*, **90** (1800): 293–326, 437–538, esp. 439–41 and Plate XX.

(5) J. Müller, 'Untersuchungen über die thermischen Wirkungen des Sonnenspectrums', *Ann. Phys.*, **105** (1858): 337–59; (trans.) 'Investigations on the thermal effects of the solar spectrum', *Phil. Mag.*, ser. 4, **17** (1859): 233–50, esp. 242.

(6) Tyndall, 'On calorescence: 2 (the italic is Maxwell's). In the published text there is a

do not think that the use of the word maximum here conduces to express the meaning. If the luminosity rises and falls (in time) the calorific power does the same and their maxima occur at the same time, but the maximum calorific effect in the spectrum, which has been spoken of before never coincides with the brightest point of the spectrum.

Experiments are then described on the distribution of heat in the spectrum of the electric light as formed by rock salt prisms and lenses. These show that the heat radiations extend far beyond the red end of the spectrum, that the maximum of heat is considerably beyond the red and that the total invisible heat is about eight times the visible. The length of the spectrum from the beginning of the green to the end of the red appears to have been about 8 millimeters. From the end of the red to the maximum about 2.75 m.m. and from the end of the red till the heat became insensible 19 m.m.

In repeating these experiments it would be of great advantage to test the purity of the spectrum by observing the absorption bands seen in it through small blue glass or still better by sodium vapour.[7]

If the focal lengths of the rock salt lenses were ascertained for any luminous ray and the index of refraction of a given invisible ray ascertained from the deviation produced by the prism of rock salt, the proper distance of the screen for receiving a pure spectrum could be calculated for any invisible part of the spectrum. It would however require several additional precautions to ascertain that the *extreme* portions of the observed heat spectrum are not partly due to scattering of the rays within the prism owing to its not being perfectly transparent with respect to such rays.

This observation does not apply to the observed maximum which is evidently a physical fact.

From the experiments in which a white heat was produced in platinum and other bodies by the concentration of invisible rays[8] it appears that a small part of the radiation from the carbons namely that which fell on the mirror

---

footnote appended to this sentence referring to Tyndall's 'Rede Lecture for 1865'; see John Tyndall, *On Radiation* (London, 1865): 30, where there is discussion of the 'material jostling of the atoms' of the incandescent substance, so that 'the light-giving waves would follow as the necessary progeny of the heat-giving vibrations'.

(7) In his report on Tyndall's paper (see note (3)) Stokes commented: 'It is not easy to connect [Tyndall's readings]...with definite points in the spectrum. I think the value and interest of the table would be increased by supplementary measures'. See Tyndall, 'On calorescence': 4–5.

(8) Focusing the radiation of an electric arc on a foil of platinised platinum, the beam was sifted of luminous radiation by transmission through a solution of iodine in carbon bisulphide; the foil was raised to incandescence and emitted light. See Tyndall, 'On calorescence': 10–14.

or lens and afterwards escaped absorption by the iodine has sufficient energy of motion to bring solid bodies to a white heat. If by any means the more rapid vibrations of the heated carbons could be deadened in the carbon itself, as the luminous radiation is deadened by iodine in the intermediate medium, we should have a non-luminous body able to render a neighbouring body white hot, and therefore the original body would have a temperature higher than white heat without emitting luminous rays. But it is probable that the absorbing power of iodine depends on its temperature and that unless it were much colder than the source of heat it would itself supply any loss of luminous rays.

The experiment of putting the eye into the focus of heat is striking[9] but is quite unnecessary as a much better evidence of non luminosity is obtained by simply looking at the carbons through the iodine. For it is better to compare a small area than a large one with total blackness in order to test its non-luminosity, since the physiological test can be best applied by looking at the boundary between the given area and total blackness.

Of course when the eye is placed *at* the focus the variation of luminosity over the mirror depends on the defects of the mirror or focussing, and the eye should see a large uniform field of light or dimness. The carbons themselves were seen directly and not by reflexion at the mirror.

In conclusion, I consider this paper, as demonstrating the power of rays of long period to heat a body to such an extent as to make it emit copiously rays of shorter period to be worthy of a place in the Philosophical Transactions as a step in the history of science, while the employment of the electric lamp as a source of radiant heat and of iodine as an absorber of the luminous rays opens the way for a more complete investigation of the non luminous heat rays by affording us a source of great intensity and it may be hoped that the wave length of many of these rays their index of refraction in rock salt and their peculiar relations to various absorbing materials may be more fully studied in consequence of this paper.[10]

J. CLERK MAXWELL
Cambridge, 1st Jan 1866[11]

---

(9) Tyndall commented: 'I do not recommend the repetition of these experiments'; 'On calorescence': 15n.

(10) In his report (see note (3)) Stokes criticised Tyndall's 'illustration of calorescence derived from the production of small waves when a huge wave of the sea dashes against a rock'. He commented: 'Everything tends to show that in phosphorescence, fluorescence, calorescence the molecules of the body are thrown into a state of agitation, and that it is their agitation, communicated to the ether, which is the source of the altered period.' Compare Tyndall's discussion as published in 'On calorescence': 5–6n, on the oscillation of atoms; and see note (6).

(11) Maxwell was in Cambridge to examine for the Mathematical Tripos.

256

FROM A LETTER TO CHARLES BENJAMIN TAYLER[1]

2 FEBRUARY 1866

From Campbell and Garnett, *Life of Maxwell*[2]

8 Palace Gardens Terrace
W.
2 February 1866

You ask for my history since I wrote to you before my marriage. We remained in Aberdeen till 1860, when the union or fusion of the Colleges took place, and I went to King's Coll., London, where I taught till last Easter,[3] when I was succeeded by W. G. Adams,[4] brother of the astronomer.[5] I have now my time fully occupied with experiments and speculations of a physical kind, which I could not undertake as long as I had public duties.

---

(1) See Volume I: 220–1.

(2) *Life of Maxwell*: 344–5; abridged.

(3) See Number 235 note (20).

(4) William Grylls Adams, St John's 1855 (Venn), who had been appointed to succeed G. R. Smalley (see Number 209 note (2)) in the lectureship in Natural Philosophy on 9 October 1863, was appointed Maxwell's successor as Professor of Natural Philosophy on 10 March 1865; see King's College London Archives, King's College Council Vol. I, minutes 276, 415.

(5) John Couch Adams, St John's 1839, Lowndean Professor of Astronomy and Geometry at Cambridge 1859 (Venn).

LETTER TO HUGH ANDREW JOHNSTONE MUNRO[1]

7 FEBRUARY 1866

From the original in the Library of Trinity College, Cambridge[2]

8 Palace Gardens Terrace
London W.
1866 Feb 7

Dear Sir

I am writing about the Dynamical Theory of Gases and am making a short statement of those who have started or embraced similar theories before from Lucretius[3] down to D Bernoulli,[4] Le Sage of Geneva under the name of Lucrèce Newtonien[5] and Clausius[6] now professor at Zurich and myself.[7] The details of the mechanics are very different in these different writers on account of their different measure of acquaintance with the theory of collision &c. With respect to those who flourished since the revival of science I can make out pretty well what they really meant but I am afraid to say anything of Lucretius because his words sometimes seem so appropriate that it is with great regret that one is compelled to cut off a great many marks from him for showing that he did not mean what he has already said so well.

Here is what I have written. Will you tell me if you think it unjust to Lucretius either in excess or defect.

---

(1) Trinity 1838, Tutor 1855–7, Junior Bursar 1862–6 (Venn); see *Titi Lucreti Cari De Rerum Natura Libri Sex*, ed. and trans. H. A. J. Munro, 2 vols. (Cambridge, 1864, $_2$1866). Garber, Brush and Everitt, *Molecules and Gases*: 83n suggest Munro as the addressee of Maxwell's letter.

(2) Trinity College, Cambridge, Add. MSS. c. 111^{10}. Previously published in *Molecules and Gases*: 82–3.   (3) Lucretius, *De Rerum Natura*: see note (1).

(4) Daniel Bernoulli, *Hydrodynamica, sive de Viribus et Motibus Fluidorum Commentarii* (Strasbourg, 1738): 200–2.

(5) G. L. Le Sage, 'Lucrèce Newtonien', *Nouveaux Mémoires de l'Académie des Sciences et Belles-Lettres de Berlin* (1782): 404–32; and in Pierre Prevost, *Notice de la Vie et des Écrits de George-Louis Lesage de Genève* (Geneva, 1805): 561–604. In his paper 'Ueber die Wärmeleitung gasförmiger Körper', *Ann. Phys.*, **115** (1862): 1–56, on 2n (see Number 207) Clausius cites Lesage's 'Physique mécanique' in *Deux Traités de Physique Mécanique* publiés par Pierre Prevost (Geneva/Paris, 1818): 1–186, a reference repeated by Maxwell in 'On the dynamical theory of gases', *Phil. Trans.*, **157** (1867): 42–88, on 50 (= *Scientific Papers*, **2**: 28).

(6) Rudolf Clausius, 'Ueber die Art der Bewegung welche wir Wärme nennen', *Ann. Phys.*, **100** (1857): 353–80; Clausius, 'Ueber die mittlere Länge der Wege...', *ibid.*, **105** (1858): 239–58.

(7) J. C. Maxwell, 'Illustrations of the dynamical theory of gases', *Phil. Mag.*, ser. 4, **19** (1860): 19–32; *ibid.*, **20** (1860): 21–37 (= *Scientific Papers*, **1**: 377–409).

'The notion of particles flying about in all directions, like the motes in a sunbeam, and causing by their impact the motion of larger bodies is to be found in the exposition of the theories of Democritus by Lucretius, but the nature of the impacts and the deviation produced in the path of the particles are described in language which we must interpret according to the physical conceptions of the age of the author that is we must get rid of every distinct physical idea which his words may have suggested to us.'[8]

Is this saying it too severely about a clever and intelligent ancient?

In particular have the Lucretian atoms an original motion all the same and in the same (downward) direction and equally accelerated (lib II 238, 239)[9] except insofar as they deviate, and so and only so come into collision (v 220 &c)[10] whereas (at v 90) spatium sine fine modoque est.[11]

The words are such a good illustration of the modern theory at v 100 lib II &c[12] that it would be a pity if they meant something quite different.

The *great intervals* between the collisions in air are in fact about $\frac{1}{400000}$ of an inch[13] but they are great compared to those in other media.

In my late capacity of Junior Moderator[14] I have to obtain a poet for Tripos day 7th April. Finding no impulse towards poesy existing at Trinity Hall I asked Gray[15] if the Trinity men were inclined that way. Can you tell

---

(8) Compare Maxwell, 'On the dynamical theory of gases': 50 (= *Scientific Papers*, **2**: 27–8).

(9) *De Rerum Natura*, ed. Munro, 2 vols. (Cambridge, $_2$1866), **1**: 92, 'omnia quapropter debent per inane quietum/aeque ponderibus non aequis concita ferri'; ('and for this reason all things must be moved and borne along with equal velocity though of unequal weights through the unresisting void', *ibid.*, **2**: 33).

(10) *De Rerum Natura*, ed. Munro, **1**: 91, 'tantum quod momen mutatum dicere possis./quod nisi declinare solerent, omnia deorsum/imbris ubi guttae, caderent per inane profundum/nec foret offensus natus nec plaga creata/principiis; ita nil umquam natura creasset'; ('you just and only just can call it a change of inclination. If they were not used to swerve, they would all fall down like drops of rain, through the deep void, and no clashing would have been begotten nor blow produced among the first beginnings: thus nature never would have produced aught', *ibid.*, **2**: 33). See Numbers 377 and 439 on the swerve of Lucretian atoms.

(11) *De Rerum Natura*, ed. Munro, **1**: 86 (Book II, 92); 'space is without end and limit' (*ibid.*, **2**: 30).

(12) *De Rerum Natura*, **1**: 87 (Book II, 100–103), 'et quaecumque magis condenso conciliatu/exiguis intervallis convecta resultant,/indupedita suis perplexis ipsa figuris,/haec validas saxi radices et ferra ferri'; ('and all that form a denser aggregation when brought together, rebound leaving trifling spaces between, held fast by their own close-tangled shapes, these form enduring bases of stone and unyielding bodies of iron and such like', *ibid.*, **2**: 30).

(13) See Maxwell's paper presented to the British Association in 1860 (Volume I: 659–60).

(14) See *The Cambridge University Calendar for the Year 1866* (Cambridge, 1866): 448.

(15) Charles Gray, Trinity 1851, Junior Dean 1862–6 (Venn).

me how the appointment is made, and whether Pollock[16] or any other Trinity man would compose a hymn worthy of the day when the names of Colleges assume their Latin forms.

I remain
Yours truly
J. CLERK MAXWELL

[16] Frederick Pollock, Trinity 1863, Browne Medal 1866 (Venn).

REPORT ON A PAPER BY JOHN TYNDALL ON RADIATION

22 FEBRUARY 1866

From the original in the Library of the Royal Society, London[1]

8 Palace Gardens Terrace
London W
1866 Feb 22

I have read Professor Tyndall's 'Sixth Memoir on Radiation and Absorption',[2] and consider it worthy of publication in the Philosophical Transactions.[3]

The author has shown by numerous instances that the behaviour of bodies with respect to radiations from dark sources is different from their behaviour with respect to visible radiations, and that the former is much more connected with simplicity of chemical constitution than the latter. He has also shown that rock salt is not equally transparent to all radiations from bodies at 100 °C but that it is less transparent to radiation from salt, and more transparent to radiation from platinum black, than to other radiations. Hence 1st All radiations from bodies at 100 °C are not alike, but differ in quality, and 2nd Rock salt has variations of absorptive power in that part of the spectrum which corresponds to rays of great wave-length such as are alone emitted from sources of low temperature. Hence if curves were drawn, the abscissae of which corresponded to wavelengths or to periods of vibration, and the ordinates to the absorptive power of a substance for radiations of such periods; the curve corresponding to rock salt which we know to have very small absorption for radiations invisible from their shortness of period as well as to visible radiations and invisible heat radiations from sources of high temperature would exhibit one or more maxima of absorption for certain rays of very long period, the numerical relation of which to the period of visible rays is not yet ascertained.

J. CLERK MAXWELL

---

(1) Royal Society, *Referees' Reports*, **6**: 294.

(2) John Tyndall, 'Sixth memoir on radiation and absorption. – Influence of colour and mechanical condition on radiant heat', *Phil. Trans.*, **156** (1866): 83–96. The paper was received by the Royal Society on 21 December 1865, and read on 18 January 1866; see the abstract in *Proc. Roy. Soc.*, **15** (1866): 5.

(3) Tyndall's five previous papers 'On the absorption and radiation of heat' had been published in *Phil. Trans.*, **151** (1861): 1–36; *ibid.*, **152** (1862): 59–98; *ibid.*, **153** (1863): 1–12; *ibid.*, **154** (1864): 201–25; *ibid.*, **154** (1864): 327–68.

DRAFTS OF 'ON THE DYNAMICAL THEORY OF GASES'[1]

LATE 1865 – EARLY 1866[2]

From the originals in the University Library, Cambridge[3]

[ON THE DYNAMICAL THEORY OF GASES]

[1] **[On the mutual action of two molecules][4]**

Let us now consider the alteration in the path of a molecule in consequence of the action of another molecule which comes near it in its course.

Let us suppose the two molecules moving with equal momenta in opposite directions so that their centre of gravity is at rest.

Let their masses be M_1, M_2, their initial velocities V_1, V_2 and their distances from the centre of gravity r_1 r_2. We shall suppose them initially so distant that ⟨the⟩ force between them vanishes and they are moving sensibly in parallel straight lines at distances b_1 b_2 from the centre of gravity.

In consequence of the mutual action between the molecules each will describe a plane curve, the two curves being symmetrical with respect to the centre of gravity, and when the molecules are again out of reach of their mutual action they will be found moving from one another with velocities V_1 V_2 on straight lines distant b_1 b_2 from the centre of gravity but inclined to the directions of the original lines of motion by an angle 2θ where θ is the angle between the asymptotes and the apse of the orbit.

If the molecules are not mere centres of force[5] but bodies capable of internal motions their paths after the encounter will be different, and their velocities may not be exactly equal before and after but as we do not know the constitution of molecules we shall treat them as if they were mere centres of force.

---

(1) J. Clerk Maxwell, 'On the dynamical theory of gases', *Phil. Trans.*, **157** (1867): 49–88 (= *Scientific Papers*, **2**: 26–78).

(2) The paper was received by the Secretary of the Royal Society on 16 May 1866; see Number 263. On its composition, see Maxwell's letters to H. R. Droop of 19 July 1865, H. A. J. Munro of 7 February 1866, and William Thomson of 27 February 1866 (Numbers 250, 257 and 260).

(3) ULC Add. MSS 7655, V, f/6. Portions of this manuscript have been published in *Molecules and Gases*: 387–97.

(4) Compare 'On the dynamical theory of gases': 56–7 (= *Scientific Papers*, **2**: 35–6).

(5) See Number 266 note (6).

The angle θ may be calculated when we know V, b and the law of force where $V = V_1 + V_2$ & $b = b_1 + b_2$.

[2] [On the mutual action of two molecules][6]

Now let the components of the velocity of M_1 be $\xi_1\,\eta_1\,\zeta_1$ those of M_2 $\xi_2\,\eta_2\,\zeta_2$ and those of the centre of gravity of M_1 & M_2 $\bar{\xi}\,\bar{\eta}\,\bar{\zeta}$. Then we know by Dynamics that the velocity of the centre of gravity will be unchanged by the mutual action and that the motion of either molecule relatively to the centre of gravity will not be affected by the circumstance that the whole system is in motion.

The components of V_1 the velocity of M_1 relative to the centre of gravity are $\xi_1 - \bar{\xi}, \eta_1 - \bar{\eta}, \zeta_1 - \bar{\zeta}$. After M_1 and M_2 have met and deflected each other from their courses the value of V_1 will be the same but its direction will be turned through an angle 2θ in the plane containing the directions of V_1 and b. Let ϕ be the angle which this plane makes with the plane containing the direction of V and parallel to the axis of x and let $\xi_1 + \delta\xi_1$ be the component velocity of M_1 in the direction of x after the mutual action of the molecules.

$$\xi_1 + \delta\xi_1 = \frac{M_1\xi_1 + M_2\xi_2}{M_1 + M_2}$$
$$+ \frac{M_2}{M_1 + M_2}\{(\xi_1 + \xi_2)\cos 2\theta + \sqrt{(\eta_1 - \eta_2)^2 + (\zeta_1 - \zeta_2)^2}\sin 2\theta \cos\phi\}$$

or

$$\xi_1 + \delta\xi_1 = \xi_1 + \frac{M_2}{M_1 + M_2}\{(\xi_2 - \xi_1)\,2\sin^2\theta + \sqrt{(\eta_2 - \eta_1)^2 + (\zeta_2 - \zeta_1)^2}\sin 2\theta \cos\phi\}.$$

There will be similar expressions for the components of the new velocity of M_1 in the other coordinate directions.

[3] [On the mutual action of molecules in motion][7]

To find the Equations of Motion of a Medium composed of Molecules in motion acting on one another with forces which are insensible at distances which are small compared with the average distance of the Molecules.

Let us begin by considering two particles whose masses are $M_1\,M_2$ at a considerable distance from each other so that the force between them is insensible. Let their velocities resolved in the coordinate directions be

---

(6) Compare 'On the dynamical theory of gases': 57 (= *Scientific Papers*, 2: 36–7).

(7) Compare 'On the dynamical theory of gases': 60 (= *Scientific Papers*, 2: 40).

$\xi_1\,\eta_1\,\zeta_1$ and $\xi_2\,\eta_2\,\zeta_2$. Let V be the velocity of M_1 relative to M_2 and let G be the velocity of the centre of gravity of M_1 & M_2. Also let b be the minimum distance to which the particles would approach if there were no action between them.

In consequence of the mutual action between M_1 & M_2 when they come near each other, each will describe a curve about G their centre of gravity in the plane of V and b and when they have passed out of each others influence each will have a velocity relative to the centre of gravity equal in magnitude to its former value but in a direction inclined 2θ to its former direction in the plane of V & b, 2θ being the angle between the asymptotes of the orbit.

Let us assume that the moving force between the particles is as the nth power of the distance inversely and that its value at distance unity is K and repulsive then the well known equation[8]

$$\frac{d^2u}{d\theta^2}+u+\frac{P}{h^2u^2}=0$$

becomes by integration and putting $u=\frac{x}{b}$ and $b=\alpha\left(\frac{K}{V^2}\frac{(M_1+M_2)}{M_2}\right)^{\frac{1}{n-1}}$

$$\theta=\int\frac{dx}{\sqrt{1-x^2-\frac{2}{n-1}\left|\frac{x}{\alpha}\right|^{n-1}}}.\qquad(9)$$

Let θ be the value of this integral taken between the limits $x=0$ and x a root of the equation

$$1-x^2-\frac{2}{n-1}\left|\frac{x}{\alpha}\right|^{n-1}=0.$$

[4] **Law of Volumes**

To determine the variation in the quantity of ⟨heat⟩ energy, put

$$Q=\tfrac{1}{2}M_1(\xi_1^2+\eta_1^2+\zeta_1^2)$$

---

(8) The orbital equation for the path under a central force P. See J. H. Pratt, *The Mathematical Principles of Mechanical Philosophy* (Cambridge, $_2$1845): 223–4, where $u=\dfrac{1}{r}$, $h=$ constant $= x\dfrac{dy}{dt}-y\dfrac{dx}{dt}$, as cited in Maxwell's undergraduate notebook 'Statics Dynamics' (ULC Add. MSS 7655, V, m/10, on f. 89).

(9) These equations are corrected in 'On the dynamical theory of gases': 60 (= *Scientific Papers*, 2: 40). On the result that $n=5$ see Number 263; and on the computation of the paths of the molecules see Number 262.

and let us first consider the value of $\frac{\delta Q}{\delta t}$ due to the action of the molecules of the second kind on those of the first in a mixed medium in equilibrium when $u\ v\ w$ are $= 0^{(10)}$

then
$$\frac{\delta Q_1}{\delta t} = \frac{k\rho_2}{M_2}\Theta_1\left\{\frac{1}{2}M_2(\xi_2^2+\eta_2^2+\zeta_2^2) - \frac{1}{2}M_1(\xi_1^2+\eta_1^2+\zeta_1^2)\right.$$
$$\left. + \frac{1}{2}(M_1-M_2)(\xi_1\xi_2+\eta_1\eta_2+\zeta_1\zeta_2)\right\}. \quad (11)$$

Since ξ_1 is independent of ξ_2 and since the mean values of both are zero the product $\xi_1\xi_2$ has zero for its mean value so that the terms $\xi_1\xi_2$, $\eta_1\eta_2$, $\zeta_1\zeta_2$ disappear and we may write the result

$$\frac{\delta Q_1}{\delta t} = \frac{k\rho_2}{M_2}\Theta_1\{Q_2-Q_1\}.$$

Similarly
$$\frac{\delta Q_2}{\delta t} = \frac{k\rho_1}{M_1}\Theta_1\{Q_1-Q_2\}$$

whence
$$\frac{\delta}{\delta t}(Q_1-Q_2) = -k\Theta_1\left(\frac{\rho_1}{M_1}+\frac{\rho_2}{M_2}\right)(Q_1-Q_2)$$

or
$$Q_1-Q_2 = Ce^{-\frac{t}{T}} \quad \text{where} \quad \frac{1}{T} = k\Theta_1\left(\frac{\rho_1}{M_1}+\frac{\rho_2}{M_2}\right). \quad (12)$$

---

(10) u, v, w are the components of the mean velocity of all the molecules which are at a given instant in a given element of volume, hence there is no motion of translation. ξ, η, ζ, are the components of the relative velocity of one of these molecules with respect to the mean velocity, the 'velocities of agitation of the molecules'. See 'On the dynamical theory of gases': 68 (= *Scientific Papers*, 2: 51).

(11) ρ_1, ρ_2 are the densities of the two systems of molecules, Θ the absolute temperature.

(12) In 'On the dynamical theory of gases': 82 (= *Scientific Papers*, 2: 69) Maxwell terms T the 'modulus of the time of relaxation'. In the introduction to 'On the dynamical theory of gases': 52–4 (= *Scientific Papers*, 2: 30–2) he introduced the concept of 'time of relaxation' as a method of defining viscosity. He suggested that the rate of relaxation of the stress F of a viscous body is related to the strain S by the equation $\frac{dF}{dt} = E\frac{dS}{dt} - \frac{F}{T}$, where E is the coefficient of elasticity for that particular kind of strain. In his paper 'On double refraction in a viscous fluid in motion', *Proc. Roy. Soc.*, 22 (1873): 46–7 (= *Scientific Papers*, 2: 379–80) he described an attempt to establish the relaxation time: 'In 1866 I made some attempts to ascertain whether the state of strain in a viscous fluid in motion could be detected by its action on polarized light' (compare Volume I: 125–7, 145–6, 148, 151–6 for his early investigation of induced double refraction in strained solids), recording that 'I observed an effect on polarized light when I compressed some Canada balsam', but that the effect was so transient that 'I have hitherto been unable to determine the rate of relaxation of that state of strain'.

Hence if Q_1 is originally different from Q_2 the values of Q_1 and Q_2 will rapidly approach to equality and will be sensibly equal in a few multiples of the very short time T, and in all movements of the media except the most violent Q_1 & Q_2 will remain equal. Now Q_1 is the actual energy of a single molecule of the first system due to the motion of agitation of its centre of gravity and Q_2 is the same for a single molecule of the second system. The energies of single molecules of mixed systems therefore tend to equality whatever the mass of each molecule may be.

Now when the gases are such that neither communicates energy to the other, their temperatures are the same and we have seen that $Q_1 = Q_2$ in this case.

But for either gas $NQ = \tfrac{3}{2}p$

therefore if both the temperature and the pressure be the same in two different gases, then N the number of molecules in unit of volume is also the same in the two gases. This is the law of Volumes of gases,[13] first discovered by Gay-Lussac from chemical considerations.[14] It is a necessary result of the Dynamical Theory of Gases.

In the case of a single gas in motion let Q be the total energy of a single molecule then

$$Q = \tfrac{1}{2}M((u+\xi)^2 + (v+\eta)^2 + (w+\zeta)^2 + \beta(\xi^2 + \eta^2 + \zeta^2))\text{\tiny(15)}$$

and $\dfrac{\delta Q}{\delta t} = M(uX + vY + wZ)$.

The general equation ( ) becomes

$$\tfrac{1}{2}\rho\frac{\partial}{\partial t}\left(u^2 + v^2 + w^2 + (1+\beta)(\xi^2 + \eta^2 + \zeta^2)\right) + \frac{d}{dx}(u\rho\xi^2 + v\rho\xi\eta + w\rho\xi\zeta)$$

$$+ \frac{d}{dy}(u\rho\xi\eta + v\rho\eta^2 + w\rho\eta\zeta)$$

$$+ \frac{d}{dz}(u\rho\xi\zeta + v\rho\eta\zeta + w\rho\zeta^2) + \tfrac{1}{2}\frac{d}{dx}(1+\beta)\rho(\xi^3 + \xi\eta^2 + \xi\zeta^2)$$

---

(13) Compare Maxwell's discussion of 'Avogadro's hypothesis' in his letter to Stokes of 30 May 1859 (Volume I: 610) and see his 'Illustrations of the dynamical theory of gases. Part I. On the motions and collisions of perfectly elastic spheres', *Phil. Mag.*, ser. 4, **19** (1860): 19–32, esp. 30 (= *Scientific Papers*, **1**: 390); 'This result agrees with the chemical law, that equal volumes of gases are chemically equivalent'.

(14) See Number 263 where Maxwell repeats his attribution to Gay-Lussac; and 'On the dynamical theory of gases': 78 (= *Scientific Papers*, **2**: 64). See also Number 375 note (2).

(15) 'β is the ratio of the total energy [of a molecule] to the energy of translation'; see 'On the dynamical theory of gases': 55 (= *Scientific Papers*, **2**: 34), and Number 207 esp. note (20).

$$+\frac{1}{2}\frac{d}{dy}(1+\beta)\rho(\xi^2\eta+\eta^3+\eta\zeta^2)+\frac{1}{2}\frac{d}{dz}(1+\beta)\rho(\xi^2\zeta+\eta^2\zeta+\zeta^3)$$
$$=\rho(uX+vY+wZ).$$

Substituting the values of $\rho X\ \rho Y\ \rho Z$

$$\frac{1}{2}\rho\frac{\partial}{\partial t}(1+\beta)(\xi^2+\eta^2+\zeta^2)+\rho\xi^2\frac{du}{dx}+\rho\eta^2\frac{dv}{dy}+\rho\zeta^2\frac{dw}{dz}$$
$$+\rho\eta\zeta\left(\frac{dv}{dz}+\frac{dw}{dy}\right)+\rho\zeta\xi\left(\frac{dw}{dx}+\frac{du}{dz}\right)+\rho\xi\eta\left(\frac{du}{dy}+\frac{dv}{dx}\right)$$
$$+\frac{1}{2}(1+\beta)\left\{\frac{d}{dx}\rho(\xi^3+\xi\eta^2+\xi\zeta^2)+\frac{d}{dy}\rho(\xi^2\eta+\eta^3+\eta\zeta^2)\right.$$
$$\left.+\frac{d}{dz}\rho(\xi^2\zeta+\eta^2\zeta+\zeta^3)\right\}=0.$$

[5]   **[Specific heat at constant volume]**[16]

The total energy of agitation of unit of volume of the medium is $\frac{3}{2}(1+\beta)p$ hence the total energy of agitation of unit of mass is

$$E=\frac{3}{2}(1+\beta)\frac{p}{\rho}.$$

If now additional energy be communicated to it in the form of heat without altering its density

$$\partial E=\frac{3}{2}(1+\beta)\frac{\partial p}{\rho}=\frac{3}{2}(1+\beta)\frac{p}{\rho}\frac{\partial\theta}{\theta}.$$

Hence the specific heat of unit of mass at constant volume is in dynamical measure

$$\frac{\partial E}{\partial\theta}=\frac{3}{2}(1+\beta)\frac{p}{\rho\theta}.$$

[Specific heat at constant pressure][17]

If the gas be now allowed to expand without receiving more heat from without till the pressure sinks to p the temperature will sink by a quantity $\partial\theta'$ such that

$$\frac{\partial\theta'}{\theta'}=\frac{2}{5+3\beta}\frac{\partial p}{p}=\frac{2}{5+3\beta}\frac{\partial\theta}{\theta}.$$

---

(16) Compare 'On the dynamical theory of gases': 79 (= *Scientific Papers*, **2**: 65).
(17) Compare 'On the dynamical theory of gases': 79–80 (= *Scientific Papers*, **2**: 66).

The total change of temperature is therefore $\partial\theta - \partial\theta' = \dfrac{3+3\beta}{5+3\beta}\partial\theta$ and the specific heat of unit of mass at constant pressure is

$$\frac{\partial E}{\partial \theta'} = \frac{5+3\beta}{2}\frac{p}{\rho\theta}.$$

The ratio of the specific heat at constant pressure to that at constant volume is $\dfrac{5+3\beta}{3+3\beta}$ a quantity which is generally denoted by the symbol γ.[18]

We have then $\beta = \dfrac{5-3\gamma}{3\gamma-3}$

and $\quad\dfrac{dE}{d\theta} = \dfrac{1}{\gamma-1}\dfrac{p}{\rho\theta}\quad$ the specific heat at constant volume

$\quad\dfrac{dE}{d\theta'} = \dfrac{\gamma}{\gamma-1}\dfrac{p}{\rho\theta}\quad$ the specific heat at constant pressure

expressions from which the specific heat of air has been calculated by Professor Rankine and found to agree with the values determined experimentally by M. Regnault.[19]

[6] [Determination of the inequality of pressure in a medium][20]

Let us next determine the variation of the pressure in the direction of x in a simple medium and make $Q = M(u+\xi)^2$ then by equation ( ) we find

$$\frac{\delta Q}{\delta t} = 2k\rho_2\Theta_2(\eta^2+\zeta^2+\xi^2) + 2M\xi X$$

whence

$$\rho\frac{\partial\overline{\xi^2}}{\partial t} + 2\left(\xi^2\rho\frac{du}{dx} + \xi\eta\rho\frac{du}{dy} + \xi\zeta\rho\frac{du}{dz} + \frac{d}{dx}\xi^3\rho\right.$$
$$\left. + \frac{d}{dy}\xi^2\eta\rho + \frac{d}{dz}\xi^2\zeta\rho\right) = \frac{6k\rho}{M}\Theta_2(p-\xi^2\rho).$$ [21]

Omitting for the present the terms involving three dimensions in $\xi\,\eta\,\zeta$

---

(18) The symbol was introduced by Poisson; see S. D. Poisson, *Traité de Mécanique*, 2 vols. (Paris, $_2$1833), **2**: 714–15; and Volume I: 608n.

(19) W. J. M. Rankine, 'On the mechanical action of heat', *Trans. Roy. Soc. Edinb.*, **20** (1853): 565–89, esp. 588–9, citing values determined by H. V. Regnault, 'Recherches sur les chaleurs spécifiques des fluides élastiques (3)', *Comptes Rendus*, **36** (1853): 676–87, esp. 685–6.

(20) Compare 'On the dynamical theory of gases': 80–3 (= *Scientific Papers*, **2**: 68–71).

(21) Maxwell terms k the 'coefficient of mutual interference' of the molecules; see 'On the dynamical theory of gases': 84 (= *Scientific Papers*, **2**: 72–3).

which refer to conduction of heat and taking the value of $\frac{\partial p}{\partial t}$ from equation ( )

$$\frac{\partial}{\partial t}(\rho\xi^2-p)+2p\frac{du}{dx}-\frac{2}{3}p\left(\frac{du}{dx}+\frac{dv}{dy}+\frac{dw}{dz}\right)=\frac{6k\rho\Theta_2}{M}(p-\xi^2\rho)$$

putting p for $\rho\xi^2$ and omitting $\xi\eta\rho$ and $\xi\zeta\rho$ in terms not involving the large coefficient $6k\rho\Theta_2$. If the motion is not very violent we may also neglect $\frac{\partial}{\partial t}(\rho\xi^2-p)$ and then we have

$$\xi^2\rho = p - \frac{M}{9k\rho\Theta_2}p\left(2\frac{du}{dx}-\frac{dv}{dy}-\frac{dw}{dz}\right)$$

with similar expressions for $\eta^2\rho$ and $\zeta^2\rho$. By transformation of coordinates we can easily obtain the expressions for $\xi\eta\rho$ $\eta\zeta\rho$ and $\zeta\xi\rho$.

They are of the form

$$\eta\zeta\rho = -\frac{M}{6k\rho\Theta_2}p\left(\frac{dv}{dz}+\frac{dw}{dy}\right).$$

Having thus obtained the values of the pressures in different directions we may substitute them in the equation of motion.

$$\rho\frac{\partial u}{\partial t}+\frac{d}{dx}(\rho\xi^2)+\frac{d}{dy}(\rho\xi\eta)+\frac{d}{dz}(\rho\xi\zeta)=X\rho$$

which becomes

$$\rho\frac{\partial u}{\partial t}+\frac{dp}{dx}-\frac{pM}{6k\rho\Theta_2}\left\{\frac{d^2u}{dx^2}+\frac{d^2u}{dy^2}+\frac{d^2u}{dz^2}+\frac{1}{3}\frac{d}{dx}\left(\frac{du}{dx}+\frac{dv}{dy}+\frac{dw}{dz}\right)\right\}=X\rho. \quad (22)$$

[Coefficient of Viscosity]

This is the equation of motion in the direction of x. The other equations may be written down by symmetry. The form of the equations is identical with that deduced by Poisson*[23] from the theory of elasticity by supposing the strain to be constantly relaxed at a given rate and the ratio of the

---

* Journal de l'Ecole Polytechnique 1829 tom XIII cah. 20 p. 139.[23]

---

(22) The equation of fluid motion: see notes (23) and (25), and Number 260.
(23) Siméon Denis Poisson, 'Mémoire sur les équations générales de l'équilibre et du mouvement des corps solides élastiques et des fluides', *Journal de l'École Polytechnique*, **13** cahier 20 (1831): 1–174, see esp. 152, equation (9).

coefficients of $\nabla^2 u$ and $\dfrac{d}{dx}\dfrac{1}{\rho}\dfrac{\partial \rho}{\partial t}$ [24] agrees with that given by Professor Stokes.†[25]

The quantity $\dfrac{pM}{6k\rho\Theta_2}$ is the coefficient of viscosity or of internal friction and is denoted by μ in the writings of Professor Stokes and in my paper on the Viscosity of Air and other Gases.[26]

In this expression Θ_2 is a numerical quantity k is a quantity depending on the intensity of the action between two molecules at unit of distance.[27] The ratio of p to ρ is proportional to the temperature from absolute zero and is independent of the density. Hence in a given gas, μ is independent of the pressure[28] and proportional to the temperature,[29] as is found by experiment.‡[30]

Putting $\qquad k = \left(\dfrac{K}{8M}\right)^{\frac{1}{2}} \quad p = MN\xi^2 \quad \rho = MN$

σ = specific gravity compared with air

$$\mu = \dfrac{2^{\frac{3}{2}}}{6\Theta_2}\dfrac{M^{\frac{1}{2}}}{K^{\frac{1}{2}}}M\xi^2.$$

Now $M\xi^2$ is the same for all gases at the same temperature, therefore μ varies as $\left(\dfrac{M}{K}\right)^{\frac{1}{2}}$ for different gases at the same temperature.

† Cambridge Phil Trans. vol VIII (1845).[25]
‡

---

(24) The fourth term (from the equation of continuity).

(25) George Gabriel Stokes, 'On the theories of the internal friction of fluids in motion, and of the equilibrium and motion of elastic solids', *Trans. Camb. Phil. Soc.*, **8** (1845): 287–319, esp. 297, equation (12) (= *Papers*, **1**: 75–129).

(26) See note (30).

(27) In 'On the dynamical theory of gases': 84–5 (= *Scientific Papers*, **2**: 73), Maxwell refers to Thomas Graham's experiments in determining values of k, the coefficient of mutual interference of the molecules of the gases. See Number 263.

(28) On the independence of μ and the density of a gas compare 'Illustrations of the dynamical theory of gases. Part I': 32 (= *Scientific Papers*, **1**: 391); his letter to Stokes of 30 May 1859 (Volume I: 610); and Numbers 207 and 252.

(29) See Numbers 248, 249 and 252.

(30) J. C. Maxwell, 'On the viscosity or internal friction of air and other gases', *Phil. Trans.*, **156** (1866): 249–68, and see Number 252. O. E. Meyer, 'Ueber die innere Reibung der Gase', *Ann. Phys.*, **125** (1865): 177–209, 401–20, 564–99 gave experimental support for Maxwell's result, which had so surprised him in 1859 (see note (28)), that the viscosity is independent of the density of a gas.

[7] [Conduction of heat][31]

We have next to determine the rate of variation of the quantity $\xi^3+\xi\eta^2+\xi\zeta^2$ in a simple medium. Putting

$$Q = M(u+\xi)(u^2+v^2+w^2+2u\xi+2v\eta+2w\zeta+(1+\beta)(\xi^2+\eta^2+\zeta^2))$$

and making u, v & w zero after the differentiations and neglecting terms of the form $\xi\eta$ in comparison with those of the form ξ^2 and remembering that terms of the forms ξ^3 and $\xi\eta^2$ are also very small we get

$$\mathcal{N}\frac{\delta Q}{\delta t} = -\frac{\sqrt{2}}{M}\sqrt{\frac{K}{M}}(1+\beta)\Theta_2\rho^2(\xi^3+\xi\eta^2+\xi\zeta^2)+2\rho\xi^2 X$$
$$+2\rho\xi\eta Y+2\rho\xi\zeta Z+(1+\beta)\rho(\xi^2+\eta^2+\zeta^2)X.$$

Hence equation ( ) becomes

$$\rho(1+\beta)(\xi^2+\eta^2+\zeta^2)\frac{\partial u}{\partial t}+2\rho\xi^2\frac{\partial u}{\partial t}+2\rho\xi\eta\frac{\partial v}{\partial t}+2\rho\xi\zeta\frac{\partial w}{\partial t}$$
$$+\rho\frac{\partial}{\partial t}(1+\beta)(\xi^3+\xi\eta^2+\xi\zeta^2)+(1+\beta)\frac{d}{dx}\rho\xi^2(\xi^2+\eta^2+\zeta^2)$$
$$= -\frac{\sqrt{2}}{M}\sqrt{\frac{K}{M}}(1+\beta)\Theta_2\rho^2(\xi^3+\xi\eta^2+\xi\zeta^2)+2\rho\xi^2 X$$
$$+2\rho\xi\eta Y+2\rho\xi\zeta Z+(1+\beta)\rho(\xi^2+\eta^2+\zeta^2)X.$$

Putting $\rho\frac{\partial u}{\partial t}+\frac{dp}{dx}$ for ρX and omitting terms in $\xi\eta$ &c

$$(1+\beta)\rho\frac{\partial}{\partial t}(\xi^3+\xi\eta^2+\xi\zeta^2)+(1+\beta)\frac{d}{dx}\rho(\xi^4+\xi^2\eta^2+\xi^2\zeta^2)$$
$$-(1+\beta)(\xi^2+\eta^2+\zeta^2)\frac{dp}{dx}-2\xi^2\frac{dp}{dx}$$
$$= \frac{\sqrt{2}}{M}\sqrt{\frac{K}{M}}\Theta_2(1+\beta)\rho^2(\xi^3+\xi\eta^2+\xi\zeta^2).$$

---

(31) Errors arose in establishing these equations; compare 'On the dynamical theory of gases': 85–6 (= *Scientific Papers*, 2: 74–5).

When the motion is steady or when it is not very violent the first term will disappear and the equation may be written

$$3(1+\beta)\frac{d}{dx}\cdot\frac{p^2}{\rho} - (5+3\beta)\frac{p}{\rho}\frac{dp}{dx} = -\sqrt{2}\sqrt{\frac{K}{M^3}}\Theta_2(1+\beta)\rho^2(\xi^3+\xi\eta^2+\xi\zeta^2)$$

or
$$(1+\beta)\rho(\xi^3+\xi\eta^2+\xi\zeta^2) = \sqrt{\frac{M^3}{2K}}\frac{1}{\Theta_2}\frac{p^2}{\rho^2}\left(2\frac{1}{p}\frac{dp}{dx}-3(1+\beta)\frac{d\theta}{dx}\right)$$
$$= \frac{3}{2}\mu\frac{p}{\rho}\left(2\frac{1}{p}\frac{dp}{dx}-3(1+\beta)\frac{1}{\theta}\frac{d\theta}{dx}\right)$$

where μ is the coefficient of viscosity. This is the quantity of heat, measured as mechanical energy which is carried over unit of area in unit of time when the pressure and temperature vary from point to point.

[8] **[Condition of equilibrium of a gas]**

A quantity of gas is in equilibrium in a vessel under the action of gravity, to determine the pressure and temperature at any point when both the pressure and temperature have assumed their final state.

The condition of mechanical equilibrium is

$$\frac{dp}{dx} = \rho g$$

where x is measured in the direction in which g acts. We have also

$$p = \tfrac{1}{3}\rho(\xi^2+\eta^2+\zeta^2)$$

and in the state of equilibrium $\xi^2 = \eta^2 = \zeta^2$.

The whole energy of a molecule M is

$$\tfrac{1}{2}M(1+\beta)(\xi^2+\eta^2+\zeta^2)$$

where $\xi\,\eta\,\zeta$ and β have values peculiar to that molecule.

Now let the molecule move so as to increase x by dx then gravity will do work upon it $= Mgdx$ and its energy will now be increased by this amount. If its energy is now greater than the mean of that of the molecules among which it has arrived it will increase the mean energy of the molecules in that part of the field, and if it is less it will diminish the mean energy but if the mean energy of these molecules is greater by $Mgdx$ than the original energy of the molecule considered, its arrival will not alter the mean energy of the surrounding molecules.

That this must be the case generally we must have

$$\frac{1+\beta}{2}\frac{d}{dx}(\xi^2+\eta^2+\zeta^2) = g$$

and if this condition be fulfilled, any molecule passing from one position to another will have the excess of its energy above the mean energy of the surrounding molecules the same throughout its path.

[9] [Effect of gravity on the temperature of a column of gas]

Since μ is independent of the density and proportional to the pressure the coefficient of conductivity for heat which is $\frac{9}{2}\frac{p}{\rho\theta}\mu(1+\beta)$[32] will also be independent of the density and will vary directly as the temperature.

The condition of there being no conduction of heat is

$$\frac{d\theta}{dp} = \frac{2}{3(1+\beta)}\frac{\theta}{p}.$$

Now when the pressure of a gas is gradually changed no heat being allowed to enter or escape

$$\frac{d\theta}{dp} = \frac{2}{5+3\beta}\frac{\theta}{p}.$$

If therefore a mass of gas under the action of gravity were to be left to itself till conduction of heat ceased, the temperature would diminish more rapidly with the height than that of a portion of gas carried up bodily. If the portion of gas were to ascend it would be warmer than the surrounding gas and would therefore tend to ascend still, and if it were to descend below its original position it would be colder than the surrounding gas and would tend to descend further. Hence the condition of final equilibrium of heat in a gas acted on by gravity is one of mechanical instability so that such a mass of gas left to itself will perpetually be converting part of its heat into visible motion or currents and the energy thus developed will be reconverted into heat by friction.[33]

If however the motion were properly regulated the energy thus developed

---

(32) See the last equation in §7.

(33) In an 'Addition made December 17, 1866' to 'On the dynamical theory of gases': 86–7 (= *Scientific Papers*, **2**: 75–6) Maxwell recollected that: 'When I first attempted this investigation [of the final equilibrium of temperature of a column of gas] I overlooked the fact that $\overline{\xi^4}$ is not the same as $\overline{\xi^2}.\overline{\xi^2}$, and so obtained as a result that the temperature diminishes as the height increases at a greater rate than it does by expansion when air is carried up in mass. This leads at once to a condition of instability, which is inconsistent with the second law of thermodynamics. I wrote to Professor Sir W. Thomson about this result, and the difficulty I had met with [Number 260], but presently discovered *one* of my mistakes, and arrived at the conclusion that the temperature would increase with the height'. This was the conclusion Maxwell stated in the paper as submitted to the Royal Society in May 1866: see Number 263, esp. note (23).

could be transferred to machinery so as to convert the invisible agitation of the gas into any other form of energy and thus form a perpetual motion. For instance if a portion of the gas were carried upwards and made to expand so as always to be at the same temperature with the surrounding gas it would be rarer than the surrounding gas and the resultant of pressure and gravity on the portion of gas would act upwards and so do work. If when at the highest point it is allowed to acquire the temperature and pressure of the surrounding gas and is then lowered and compressed so as to be always at the temperature of the surrounding gas, it will be denser than the surrounding gas and the resultant of gravity and pressure will act downwards and still do work. Thus from a mass of gas acted on by gravity energy may be abstracted to any amount, and the gas cooled to a corresponding extent.

This result is directly opposed to the second law of Thermodynamics which affirms that 'it is impossible by means of inanimate material agency to derive mechanical effect from any portion of matter by cooling it below the temperature of the coldest part of the surrounding objects.'*[34]

I think it necessary to confirm a result so much opposed to so important a doctrine by a more elementary investigation in which we do not require to consider the precise nature of the action between the molecules or to determine the coefficient of conductivity.[35]

* W. Thomson. On the Dynamical Theory of Heat Trans. Edin. 1851 p 265[34]

---

(34) William Thomson, 'On the dynamical theory of heat', *Trans. Roy. Soc. Edinb.*, **20** (1851): 261–88, on 265 (= *Math. & Phys. Papers*, **1**: 179). Maxwell modified Thomson's wording slightly: compare Number 277 note (9).

(35) See Numbers 260 and 263.

LETTER TO WILLIAM THOMSON

27 FEBRUARY 1866

From the original in the University Library, Glasgow[1]

8 Palace Gardens Terrace
London W.
1866 Feb 27

Dear Thomson

In working at the Dynamical Theory of Gases I have come on the following paradox, which I intend to think about, but I should be obliged to you for the benefit of your views.[2]

1st Suppose $\overline{\xi^2}$ to represent the mean square of the velocity of a molecule in direction of x it is easy to show that

$$p = \rho\overline{\xi^2}.$$

2nd If $\overline{\eta^2}$ & $\overline{\zeta^2}$ be the mean squares of the velocities in the other two directions and if β be the ratio of the energy of rotation or other internal motion to that of translation then the mean total energy of a molecule will be

$$\frac{1}{2}M(\overline{\xi^2}+\overline{\eta^2}+\overline{\zeta^2})(1+\beta)$$

and that of unit of volume

$$\frac{3}{2}(1+\beta)\rho\xi^2 = \frac{3}{2}(1+\beta)p$$

and that of unit of mass

$$\frac{3}{2}(1+\beta)\frac{p}{\rho}.$$

3rd Now let unit of mass be enclosed in volume V and let V become $V+dV$ then work $= pdV$ is done and we must have

$$d\left(\frac{3}{2}(1+\beta)pV\right)+pdV = 0$$

or since

$$pV = \xi^2 \quad \text{and} \quad V = \frac{1}{\rho}$$

$$\frac{3}{2}(1+\beta)\frac{d.\xi^2}{\xi^2} = \frac{d.\rho}{\rho}.$$

---

(1) Glasgow University Library, Kelvin Papers, M 19.
(2) See James Clerk Maxwell, 'On the dynamical theory of gases', *Phil. Trans.*, **157** (1867): 49–88, esp. 86–7 (= *Scientific Papers*, **1**: 75–6). Compare Number 259 §8 and §9.

All this is the ordinary theory putting

$$\frac{3}{2}(1+\beta) = 1-\gamma \quad \text{and} \quad \xi^2 = CT(\text{emperature}).$$

Now comes the difficulty.

4th To determine the conditions of equilibrium of temperature in a heavy gas.

The mean energy of a molecule is

$$\frac{1}{2}M(\xi^2+\eta^2+\zeta^2)(1+\beta).$$

If it ascends a distance dx against a force g this is diminished by $gMdx$.

If its mean energy thus diminished is greater than that of the molecules in the stratum into which it has come it will increase the mean energy there if less it will diminish it therefore for eq^m of heat

$$gMdx + d\left(\frac{1}{2}M(\xi^2+\eta^2+\zeta^2)(1+\beta)\right) = 0$$

or

$$gdx + \frac{3}{2}(1+\beta)d\bar{\xi}^2 = 0.$$

Now

$$gdx = -\frac{dp}{\rho} =$$

$$\therefore \frac{3}{2}(1+\beta)\frac{d.\bar{\xi}^2}{\bar{\xi}^2} = \frac{dp}{p}.$$

This is the condition of no conduction of heat up or down in a heavy gas.

Now since $p = \rho\bar{\xi}^2$, $\quad \dfrac{dp}{p} = \dfrac{d\rho}{\rho} + \dfrac{d\xi^2}{\xi^2}.$

If then a mass of gas under gravity is left to itself the law of temperature will be

$$\frac{dT}{T} = \frac{2}{3(1+\beta)}\frac{dp}{p}$$

whereas if the pressure of the gas is changed dp

$$\frac{dT}{T} = \frac{2}{5+3\beta}\frac{dp}{p}$$

so that the temperature in a vertical column decreases faster with the pressure than that of a portion of gas carried up the column bodily.

Now for the paradox

5th   Take a large mass of gas and let it come into thermic equilibrium. Take a small portion in a cylinder & piston without weight or counterbalanced. Raise it and let it expand so as to have the same pressure with the surrounding gas, then as it is hotter it will be lighter and will be buoyant, so that, as it goes up it will do work. When it comes to the top let it remain till it cools to the surrounding temperature then lower it keeping the pressure equal to the surrounding pressure then it will be colder and therefore denser than the surrounding gas and will sink with a force which may be made to do work.

Thus by means of material agency mechanical effect is derived from the gas under gravity by cooling it below the temperature of the coldest of the surrounding objects. See Thomson Dyn Θ of H 2nd Law.[3]

Whether the dyn. Θ. of Gases is good or not 1 2 & 3 are good mechanics and true of gases. 4 is the only difficulty and the only way out of it seems to be that in the case supposed a molecule moving upwards has not the same mean energy as one moving horizontally or downwards, at the same height. This would involve different pressures in different directions and is otherwise objectionable. So there remains as far as I can see a collision between Dynamics & thermodynamics.

I have just heard Mr Everetts paper at the R S about elasticity of glass.[4] The method is superior to Kirchhoff's[5] in as much as the flexure is produced by couples so as to be uniform over the length of the rod as the torsion is, whereas Kirchhoffs makes the moment greatest in the middle so that the flexure and torsion have different forms for integration whereas here they are the same, and therefore σ[6] is more to be trusted. But Kirchhoffs apparatus was more symmetrical and better adapted to measurement.

Have four equal weights and put them

1st   at $A\,B, A'\,B'$ for torsion $+$
2      $B\,C\,B'\,C'$ flexure $+$
3      $C\,D\,C'\,D'$ torsion $-$
       $D\,A\,D'\,A'$ flexure $-$.

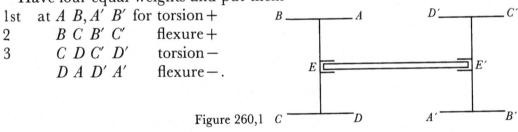

Figure 260,1

---

(3) William Thomson, 'On the dynamical theory of heat', *Trans. Roy. Soc. Edinb.*, **20** (1851): 261–88, on 265 (= *Math. & Phys. Papers*, **1**: 179).   (4) See Number 261 esp. notes (3) and (4).

(5) Gustav Kirchhoff, 'Ueber das Verhältniss der Quercontraction zur Längendilatation bei Stäben von federhartem Stahl', *Ann. Phys.*, **108** (1859): 369–92.

(6) See Number 261 esp. note (6).

The results seem so good that it would be worth while to correct for the deviation of the arm of the couple from the horizontal.

I made a new set of exp^{ts} on viscosity of air and came within $\frac{1}{150}$ of what I got in summer (corrected for temperature of course). If you want the results for your book or anything else here they are.

$$\text{Coeff}^t \text{ of friction } \mu \text{ dimension } \frac{M}{LT}$$

$$\text{at } 62\,°F \; \mu = .09362 \frac{\text{grains}}{\text{feet seconds}} \quad {}^{(7)}$$

$$\mu = .01878\,(1+\alpha\theta)\frac{\text{grammes}}{\text{metres seconds}} \text{ centigrade scale for } \theta.$$

μ is quite independent of the pressure and proportional to the absolute temperature from 50° to 185 °F.

This value is about double Stokes[8] and about half Meyer's.[9]

Hydrogen is .516 of air by my expts. Graham by transpiration gets .485 but he required less hydrogen and less time for his exp^{ts} and I think got purer gas. Carbonic acid .859 by me .807 by Graham.[10] All these gases are dry. Damp air is a very little smoother than dry about $\frac{1}{60}$ part for pressure 4 in temp. 70 °F. Hydrogen and air, equal vols about $\frac{15}{16}$ of air.

Results of dynamical theory not yet tested.

1 Coefficient of conductivity for heat (measured as energy) $= \dfrac{9(1+\beta)}{2}\dfrac{p}{\rho\theta}\mu$

where μ is the coefft of friction or viscosity.[11]

2 Equations of motion are of the form

$$\rho\frac{\partial u}{\partial t} + \frac{dp}{dx} - \mu\left(\frac{d^2u}{dx^2} + \frac{d^2u}{dy^2} + \frac{d^2u}{dz^2}\right) - \frac{\mu}{3}\frac{d}{dx}\left(\frac{du}{dx} + \frac{dv}{dy} + \frac{dw}{dz}\right)$$

the same as Stokes.[12] For different gases

$\dfrac{1}{\mu} \propto \sqrt{\dfrac{M}{K}}$ where M = mass of molecule K force at unit distance.

---

(7) The value cited in 'On the dynamical theory of gases': 83 (= *Scientific Papers*, **2**: 71). Compare Number 252.

(8) G. G. Stokes, 'On the effect of the internal friction of fluids on the motion of pendulums', *Trans. Camb. Phil. Soc.*, **9**, part 2 (1851): [8]–[106], esp. 65 (= *Papers*, **3**: 1–136).

(9) O. E. Meyer, 'Ueber die Reibung der Flüssigkeiten', *Ann. Phys.*, **113** (1861): 55–86, 193–238, 383–425, esp. 383.

(10) Thomas Graham, 'On the motion of gases. Part II', *Phil. Trans.*, **139** (1849): 349–401, esp. 364; and see Number 252 note (13).

(11) See Number 259 §9.   (12) See Number 259 §6, esp. note (25).

3   Mixed gases diffuse till the law of density for each is the same as if the others were away. The equation of diffusion is

$$u_1 p_1 = \frac{D}{p_1 + p_2}\left(X\rho_1 - \frac{dp_1}{dx}\right)$$

where u_1 is vel^y and p_1 the pressure of one gas
p_2 of the other

D is a coeff^t depending on the two gases mutual action.[13] It is independent of density and varies with square of temperature therefore since it is divided by $p_1 + p_2$ the actual rate of diffusion will be as the temperature and inversely as the density.

B Stewart[14] is busy with his 'Chimæra bombylans in vacuo'.[15]

I am going to see the new electrical machine at the R I[16] which I take to be a foreign development of C F Varleys multiplier.[17] There is no doubt that it is the right thing in electrical machines to have no friction but to work up the electricity by induction.

Yours truly
J. CLERK MAXWELL

(13) Compare 'On the dynamical theory of gases': 75 (= *Scientific Papers*, **2**: 60); '*D* is the volume of gas reduced to unit of pressure which passes in unit of time through unit of area when the total pressure is uniform and equal to *p*, and the pressure of either gas increases or diminishes by unity in unit of distance. *D* may be called the coefficient of diffusion.'

(14) The experiments by Balfour Stewart and P. G. Tait, 'On the heating of a disc by rapid rotation *in vacuo*'; see Numbers 244 note (4), 245 note (7) and 262 note (12).

(15) A misquotation from Rabelais, *Pantagruel*, Book II, chap. 7; 'Quaestio subtilissima, utrum Chimæra in vacuo bombinans possit comedere secundas intentiones.' See Volume I: 493.

(16) The Holtz electrical machine: see W. Holtz, 'Ueber eine neue Elektrisirmaschine', *Ann. Phys.*, **126** (1865): 157–71; (trans.) 'On a new electrical machine', *Phil. Mag.*, ser. 4, **30** (1865): 425–33. See the *Treatise*, **1**: 260 (§212).

(17) C. F. Varley's instrument, a patent of 1860, is mentioned by Maxwell in the *Treatise*, **1**: 257n (§210): 'Specification of Patent, Jan. 27, 1860, No. 206'. See Number 302 esp. note (2).

REPORT ON A PAPER BY JOSEPH DAVID EVERETT[1] ON THE RIGIDITY OF GLASS

1 MARCH 1866

From the original in the Library of the Royal Society, London[2]

REPORT ON Dr EVERETTS PAPER ACCOUNT OF EXPERIMENTS ON THE FLEXURAL AND TORSIONAL RIGIDITY OF A GLASS ROD; LEADING TO THE DETERMINATION OF THE RIGIDITY OF GLASS[3]

The experiments here described[4] are in some respects similar to those made by M. Kirchhoff on steel rods Pogg. cviii p369 or Phil Mag 1862 Jany p28[5] in which the flexure and the torsion of the same rod is determined and the relation of the Lateral Contraction to the Longitudinal Extension is estimated.[6] This relation is of great importance in the theory of Elastic Solids, since if we assume elasticity to arise from the direct action of molecules on one another by attractive or repulsive forces acting along the line of centres, this ratio can be shown to be $\frac{1}{4}$,[7] provided the displacement of each

---

(1) Assistant to Hugh Blackburn, Professor of Mathematics at Glasgow, 1864; Professor of Natural Philosophy, Queen's College, Belfast 1867 (*DNB*).

(2) Royal Society, *Referees' Reports*, **6**: 117.

(3) J. D. Everett, 'Account of experiments on the flexural and torsional rigidity of a glass rod, leading to the determination of the rigidity of glass', *Phil. Trans.*, **156** (1866): 185–91. The paper was received by the Royal Society on 1 February 1866, and read on 22 February 1866; see the abstract in *Proc. Roy. Soc.*, **15** (1866): 19–20.

(4) Everett's experiments were carried out in William Thomson's laboratory at Glasgow University in the summer of 1865, following a plan devised by Thomson, who communicated the paper to the Royal Society; see Everett, 'Account of experiments on the flexural and torsional rigidity of a glass rod': 185. Thomson had himself recently reported work on the subject to the Royal Society; see William Thomson, 'On the elasticity and viscosity of metals', *Proc. Roy. Soc.*, **14** (1865): 289–97.

(5) Gustav Kirchhoff, 'Ueber das Verhältniss der Quercontraction zur Längendilatation bei Stäben von federhartem Stahl', *Ann. Phys.*, **108** (1859): 369–92; (trans.) 'On the relation of the lateral contraction to the longitudinal expansion in rods of spring steel', *Phil. Mag.*, ser. 4, **23** (1862): 28–47.

(6) Everett denotes this relation by the symbol σ, and terms it 'Poisson's ratio'; see 'Account of experiments on the flexural and torsional rigidity of a glass rod': 189. See notes (7) and (9).

(7) As stated by Siméon Denis Poisson, 'Mémoire sur l'équilibre et le mouvement des corps élastiques', *Mémoires de l'Académie Royale des Sciences de l'Institut de France*, **8** (1829): 357–570, 623–7, on 451. This value is a consequence of Poisson's molecular force law and assumption of an invariable ratio between the linear rigidity and the compressibility of the volume of elastic solids: see note (9).

molecule is a function of its position in the body.⁽⁸⁾ If however the displacement of each molecule is a function of a different form from that of the others, the ratio may be different, and if the molecules are in a state of motion or if the elasticity is in part due to the pressure of molecular atmospheres, the ratio will be greater than $\frac{1}{4}$.⁽⁹⁾

The torsional elasticity of any portion of a rod of any form depends on the moment of inertia of the section about its centre of gravity in its own plane.

The flexural elasticity of the same portion of the rod as regards bending in a given plane depends on the moment of inertia of the section about a diameter perpendicular to that plane. Now if two diameters be taken at right angles to each other the sum of the moments of inertia is equal to the moment of inertia about an axis perpendicular to the plane. Hence by comparing the torsion of a portion of a rod with the flexure produced first in one plane and then in a plane at right angles the ratio of the rigidity to the longitudinal elasticity can be determined without knowing the form of the section.

In experiments on torsion, the moment of twisting is the same at every section of the rod. It is desirable therefore that in the experiments on flexure the moment of bending should be uniform for every section. This condition is fulfilled in Dr Everetts experiments by applying two equal and opposite couples at the ends of the rod. In M Kirchhoffs experiments the rod was supported at the middle and loaded at the end so that the moment of bending decreased from the middle to the ends so that the result will depend more on the stiffness of the middle of the rod than on that of the ends. In this respect Dr Everetts method is to be preferred and I think this should be stated. The form of the apparatus for applying the force might I think be improved by an arrangement like this.

---

(8) In his paper 'On the equilibrium of elastic solids', *Trans. Roy. Soc. Edinb.*, **20** (1850): 87–120, esp. 87 (= *Scientific Papers*, **1**: 31), Maxwell had termed this 'the assumption of Navier'. For his discussion of theories of elasticity see Volume I: 133–5.

(9) Rejecting Poisson's molecular force law and assumption of an invariable ratio between linear rigidity and compressibility of volume, Stokes introduced two arbitrary independent coefficients of elasticity; see G. G. Stokes, 'On the theories of the internal friction of fluids in motion, and of the equilibrium and motion of elastic solids', *Trans. Camb. Phil. Soc.*, **8** (1845): 287–319 (= *Papers*, **1**: 75–129). In 'On the equilibrium of elastic solids' Maxwell followed Stokes' method; see Volume I: 133–5, 138–40, 142–4. In experiments on glass, Guillaume Wertheim had obtained an experimental value of $\frac{1}{3}$ for 'Poisson's ratio', at variance with Poisson's theoretical value; see Guillaume Wertheim, 'Mémoire sur l'équilibre des corps solides homogènes', *Ann. Chim. Phys.*, ser. 3, **23** (1848): 52–95, esp. 55, 57. See also G. Wertheim, 'On the cubical compressibility of certain solid homogeneous bodies', *Phil. Mag.*, ser. 4, **21** (1861): 447–51.

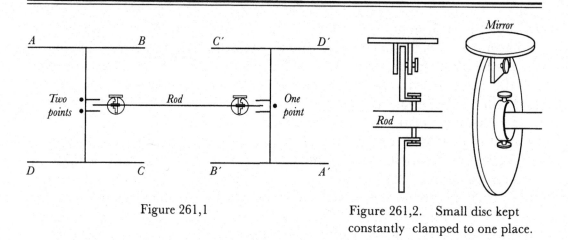

Figure 261,1

Figure 261,2. Small disc kept constantly clamped to one place.

The Weights to be placed on $ABA'B'$ then on $BCB'C'$ and so on. The flexibility of the supports of the mirrors should be carefully tested.[10]

I also think that since the points marked C, E in the figure in the paper are not in the same horizontal plane, a small alteration in the direction of the arm will make an appreciable alteration on the value of the moment.[11] These points therefore should either be placed in the same horizontal line or the angle of the line joining them should be measured. I think that the accuracy of the results obtained warrants this refinement.[12]

The value of σ[13] found by Dr Everett for glass is .258
That found by Wertheim[14] by a different method is about .33 crystal
          Kirchhoff[15] for   steel   .296
                             brass   .387

These are all greater than .25 as they ought to be[16] but Dr Everetts is much

---

(10) Everett had measured the bending produced in a cylindrical rod by means of 'two mirrors, rigidly attached to the rod...which form by reflexion upon a screen two images of a fine wire placed in front of a lamp-flame'; Everett, 'Account of experiments on the flexural and torsional rigidity of a glass rod': 185.

(11) The arm CE provides a twisting couple to a rod secured at C; see Plate XVI Fig. 3 in *Phil. Trans.*, **156** (1866).

(12) In a subsequent series of experiments Everett modified his apparatus on the lines Maxwell suggests: see Number 269.

(13) See note (6).   (14) See note (9).
(15) See note (5).   (16) See notes (7) and (9).

the smallest. By experiments in 1850[17] I made $\sigma = .267$ for iron and $.332$ for glass.[18]

I consider Dr Everetts paper worthy of publication, the reference to Kirchhoffs paper being made a little fuller as the methods are similar.

JAMES CLERK MAXWELL
1866 March 1

(17) Early in 1850, as an intended 'Appendix' to his paper 'On the equilibrium of elastic solids', Maxwell recorded the results of 'some rough experiments on the twisting and bending of cylindric rods', iron and brass wires and glass rods; see Volume I: 179–83. These experiments were continued in July 1850; see Volume I: 193–4.

(18) In his personal copy of 'On the equilibrium of elastic solids' reprinted from *Trans. Roy. Soc. Edinb.*, **20** (1850): 87–120 (Cavendish Laboratory, Cambridge), Maxwell recorded 'Results of Experiments July 1850' on the bending of iron wires. He subsequently appended the values for σ mentioned here to this record of his July 1850 experiments. These values were cited by Everett ('Professor J. Clerk Maxwell, by experiments in 1850, glass .332, iron .267') in his 'Account of experiments on the flexural and torsional rigidity of a glass rod': 191.

LETTER TO PETER GUTHRIE TAIT

4 APRIL 1866
From the original in the University Library, Cambridge[1]

Glenlair
Dalbeattie
1866 April 4

Dear Tait

I have not access to Legendre[2] here. Could you get for me or ask one of your students to get for me the following values of log F_c or

$$\int_0^{\frac{\pi}{2}} \frac{d\psi}{\sqrt{1-\sin^2\phi \sin^2\psi}} \quad [3]$$ for these values of ϕ.

	Log F_c
$\phi = 30°$	0.226793
32°	
34°	
36°	
38°	
40°	0.252068
42°	

I have put down the values for 30° & 40° that there may be no mistake as to the table of F_c. It is the 1st or 2nd table of Complete Functions.[4] I have got all the values required except those which occur in a place I want more accuracy.[5]

---

(1) ULC Add. MSS 7655, I, b/5. Previously published in *Molecules and Gases*: 413–14.

(2) A. M. Legendre, *Traité des Fonctions Elliptiques et des Intégrales Eulériennes, Avec des Tables pour en faciliter le calcul numérique*, 2 vols. (Paris, 1825–6).

(3) In Legendre's classification of elliptic integrals, this is an integral of the first kind (the simplest of the elliptic transcendentals), of the form $F_c = \int (1/\Delta)\, d\psi$, where $\Delta = \sqrt{1-c^2\sin^2\psi}$ and $0 < c < 1$; see Legendre, *Fonctions Elliptiques*, **1**: 14–18. The modulus of the elliptic integral $c = \sin\phi$.

(4) This is the first table 'contenant les logarithmes des fonctions complètes'; see Legendre, *Fonctions Elliptiques*, **2**: 227–30. In his reply (see note (15)) Tait copied out the requested values.

(5) Maxwell required the values of the elliptic integrals to calculate the paths described by molecules about a centre of force repelling inversely as the fifth power of the distance. See J. C. Maxwell, 'On the dynamical theory of gases', *Phil. Trans.*, **157** (1867): 49–88, on 60–1 (= *Scientific Papers*, **2**: 41–2). Assuming that the molecules originally moved with equal velocities

I hope to hear soon of you and Thomson coming out.[6] If you do not come out soon I shall not be able to tickle the Questionists next Jan[y(7)] with the Scotch School in a lawful manner. I suppose you know that Laplace's Coeff[ts (8)] and Fig $\oplus$[9] are lawful. If you were out I could set things that I can only set now with ten lines of explanation or problem upon problem, that is if Thomson quotes correct in his papers.[10]

The dynamical theory of Viscosity of gases, conduction of Heat in d° and interdiffusion of d° with absolute measures of most things will soon be out. That is what F_c is for.[11]

Stewart is buzzing away with the Chimæra[12] at Kew.[13] He should have a sulphuric acid vacuum gauge such as you and Andrews used[14] to observe

---

in parallel paths, he computes the way in which their deflections depend on the distance of the path from the centre of force. See Number 259 §3.

(6) W. Thomson and P. G. Tait, *Treatise on Natural Philosophy* (Oxford, 1867). But see Tait's reply (note (15)).

(7) Maxwell had been appointed Examiner for the Cambridge Mathematical Tripos. See *The Cambridge University Calendar for the Year 1867* (Cambridge, 1867): 459. The term 'questionists' was the 'appellation of the students during the last six weeks of preparation' for the examination; see Volume I: 330.

(8) Spherical harmonics; see note (10). For a standard contemporary account see J. H. Pratt, *The Mechanical Principles of Mechanical Philosophy, and their Application to the Theory of Universal Gravitation* (Cambridge, $_2$1845): 159–75.

(9) Figure of the earth; see Thomson and Tait, *Natural Philosophy*: 399, and note (10).

(10) William Thomson made repeated reference to 'Thomson and Tait's *Natural Philosophy*, chap. i, Appendix B' (the treatment of spherical harmonic analysis in *Natural Philosophy*: 140–60) in his paper 'Dynamical problems regarding elastic spheroidal shells and spheroids of incompressible liquid', *Phil. Trans.*, **153** (1863): 583–616, esp. 585–6 (= *Math. & Phys. Papers*, **3**: 351–94); 'we shall call any homogeneous function of (x, y, z) which satisfies the equation $\nabla^2 V = 0$ a "spherical harmonic function", or more shortly, a "spherical harmonic"... spherical surface-harmonics of integral order, have been generally called "Laplace's coefficients" by English writers.' On the application of these methods to the problem of the rigidity of the earth see 'Dynamical problems regarding elastic spheroidal shells': 606–10; and Thomson, 'On the rigidity of the earth', *Phil. Trans.*, **153** (1863): 573–82. See Number 277 note (5).

(11) See note (5).

(12) Balfour Stewart and P. G. Tait, 'On the heating of a disc by rapid rotation *in vacuo*', *Proc. Roy. Soc.*, **15** (1866): 290–9. On the term 'chimæra' see Number 260 note (15). On Stewart and Tait's experiments see Numbers 244 note (4) and 245 note (7).

(13) Balfour Stewart was Director of the Kew Observatory (*DNB*).

(14) Thomas Andrews and P. G. Tait, 'On the volumetric relations of ozone, and the action of the electric discharge on oxygen and other gases', *Phil. Trans.*, **150** (1860): 113–31, esp. 114–15 and Plate III, where they describe a vacuum gauge to determine minute changes in the volume of a gas.

changes of pressure in the rarefied air (indicating changes of temp. due to friction of air) which will be proportionally greater as the air is rarer.

Yours truly,
J. CLERK MAXWELL[15]

---

(15) In his reply of 6 April 1866 (ULC Add. MSS 7655, I, a/2) Tait listed the requested values from Legendre's first table of elliptic integrals.

'Coll. Library Edin^h 6/4/66

							For 0°.1		
ϕ		Log F'			Diff I			II	III
30°	0.226	793	259	758	211	349	731	796 387	1060
32	0.231	172	806	867	227	486	050	818 789	1188
34	0.235	879	485	458	244	095	463	843 883	1332
36	0.240	923	287	876	261	235	001	872 015	1492
38	0.246	315	415	669	278	969	140	903 590	1677
40	0.252	068	441	749	297	371	255	939 099	1886
42	0.258	196	504	876	316	525	426	979 129	2133

⌊Splendid exercise in interpolation. When are we (if ever) to see you in Edinburgh.⌋ / Dear Maxwell, / There they are, as large as life. Legendre gives them for every tenth of a degree so you may get any amount more if you want them. Thomson & I will be out certainly in May – & you will find ample materials to justify you in giving P_i & Fig $\oplus$. But perhaps you would like a few sheets now – If so, say so. / I'll take Stewart to task about the Chimæra next week – He is here, but too busy at present. / Yours truly / P. G. Tait.' The letter is annotated by Maxwell on the *verso* with some preliminary calculations relating to his computation of the paths of particles; see note (5).

ABSTRACT OF PAPER 'ON THE DYNAMICAL THEORY OF GASES'

[16 MAY 1866][1]

From the *Proceedings of the Royal Society*[2]

ON THE DYNAMICAL THEORY OF GASES[3]

By J. Clerk Maxwell, F.R.S. L. & E.

Received May 16, 1866

(Abstract)

Gases in this theory are supposed to consist of molecules in motion, acting on one another with forces which are insensible, except at distances which are small in comparison with the average distance of the molecules. The path of each molecule is therefore sensibly rectilinear, except when two molecules come within a certain distance of each other, in which case the direction of motion is rapidly changed, and the path becomes again sensibly rectilinear as soon as the molecules have separated beyond the distance of mutual action.

Each molecule is supposed to be a small body consisting in general of parts capable of being set into various kinds of motion relative to each other, such as rotation, oscillation, or vibration, the amount of energy existing in this form bearing a certain relation to that which exists in the form of the agitation of the molecules among each other.

The mass of a molecule is different in different gases, but in the same gas all the molecules are equal.

The pressure of the gas is on this theory due to the impact of the molecules on the sides of the vessel, and the temperature of the gas depends on the velocity of the molecules.

The theory as thus stated is that which has been conceived, with various degrees of clearness, by D. Bernoulli,[4] Le Sage and Prevost,[5]

---

(1) The date the paper was received by the Royal Society. The paper was read on 31 May 1866: see note (2). (2) *Proc. Roy. Soc.*, **15** (1866): 167–71.

(3) Published in *Phil. Trans.*, **157** (1867): 49–88 (= *Scientific Papers*, **2**: 26–78). There is a referee's report by William Thomson: see his letter to Stokes of 13 October 1866 (Royal Society, *Referees' Reports*, **6**: 179; printed in Wilson, *Stokes–Kelvin Correspondence*, **1**: 327–30; and see Number 266 notes (4), (6) and (8)).

(4) Daniel Bernoulli, *Hydrodynamica* (1738); see Number 257 note (4).

(5) G. L. Le Sage, 'Lucrèce Newtonien' (1782), and *Deux Traités de Physique Mécanique* (1818) publiés par Pierre Prevost; see Number 257 note (5).

Herapath,[6] Joule,[7] and Krönig,[8] and which owes its principal developments to Professor Clausius.[9] The action of the molecules on each other has been generally assimilated to that of hard elastic bodies, and I have given some application of this form of the theory to the phenomena of viscosity, diffusion, and conduction of heat in the Philosophical Magazine for 1860.[10] M. Clausius has since pointed out several errors in the part relating to conduction of heat,[11] and the part relating to diffusion also contains errors.[12] The dynamical theory of viscosity in this form has been re-investigated by M. O. E. Meyer, whose experimental researches on the viscosity of fluids have been very extensive.[13]

In the present paper the action between the molecules is supposed to be that of bodies repelling each other at a distance, rather than of hard elastic bodies acting by impact; and the law of force is deduced from experiments on the viscosity of gases to be that of the inverse fifth power of the distance, any other law of force being at variance with the observed fact that the viscosity is proportional to the absolute temperature. In the mathematical application of the theory, it appears that the assumption of this law of force leads to a great simplification of the results, so that the whole subject can be treated in a more general way than has hitherto been done.

I have therefore begun by considering, first, the mutual action of two molecules; next that of two systems of molecules, the motion of all the molecules in each system being originally the same. In this way I have

---

(6) John Herapath, *Mathematical Physics; or the Mathematical Principles of Natural Philosophy: with a Development of the Causes of Heat, Gaseous Elasticity, Gravitation, and other Great Phenomena of Nature*, 2 vols. (London, 1847). Maxwell had been familiar with Herapath's book in 1859; see Volume I: 610–11. Garber, Brush and Everitt, *Molecules and Gases*: 80–1, publish a letter of Herapath's dated 23 February 1864, which they believe to be addressed to Maxwell.

(7) James Prescott Joule, 'Some remarks on heat, and the constitution of elastic fluids', *Memoirs of the Literary and Philosophical Society of Manchester*, **9** (1851): 107–14 (read 3 October 1848); and in *Phil. Mag.*, ser. 4, **14** (1857): 211–16.

(8) A. Krönig, 'Grundzuge einer Theorie der Gase', *Ann. Phys.*, **99** (1856): 315–22.

(9) R. Clausius, 'Ueber die Art der Bewegung welche wir Wärme nennen', *Ann. Phys.*, **100** (1857): 353–80; Clausius, 'Ueber die mittlere Länge der Wege...', *ibid.*, **105** (1858): 239–58.

(10) J. C. Maxwell, 'Illustrations of the dynamical theory of gases', *Phil. Mag.*, ser. 4, **19** (1860): 19–32; *ibid.*, **20** (1860): 21–37 (= *Scientific Papers*, **1**: 377–409).

(11) R. Clausius, 'Ueber die Wärmeleitung gasförmiger Körper', *Ann. Phys.*, **115** (1862): 1–56; see Number 207, esp. notes (9) and (39).

(12) See Maxwell's discussion of diffusion in his letter to William Thomson of 27 February 1866 (Number 260).

(13) O. E. Meyer, 'Ueber die innere Reibung der Gase', *Ann. Phys.*, **125** (1865): 177–209, 401–20, 564–99.

determined the rate of variation of the mean values of the following functions of the velocity of molecules of the first system –

α, the resolved part of the velocity in a given direction.

β, the square of this resolved velocity.

γ, the resolved velocity multiplied by the square of the whole velocity.

It is afterwards shown that the velocity of translation of the gas depends on α, the pressure on β, and the conduction of heat on γ.

The final distribution of velocities among the molecules is then considered, and it is shown that they are distributed according to the same law as the errors are distributed among the observations in the theory of 'Least Squares', and that if several systems of molecules act on one another, the average *vis viva* of each molecule is the same, whatever be the mass of the molecule. The demonstration is of a more strict kind than that which I formerly gave, and this is the more necessary, as the 'Law of Equivalent Volumes', so important in the chemistry of gases, is deduced from it.

The rate of variation of the quantities α, β, γ in an element of the gas is then considered, and the following conclusions are arrived at.

(α) 1st. In a mixture of gases left to itself for a sufficient time under the action of gravity, the density of each gas at any point will be the same as if the other gases had not been present.

2nd. When this condition is not fulfilled, the gases will pass through each other by diffusion. When the composition of the mixed gases varies slowly from one point to another, the velocity of each gas will be so small that the effects due to inertia may be neglected. In the quiet diffusion of two gases, the volume of either gas diffused through unit of area in unit of time is equal to the rate of diminution of pressure of that gas as we pass in the direction of the normal to the plane, multiplied by a certain coefficient, called the coefficient of interdiffusion of these two gases. This coefficient must be determined experimentally for each pair of gases. It varies directly as the square of the absolute temperature, and inversely as the total pressure of the mixture. Its value for carbonic acid and air, as deduced from experiments given by Mr. Graham in his paper on the Mobility of Gases,*[14] is

$$D = 0.0235,\text{[15]}$$

the inch, the grain, and the second being units. Since, however, air is itself a

---

* Philosophical Transactions. 1863.[14]

(14) Thomas Graham, 'On the molecular mobility of gases', *Phil. Trans.*, **153** (1863): 385–405, esp. 404–5 for experiments on the interdiffusion of carbon dioxide and air.

(15) See Number 260 note (13).

mixture, this result cannot be considered as final, and we have no experiments from which the coefficient of interdiffusion of two pure gases can be found.

3rd. When two gases are separated by a thin plate containing a small hole, the rate at which the composition of the mixture varies in and near the hole will depend on the thickness of the plate and the size of the hole. As the thickness of the plate and the diameter of the hole are diminished, the rate of variation will increase, and the effect of the mutual action of the molecules of the gases in impeding each other's motion will diminish relatively to the moving force due to the variation of pressure. In the limit, when the dimensions of the hole are indefinitely small, the velocity of either gas will be the same as if the other gas were absent. Hence the volumes diffused under equal pressures will be inversely as the square roots of the specific gravities of the gases, as was first established by Graham†;[16] and the quantity of a gas which passes through a thin plug into another gas will be nearly the same as that which passes into a vacuum in the same time.

(β) By considering the variation of the total energy of motion of the molecules, it is shown that,

1st. In a mixture of two gases the mean energy of translation will become the same for a molecule of either gas. From this follows the law of Equivalent Volumes, discovered by Gay-Lussac from chemical considerations; namely, that equal volumes of two gases at equal pressures and temperatures contain equal numbers of molecules.[17]

2nd. The law of cooling by expansion is determined.

3rd. The specific heats at constant volume and at constant pressure are determined and compared. This is done merely to determine the value of a constant in the dynamical theory for the agreement between theory and experiment with respect to the values of the two specific heats, and their ratio is a consequence of the general theory of thermodynamics, and does not depend on the mechanical theory which we adopt.[18]

4th. In quiet diffusion the heat produced by the interpenetration of the gases is exactly neutralized by the cooling of each gas as it passes from a dense to a rare state in its progress through the mixture.

5th. By considering the variation of the difference of pressures in different directions, the coefficient of viscosity or internal friction is determined, and the equations of motion of the gas are formed. These are of the same form as

† 'On the Law of the Diffusion of Gases'. Transactions of the Royal Society of Edinburgh, vol. xii. (1831).[16]

(16) Thomas Graham, 'On the law of the diffusion of gases', *Trans. Roy. Soc. Edinb.*, **12** (1832): 222–58.

(17) On Gay-Lussac and 'Avogadro's hypothesis' see Number 259 §4 and note (13).

(18) See Number 259 §5.

those obtained by Poisson[19] by conceiving an elastic solid the strain on which is continually relaxed at a rate proportional to the strain itself.

As an illustration of this view of the theory, it is shown that any strain existing in air at rest would diminish according to the values of an exponential term the modulus of which is $\frac{1}{5,100,000,000}$ second, an excessively small time, so that the equations are applicable, even to the case of the most acute audible sounds, without any modification on account of the rapid change of motion.

This relaxation is due to the mutual deflection of the molecules from their paths. It is then shown that if the displacements are instantaneous, so that no time is allowed for the relaxation, the gas would have an elasticity of form, or 'rigidity', whose coefficient is equal to the pressure.

It is also shown that if the molecules were mere points, not having any mutual action, there would be no such relaxation, and that the equations of motion would be those of an elastic solid, in which the coefficient of cubical and linear elasticity have the same ratio as that deduced by Poisson from the theory of molecules at rest acting by central forces on one another.[20] This coincidence of the results of two theories so opposite in their assumptions is remarkable.

6th. The coefficient of viscosity of a mixture of two gases is then deduced from the viscosity of the pure gases, and the coefficient of inter-diffusion of the two gases. The latter quantity has not as yet been ascertained for any pair of pure gases, but it is shown that sufficiently probable values may be assumed[21] which being inserted in the formula agree very well with some of the most remarkable of Mr. Graham's experiments on the Transpiration of Mixed Gases.*[22] The remarkable experimental result that the viscosity is independent of the pressure and proportional to the absolute temperature is a necessary consequence of the theory.

(γ) The rate of conduction of heat is next determined, and it is shown

1st. That the final state of a quantity of gas in a vessel will be such that the temperature will increase according to a certain law from the bottom to the top.[23] The atmosphere, as we know, is colder above. This state would be

* Philosophical Transactions, 1846.[22]

(19) See Number 259 §6, esp. note (23).
(20) See 'On the dynamical theory of gases': 81–2 (= *Scientific Papers*, **2**: 69–70); and G. G. Stokes, 'On the theories of the internal friction of fluids in motion, and of the equilibrium and motion of elastic solids', *Trans. Camb. Phil. Soc.*, **8** (1845): 287–319, esp. 311, equation (29) (= *Papers*, **1**: 75–129). See Number 261 notes (7), (8) and (9). (21) See note (14).
(22) Thomas Graham, 'On the motion of gases', *Phil. Trans.*, **136** (1846): 573–632.
(23) On Maxwell's derivation of this result see Number 259 note (33); and for its subsequent correction see Number 266 esp. note (8). For his original conclusion that the temperature decreases as the height increases see Numbers 259 §9 and 260.

produced by winds alone, and is no doubt greatly increased by the effects of radiation. A perfectly calm and sunless atmosphere would be coldest below.

2nd. The conductivity of a gas for heat is then deduced from its viscosity, and found to be
$$\frac{5}{3}\frac{1}{\gamma-1}\frac{p_0}{\rho_0\theta_0}\frac{\mu}{S}^{(24)};$$
where γ is the ratio of the two specific heats, p_0 the pressure, and ρ_0 the density of the standard gas at absolute temperature θ_0. S the specific gravity of the gas in question, and μ its viscosity. The conductivity is, like the viscosity, independent of the pressure and proportional to the absolute temperature. Its value for air is about 3500 times less than that of wrought iron, as determined by Principal Forbes.[25] Specific gravity is .0069.

For oxygen, nitrogen, and carbonic oxide, the theory gives the conductivity equal to that of air. Hydrogen according to the theory should have a conductivity seven times that of air, and carbonic acid about $\frac{7}{9}$ of air.

---

(24) Boltzmann subsequently discovered an error in Maxwell's calculation: the factor $\frac{5}{3}$ should be corrected to $\frac{5}{2}$. See Ludwig Boltzmann, 'Weitere Studien über das Wärmegleichgewicht unter Gasmolekülen', *Wiener Berichte*, **66**, Abtheilung II (1872): 275–370, esp. 332. See Number 425, esp. note (5).

(25) J. D. Forbes, 'Experimental inquiry into the laws of the conduction of heat in bars, and into the conducting power of wrought iron', *Trans. Roy. Soc. Edinb.*, **23** (1862): 133–46, esp. 145.

REPORT ON A PAPER BY THOMAS GRAHAM ON THE ABSORPTION AND SEPARATION OF GASES

17 JULY 1866

From the original in the Library of the Royal Society, London[1]

REPORT TO THE COMMITTEE OF PAPERS ON Mr GRAHAM'S PAPER ON THE ABSORPTION AND DIALYTIC SEPARATION OF GASES BY COLLOID SEPTA. PARTS I & II[2]

Mr Graham has on former occasions investigated the resistance opposed to the motion of gases by porous septa[3] and by capillary tubes.[4] He has also investigated the passage of liquids through the substance of that class of bodies to which he has applied the epithet colloid.[5] In the present paper he considers the apparent passage of gases through septa which are not known to be porous, such as Caoutchouc[6] Platinum & Iron.[7]

---

(1) Royal Society, *Referees' Reports*, **6**: 138.

(2) Thomas Graham, 'On the absorption and dialytic separation of gases by colloid septa', *Phil. Trans.*, **156** (1866): 399–439. The paper was received by the Royal Society on 20 June 1866, and read on 21 June 1866; see the abstract in *Proc. Roy. Soc.*, **15** (1866): 223–4. In his paper on 'Liquid diffusion applied to analysis', *Phil. Trans.*, **151** (1861): 183–224, esp. 183, 186, Graham introduced the terms 'dialysis' and 'colloid'. Distinguishing 'colloids' from 'crystalloids', he noted that the 'softness of the gelatinous colloid partakes of fluidity', and that a 'colloid' was 'a medium for liquid diffusion'. He defined 'dialysis' as 'the method of separating by diffusion through a septum of gelatinous matter'. Thus, as he explained in 'On the absorption and dialytic separation of gases by colloid septa': 399, 'dialysis involves the passage of a substance through a septum composed of soft colloid matter, such as must be wholly destitute of open channels, and therefore be impermeable to gas as such'.

(3) Thomas Graham, 'On the molecular mobility of gases', *Phil. Trans.*, **153** (1863): 385–405.

(4) Thomas Graham, 'On the motion of gases', *Phil. Trans.*, **136** (1846): 573–632; *ibid.*, **139** (1849): 349–401.

(5) Graham, 'Liquid diffusion applied to analysis'; see note (2).

(6) See 'Part I – Action of a septum of caoutchouc' of Graham's 'On the absorption and dialytic separation of gases by colloid septa': 399–415, esp. 404, where Graham noted that 'a film of rubber appears to have no porosity, and to resemble a film of liquid in its relation to gases', and that 'liquids and colloids have an unbroken texture'.

(7) See 'Part II – Action of metallic septa at red heat' of Graham's 'On the absorption and dialytic separation of gases by colloid septa': 415–39, esp. 415, where he discussed the recent 'surprising passage of gases through the homogeneous substance of a plate of fused platinum or of iron at a red heat', discovered by H. Sainte-Claire Deville and L. Troost, 'Sur la perméabilité du fer à haute température', *Comptes Rendus*, **57** (1863): 965–7.

Mr Graham in this paper considers the passage of the gas from the one side of the septum to the other to be the result of a process more allied to that of liquid diffusion than to that of gaseous diffusion, he shows that the substances of which the septa are composed have the power of absorbing the gases which are observed to pass through them, and of giving out these gases under a reduced pressure or a higher temperature, and he considers that the physical state of the gas when absorbed is that of a liquid.

The connexion between the 'penetrativeness' of a gas[8] and its capacity of being absorbed by the substance through which it penetrates, together with its loss of the gaseous state while within the substance of the septum, are the theoretical principles brought out in the investigation, in addition to several new methods of procedure, many new facts, and a number of practical suggestions.

The relative velocity of passage of gases through porous septa has been shown by Mr Graham to depend entirely on the specific gravity of the gases and not on their chemical relation to the substance of the septum.[9] The flow seems to be regulated by strictly mechanical principles as much as that of gases through small holes. In the cases now discussed the relative velocity of the gases is not that of their specific gravities or of their viscosities but has reference to the relation of each gas to the particular septum employed.

If we assume that a molecule is perfectly free when in the gaseous state, then if we find it so far connected with another substance as to be affected by the chemical nature of that substance, we may conclude that the molecule is not in the gaseous state.

In the case of a gas absorbed by a liquid the whole is manifestly liquid, but when the absorbing substance is solid we may suppose either that the gas has entered into its pores and has been there condensed, or that the gas has been taken into the substance of the body. If the body is such that a portion highly charged with the absorbed substance parts with it to portions having a smaller charge, then the absorption will take place not only at the surface but throughout the body, and if at the opposite boundary of the body the conditions are favourable to the escape of the absorbed substance it will pass through the body.

Now a colloid body, according to Mr Graham, is one which can take up a little more or less of certain substances into itself independently of any true mechanical or geometrical porosity.

The explanation given by M. Deville of the passage of gases through iron

---

(8) Graham's term; see 'On the absorption and dialytic separation of gases by colloid septa': 402.

(9) Graham, 'On the molecular mobility of gases'.

and platinum[10] is apparently inconsistent with that given by Mr Graham. M. Devilles explanation is mechanical. The metals are expanded by heat till those gases which have the smallest molecules can penetrate the intermolecular spaces. If the order of penetration of the gases is different in different metals it must be due to the relation between the shape of the intermolecular pores and that of the molecules of each particular gas.

Mr Grahams explanation if I understand it right leads him to look for the phenomenon not among 'crystallised masses'[11] of metals having planes of cleavage &c but among amorphous masses whose molecules may interchange place without any breach of continuity.[12] When a portion of such a mass is charged with a substance capable of being absorbed by it, then there is such an interchange of molecules of that substance as to diffuse it through the mass. This diffusion however may not be possible except at a high temperature, which by increasing the excursions of and the velocity of the molecules, enables them to pass from one part of the mass to another.

This view of the matter leads to enquiries as to the relation between colloids and the absorbed gases within them, but tells us nothing about the absolute distances of the molecules of solids.

I consider Mr Graham's paper an important contribution to our knowledge of the physical states of matter, as well as to that of the properties of particular gases and solids, and that it ought to be printed in the Philosophical Transactions.

The knowledge of the penetration of iron by carbonic oxide may be useful to those who wish to improve the manufacture of steel[13] and the complete separation of hydrogen from other gases by a septum of heated platinum may afford the means of making experiments on the mechanical equivalent of chemical affinity, if we can overcome the affinity of hydrogen for other substances by inequality of pressure at a higher temperature.

JAMES CLERK MAXWELL
17 July 1866

---

(10) H. Sainte-Claire Deville, 'Note sur le passage des gaz au travers des corps solides homogènes', *Comptes Rendus*, **59** (1864): 102–7.

(11) Sainte-Claire Deville's term 'masses cristallisées' ('Note sur le passage des gaz': 102), as cited by Graham, 'On the absorption and dialytic separation of gases by colloid septa': 416.

(12) See Graham's distinction between 'colloids' and 'crystalloids' (note (2)).

(13) A point also made by William Allen Miller in his brief report on Graham's paper dated 4 July 1866 (Royal Society, *Referees' Reports*, **6**: 137): 'iron absorbs not only hydrogen but takes up a notable proportion of carbonic oxide which may have an important influence in the process of the conversion of iron into steel during cementation.'

REPORT ON A PAPER BY EDWARD WYNDHAM TARN[1] ON THE STABILITY OF DOMES

18 DECEMBER 1866

From the original in the Library of the Royal Society, London[2]

REPORT ON A PAPER ON THE STABILITY OF DOMES BY E. W. TARN

PART II[3]

In reporting on the second part of this paper I am obliged to make a few remarks on the paper as a whole,[4] and on the subject of Domes.

Mr Tarn has considered the equilibrium of arches, differing from common arches in being bounded laterally by two planes, passing through the crown of the arch, and inclined at an angle of 2°.[5] If a number of these were placed symmetrically about an axis, but not in contact they would form a crown, such as surmounts certain towers and steeples. A dome differs from a crown in that the component segments are in contact, and therefore are capable of exerting a lateral pressure which ought to be considered in treating of domes. I have not been able to find in any part of Mr Tarns paper any mention of this lateral pressure. He rightly says that 'domes of various sizes and forms have been erected for centuries past'[6] so that the *form* of the dome is in some measure indeterminate, but he does not give the reason why the form of the dome is not so determinate as that of the arch. Arches of various forms have been erected, but their stability has depended on the fact that their ribs had a finite depth, and that they were supported by masonry outside, but a dome, indefinitely thin, will be stable whatever be its form provided certain conditions be fulfilled. This arises from the lateral support given by the pressure of the sectors on each other in the direction of horizontal tangents to the dome, and the condition of stability of a dome of masonry is that this

---

(1) University College London 1843, Associate of the Royal Institute of British Architects 1855 (Boase).

(2) Royal Society, *Referees' Reports*, **6**: 276.

(3) E. Wyndham Tarn, 'On the stability of domes. – Part II' (Royal Society, AP. 48.8). The paper was received by the Royal Society on 23 October 1866, and read on 22 November 1866; see the abstract in *Proc. Roy. Soc.*, **15** (1866): 266–8.

(4) The first part of Tarn's paper 'On the stability of domes' had been published in *Proc. Roy. Soc.*, **15** (1866): 182–8; the paper was received on 5 May 1866, and read on 31 May 1866. While the first part of the paper is concerned with spherical domes, the second part considered domes of other forms than the spherical.

(5) This angle is denoted ϕ by Tarn. (6) Tarn, 'On the stability of domes': 182.

pressure shall not be negative (that is a tension) which would throw the stress on the cement or the bond of the masonry. This condition with its consequence is correctly stated in Prof. Rankines Applied Mechanics Art 234 p 265[7] and may be thus stated.

Let W be the weight of a part of the dome above the circular joint at which the inclination of the surface of the dome to the horizon is θ and let r be the mean radius of the joint, P the pressure in the meridian and Q the lateral pressure N the length of the normal and R the radius of curvature of the meridian section.

Then
$$2\pi Pr \sin\theta = W$$
$$\frac{P}{R} + \frac{Q}{N} = \frac{dW}{d\theta}\frac{\cos\theta}{2\pi Rr}$$

whence
$$Q = \frac{1}{2\pi R}\frac{d}{d\theta} \cdot (W \cot\theta).$$

If $W \cot\theta$ always increases with θ, Q will be positive and the dome will stand if Q be negative the dome will split unless held together by a belt by cement or the friction of overlapping stones.

This is the theory of a dome indefinitely thin, a thick shell is more stable.

I think the author should have said something about Q, the lateral thrust since it is the feature which distinguishes domes from arches, and is most important in the mechanical theory. We do not see, from the paper, that it is possible to build a dome with a round hole at the top.

In the second part, Equation A, page 4, is not correct. It should be $P = \delta\iiint r(r\sin\overline{\alpha+\theta} - OZ)\,dr\,d\theta\,d\phi$.[8] The error introduced is not large. He also states that the ordinary rules for finding maxima will not apply to the case of the quantity N'.[9] I think the rules apply well enough, though the operation might be found tedious.

The mathematics, on the whole, is superior to the mechanics, especially in the paraboloidal dome. In the Ogival dome, p. 29,[10] the upper part would

---

(7) W. J. M. Rankine, *A Manual of Applied Mechanics* (London/Glasgow, 1858): 265–6.

(8) P is the weight of the portion of rib above a given joint; δ the weight of a cubic foot of the material of the dome; r and R the internal and external radii of the dome; the angles α and θ corresponding to various shapes of 'Gothic' dome; OZ the distance between the centre of the arc of the rib and its vertical axis; and ϕ as stated above (note (5)). Tarn's expression reads: $P = \delta\iiint r^2(\sin(\alpha+\theta) - \sin\alpha)\,dr\,d\theta\,d\phi$; and see also 'On the stability of domes': 183 (for spherical domes).

(9) Maxwell here is referring to Tarn's discussion in 'On the stability of domes': 184.

(10) Tarn, 'On the stability of domes. – Part II': f. 29; 'There is another form of Dome commonly used in Eastern countries...sometimes called the "Ogival" dome, the contour being a curve which has a point of "contrary flexure"'.

not stand at all on the authors principle of neglecting the lateral thrust. If such an arch were built of this form, it would fall at once. It is only on account of the lateral thrust that the upper part of this dome can stand.

On the whole I think that a good deal of mathematical power has been expended on this paper with small mechanical effect, as the author has never alluded to the true reason why domes stand when built, though it is stated in various books. I think the Society should not be responsible for the printing of the paper at large in the Proceedings,[11] unless the author takes the true theory into account, (which, from the style of this paper, I have no doubt he could do,) or else gives reasons why he should do without it.

JAMES CLERK MAXWELL
1866 Dec 18

(11) Part II of Tarn's paper was only printed in abstract: see note (3).

266

LETTER TO GEORGE GABRIEL STOKES

18 DECEMBER 1866

From the original in the University Library, Cambridge[1]

8 Palace Gardens Terrace
W
1866 Dec 18

Dear Stokes

I enclose a report on Mr Tarn's paper[2] and Thomson's report on mine.[3] Thomsons theory of matter being continuous but much more dense at one place than another is a molecular theory, for the dense portions constitute a finite number of molecules and I do not assert nor does any one since Lucretius that the space between the molecules is absolutely empty.[4]

I take Statics to be the theory of systems of forces without considering what they act on

Kinetics to be the theory of the motions of systems without regard to the forces in action

Dynamics to be the theory of the motion of bodies as the result of given forces

and Energetics to be the theory of the communication of energy from one body to another.

I therefore call the theory a dynamical theory because it considers the motions of bodies as produced by certain forces.[5]

I think I have stated plainly enough the difference between my molecules and pure centres of force.[6] I do not profess to have a dynamical theory of the molecule itself.

---

(1) ULC Add. MSS 7656, M 424. First published in Larmor, *Correspondence*, 2: 27–8.

(2) Number 265.

(3) William Thomson's letter to Stokes of 13 October 1866 (see Number 263 note (3)) is a report on Maxwell's paper 'On the dynamical theory of gases', *Phil. Trans.*, **157** (1867): 49–88 (= *Scientific Papers*, **2**: 26–78).

(4) In his report on Maxwell's paper (see note (3)) Thomson had questioned the word 'homogeneous' in Maxwell's initial assertion that 'Theories of the constitution of bodies suppose them either to be continuous and homogeneous, or to be composed of a finite number of distinct particles or molecules'; see 'On the dynamical theory of gases': 49 (= *Scientific Papers*, **2**: 26). Thomson suggested 'all space to be full but the properties of known bodies to be due to...vast variations of density from point to point' (Wilson, *Stokes–Kelvin Correspondence*, **1**: 330).

(5) On Maxwell's use of the terms 'kinetics' and 'dynamics' compare Volume I: 665–6 and Number 377 esp. note (4).

(6) See Maxwell's statement in 'On the dynamical theory of gases': 54–5 (= *Scientific Papers*,

I have considered the equilibrium of heat in a vertical column and find I made a mistake in eq^n 143.$^{(7)}$ I now make the temperature the same throughout, and have inserted (on two pages) an addition to that effect which I mean to be instead of p. 60.$^{(8)}$

I have also amended equation (54) in which the effect of external forces was omitted by mistake in writing out and copying from eq^n 47.$^{(9)}$

The result is a corroboration of the theory of the distribution of velocities as the errors are in the theory of 'Least Squares' for we require to have

$$\overline{\xi^4} = 3\,\overline{\xi^2}.\overline{\xi^2},$$

which agrees with that theory.$^{(10)}$

I think something might be done to the statical theory of elasticity with centres of force whose displacement is a function of the index of the molecule

---

2: 33); 'The molecules of a gas in this theory are those portions of it which move about as a single body. These molecules may be mere points, or pure centres of force endowed with inertia, or the capacity of performing work while losing velocity. They may be systems of several such centres of force, bound together by their mutual actions'. Thomson had commented: 'It should...be explained...that the molecules are regarded *not* as centres of force but as really (according with their name) little heaps of matter' (Wilson, *Stokes–Kelvin Correspondence*, 1: 328).

(7) Maxwell, 'On the dynamical theory of gases': 85–6 (= *Scientific Papers*, 2: 74–5).

(8) See the 'Addition made December 17, 1866' on the 'Final equilibrium of temperature' appended to 'On the dynamical theory of gases': 86–7 (= *Scientific Papers*, 2: 75–6). On Maxwell's original conclusion that the temperature of a column of gas diminishes as the height increases, see Numbers 259 §9 and 260; and for his revision, concluding that the temperature would increase with the height (as stated in the paper as submitted to the Royal Society in May 1866), see Numbers 259 note (33) and 263. Thomson discussed the problem in his report on Maxwell's paper, acknowledging that 'What the flaw may be in Maxwell's investigation if any I have not been able to see.' (Wilson, *Stokes–Kelvin Correspondence*, 1: 329). In the 'Addition' to his paper Maxwell concluded that: 'if the temperature of any substance, when in thermic equilibrium is a function of the height, that of any other substance must be the same function of the height. For if not, let equal columns of the two substances be enclosed in cylinders impermeable to heat, and put in thermal communication at the bottom. If, when in thermal equilibrium, the tops of the two columns are at different temperatures, an engine might be worked by taking heat from the hotter and giving it to the cooler, and the refuse heat would circulate round the system till it was all converted into mechanical energy, which is in contradiction to the second law of thermodynamics.'

(9) Maxwell, 'On the dynamical theory of gases': 67 (= *Scientific Papers*, 2: 49–50).

(10) Maxwell, 'On the dynamical theory of gases': 87 (= *Scientific Papers*, 2: 76); and see Number 259 notes (10) and (33). For Maxwell's subsequent discussion of his conclusion 'that the temperature in gases, when in thermal equilibrium, is independent of height', see Numbers 457, 472, 473 and 481. This conclusion was later challenged by Joseph Loschmidt, 'Über den Zustand des Wärmegleichgewichtes eines Systems von Körpern mit Rücksicht auf die Schwerkraft. I', *Wiener Berichte*, **73**, Abtheilung II (1876): 128–42, esp. 135–9.

as well as of its initial coordinates, the number of kinds of indices being small and the groups of n particles being originally of the same form, but it would require an investigation to itself.[11]

I remain
Yours truly
J. CLERK MAXWELL

Professor Stokes

I shall be at Cambridge from 26 Dec to 26 Jan at Trinity.[12]

---

(11) In his report on Maxwell's paper Thomson had alluded to molecular explanations of elasticity: 'a solid violating Poisson's condition [$\sigma = 1/4$] could be built up of small parts (molecules) each fulfilling it' (Wilson, *Stokes–Kelvin Correspondence*, **1**:330).

(12) Maxwell had been appointed Examiner for the Mathematical Tripos in 1867; see *The Cambridge University Calendar for the Year 1867* (Cambridge, 1867): 459.

LETTER TO JAMES JOSEPH SYLVESTER[1]
21 DECEMBER 1866
From the original in Columbia University Library[2]

8 Palace Gardens Terrace
London W
1866 Dec 21

Dear Sir

Some days ago my attention was called to the Cartesian Ovals by a statement of yours in the Philosophical Magazine[3] that the R. S. Laureat (Chasles,[4] not Tennyson)[5] had discovered that they had 3 foci,[6] which as you say is a remarkable bit of mathematics.[7] I tried to establish a third focus when I began mathematics about the [year] 1846 and several times afterwards.[8] My reason was that I had drawn all the kinds of them with pins and threads on paper and was struck with the visible resemblance of two kinds in one of which the

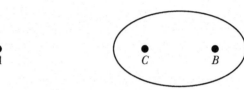

Figure 267,1

---

(1) It seems certain that the letter was addressed to Sylvester: see note (7).

(2) D. E. Smith Special MS Collection, Rare Book and Manuscript Library, Columbia University, New York.

(3) In the January 1866 number: see note (7).

(4) Michel Chasles had been awarded the Copley Medal of the Royal Society in 1865 'for his Historical and Original Researches in Pure Geometry'; see *Proc. Roy. Soc.*, **14** (1865): 493–6.

(5) The Poet Laureate.

(6) In 'Note XXI. Sur les ovales de Descartes, ou lignes aplanétiques' of his *Aperçu Historique sur l'Origine et le Développement des Méthodes en Géométrie* (Brussels, 1837), in *Mémoires couronnés par l'Académie Royale des Sciences et Belles-Lettres de Bruxelles,* **11** (1837): 350–3, esp. 352, Chasles had observed: 'qu'*au lieu de deux foyers seulement, elles en ont toujours trois*: c'est-à-dire, qu'outre les deux foyers qui servent à leur description, elles en ont un troisième qui joue le même rôle, avec l'un des deux premiers, que ces deux-ci ensemble.'

(7) Sylvester had remarked on 'the knowledge of the existence of a third focus to the Cartesian ovals, that remarkable discovery of our illustrious Royal Society *Laureate* of the year...', adding that 'I am not aware that M. Chasles has ever disclosed that *aperçu* which led him to this unlooked for discovery', in his 'Astronomical prolusions: commencing with an instantaneous proof of Lambert's and Euler's theorems, and modulating through a construction of the orbit of a heavenly body from two heliocentric distances, the subtended chord, and the periodic time, and the focal theory of Cartesian ovals, into a discussion of motion in a circle and its relation to planetary motion', *Phil. Mag.*, ser. 4, **31** (1866): 52–76, esp. 61–2.

(8) But see Maxwell's manuscript paper 'Oval' (Volume I: 47–54), written in 1847, where he seems unaware that a Cartesian oval has three foci.

foci are A and B in the other A & C.⁽⁹⁾ My other reason for which I renewed the search was to find out what Descartes means by what he says in his Geometria Lib. II p 61 where he has a figure like this⁽¹⁰⁾ in which FE is a rule centred at F and the string goes from E round the pencil at C to K back to C and then is fastened at G so that

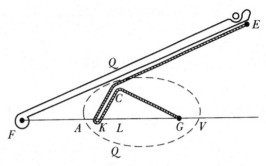

Figure 267,2

$$EC + 2CK + CG = \text{const.}$$

He makes $FA = AG$

$$FL = \mu LG^{(11)}$$

$$AK = KL$$

$$EC + 2CK + CG = GA + AL + FE - AF$$

then $FK = \dfrac{3\mu + 1}{4(\mu + 1)} FC$

and the oval is either

$$FC + \mu GC = \frac{\mu + 1}{2} FG$$

or $\quad + FC - \dfrac{2\mu}{\mu + 1} KC = \dfrac{3\mu + 1}{2(\mu + 1)^2} FG$

or $\quad GC + \dfrac{2}{\mu + 1} KC = \dfrac{\mu}{2} \dfrac{\mu + 3}{(\mu + 1)^2} FG.$

So that Descartes has not only found out a case of the 3ʳᵈ focus but has overcome the difficulty of describing ovals with strings when the value of μ is incommensurable.⁽¹²⁾ He has (as far as I know) lost the credit of it

---

(9) See Maxwell's manuscript paper 'Observations on circumscribed figures having a plurality of foci, and radii of various proportions' (Volume I: 35–42), written in February 1846.

(10) *Geometria, à Renato Des Cartes. Anno 1637 Gallicè edita; nunc autem Cum Notis Florimondi De Beaune,...In linguam Latinam versa, & commentariis illustrata, Operâ atque studio Francisci à Schooten...* (Leiden, 1649): 61.

(11) See George Salmon, *A Treatise on the Higher Plane Curves* (Dublin, 1852): 119, where 'a Cartesian oval is defined as the locus of a point whose distances from two given foci [ρ, ρ'] are connected by the relation $m\rho + n\rho' = c$.' Here $\mu = m/n$.

(12) In Maxwell's method of description of ovals in his 'Observations on circumscribed figures having a plurality of foci', a tracing pin describes an oval by moving so that m times its distance from one focus (ρ) together with n times its distance from another focus (ρ') is equal to

1ˢᵗ   by being too short (though not obscure)
2ⁿᵈ by using the words etiamsi hæ Ovales ejusdem fermé naturæ videntur, p 62⁽¹³⁾
3ʳᵈ by erroneous statements about reflexion⁽¹⁴⁾ which made men set this paragraph down as a mistake.

I suppose you know that rays from G in a medium whose index is μ falling on the part of QVQ which is beyond the tangent from F, will after refraction proceed in directions which touch the caustic produced by rays from F *reflected* at QVQ supposing the refractive medium abolished and QVQ a reflecting surface.⁽¹⁵⁾

---

a constant quantity; m and n are determined by the number of times the thread is wrapped round the pins placed at the two given foci. J. D. Forbes remarked in his published 'On the description of oval curves and those having a plurality of foci. By Mr Clerk Maxwell junior; with remarks by Professor Forbes', *Proc. Roy. Soc. Edinb.*, **2** (1846): 89–91 (= *Scientific Papers*, **1**: 1–3), that 'it probably has not been suspected that so easy and elegant a method exists of describing these curves by the use of a thread and pins whenever the powers of the foci [m, n] are commensurable'. Maxwell thus recognises that the restriction that $\mu(m/n)$ is rational does not limit Descartes' description of ovals.

(13) 'Ad hæc, etiamsi hæ Ovales ejusdem fermè naturæ videntur, ipsæ nihilominus quatuor diversorum sunt generum, quorum unumquodque sub se infinita ali genera continet, & unumquodque rursus tot diversas species, quot facit Ellipsum aut Hyperbolarum genus.' ('Although these ovals seem to be of nearly the same nature, they nevertheless belong to four different classes, each containing an infinity of other classes, and each of which again so many different kinds, as does the class of ellipses or of hyperbolas.'); Descartes, *Geometria*: 62.

(14) First noticed by Maxwell in a letter to his father of April 1847 (Volume I: 62). In discussing the reflective properties of ovals Descartes supposes an oval as the concave surface of a mirror 'ex tali materiâ constaret, ut vim horum radiorum...diminuat' ('composed of such matter that the force of the rays is diminished' in a given proportion). He supposes an incident ray to be reflected at the angle with which it would be refracted were the oval supposed to be the surface of a lens: 'ut etiam reflexionum anguli non secus ac refractionum inæquales existant'; Descartes, *Geometria*: 63.

(15) In his note 'Sur les ovales de Descartes' Chasles had pointed out that 'M. Quetelet, dans sa belle théorie des *caustiques secondaires*...a trouvé que les caustiques secondaires produites par la réflexion et la réfraction dans un cercle éclairé par un point lumineux, sont les *ovales de Descartes*, ou lignes aplanétiques'; Chasles, *Aperçu Historique*: 350. See Adolphe Quetelet, 'Mémoire sur une nouvelle manière de considérer les caustiques, produites soit par réflexion soit par réfraction', *Nouveaux Mémoires de l'Académie Royale des Sciences et Belles-Lettres de Bruxelles*, **3** (1826): 89–140; Quetelet, 'Démonstration et développemens des principes fondamentaux de la théorie des caustiques sécondaires', *ibid.*, **5** (1829); and in his 'Supplément au Traité de la lumière de Sir J. F. W. Herschel' appended to Herschel's *Traité de la Lumière*, (trans.) P. F. Verhulst and A. Quetelet, 2 vols. (Paris, 1829–33), **2**: 380–407. See Salmon, *Higher Plane Curves*: 118–19; and Arthur Cayley, 'A memoir upon caustics', *Phil. Trans.*, **147** (1857): 273–312.

Descartes Geometry is a book studied by Newton and all the mathematicians since so I daresay this proposition has been well known though I never understood it till now. If you do not know of Descartes discovery I shall think it worth republishing for the honour of old Renatus.[16]

I remain
Yours truly
J. CLERK MAXWELL

(16) Following Sylvester's discussion of Cartesian ovals, on 19 March 1866 Morgan William Crofton read a paper to the newly instituted London Mathematical Society 'On certain properties of the Cartesian ovals, treated by the method of vectorial co-ordinates', *Proceedings of the London Mathematical Society*, **1** (1866): 5–18, esp. 5–7, giving a proof of the third focus, and declaring that: 'The Cartesian ovals seem at all times to have attracted considerable attention, though no great success has attended the attempts made to investigate their properties. Of these the most remarkable which has been discovered is that of the third focus, given by Chasles without proof'. For discussion of the third focus of Cartesian ovals see F. Gomes Teixeira, *Traité des Courbes Spéciales Remarquables*, 2 vols. (Coimbra, 1908–9), **1**: 220–1.

LETTER TO GEORGE GABRIEL STOKES

27 FEBRUARY 1867

From the original in the University Library, Cambridge[1]

8 Palace Gardens Terrace
W.
1867 Feb. 27.

Dear Sir

I find that I have made two mistakes in a paper I have sent to the R.S.[2] about Siemens & Wheatstones machines.[3]

It is all right about the *first* kind of commutator.[4]

In finding the effect of the second kind of commutator which breaks one of the circuits I have omitted to consider the effect of the stoppage on the other coil by induction. I send you the result taking the inductive effect into account.[5]

The second mistake was in the case of two currents always disconnected. Such a system cannot maintain currents by its motions.

The result I came to arose from neglecting the inductive effect of stopping the current.

In fact a closed circuit cannot have a current always in one direction produced by any inductive action.

The nearest approach to it is to take a long flexible magnet and wind it on the coil like as a silk is wound to cover a wire. During the winding a current

---

(1) ULC Add. MSS 7656, M 425. First published in Larmor, *Correspondence*, **2**: 28.

(2) J. Clerk Maxwell, 'On the theory of the maintenance of electric currents by mechanical work without the use of permanent magnets', *Proc. Roy. Soc.*, **15** (1867): 397–402 (= *Scientific Papers*, **3**: 79–85). The paper was received on 28 February 1867, and read on 14 March 1867.

(3) Concerned with the self-excitation of a dynamo. See Charles William Siemens, 'On the conversion of dynamical into electrical force without the aid of permanent magnetism', *Proc. Roy. Soc.*, **15** (1867): 367–9; and Charles Wheatstone, 'On the augmentation of the power of a magnet by the reaction thereon of currents induced by the magnet itself', *Proc. Roy. Soc.*, **15** (1867): 369–72. The papers were read on 14 February 1867. These self-exciting magneto-electrical machines consisted of a fixed and a moveable electromagnet connected by a commutator.

(4) Maxwell, 'On the theory of the maintenance of electric currents': 399–401 (= *Scientific Papers*, **2**: 81–3). He considers four different arrangements of the contacts of the commutator with the two coils of the electromagnets. In the first kind of commutator the circuits of both coils are uninterrupted.

(5) In the second kind of commutator the circuits are closed, so the currents in them are independent: 'The second circuit is then broken, and the current in it is thus stopped. This produces an effect on the first circuit by induction'; see Maxwell, 'On the theory of the maintenance of electric currents': 401 (= *Scientific Papers*, **2**: 83).

will go in one direction and during the unwinding it will go in the other direction.

The part relating to two independent coils is therefore all wrong.

If you can allow that part to be cut out, and the enclosed to be substituted for what relates to commutators of the 2nd kind it will prevent a false statement from going beyond you and me.

Yours truly
J. CLERK MAXWELL.

REPORT ON A PAPER BY JOSEPH DAVID EVERETT ON THE DETERMINATION OF RIGIDITY

4 MARCH 1867

From the original in the Library of the Royal Society, London[1]

REPORT ON Dr EVERETT'S ACCOUNT OF EXPERIMENTS ON TORSION AND FLEXURE FOR THE DETERMINATION OF RIGIDITIES[2]

These experiments are a continuation of a former series[3] with better apparatus and a greater number of substances.[4] In my report on the former paper[5] I stated my opinion of the advantages of M. Kirchhoff's method of experimenting on the torsion and flexure of the same rod[6] in order to determine Poissons ratio,[7] and of the improvement introduced by Dr Everett in making the moment of flexure uniform throughout the length of the rod and in having no external force applied to the part of the rod whose bending is observed.

I have therefore only to report on the changes and additions which Dr Everett has since made.

He now clamps one end of the rod and applies a couple to the other by means of a cross piece weighted at the end of one of its limbs and supported in the centre by a balance. This is an improvement on the jointed apparatus formerly used[8] but a correction is required on account of the middle point of support not being in the plane of the points of suspension of the weights.[9] There seems no mechanical reason why the five points should not be placed

---

(1) Royal Society, *Referees' Reports*, **6**: 118.

(2) J. D. Everett, 'Account of experiments on torsion and flexure for the determination of rigidities', *Phil. Trans.*, **157** (1867): 139–53. The paper was received by the Royal Society on 25 January 1867, and read on 7 February 1867; see the abstract in *Proc. Roy. Soc.*, **15** (1867): 356.

(3) J. D. Everett, 'Account of experiments on the flexural and torsional rigidity of a glass rod, leading to the determination of the rigidity of glass', *Phil. Trans.*, **156** (1866): 185–91.

(4) In the paper under review Everett carried out experiments on rods of glass, brass and steel.

(5) Number 261.

(6) Gustav Kirchhoff, 'Ueber das Verhältniss der Quercontraction zur Längendilatation bei Stäben von federhartem Stahl', *Ann. Phys.*, **108** (1859): 369–92.

(7) The ratio of lateral contraction to longitudinal extension; see Number 261 notes (6), (7) and (9).

(8) Compare Maxwell's suggestions for improving the apparatus in Number 261.

(9) See Everett, 'Account of experiments on torsion and flexure': 143.

in one plane so as to get rid of the principal part of this correction which is uncertain, as no direct measure of the rotation of the cross &c were made.

The cone of support n might be screwed into a mortice hole in the stem of the apparatus and supported by a semistirrup hanging from the balance arm.[10]

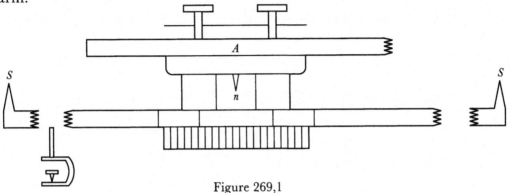

Figure 269,1

The counterpoise should be equal to the weight of this apparatus together with half the weight of the rod experimented on and the centre of gravity of this apparatus together with half the rod at A should coincide nearly with n.

No statement is made as to the horizontality of the cross piece. Its deviation from horizontality when the weights are on should be ascertained (roughly at least).

The method of observing with telescopes and a scale is better than that with a lamp and its image. The method of correction for the obliquity of the ray is not stated as fully as other parts of the paper are developed.

If AB is the plane of the scale AM the direction of the axis of the telescope B the point on the scale seen at the cross wires, MN the normal then by geometry $AN:NB::AM:MB$ and ANB is a straight line.

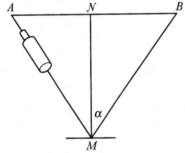

Figure 269,2

If $NMB = \alpha$ and if in the mean position MN is perpendicular to the scale then for a small displacement BB' where $BC = x$ and $CB' = y$ we have a corresponding displacement of the normal NN' where $NL = \xi$ and $LN' = \eta$

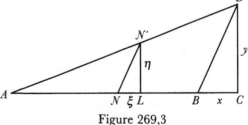

Figure 269,3

---

(10) Compare Everett's apparatus in *Phil. Trans.*, **157** (1867): Plate IX, Fig. 1.

and
$$\xi = \frac{x}{2\sec^2\alpha} \quad \eta = \frac{y}{2}.$$

The mirrors should be adjusted to be horizontal which may be done by observing the reflexion of a plumb line in them.

The telescopes should then be adjusted[11] each in a plane through its own mirror perpendicular to the rod and at equal angles with the vertical such that the ray from the scale to the mirror always clears the top of the observers forehead in all the conditions of torsion.

If this angle be α then we have for torsion if c be the height of scale above the mirror and θ the angle of torsion x & y the scale readings

$$\tan\theta = \frac{2c\tan\alpha + x}{c + \sqrt{c^2 + cx\sin 2\alpha + (x^2 + y^2)\cos^2\alpha}} - \tan\alpha$$

and if ϕ is the angle of flexure

$$\tan\phi = \frac{y}{c + \sqrt{c^2 + cx\sin 2\alpha + (x^2 + y^2)\cos^2\alpha}}.$$

The value of Poissons ratio obtained by Dr Everett for glass is decidedly less than .25[12] being .229.[13] Well annealed glass is probably as isotropic as any substance we can find. A piece of the rod from $\frac{1}{2}$ inch to 1 inch long may be examined by passing polarized light through it longitudinally and if the light is unaffected the glass may be considered not only isotropic but free from strain. Most glass rods are in a state of constraint but this does not imply any want of isotropy in the substance but only the existence of forces.

Whether by pressure and heat a piece of glass can be made to have through its whole extent a doubly refractive power of the same kind and direction not depending on the actual existence of unequal pressures, I cannot say. It can be done with dried gelatine.[14]

The value of σ[15] for brass[16] comes very near its absolute limit $\frac{1}{2}$ and ought to be carefully tested.

---

(11) 'The effect produced was observed, in Kirchhoff's experiments, by means of two telescopes looking down into two mirrors which reflected a scale of lines crossing each other at right angles placed horizontally overhead.'; Everett, 'Account of experiments on torsion and flexure': 139.

(12) See Number 261, esp. note (7).

(13) Everett, 'Account of experiments on torsion and flexure': 145. Compare the value of 0.258 found in his former paper (see Number 261).

(14) On Maxwell's interest in photoelasticity see Volume I: 117, 125–7, 151–6, 488–9.

(15) Poisson's ratio: see Number 261 note (6).

(16) Everett, 'Account of experiments on torsion and flexure': 148, gives a value of 0.469 for brass.

Lead is said to be very uniform in its properties when pressed into wires. If it is not too plastic it would be desirable to try its elasticity.

In conclusion I think that only one set of experiments should have all their numbers given in full. The others should be reduced and corrected and the results given, stating in each case the amount of discordance of the observations in the form of 'probable error' of single observations or of the result.[17] In other respects I think that both for method and results this paper is worthy to be printed in the Transactions.

J. CLERK MAXWELL

1867 March 4

---

(17) This recommendation was not followed.

REPORTED COMMENTS ON BRODIE'S CHEMICAL CALCULUS[1]

6 JUNE 1867[2]

From a report on a meeting of the Chemical Society in *Chemical News*[3]

Professor Clerk Maxwell said he confessed that when he came into the room his feelings received a wholesome shock from two of the statements in the diagrams – first, that space was a chemical substance, and second, that hydrogen and mercury were operations. He now, however, understood what was meant. The present [calculus] seemed to be an endeavour to cause the symbols of chemical substances to act in the formulae according to their own laws. The formulae at present used were made to express many valuable properties of chemical substances, just as a great many formulae were employed to represent the syllogism in logic, which required a logical mind to form them, to understand them, and to reason upon them. The only successful attempt to introduce a new system in the logical representation was that of Mr. Boole, who accomplished it by the metaphysical and mathematical conception that x^2 was equal to x.[4] In Sir Benjamin Brodie's system α did not mean exactly 'hydrogen', but 'make hydrogen'; that is, take the cubic centimetre of space, and put hydrogen into it of the proper pressure and temperature. But if they were to compress into that space another volume of hydrogen, that would not be α^2, because it would increase the pressure to double what it was before. If it were possible to get α^2, they would require to combine two volumes together by a process unknown to chemists, keeping the pressure and temperature as before.[5] There was, in this respect, no doubt, an idea which differed from the mere collocation of symbols. The unit of ponderable matter described in the system was one

---

(1) Benjamin Collins Brodie, 'The calculus of chemical operations; being a method for the investigation, by means of symbols, of the laws of the distribution of weight in chemical change. Part I. On the construction of chemical symbols', *Phil. Trans.*, **156** (1866): 781–859.

(2) See note (3).

(3) A meeting of the Chemical Society on 6 June 1867; B. C. Brodie, 'On the mode of representation afforded by the chemical calculus, as contrasted with the atomic theory', *Chemical News*, **15** (1867): 295–305, on 303.

(4) See George Boole, *An Investigation of the Laws of Thought, on which are founded the Mathematical Theories of Logic and Probabilities* (London, 1854): 31. Brodie made no reference to Boole in his Chemical Society lecture; but compare Brodie, 'The calculus of chemical operations': 794–803, esp. 801n, where he refers to the logical relation $x^2 = x$ in Boole's system of logic.

(5) On Maxwell's comments see D. M. Dallas, 'The chemical calculus of Sir Benjamin Brodie', in *The Atomic Debates*, ed. W. H. Brock (Leicester, 1967): 49–50.

which had been derived by chemists from chemical considerations alone. It had also been advocated by physicists from considerations derived from the theory of heat. In order to decide with certainty on the truth or falsehood of the atomic theory, it would be necessary to consider it from a dynamical point of view. He meant that kind of dynamics treated of in books on mechanics. It was worth while to direct the attention of chemists to the fact that a belief in atoms conducted necessarily to exactly the same definition as was given there – namely,[6] that for every kind of substance the number of atoms, or molecules, in the gaseous state, occupying the space of a litre, at a temperature of 0 degrees, and of a pressure of 760 millimetres,[7] must necessarily be the same.[8] That was a consequence which could be deduced from purely dynamical considerations on the supposition advocated by Professor Clausius and others, that gases consists of molecules floating about in all directions, and producing pressure by their impact.[9] That theory was now under probation among chemists, physicists, and others. The next step was one which might be far off – the finding of the number of these molecules. That number was a fixed one; and when it could be arrived at, we should have another unit of ponderable matter – that of a fixed molecule.[10]

(6) Brodie's definition of a 'unit of matter'; see Brodie, 'On the mode of representation afforded by the chemical calculus': 298.
(7) Of mercury.
(8) 'Avogadro's hypothesis': see Number 259 §4, esp. note (13).
(9) See Number 263, esp. note (9).
(10) See Number 470.

LETTER TO WILLIAM HUGGINS[1]

10 JUNE 1867

From the *Philosophical Transactions of the Royal Society*[2]

ON THE INFLUENCE OF THE MOTIONS OF THE HEAVENLY BODIES ON THE INDEX OF REFRACTION OF LIGHT

Let a source of light be such that it produces n disturbances or vibrations per second, and let it be at such a distance from the earth that the light requires a time T to reach the earth. Let the distance of the source of light from the earth be altered, either by the motion of the source of light, or by that of the earth, so that the light which emanates from the source t seconds afterwards reaches the earth in a time T'.

During the t seconds nt vibrations of the source of light took place, and these reached the earth between the time T and the time $t+T'$, that is, during $t+T'-T$ seconds. The number of vibrations which reached the earth per second was therefore no longer n, but $n\dfrac{t}{t+T'-T}$.

If v is the velocity of separation of the source of light from the earth, and V the velocity of light between the bodies relative to the earth, then $vt = V(T'-T)$, and the number of vibrations per second at the earth will be $n\dfrac{V}{V+v}$.

If V_0 is the velocity of propagation of light in the luminiferous medium, and if v_0 is the velocity of the earth,

$$V = V_0 - v_0,$$

---

(1) William Huggins, astronomer and astrophysicist, FRS 1865, Royal Medal 1866, Hon. Sec. Royal Astronomical Society 1867–70 (*DNB*).

(2) Published by William Huggins in his paper 'Further observations on the spectra of some of the stars and nebulæ, with an attempt to determine therefrom whether these bodies are moving towards or from the earth, also observations of the spectra of the sun and of Comet II., 1868', *Phil. Trans.*, **158** (1868): 529–64, on 532–5. In an introduction to his paper, Huggins explained the circumstances of Maxwell's letter: 'The subject of the motions of the heavenly bodies on the index of refraction of light had already...in 1864, occupied the attention of Mr. J. C. Maxwell, F.R.S., who had made some experiments in an analogous direction. In the spring of last year, at my request, Mr. Maxwell sent to me a statement of his views and of the experiments which he had made.' (on 530). For Maxwell's experiments see Number 227.

and the wave-length will be increased by a fraction of itself equal to

$$\frac{v}{V_0 - v_0}.$$

Since v_0 only introduces a correction which is small compared even with the alteration of wave-length, it cannot be determined by spectroscopic observations with our present instruments, and it need not be considered in the discussion of our observations.

If, therefore, the light of the star is due to the combustion of sodium, or any other element which gives rise to vibrations of definite period, or if the light of the star is absorbed by sodium vapour, so as to be deficient in vibrations of a definite period, then the light, when it reaches the earth, will have an excess or defect of rays whose period of vibration is to that of the sodium period as $V+v$ is to V.

As an example, let us suppose the star to be fixed and the earth to be moving directly away from the star with the velocity due to its motion round the sun. The coefficient of aberration indicates that the velocity of light is about 10,000 times that of the earth in its orbit,[3] and it appears from the observations of Ångström[4] and Ditscheiner[5] that the wave-length of the less refrangible of the lines forming D exceeds that of the other by about one-thousandth part of itself. Hence, if the lines corresponding to D in the light of the star are due to sodium in the star, these lines in the starlight will be less refrangible than the corresponding lines in a terrestrial sodium-flame by about a tenth part of the difference between D_1 and D_2.

When the earth is moving towards the star, the lines will be more refrangible than the corresponding terrestrial lines by about the same quantity.

The effect of the proper motion of stars would of course have to be compounded with the effect of the earth's own motion, in order to determine the velocity of approach or separation.

To observe these differences of the light from stars, a *spectroscope* is necessary, that is, an instrument for separating the rays of different periods; and it is immaterial in what direction the refraction of the light through the

---

(3) See the value cited in Number 238, esp. note (26).

(4) A. J. Ångström, 'Neue Bestimmung der Länge der Lichtwellen, nebst einer Methode, auf optische Wege die fortschreitende Bewegung des Sonnensystems zu bestimmen', *Ann. Phys.*, **123** (1864): 489–505; (trans.) 'On a new determination of the lengths of waves of light, and of a method of determining, by optics, the translatory motion of the solar system', *Phil. Mag.*, ser. 4, **29** (1865): 489–501, esp. 491–2.

(5) Leander Ditscheiner, 'Bestimmung der Wellenlängen der Fraunhofer'schen Linien des Sonnenspectrums', *Wiener Berichte*, **50**, Abtheilung II (1865): 296–341, esp. 340.

prisms takes place, because the *period* of the light is the thing to be observed by comparison with that of a terrestrial flame.

If, instead of a spectroscope, an achromatic prism were used, which produces an equal deviation on rays of different periods, no difference between the light of different stars could be detected, as the only difference which could exist is that of their period.[6]

If the motion of a luminiferous medium in the place where the experiment is made is different from that of the earth, a difference in the deviation might be expected according to the *direction* of the ray within the prisms, and this difference would be nearly the same whatever the source of the light.

There are therefore two different and independent subjects of experiment. The one is the alteration in the period of vibration of light due to the relative motion of the stars and the earth.[7] The fact of such an alteration is independent of the form under which we accept the theory of undulations, and the possibility of establishing its existence depends on the discovery of lines in the stellar spectra, indicating by their arrangement that their origin is due to the existence of substances in the star having the same properties as substances found on the earth. Any method of observing small differences in the period of vibration of rays, if sufficiently exact, will enable us to verify the theory, and to determine the actual rate of approach or separation between the earth and any star.

The other subject of experiment is the relation between the index of refraction of a ray and the direction in which it traverses the prism. The essentials of this experiment are entirely terrestrial, and independent of the source of light, and depend only on the relative motion of the prism and the luminiferous medium, and on the direction in which the ray passes through the prism.

The theory of this experiment, however, depends on the form in which we accept the theory of undulations. In every form of the theory, the index of refraction depends on the retardation which a ray experiences on account of having to traverse a dense medium instead of a vacuum. Let us calculate this retardation.

Let there be a transparent medium whose thickness is a, and let it be supposed fixed. Let the luminiferous ether be supposed to move with velocity v in air, and with velocity v' within the medium. Let light be propagated

---

(6) See Number 227 note (11).

(7) The experiment addressed by Huggins. He found some evidence of the motion of the stars relative to the earth from observations of the spectral lines of Sirius as compared with the hydrogen spectrum; see his 'Further observations on the spectra of some of the stars and nebulæ': 546–50.

through the ether with velocity V in air and with velocity V' within the medium. Then the absolute velocity of the light will be $v+V$ in air and $v'+V'$ within the medium, and the retardation, or difference of *time* in traversing a thickness a of the medium and an equal thickness of air, will be

$$a\left(\frac{1}{v'+V'}-\frac{1}{v+V}\right);$$

and the retardation in *distance* reckoned as at the velocity, V will be

$$a\left\{\frac{V}{V'}-1-\frac{v'}{V}\left(\frac{V^2}{V'^2}-\frac{v}{v'}\right)+\frac{v'^2}{V^2}\left(\frac{V^3}{V'^3}-\frac{v^2}{v'^2}\right)-\&c.\right\}.$$

Now, according to every form of the theory, $\frac{V}{V'}=\mu$, the index of refraction, and according to Fresnel's form of the theory, in which the density of the medium varies as μ^2,[8] the equation of continuity requires that $\frac{v}{v'}=\mu^2$. In this case the second term disappears and the retardation is $a(\mu-1)+$ terms in $\frac{v'^2}{V^2}$, which may be neglected, as V is more than 10,000 times v.

Hence, on Fresnel's theory, the retardation due to the prism is not sensibly affected by the motion of the earth. The same would be true on the hypothesis that the luminiferous ether near the earth's surface moves along with the earth, whatever the form of the theory of the medium.

Since the deviation of light by the prism depends entirely on the retardation of the rays within the glass, no effect of the earth's motion on the refrangibility of light is to be expected.[9] Professor Stokes (Phil. Mag. 1846, p. 63)[10] has also given a direct proof of this statement, and the experiment of Arago[11] confirms it to a certain degree of exactness.

In order to test the equality of the index of refraction for light moving in

---

(8) [A. J. Fresnel,] 'Lettre de M. Fresnel à M. Arago, sur l'influence du mouvement terrestre dans quelques phénomènes d'optique', *Ann. Chim. Phys.*, **9** (1818): 57–66, esp. 62. Fresnel assumes that isotropic media differ optically only in density; his argument is discussed by G. B. Airy, *Mathematical Tracts on the Lunar and Planetary Theories...and the Undulatory Theory of Optics* (Cambridge, $_3$1842): 340. See also Number 227 esp. note (6).

(9) Compare Maxwell's conclusion in Number 227; and see his letter to Stokes of 6 May 1864 (Number 228, esp. note (5)).

(10) Read: G. G. Stokes, 'On Fresnel's theory of the aberration of light', *Phil. Mag.*, ser. 3, **28** (1846): 76–81 (= *Papers*, **1**: 141–7).

(11) François Arago, 'Mémoire sur la vitesse de la lumière, lu à la première Classe de l'Institut, le 10 décembre 1810', *Comptes Rendus*, **36** (1853): 38–49.

opposite directions through a prism, I employed in 1864 the following arrangement.[12]

I made use of a spectroscope constructed by Mr. Becker,[13] and provided with a tube at right angles to the axis of the observing-telescope, carrying a transparent plate of parallel glass placed between the object-glass and its focus, so as to reflect the light which enters the tube along the axis of the telescope towards the object-glass. In this tube is placed a screen with a vertical slit, in the middle of which is a vertical spider-line so arranged that its virtual image formed by the first surface of the glass plate coincides with the crossing of the spider-lines of the telescope at the principal focus of the object-glass. This coincidence is tested by observing the cross lines through the other telescope, with the two telescopes facing each other. The eyepiece of the second telescope is then removed, and a plane mirror is placed at the focus of the object-glass, perpendicular to the axis, and the telescopes are so adjusted that light entering by the side tube is reflected down the axis of the first telescope, traverses the prisms in succession, enters the second telescope, is reflected by the mirror at its focus, and emerges from the telescope parallel to its direction at incidence; it then traverses the prisms in the reverse order, and is brought to a focus at the cross lines of the first telescope.

If the deviation of the rays in passing through the prisms from east to west differs from that produced during their passage from west to east, the image of the vertical spider-line formed by the rays which have traversed the prisms twice will not coincide with the intersection of the spider-lines as before.

I have found, however, that when the instrument is properly adjusted, the coincidence is so perfect with respect to rays of all refrangibilities, that the image of the vertical spider-line is seen with perfect distinctness, though the rays which form it have passed twice through three prisms of 60°.

If we observe the coincidence of this image with the intersection of the spider-lines at the focus when the rays pass through the prisms first in the direction of the earth's motion and return in the opposite direction, we may then reverse the whole instrument, so that the rays pursue an opposite path with respect to the earth's motion. I have tried this experiment at various times of the year since the year 1864, and have never detected the slightest effect due to the earth's motion. If the image of the spider-line is hid by the intersection of the cross lines in one position, it remains hid in precisely the same way in the other position, though a deviation corresponding to one-twentieth of the distance of the components of the line D could be easily detected.

---

(12) Number 227.   (13) See Number 214 note (5).

On the other hand, M. Fizeau*[14] has observed a difference in the rotation of the plane of polarization according as the ray travels in the direction of the earth's motion or in the contrary direction, and M. Ångström has observed a similar difference in phenomena of diffraction.[15] I am not aware that either of these very difficult observations has been confirmed by repetition.

In another experiment of M. Fizeau, which seems entitled to greater confidence, he has observed that the propagation of light in a stream of water takes place with greater velocity in the direction in which the water moves than in the opposite direction, but that the acceleration is less than that which would be due to the actual velocity of the water, and that the phenomenon does not occur when air is substituted for water.[16] This experiment seems rather to verify Fresnel's theory of the ether; but the whole question of the state of luminiferous medium near the earth, and of its connexion with gross matter, is very far as yet from being settled by experiment.[17]

JAMES CLERK MAXWELL

June 10, 1867.

* Ann. de Chimie et de Physique, Feb. 1860.[14]

---

(14) Hippolyte Fizeau, 'Sur une méthode propre a rechercher si l'azimut de polarisation du rayon réfracté est influencé par le mouvement du corps réfringent – essai de cette méthode', *Ann. Chim. Phys.*, ser. 3, **58** (1860): 129–63.

(15) Ångström, 'On a new determination of the lengths of waves of light': 497–501.

(16) H. Fizeau, 'Sur les hypothèses relatives a l'ether lumineux...', *Ann. Chim. Phys.*, ser. 3, **57** (1859): 385–404. See Number 227 note (4).

(17) Maxwell summarized the argument of his letter to Huggins on discussing the problem of the relative motion of the ether in his article on 'Ether', in *Encyclopaedia Britannica* (9th edn), **8** (Edinburgh, 1879): 568–72, esp. 571 (= *Scientific Papers*, **2**: 769–70).

BRITISH ASSOCIATION PAPER ON A STEREOSCOPE

[SEPTEMBER 1867]

From the *Report of the British Association for 1867*[1]

ON A REAL IMAGE STEREOSCOPE[2]

In all stereoscopes there is an optical arrangement, by which the right eye sees an image of one picture and the left eye that of another.[3] These images ought to be apparently in the same place, and at the distance of most distinct vision. In ordinary stereoscopes these images are virtual, and the observer has to place his two eyes near two apertures, and he sees the united images, as it were, behind the optical apparatus. In the stereoscope made for the author by Messrs. Elliott Brothers the observer stands at a short distance from the apparatus, and looks with both eyes at a large lens, and the image appears as a real object close to the lens. The stereoscope consists of a board about 2 feet long, on which is placed, first, a vertical frame to hold the pair of pictures, which may be an ordinary stereoscopic slide, turned upside down; secondly, a sliding piece near the middle of the board containing two lenses of 6 inches focal length, placed side by side, with their centres about $1\frac{1}{4}$ inch apart; and thirdly, a frame containing a large lens of about 8 inches focal length and 3 inches diameter. The observer stands with his eyes about 2 feet from the large lens. With his right eye he sees the real image of the left-hand picture formed by the left-hand lens in the air, close to the large lens, and with the left eye he sees the real image of the other picture formed by the other lens in the same place. The united images look like a real object in the air, close to the large lens. This image may be magnified or diminished at pleasure by sliding the piece containing the two lenses nearer to, or further from, the pictures.

---

(1) *Report of the Thirty-seventh Meeting of the British Association for the Advancement of Science; held at Dundee in September 1867* (London, 1868), part 2: 11.

(2) Maxwell gave an account of the principles of his real image stereoscope in his paper 'On the cyclide', *Quarterly Journal of Pure and Applied Mathematics*, **11** (1867): 111–26, esp. 115n (= *Scientific Papers*, **2**: 148n). For the use of the stereoscope in drawing figures of surfaces see Numbers 274, 275, 277 and 279.

(3) Maxwell had first expressed interest in Charles Wheatstone's mirror or reflecting stereoscope and David Brewster's lenticular or refracting telescope in October 1849: see Volume I: 119. He devised a reflecting stereoscope in 1856; see Volume I: 391.

Plate V. Maxwell's real image stereoscope (1867), showing a stereogram of Steiner's surface (Number 272).

273

ON RECIPROCAL FIGURES AND DIAGRAMS OF FORCES

circa SEPTEMBER 1867

From *The Engineer* (1867)[1]

ON THE APPLICATION OF THE THEORY OF RECIPROCAL POLAR FIGURES[2] TO THE CONSTRUCTION OF DIAGRAMS OF FORCES*

Professor Rankine, in the *Philosophical Magazine* for February, 1864, has described a pair of reciprocal figures in three dimensions.[3] The reciprocity consists in the fact that they may be placed so that every straight line in the one figure is perpendicular to a plane face of the other, and every point of concourse of straight lines in the one figure corresponds in the other figure to a closed polyhedron. If these conditions be fulfilled, and if forces act between each connected pair of points in the first figure proportional to the areas of the plane faces of the second figure, which are perpendicular to the lines joining the pair of points, then this system of forces will keep all the points in equilibrium. In the *Philosophical Magazine* for April 1864, I have stated the conditions under which the construction of such reciprocal figures is possible.[4] I now propose to explain the connection between Professor Rankine's figure and the diagrams of forces for plane frames by means of the theory of reciprocal polars with respect to the sphere.

* British Association, Section G[5]

---

(1) *The Engineer*, **24** (8 November 1867): 402.

(2) The reference is to the method of reciprocal polars in projective geometry, introduced by J. V. Poncelet in the 1820s, and widely familiar. See especially Michel Chasles, *Aperçu Historique sur l'Origine et le Développement des Méthodes en Géométrie* (Brussels, 1837) and his supplementary 'Mémoire de géométrie sur deux principes généraux de la science: la dualité et l'homographie' in *Mémoires couronnés par l'Académie Royale des Sciences et Belles-Lettres de Bruxelles*, **11** (1837): 575–848; and Chasles, *Traité de Géométrie Supérieure* (Paris, 1852). Maxwell refers to Chasles' projective geometry in Number 373. The work of Chasles and Poncelet is presented by John Mulcahy, *Principles of Modern Geometry, with numerous applications to Plane and Spherical Figures* (Dublin, 1852, $_2$1862); Maxwell referred to Mulcahy's text in 1853 and 1856 (see Volume I: 230n, 485). See also Numbers 334, 472 §1, and 480.

(3) W. J. M. Rankine, 'Principle of the equilibrium of polyhedral frames', *Phil. Mag.*, ser. 4, **27** (1864): 92.

(4) J. Clerk Maxwell, 'On reciprocal figures and diagrams of forces', *Phil. Mag.*, ser. 4, **27** (1864): 250–61 (= *Scientific Papers*, **1**: 514–25).

(5) The abstract published in the British Association *Report* is reproduced as the Appendix *infra*.

Let any closed polyhedron with plane faces be taken, and let a system of triangles be described whose bases are the edges of the polyhedron and whose vertices are at the point P. Next let the polar reciprocal of the polyhedron be constructed with respect to a sphere whose centre is at P, and let triangles be described with their bases on the edges of this polyhedron and their vertices at P. Then every face of one polyhedron will be polar to a summit of the other, and every edge of the one to a corresponding edge of the other, by the theory of reciprocal polars.

The polyhedra with the accompanying triangles will also satisfy Professor Rankine's condition, for every face of either polyhedron will be perpendicular to the line joining P with the corresponding summit of the other, and every triangle whose vertex is at P will be perpendicular to the lines in the other figure which is polar to its base. Every summit of the one polyhedron corresponds to the pyramid in the other whose vertex is P, and whose base is the polar of the summit, and the polyhedron itself in the one figure corresponds to the point P in the other. Either figure may be taken to represent a jointed frame whose angles are acted on by forces whose direction passes through P, and the other figure will then represent the magnitude of each force by the area of the face which is perpendicular to the line of action of the force.

In order to pass from this case to that of plane frames, let any point Q be taken within one of the polyhedra, and let a plane be drawn through Q perpendicular to PQ. Next let the distance of every point of the polyhedron from this plane be diminished in the ratio of n to 1, and let the distance of P from the plane be increased in the ratio of 1 to n, and let the figure which is reciprocal to this altered figure be described. Then, when n is indefinitely increased, both the polyhedra will tend to become plane figures of finite dimensions, which are reciprocal figures in the sense that every line of the one is perpendicular to the corresponding line in the other, and that lines which meet in a point correspond to lines forming a closed polygon. I have proved in my former paper that the condition of a reciprocal figure being possible is the same as that of the figure being the projection of a polyhedron with plane sides,[6] and by the construction which I have now described, when this condition is fulfilled, the reciprocal figure may be drawn.

In calculating the equilibrium of frames, such as those of roofs and bridges, after resolving the weight of each piece into two parts applied at its extremities, we have a frame without weight acted on by external forces applied at its joints. If a diagram of forces without redundant lines is possible,

---

(6) Maxwell, 'On reciprocal figures and diagrams of forces': 252–8 (= *Scientific Papers*, **1**: 516–22).

every line of the frame must form a side of two, and only two, closed polygons answering to the two, and only two extremities of the corresponding line in the diagram of forces. Such a diagram can only be drawn when the external forces are applied at points on the boundary of the frame. For any line in the frame to the extremities of which external forces are applied forms part of a polygon of which the directions of the external forces are sides. If it is part of the boundary of the frame, it forms a side of one other polygon only and the reciprocal diagram is possible, but if it is in the interior of the frame it is a side of more than one other polygon, and it cannot be represented in the reciprocal diagram by a single line. In the complete diagram the line would be repeated till all the polygons of which the original line formed a side were represented by the extremities of the different repetitions of the line. In most actual cases, however, the external forces can be represented by a series of weights placed on the joints of the upper and lower boundaries of the frame, and a diagram can be drawn representing at once the magnitude and direction of the stresses. The construction of such diagrams is easy, and affords a security against errors, since if any mistake is made the diagram cannot be completed. Since all the weights on the upper boundary of the frame act towards one point at an infinite distance, the lines representing them will form part of a polygon, and since they are all parallel, the lines will be successive portions of the same straight line. The same will be true of the weights on the lower boundary. The vertical lines corresponding to these two sets of weights, together with the forces supporting the whole structure, will form a closed polygon. If the supporting forces are vertical, this polygon will be reduced to a vertical line folded on itself.

The diagram for a roof may be thus constructed:– Let A_1, A_2, &c, be the different divisions of the rafters beginning at the left side of the figure. Let a_1, a_2, &c, be the stresses in these pieces. Let B_1, B_2, &c, be the different pieces

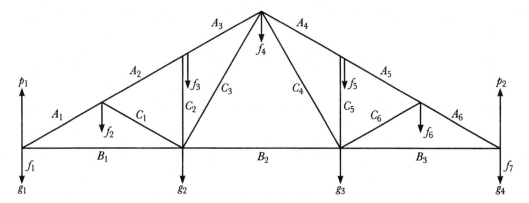

Figure 273,1

of the tie beam, and b_1, b_2, &c, the stresses in them. Let C_1, C_2, &c, be the different pieces of the frame between the rafters and the tie beam, and let c_1, c_2, &c, be the stresses in them. Let f_1, f_2, &c, be the weights applied at the end of the rafters and at the different joints of them, and let g_1, g_2, &c, be the weights at the extremities of the pieces of the tie beam. Let p_1, p_2, be the forces supporting the entire structure. It is easiest to calculate these in the ordinary way by taking moments.

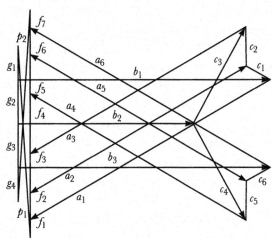

Figure 273,2

To construct the diagram draw a vertical line and measure successive portions upwards representing f_1, f_2, &c. From the bottom of this line draw p upwards (if p is vertical the two lines will coincide). From the top of p measure segments g_1, g_2, &c, downwards in succession. The line joining the bottom of this line with the top of the line of f_1, f_2, &c, will represent p_2. Next, from the point of division between f_1 and f_2 draw a_1 parallel to A_1, and from the points of division between f_2 and f_3 draw a_2 parallel to A_2, and so on. In the same way from the point g_1, g_2 draw b_1 parallel to B_1, and so on. Then, since at the foot of the first rafter the forces are f_1, a_1, b_1, g_1, p, these must form a polygon, and therefore the lines a_1 and b_1 terminate at their point of intersection. We may then go on to determine all the other forces by drawing lines parallel to c_1, c_2, &c, as in the figure, always remembering that forces acting at a point in the roof must form a closed polygon in the diagram, and that the forces along pieces which form a closed polygon in the roof must meet at a point in the diagram.

APPENDIX: BRITISH ASSOCIATION PAPER ON DIAGRAMS OF FORCES

[SEPTEMBER 1867]

From the *Report of the British Association for 1867*[7]

ON THE THEORY OF DIAGRAMS OF FORCES AS APPLIED TO ROOFS AND BRIDGES

A roof is made up of a series of vertical frames. A diagram of forces is a figure consisting of straight lines, which represent, both in magnitude and direction, the tensions and pressures in the different pieces between the joints of the frame. The pieces of the frame and the weights acting on it are denoted by capital letters, and the corresponding lines of the diagram by small letters. The diagram is constructed by the following rule, which is sufficient for the purpose:– The frame, including the vertical lines representing the weights, and the diagrams of forces, are reciprocal figures, such that every line in the one is parallel to the corresponding line in the other, and every set of lines which meet in a point in the one figure form a closed figure in the other. It follows from this that the weights, which are all vertical forces, are represented by the parts of one vertical line. The first extension of the principle of the diagram of forces was made by Dr. Rankine in his 'Applied Mechanics'.[8] The theory was generalized by the author in the Philosophical Magazine in April 1864.[9] In the present paper it is shown to be connected with the theory of reciprocal polars in solid geometry, and rules for the construction of diagrams are given. The advantage of the method is that its construction requires only a parallel ruler, and that every force is represented to the eye at once by a separate line, which may be measured with sufficient accuracy for all purposes with less trouble than the forces can be found by calculation. It also affords security against error, as, if any mistake is made, the diagram cannot be completed.

---

(7) *Report of the Thirty-seventh Meeting of the British Association for the Advancement of Science; held at Dundee in September 1867* (London, 1868), part 2: 156.

(8) W. J. M. Rankine, *A Manual of Applied Mechanics* (London/Glasgow, 1858): 137–40.

(9) See note (4).

274
LETTER TO WILLIAM THOMSON
14 SEPTEMBER 1867
From the original in the University Library, Glasgow[1]

Glenlair
Dalbeattie
1867 Sept 14

Dear Thomson

I send you per book post a copy of my paper on the maintenance of electric currents[2] enclosing stereograms of[3]

I Icosihedron inscribed in Octahedron. This is one of two cases right & left handed. Every face of the Octahedron has in it a face of the Icosihedron with a twist to the right or left hand thus.

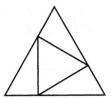

Figure 274,1

The alternate sides of the octahedron are right or left handed, and if the two tetrahedra be formed by producing the sides of the octahedron the one tetrahedron will be righthanded and the other lefthanded with regard to the icosihedron.

II Part of the elliptic paraboloid near its vertex showing the umbilici and lines of curvature.

III Lines of curvature of a hyperbolic paraboloid near the vertex. Both figures are here symmetrical in themselves but give the negative curvature in the stereoscope.

IV Lines of curvature of the ellipsoid.[4]

---

(1) Glasgow University Library, Kelvin Papers M 20.

(2) J. Clerk Maxwell, 'On the theory of the maintenance of electric currents by mechanical work without the use of permanent magnets', *Proc. Roy. Soc.*, **15** (1867): 397–402 (= *Scientific Papers*, **2**: 79–85). See Number 268.

(3) The stereograms listed below are preserved in ULC Add. MSS 7655, V, i/11, where a number of the original drawings are also preserved. See Plates VI and VII. Some of the stereograms mentioned here were exhibited to the London Mathematical Society on 23 January 1868: see Number 279. See also Numbers 275 and 277; and on the stereoscope see Number 272 and Plate V. The proof of the stereogram of the elliptic paraboloid carries the following explanation on the *verso*: 'II Lines of Curvature of an Elliptic Paraboloid / General Equation of the confocal system / $\dfrac{x^2}{p+a}+\dfrac{y^2}{p-a}+4(z-p) = 0.$ / If $p, a, q, -a, r$ be in order of magnitude and if q and r be substituted for p, the point of intersection of the three confocal surfaces $p\,q\,r$ is / $x^2 = -2\dfrac{(p+a)(q+a)(r+a)}{a}$ / $y^2 = 2\dfrac{(p-a)(q-a)(r-a)}{a}$ / $z = p+q+r.$ / In the figure $a = 2$, $p = 4$ / q & r from $+2$ to -4.'

(4) Maxwell's proof of this stereogram (see note (3)) carries the following explanation on the

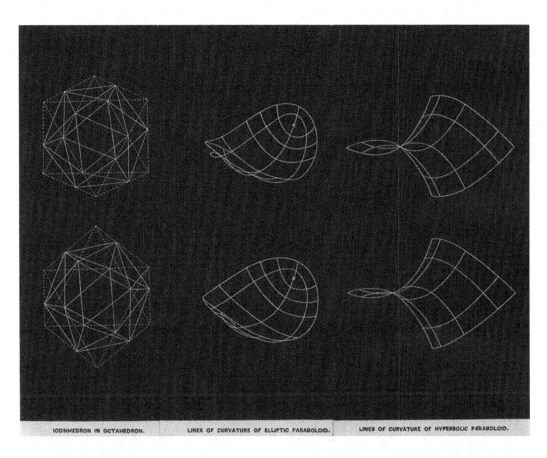

Plate VI. Stereograms (1867) of icosihedron in octahedron, lines of curvature of elliptic paraboloid and lines of curvature of hyperbolic paraboloid (Number 274).

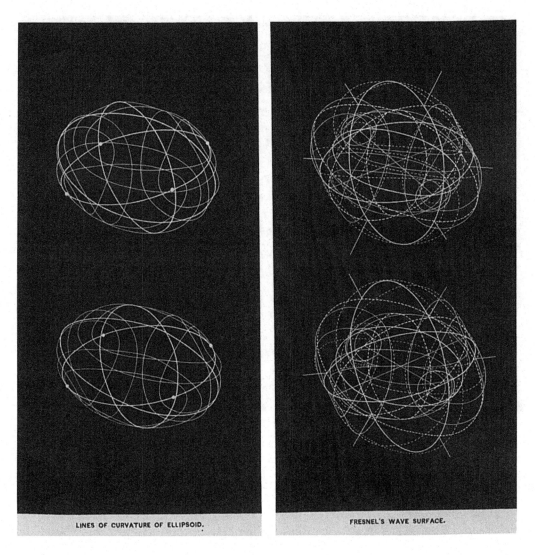

Plate VII. Stereograms (1867) of lines of curvature of ellipsoid and Fresnel's wave surface (Number 274).

V Wave surfaces of the same ellipsoid.[5] The dotted lines follow the direction of the planes of polarization at every point and are all spherical curves on the wave surface. The continuous lines are perpendicular to these or in the direction of Fresnels vibration. They are all intersections of the wave surface with ellipsoids similar to IV.

The two lines which cross at the centre pass through the conical points where the inner sheet which is like a pulpit cushion meets the outer sheet which is like an apple with two stalk holes and two blossom holes.

The six spines sticking out are the ends of the principal axes projecting beyond the surface to a fixed distance. They show where the principal sections are.

The other four are figures of the Cyclide or surface all whose lines of curvature are circles and all whose normals pass through two confocal conics (the skeleton curves of a confocal system of quadric surfaces. See my paper in next number of Q J of P & A M).[6]

---

verso: 'IV. Lines of Curvature of an Ellipsoid / Equation of the Confocal System / $\frac{x^2}{\rho^2-a^2}+\frac{y^2}{\rho^2-b^2}+\frac{z^2}{\rho^2-c^2} = 1.$ / If ρ, c, μ, b, v, a be in descending order of magnitude and if μ and v be substituted for ρ, the point of intersection of the three confocal surfaces is given by $x^2 = -\frac{(\rho^2-a^2)(\mu^2-a^2)(v^2-a^2)}{(c^2-a^2)(a^2-b^2)}$ and two other equations for y & z which may be written down from symmetry. In the figure, for the ellipsoid $a^2 = 0$, $b^2 = 3$, $c^2 = 6$, $\rho^2 = 9$. / For the hyperboloids of one sheet $\mu^2 = 6, 5, 4$ and 3. / For the hyperboloids of two sheets $v^2 = 3, 2, 1$ and 0. / The umbilici are indicated by dots.'

(5) Maxwell's proof of this stereogram (see note (3)) carries the following explanation on the *verso*: 'V. Fresnels Biaxial Wave Surface. / Formed by Fresnels construction from the Ellipsoid N°IV. / Points on the outer and inner sheet respectively are found from the equations

$$x_1^2 = \frac{(\rho^2-b^2)(\rho^2-c^2)(\mu^2-a^2)(v^2-a^2)}{(c^2-a^2)(a^2-b^2)(\rho^2-\mu^2)}$$

$$x_2^2 = \frac{(\rho^2-b^2)(\rho^2-c^2)(\mu^2-a^2)(v^2-a^2)}{(c^2-a^2)(a^2-b^2)(\rho^2-v^2)}$$

with similar equations for y & z. / The straight lines which intersect at the centre are the optic axes joining the two pairs of conical points where the two sheets meet. / The short straight lines are portions of the three principal axes projecting beyond the outer sheet. / The continuous lines are in the direction of vibration at every point and are the intersections of the Wave Surface with ellipsoids similar to N°IV. / The dotted lines are in the direction of the plane of polarization and are the intersections of the Wave Surface with concentric spheres. / The strong lines are the principal sections.' See Number 320 note (8).

(6) J. Clerk Maxwell, 'On the cyclide', *Quarterly Journal of Pure and Applied Mathematics*, **11** (1867): 111–26 (= *Scientific Papers*, **2**: 144–59). The four cyclides here listed are described and illustrated in this paper: on the definition of the 'cyclide' he cites Charles Dupin, *Applications de Géométrie et de Mécanique* (Paris, 1822): 200–10.

VI is a horned cyclide with the skeleton curves and the lines thro which the circular sections pass dotted.
VII a ring cyclide
VIII a spindle cyclide
IX a parabolic ring cyclide.

Here is something which might be considerably extended.

Let $A\ B\ C\ D$ be four bodies then if operation F acts between A and B and produces the effect E between C and D then will the same operation F acting between C & D produce the same effect E between A & B.

Examples of Operations	Effects
Tension or Pressure in the direction AB	Elongation or contraction in CD
Difference of Potential	Electric Current
Difference of Potential	Electric Charge

I have proved this kind of reciprocity for all elastic frameworks[7] (Case I) for systems of linear conductors such as the electric balance and others more complicated[8] (Case II) and Case III is Greens doctrine of the Greenish Function[9] as extended by Riemann[10] & others.[11] If there is any thing which has a rotatory property of conduction &c the prop. does not hold for it.

Yours truly
J. CLERK MAXWELL

---

(7) See Number 273. (8) See Maxwell, *Treatise*, **1**: 335–6 (§281).

(9) See Maxwell, *Treatise*, **1**: 91–2 (§§88–9) for his discussion of Green's reciprocity theorem and Green's function; and see George Green, *An Essay on the Application of Mathematical Analysis to the Theories of Electricity and Magnetism* (Nottingham, 1828): 18–20 (= *Mathematical Papers of the Late George Green*, ed. N. M. Ferrers (London, 1871): 36–9).

(10) Bernhard Riemann, 'Ueber die Fortpflanzung ebener Luftwellen von endlicher Schwingungsweite', *Abhandlungen der Mathematischen Classe der Königlicher Gesellschaft der Wissenschaften zu Göttingen*, **8** (1860): 43–65.

(11) Maxwell may well have had in mind papers by Carl Neumann and Enrico Betti. See Carl Neumann, 'Ueber die Integration der partiellen Differential-gleichung: $\frac{\partial^2 \phi}{\partial x^2}+\frac{\partial^2 \phi}{\partial y^2}=0$',

Journal für die reine und angewandte Mathematik, **59** (1861): 335–66, esp. 336–9, where Neumann introduces the 'Greensche Function' (denoted G, as in the *Treatise*, **1**: 113–15 (§101)), and where his discussion is similar to Maxwell's in the *Treatise*. Maxwell refers to Neumann's paper in the *Treatise*, **1**: 234 (§190); and see Number 337. See also Betti's discussion of the 'funzione di Green' in his 'Teorica delle forze che agiscono secondo la legge di Newton e sua applicazione alla elettricità statica', *Nuovo Cimento*, **18** (1863): 385–402; *ibid.*, **19** (1863): 59–75, 77–95, 149–75, 357–77; *ibid.* **20** (1864): 19–39, 121–41; see esp. *ibid.*, **19** (1863): 165–9. Maxwell refers to Betti's paper in his letter to Tait of 11 December 1867 (Number 277).

LETTER TO PETER GUTHRIE TAIT

13 NOVEMBER 1867

From the original in the University Library, Cambridge[1]

Glenlair
Dalbeattie
1867 Nov 13

Dear Tait

If you have any spare copies of your translation of Helmholtz on 'Water Twists'[2] I should be obliged to you if you could send me one.

I set the Helmholtz dogma to the Senate house in '66,[3] and got it very nearly done by some men, completely as to the calculation nearly as to the interpretation.

Thomson has set himself to spin the chains of destiny out of a fluid plenum[4] as M. Scott set an eminent person to spin ropes from the sea sand,[5] and I saw you had put your calculus in it too.[6] May you both prosper and disentangle your formulae in proportion as you entangle your wurbles. But I fear that the simplest *indivisible* whorl is either two embracing wurbles or a worble embracing itself.[7]

For a simple enclosed worble may be easily split and the parts separated but two embracing worbles preserve each others solidarity thus

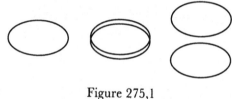

Figure 275,1

---

(1) ULC Add. MSS 7655, I, b/6. Previously published (in part) in Knott, *Life of Tait*: 106.

(2) Hermann Helmholtz, 'On the integrals of the hydrodynamical equations, which express vortex-motion', *Phil. Mag.*, ser. 4, **33** (1867): 485–512; trans. by P. G. Tait of Helmholtz's paper 'Über Integrale der hydrodynamischen Gleichungen, welche den Wirbelbewegungen entsprechen', *Journal für die reine und angewandte Mathematik*, **55** (1858): 25–55.

(3) Question 5 in the Mathematical Tripos paper on the afternoon of Friday 19 January 1866, confirmed by Maxwell's mark book (ULC Add. MSS 7655, V, k/8(iv)). See Number 254 note (1).

(4) William Thomson's paper 'On vortex motion', *Trans. Roy. Soc. Edinb.*, **25** (1869): 217–60 (= *Math. & Phys. Papers*, **4**: 13–66) was read to the Royal Society of Edinburgh on 29 April 1867; see *Proc. Roy. Soc., Edinb.*, **6** (1867): 167. See Number 295 note (2).

(5) Maxwell may be associating 'the wondrous Michael Scott' of Sir Walter Scott's *The Lay of the Last Minstrel* (canto II, xiii) with the legend recounted in Samuel Butler's *Hudibras* (part I, canto i, *ll.* 157–8): 'And, with as delicate a hand, / Could twist as tough a rope of sand.'

(6) In his paper 'On vortex atoms', *Proc. Roy. Soc. Edinb.*, **6** (1867): 94–105 (= *Math. & Phys. Papers*, **4**: 1–12) Thomson described Tait's demonstration of smoke rings, which had stimulated his speculations.   (7) See also Number 307 esp. note (7).

though each may split into many every one of the one set must embrace every one of the other.

So does a knotted one.

I send you one or two stereograms of Cyclides ellipsoids & a parabolic hyperboloid. I have several more which I will send you when they are more perfect. I have got the Wave Surface and a magnified view of the point of adhesion also the surface of centres of an ellipsoid, &c &c,[8] but the engraver has to make some improvements on them.

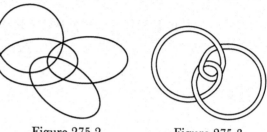

Figure 275,2   Figure 275,3

Yours truly
J. CLERK MAXWELL

---

(8) See Number 274 and Plates VI, VII and VIII.

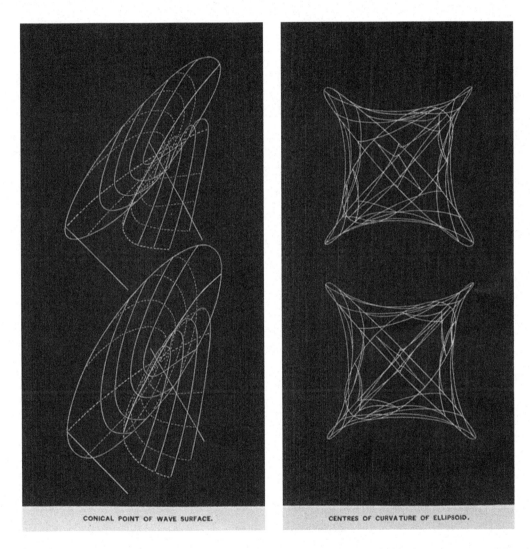

Plate VIII. Stereograms (1867) of conical point of wave surface and centres of curvature of ellipsoid (Number 275).

LETTER TO PETER GUTHRIE TAIT

4 DECEMBER 1867

From the original in the University Library, Cambridge[1]

Glenlair
Dalbeattie
1867 Dec 4

Dear Tait

I have yours of the 27th ult.[2]

Of course
$$x_1 = C e^{-\frac{k}{2}t} \cos\left(\sqrt{n^2 - \frac{k^2}{4}}\, t + \alpha\right)$$
$$y_1 = C' e^{-\frac{k}{2}t} \cos\left(\phantom{\sqrt{n^2 - \frac{k^2}{4}}\, t} + \beta\right)$$

gives your log. spiral when $C = C'$ & $\alpha + \beta = \frac{\pi}{2}$ where $\sqrt{\frac{k^2}{4} - n^2}$ is real, make it ω_2 for short,

---

(1) ULC Add. MSS 7655, I, b/7.

(2) In his letter of 27 November 1867 (ULC Add. MSS 7655, I, a/3) Tait had written: 'Dear Maxwell, / I was sorry not to meet you at Glasgow – for various reasons. / One *selfish* one I must state. A particle resisted *as the vel.*^y, and attracted *as the dist*^{ce} moves with uniform ∠^r vel in a log. spiral. The projection of this on any line gives a very pretty geometrical solution of §342 of T & T'. But what does the curve become when $\frac{k^2}{4} - n^2$ is positive? (There is an error in §342: $\frac{k^2}{4} - n^2$ being written for $n^2 - \frac{k^2}{4}$). It seems to be a curve derived from a hyperbola as the log. spiral is derived from the circle. Whence the difficulty of giving a geometrical solution in this last case? What is the path? / Your note to T. has some little bearing on an experiment I had been getting ready for – i.e. making an electrified piece of vulcanite into a magnet by spinning it violently. I am nearly ready to make the trial, having got a multiplying train of great power. Can I do anything for you with it? / I am delighted to hear you are going to do a Senate-House Treatise on Electricity. The sooner the better. / Yours truly / P. G. Tait'. Tait's discussion, relating to §342 of Thomson and Tait, *Natural Philosophy*: 276, also relates to §6 of his 'Note on the hodograph', *Proc. Roy. Soc. Edinb.*, **6** (1867): 221–6, esp. 224–6 (read 16 December 1867): 'A point describes a logarithmic spiral with uniform angular velocity about the pole – find the acceleration'. In §342 of their *Natural Philosophy* Thomson and Tait consider the motion of a particle resisted as the velocity; the rate of retardation due to unit velocity is k; n^2 is the rate of acceleration when the displacement is unity; 'then the motion is of the oscillatory or non-oscillatory class according as $k < 2n$ or $k > 2n$'. See Tait's reply to Maxwell's letter (Number 277 note (2)). Maxwell subsequently applied Tait's treatment of the acceleration of a particle describing a logarithmic spiral with uniform angular velocity about the pole, in discussing the damped vibrations of a magnetic needle in *Treatise*, **2**: 336–43 (§§731–42). On the hodograph see Number 472 §1.

then
$$x_2 = Ce^{-\frac{k}{2}t}\cosh(\omega t + \alpha)$$
and if you choose your conditions
$$y = Ce^{-\frac{k}{2}t}\sinh(\omega t + \alpha)$$
where
$$\cosh\theta = \frac{1}{2}(e^\theta + e^{-\theta}) \;\&\; \sinh\theta = \frac{1}{2}(e^\theta - e^{-\theta})$$
above
$$x_1^2 + y_1^2 = C^2 e^{-kt}$$
below
$$x_2^2 - y_2^2 = C^2 e^{-kt}$$
above
$$\frac{y}{x} = \tan\theta_1 = \tanh\omega_1 t$$
below
$$\frac{y}{x} = \tan\phi_2 = \tanh\omega_2 t.$$

Therefore – In the 1st case make a set of circles whose radii are $r_1\ r_2$ &c and a set of radii whose angles are $\theta_1\ \theta_2$ &c.

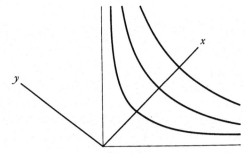

Figure 276,1   Figure 276,2

In the 2nd case make a set of hyperbolas whose eq^{ns} are
$$x_1^2 - y_1^2 = r_1^2$$
$$x_2^2 - y_2^2 = r_2^2$$
&c
and a set of radii whose angles are
$$\phi_1 = \tan^{-1}\frac{e^{\theta_1} - e^{-\theta_1}}{e^{\theta_1} + e^{-\theta_1}} \quad \phi_2 = \tan^{-1}\frac{e^{\theta_2} - e^{-\theta_2}}{e^{\theta_2} + e^{-\theta_2}}.$$

Then the first curve will lie among the circles and radii as the second lies among the hyperbolas and radii.

If this throws any light on the question well, but if not, as I think what does it signify.

I hope to hear of your vulcanite magnet drawing.[3] Thomson mentioned

---

(3) Tait's reference to Maxwell's 'note to T[homson]' (not extant) in relation to his projected experiment, may relate to Maxwell's discussion in the *Treatise*, **2**: 370 (§770) of the possibility

it in his letter to me of which the style was so entêté that there could be no doubt that it was not uninspired, or else T had been accented.[4]

At present I suppose that the superficial tension of water across a line 1 metre long

is 33.5 *grammes weight* at 43° Fah^t and
29 .... at 52°.

But I expect better results soon as at present my optical method is better than my readings and I cannot work with warm water on account of the steam dimming the glass. I expected more difficulty in the measurement of level, and used an indirect method by pouring measured quantities of water into a wide cylinder. I now find that I can measure the height of the surface directly and will require only a few drops to work on.[5]

Many thanks for your 3 pamphlets and for the page printed on one side from T & T'.[6]

I have amused myself with knotted curves for a day or two.[7] It follows from electromagnetism that if ds and $d\sigma$ are elements of two closed curves and r the distance between them and if $l\,m\,n$, $\lambda\,\mu\,\nu$, and $L\,M\,N$ are the direction cosines of $ds\,d\sigma$ & r respectively

then
$$\iint \frac{ds\,d\sigma}{r^2} \begin{vmatrix} L & M & N \\ l & m & n \\ \lambda & \mu & \nu \end{vmatrix}$$
$$= \iint \frac{ds\,d\sigma}{r^2} \left[\left(1 - \overline{\frac{dr}{ds}}\Big|^2\right)\left(1 - \overline{\frac{dr}{d\sigma}}\Big|^2\right) - \left(r\frac{d^2 r}{ds\,d\sigma}\right)^2 \right]^{\frac{1}{2}}$$
$$= 4\pi n$$

---

that an electrified body in motion produces magnetic effects. Maxwell there discussed measuring the magnetic effect of a 'non-conducting disk revolving in the plane of the magnetic meridian'. Compare Henry Rowland's detection of the magnetic effects of the convection current; see 'Versuche über die elektromagnetische Wirkung elektrischer Convection', *Monatsberichte der Akademie der Wissenschaften zu Berlin* (1876): 211–16.

(4) That is: written by Tait (T'). See Number 277 note (2) for Tait's response, and Maxwell's further comments in his letter to Tait of 23 December 1867 (Number 278).

(5) See Number 292. On Tait's interest in surface tension see his paper 'On some capillary phenomena', *Proc. Roy. Soc., Edinb.*, **5** (1866): 593–4.

(6) Thomson and Tait, *Natural Philosophy*.

(7) Perhaps suggested by reading Helmholtz on 'vortex motion': see Number 275 esp. note (2). On Helmholtz's theorems which express the analogy between hydrodynamics and electromagnetism see Number 295 esp. note (7).

the integration being extended round both curves and n being the algebraical number of times that one curve embraces the other in the same direction.[8]

Figure 276,3   Figure 276,4   Figure 276,5

If the curves are not linked together $n = 0$ but if $n = 0$ the curves are not necessarily independent. In fig [276, 3] the two closed curves are inseparable but $n = 0$. In fig [276, 4] the 3 closed curves are inseparable but $n = 0$ for every pair of them. Fig [276, 5] is the simplest single knot on a single curve. The simplest equation I can find for it is $r = b + a\cos\frac{3}{2}\theta \quad z = c\sin\frac{3}{2}\theta$
when c is $-^{ve}$ as in the figure the knot is right handed
when c is $+^{ve}$ it is left handed.
A right handed knot cannot be changed into a left handed one.[9]

$$x = \sin 2\theta$$
$$y = \sin 3\theta$$
$$z = \sin(5\theta + \gamma)$$

is knotted in different degrees according to the value of γ. When $\gamma = 0$ it is not knotted at all when $\gamma = \dfrac{\pi}{3}$ it begins to be knotted and when $\gamma = \dfrac{7}{12}\pi$ it is knotted in a different way but to the same degree.

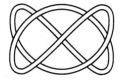 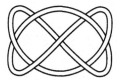 

Figure 276,6. $\gamma = 0$ no knot   Figure 276,7. $\gamma = \frac{\pi}{3}$ Figure 276,8. $\gamma = \frac{7}{12}\pi$

---

(8) See also Number 318. For further discussion see the *Treatise*, **2**: 40–1 (§421), where Maxwell makes reference to Gauss' discovery of this integral and discussion of the 'Geometry of Position': see Gauss, *Werke*, **5** (Göttingen, 1867): 605. On the electromagnetic interpretation of this integral, discussed by Maxwell in the *Treatise* §421, see 'Theorem A' of Maxwell's 'Note on the electromagnetic theory of light', in *Phil. Trans.*, **158** (1868): 652–7, esp. 653–4 (= *Scientific Papers*, **2**: 138–9).

(9) On the topology of knots see Johann Benedict Listing, 'Vorstudien zur Topologie', in *Göttinger Studien. 1847. Erste Abtheilung: Mathematische und naturwissenschaftliche Abhandlungen* (Göttingen, 1847): 811–75, esp. 862–4. See Number 370 notes (6) and (7).

Figure 276,9. $\gamma = \frac{\pi}{3}$, a knot = a righthanded twist of $4\frac{1}{2}\pi$ and then the ends linked together.

Figure 276,10. The twist of $\frac{9}{2}\pi$

Yours truly
J. CLERK MAXWELL

LETTER TO PETER GUTHRIE TAIT

11 DECEMBER 1867

From the original in the University Library, Cambridge[1]

Glenlair
Dalbeattie
1867 Dec 11

Dear Tait

Here is a different construction.[2] Of course a rotatory construction like your log spiral will not do so let us make time a straight line instead of a circle & become progressionists instead of cyclicists   let space be vertical   time horizontal   and let x be the space from origin

---

(1) ULC Add. MSS 7655, I, b/8. Published in part in Knott, *Life of Tait*: 213–14.

(2) Reply to Tait's letter (a reply to Number 276) of 6 December 1867 (ULC Add. MSS 7655, I, a/4). 'Dear Maxwell, / Many thanks for your letter, though you don't solve my difficulty about giving frictional or other resistance its true place by *geometrical* methods when too strong. I have tried several times, and got one (luckily the most important case) but the other is hopelessly complex. / Please to remember that you are a fellow of the R.S.E., and be good enough to send us a paper on Knots & their possible equations in 3 dimensions. We devised all your figures (and many more) long ago – (Crum Brown & I, working for Thomson) – but we never tried EQUATIONS. Give us a paper on them like a good fellow; whether for the *Trans*. or merely for the *Proc.*. / Give me also a reference as to your capillary investigations – for I am about to establish a working Laboratory for students, and will be delighted to get any hints as to keeping them to work & *useful* work. / Thomson's letter *was* rather ambiguous, seeing that I dictated one half & he the other, and that it was not written by him but by his nephew, whose hand is somewhat similar to his. / Nevertheless I hope your Treatise on Electricity will go on soon – whips & scorpions notwithstanding. / HALF the edition of our first vol. of Nat. Phil. is already sold!!! It was published only 3 months ago. / You may understand my desire for a solution of the COSH question when I tell you that it would be extremely useful in our smaller volume now going through the press. / Are you sufficiently up to the history of Thermodynamics to critically examine & put right a little treatise I am about to print – and will you kindly apply your critical powers to it? / You would greatly oblige me by doing so, as Clausius & others have cut up very rough about bits referring to them. I dont pretend to know the subject thoroughly and would be glad of your help. The fact seems to me to be that both Clausius & Rankine are about as obscure in their writings as anyone can well be. / Shall we never see you in Edin^h? / Yours ever, / P. G. Tait / P.S. Ponder this proposition. A man of your *originality*, and *fertility*, and *leisure*, is undoubtedly bound to furnish to the chief Society of his native land, numerous papers, however short.' See Thomson and Tait's treatment of the motion of a particle in a logarithmic spiral in their *Elements of Natural Philosophy. Part I* (Oxford, 1873): 95–6, where they reprint §6 of Tait's 'Note on the hodograph' (see Number 276 note (2)). On the circumstances surrounding the publication of Tait's *Sketch of Thermodynamics* (Edinburgh, 1868) see Number 278 note (2). In seeking to solicit a paper from Maxwell for the Royal Society of Edinburgh, Tait was writing as one of the Secretaries of the Society; see *Proc. Roy. Soc. Edinb.*, **6** (1867): 173.

$$y = x + a\frac{dx}{dt}$$

$$z = y + b\frac{dz}{dt}$$

$$= x + (a+b)\frac{dx}{dt} + ab\frac{d^2x}{dt^2}.$$

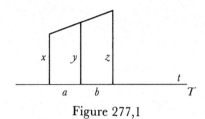

Figure 277,1

Now let us take your case in which

$$\frac{d^2x}{dt^2} = -n^2 x - k\frac{dx}{dt}$$

then $z = (1 - abn^2)x + (a + b - abk)\frac{dx}{dt}$.

If
$$a = \frac{1}{2}\frac{k}{n^2} \pm \frac{\sqrt{k^2 - 4n^2}}{2n^2}$$

$$b = \frac{1}{2}\frac{k}{n^2} \mp \frac{\sqrt{k^2 - 4n^2}}{2n^2}$$

then $z = 0$ always.
Hence the following construction.

Let OP be the original value of x.
Draw PQ horizontal = unit of time
    QR vertical = initial velocity
    and join PR & produce.
Make $OA' = a$ $OB' = b$ $OC = a+b$
Draw $B'B$ $A'A$ vertical Join BC AC

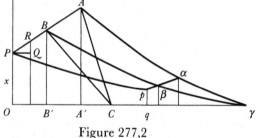

Figure 277,2

From A draw the logarithmic curve $A\alpha$ with const. subtangent $= b$.
From B draw the log curve $B\beta$ with subtangent a.
Let $\gamma\alpha$ & $\gamma\beta$ be tangents from the same point γ on the axis.

Join $\alpha\beta$ & produce. Make $\gamma q = a+b$ and draw qp to meet $\alpha\beta$. p is on a curve such that if $Oq = t$ $qp = x$.

To draw the log. curves exactly.

Draw vertical lines at equal intervals h.
Let P_1 be the beginning of the curve. Make

$$\alpha = \frac{h}{1 - e^{\frac{-h}{a}}}$$

where a is the true subtangent.

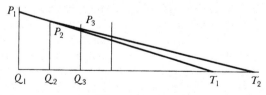

Figure 277,3

Make $Q_1 T_1 = \alpha_1$. Join $P_1 T_1$ cutting Q_2 in P_2. P_2 is a point in the curve. Make $Q_2 T_2 = \alpha_2$ & so on. This gives a series of points in the true curve.

The best way to draw a catenary is to draw two log curves in this way join corresponding points PP' and bisect PP' in Q. Q is a point in the catenary & PP' is a tangent if the log curves are properly drawn wh: is easy.

It is good in drawing curves to have tangents ready made, since a point & its tangent is as good as two points in theory & better in practice.

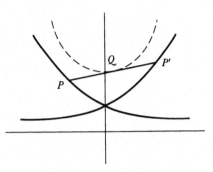

Figure 277,4

With regard to knots I have drawn stereoscopically $x = \sin 2\theta$ $y = \sin 3\theta$ $z = \cos 7\theta$ which is the first case of a real web that I have got.[3]

If the middle crossing be reversed  it becomes a knot of the simplest kind.

I have not got any R.S.E. matter on this but if they would like could knit het again. I have considerably improved the theory of reciprocal rectilinear figures & diagrams of forces, which appeared in Phil Mag. Ap. 1864.[4]

Figure 277,5

I am glad people are buying T & T'. May it sink into their bones! I shall not see it till I go to London. I believe you call Laplaces Coeffts Spherical Harmonics.[5] Good. Do you know that every Sp. Harm. of degree n has n axes? I did not till recently. When you know the directions of the axes (or their poles on the sphere) you have got your harmonic all but its strength.[6] For one of the 2nd degree they are the poles of the two circular equipotential lines on the sphere. I have a picture of them.[7]

I do not know in a controversial manner the history of thermodynamics, that is I could make no assertions about the priority of authors without

---

(3) See Plate IX and Number 279: Appendix.

(4) See Number 273, esp. note (4).

(5) See Number 262, esp. notes (8) and (10). See Thomson and Tait, *Natural Philosophy*: 140; 'The mathematical method of "Laplace's Co-efficients"... here called *spherical harmonic analysis*'.

(6) See Maxwell's discussion in the *Treatise*, **1**: 157–80, esp. 162 (§§128–46, esp. §131), where he refers to Gauss' note on 'Geometrische Bedeutung der Kugelfunctionen', published in his *Werke*, 5 (Göttingen, 1867): 631 (and see Number 276 note (8)). See Numbers 281, 293, 294 and 295.

(7) See Plate X and Number 279: Appendix.

Plate IX. Stereograms (1867) of Gordian knots (Number 277).

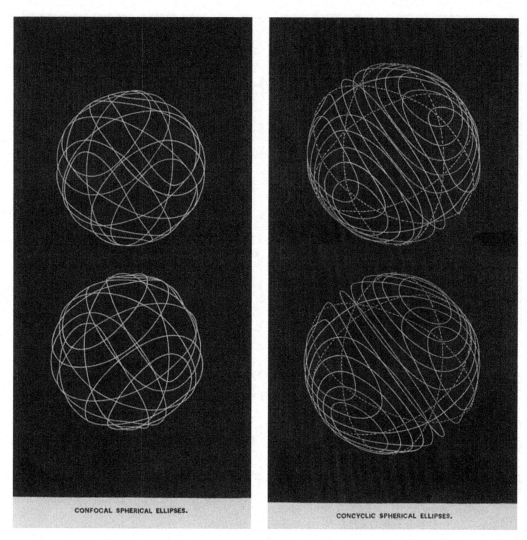

Plate X. Stereograms (1867) of confocal spherical ellipses and concyclic spherical ellipses, showing spherical harmonics of the second degree (Number 277).

referring to their actual works. If I can help you in any way with your book I shall be glad, as any contributions I could make to that study are in the way of altering the point of view here & there for clearness or variety and picking holes here & there to ensure strength & stability.

As for instance I think that you might make something of the theory of absolute scale of temperature[8] by reasoning pretty loud about it and paying it due honour, at its entrance. To pick a hole – say in the 2nd law of Θ^{cs},[9] that if two things are in contact the hotter cannot take heat from the colder without external agency.[10]

Now[a] let A & B be two vessels divided by a diaphragm and let them contain elastic molecules in a state of agitation which strike each other and the sides.

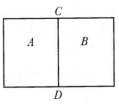

Figure 277,6

Let the number of particles be equal in A & B but let those in A have the greatest energy of motion. Then even if all the molecules in A have equal velocities, if oblique collisions occur between them their velocities will become unequal & I have shown that there will be velocities of all magnitudes in A and the same in B only the sum of the squares of the velocities is greater in A than in B.[11]

When a molecule is reflected from the fixed diaphragm CD no work is lost or gained.

If the molecule instead of being reflected were allowed to go through a hole

---

(a) {Thomson} All very well now. But when is then?

(8) See Number 207 note (15).

(9) The term 'thermo-dynamics' was first used by William Thomson, 'On the dynamical theory of heat. Part V. Thermo-electric currents', *Trans. Roy. Soc. Edinb.*, **21** (1854): 123–71, on 123 (= *Math. & Phys. Papers*, **1**: 232). The terms 'thermodynamics' and the 'second law of thermodynamics' became conventional; see W. J. M. Rankine *A Manual of the Steam Engine* (London/Glasgow, 1859): 299, 307. For Thomson's statement of the second law of thermodynamics see his paper 'On the dynamical theory of heat', *Trans. Roy. Soc. Edinb.*, **20** (1851): 261–88, esp. 265 (= *Math. & Phys. Papers*, **1**: 179): 'It is impossible, by means of inanimate material agency, to derive mechanical effect from any portion of matter by cooling it below the temperature of the coldest of the surrounding objects.'

(10) Compare Thomson's statement of Clausius' version of the second law of thermodynamics: 'It is impossible for a self-acting machine, unaided by any external agency, to convey heat from one body to another at a higher temperature'; Thomson, 'On the dynamical theory of heat': 266 (= *Math. & Phys. Papers*, **1**: 181). Thomson declared that the two forms of the second law of thermodynamics were logically equivalent.

(11) In his papers 'Illustrations of the dynamical theory of gases', *Phil. Mag.*, ser. 4, **19** (1860): 19–32; *ibid.*, **20** (1860): 21–37 (= *Scientific Papers*, **1**: 377–409); and 'On the dynamical theory of gases', *Phil. Trans.*, **157** (1867): 49–88 (= *Scientific Papers*, **2**: 26–78).

in CD no work would be lost or gained, only its energy would be transferred from the one vessel to the other.

Now conceive a finite being[12] who knows the paths and velocities of all the molecules by simple inspection but who can do no work, except to open and close a hole in the diaphragm, by means of a slide without mass.

Let him first observe the molecules in A and when he sees one coming the square of whose velocity is less than the mean sq. vel. of the molecules in B let him open the hole & let it go into B. Next let him watch for a molecule in B the square of whose velocity is greater than the mean sq. vel. in A and when it comes to the hole let him draw the slide & let it go into A, keeping the slide shut for all other molecules.

Then the number of molecules in A & B are the same as at first but the energy in A is increased and that in B diminished that is the hot system has got hotter and the cold colder & yet no work has been done, only the intelligence of a very observant and neat fingered being has been employed.

Or in short if heat is the motion of finite portions of matter and if we can apply tools to such portions of matter so as to deal with them separately then we can take advantage of the different motion of different portions to restore a uniformly hot system to unequal temperatures or to motions of large masses. Only we can't, not being clever enough.[b]

Is your book on Quaternions out yet?[13]

I see
$$\triangleleft = i\frac{d}{dx} + j\frac{d}{dy} + k\frac{d}{dz}$$
and
$$V = \triangleleft F\rho$$

(b) {Thomson} Very good. Another way is to reverse the motion of every particle of the universe and preside over the unstable motion thus produced.[14]

(12) William Thomson's term 'demon' – see his 'The kinetic theory of the dissipation of energy', *Nature*, 9 (1874): 441–4, esp. 442n (= *Math. & Phys. Papers*, 5: 12n) where he ascribes the term to Maxwell – did not receive Maxwell's approbation. In an undated note to Tait (ULC Add. MSS 7655, V, i/11a), which will be published in Volume III (and see Knott, *Life of Tait*: 215), he suggested that Tait 'Call him no more a demon but a valve'; see the Introduction esp. notes (52) and (53). For Maxwell's subsequent discussion of this argument, aimed to show that the second law of thermodynamics is an irreducibly statistical law which applies to systems of molecules, not to the spontaneous fluctuations of individual molecules, see his letter to J. W. Strutt of 6 December 1870 (Number 350) and the *Theory of Heat* (London, 1871): 308–9 (the draft version of this portion of its text being reproduced in Number 350: Appendix).

(13) P. G. Tait, *An Elementary Treatise on Quaternions* (Oxford 1867).

(14) See Thomson's subsequent discussion in his paper 'The kinetic theory of the dissipation of energy'; if 'the motion of every particle in the universe were precisely reversed at any instant, the course of nature would be simply reversed for ever after'. See Number 350 note (4). For Maxwell's discussions of time-reversal see Numbers 286 esp. note (12) and 350.

in your paper in RSE Proceedings 1862

also $$\triangleleft^2 = -\left(\frac{d^2}{dx^2}+\frac{d^2}{dy^2}+\frac{d^2}{dz^2}\right).$$ (15)

Lamé (Fonctions Inverses)[16] & (Coordonnées Curvilignes)[17] calls V the 1st differential parameter
and $\Delta^2 F\rho$ the 2nd diffl param^r[18] with other names besides. Good. But –
Betti Nuovo Cimento 1866[19] a good mathematician

calls $$\Delta^2 V = \frac{d^2V}{dx^2}+\frac{d^2V}{dy^2}+\frac{d^2V}{dz^2}$$

and $$\Delta V = \overline{\frac{dV}{dx}}\Big|^2 + \overline{\frac{dV}{dy}}\Big|^2 + \overline{\frac{dV}{dz}}\Big|^{2}$$ (20)

which is, to say the least, an atrocious combination. Is there any virtue in turning Δ round 30°?[21]

[c]Yours truly
[d]J. Clerk Maxwell[22]

(c) {Thomson} I should prefer $(+\tfrac{1}{12}\Delta)$. But the truth is ∇^2 (NB on even keel).
(d) {Tait} C over ▷
O.T. Tatlock[23] has returned the proof[24] corrected & somewhat changed by Rankine. Do you now adopt it, and may I print off with a clear conscience? If not pray Criticize fully (in writing) his remarks on Clausius,[25] that U & the Jewel[26] may get justice. Also say what occurs to you about the enclosed WHICH RETURN speedily. The *mixing* of the gases which is an objection to the text may easily be got over by waiting longer till two (one from each vessel) impinge centrically. What then? / Y^{rs} T'.

(15) P. G. Tait, 'Formulae connected with small continuous displacements of the particles of a medium', *Proc. Roy. Soc. Edinb.*, **4** (1862): 617–23; i, j, k are unit vectors at right angles to each other.

(16) Gabriel Lamé, *Leçons sur les Fonctions Inverses des Transcendantes et les Surfaces Isothermes* (Paris, 1857): 2. See also Maxwell, *Treatise*, **1**: 181–90 (§§147–54) for substantial reference to Lamé's book.

(17) Gabriel Lamé, *Leçons sur les Coordonnées Curvilignes et leurs Diverses Applications* (Paris, 1859): 6.

(18) Lamé, *Coordonnées Curvilignes*: 6; 'paramètres differentiels du premier ordre, et du second ordre, de la fonction-de-point F. On peut les désigner par les symboles $\Delta_1 F$ et $\Delta_2 F$.'

(19) Enrico Betti, 'Teorica delle forze che agiscono secondo la legge di Newton e sua applicazione alla elettricità statica', *Nuovo Cimento*, **18** (1863): 385–402; *ibid.*, **19** (1863): 59–75, 77–95, 149–75, 357–77; *ibid.*, **20** (1864): 19–39, 121–41.

(20) Betti, 'Teorica delle forze', *Nuovo Cimento*, **18** (1863): 389; *ibid.*, **19** (1863): 68.

(21) In his *Quaternions*: 221, 267, 307 Tait wrote ∇. See Number 347.

(22) Tait's reply is dated 13 December 1867 (ULC Add. MSS 7655, I, a/5): 'P.S. We are open to an offer from you to give us an evening's discourse on any subject you like (scientific of course). Name your day & your subject, and we'll book it eagerly. / Dear Maxwell, / 1) Can't you contrive, like your neighbour Dudgeon of Carssen, or like Fox Talbot, to spend a winter now

& then in Edin^h? In that case we should at once put you on the Council of the R.S.E. and get some good out of you. Also you should have the run of my laboratory (which is shortly to be considerably increased) as well as those of Playfair, Crum Brown, &c. Ponder the point. Good. / 2) Thanks for time horizontal, &^{c} & the dodge about drawing logarithmic curves, which may be very useful to me. I fear I can't avail myself of your system for our *elementary* book, for w^h my spiral is well fitted. / 3) I read the extract of y^r note about a paper on "Theory of reciprocal rectil^r figs. & diagrams of forces" to the Council R.S.E. this afternoon; and you are booked for the paper as soon as you can send it. / 4) I don't see why you shouldn't send us a "Note" on "Nots" with a stereogram or two for our Proceedings. It would give you no trouble to do this – though it might bother you to get ready a paper for the Transactions. / 5) I suppose your tension of films goes to the London R.S. – else we should be glad of a few scraps. / 6) I object to your infinitely sharp individual that he *lets his gases mix*, and so spoils the theorem. But let him wait long enough to catch a quick one from the colder medium & a slow one from the hotter w^h are moving in the same line so as to impinge centrically when he moves the slide. How many Darwinian ages will that require? And, when he has caught these two, won't he have to wait longer for a repetition? Good. / 7) The Quaternions have been out just as long as THE Book, but I have not yet heard how they sell, and whether they have sold anybody yet. / 8) Δ is required in 4^{ions} for its finite diff^{ce} meaning – so we do $\triangleleft$ or ∇ for the flux. I didn't know that Lamé had a $\triangleleft$, though I knew he had a $\triangleleft^2 = \left(\dfrac{d}{dx}\right)^2 + ...$, and a δ (I think) for Betti's $\left(\dfrac{dF}{dx}\right)^2 + ...$ But it is a long time I looked at his papers. Still if he had a $\triangleleft$, and not merely separate parts of it such as $\dfrac{dF}{dx}$, &^{c} *he must have anticipated Hamilton in discovering 4^{ions}*, so I wish you would give me the reference.

/ 9) If you read the last 20 or 30 pages of my book I think you will see that 4^{ions} are worth getting up, for there it is shown that they go into that $\triangleleft$ business like greased lightning. Unfortunately I cannot find time to work steadily at them. / 10) I'll send you a copy of my first two Chapters on Thermodynamics in a day or two, when I hear from Rankine, meanwhile let me know your mind on the graver subjects propounded at the threshold of this note. / y^{rs} / P. G. Tait'. Tait is alluding to 'Chapter XI. Physical applications' of his *Quaternions*: 276–311.

(23) See Number 332 note (2).

(24) Of Tait's *Sketch of Thermodynamics*: see Number 278 note (2).

(25) See Tait's discussion of Rankine's 'Thermodynamic function' and Clausius' 'Aequivalenzwerth' as published in his *Sketch of Thermodyamics*: 29. In the second edition of the *Sketch of Thermodynamics* (Edinburgh, $_2$1877): xv Tait admitted that the first edition contained 'paragraphs written for me by Rankine'. See also Number 278 note (2).

(26) James Prescott Joule.

278

LETTER TO PETER GUTHRIE TAIT

23 DECEMBER 1867

From the original in the University Library, Cambridge[1]

Glenlair
Dalbeattie
1867 Dec 23

Dear Tait

I have received your histories of Thermodynamics & Energetics,[2] and will examine them, along with Robertson on the Unconditioned[3] who holds that our ultimate hope of sanity lies in sticking to metaphysics and letting physics go down the wind.

I have read some metaphysics of various kinds and find it more or less ignorant discussion of mathematical and physical principles, jumbled with a little physiology of the senses. The value of the metaphysics is equal to the mathematical and physical knowledge of the author divided by his confidence in reasoning from the names of things.[4]

---

(1) ULC Add. MSS 7655, I, b/9. Published in part in Knott, *Life of Tait*: 215–16.

(2) Two draft chapters of Tait's *Sketch of Thermodynamics* (Edinburgh, 1868), the 'Historical sketch of the dynamical theory of heat' and the 'Historical sketch of the science of energy', were 'printed privately for class use in 1867', according to Knott, *Life of Tait*: 213. These were, presumably, the texts of the 'histories' which Maxwell acknowledged receiving. Tait had already sent copies to Helmholtz, Rankine and Clausius. Helmholtz replied by defending Julius Robert Mayer's contribution to the formulation of the principle of the conservation of energy (see Tait, *Sketch of Thermodynamics*: v–vii). Rankine amended Tait's text (see Number 277 note (25)); while Clausius, as Tait put it, 'cut up very rough' (see Number 277 note (2)). Clausius gave an account of the 'Tendenz des Buches "*Sketch of Thermodynamics*" von Tait' in his *Die mechanische Wärmetheorie*, 2 vols. (Braunschweig, 1876–9), **2**: 324–30. These two draft chapters of Tait's *Sketch of Thermodynamics* were based on two articles, 'The dynamical theory of heat' and 'Energy', published in the *North British Review*, **40** (1864): 40–69, 337–68.

(3) Alexander Robertson, *The Philosophy of the Unconditioned* (London, 1866), a response to John Stuart Mill, *An Examination of Sir William Hamilton's Philosophy and of the Principal Philosophical Questions discussed in his Writings* (London, 1865). The reviewer (probably H. L. Mansel) in the *Contemporary Review*, **2** (1866): 584–9 criticised Robertson's philosophical incompetence. For a sophisticated defence of Hamilton see [H. L. Mansel,] 'The philosophy of the conditioned: Sir William Hamilton and John Stuart Mill', *Contemporary Review*, **1** (1866): 31–49, 185–219.

(4) Tait scathingly dismissed metaphysical arguments on 'what is heat?' and any 'metaphysical pretender to discovery of the laws of nature' in his *Sketch of Thermodynamics*: 1–2. Compare Maxwell's comments on the 'obtrusive antinomies' in Tait's denunciation of metaphysics (while himself making implicit appeal to metaphysical principles), in his review of the second (1877) edition of 'Tait's "Thermodynamics"', *Nature*, **17** (1878): 257–9, 278–80, esp. 257 (= *Scientific Papers*, **2**: 661).

You have also some remarks on the sensational system of philosophising (sensational in the American not the psychological sense). Beware also of the hierophantic or mystagogic style. The sensationalist says 'I am now going to grapple with the Forces of the Universe and if I succeed in this extremely delicate experiment you will see for yourselves exactly how the world is kept going'. The Hierophant says 'I do not expect to make you or the like of you understand a word of what I say, but you may see for yourselves in what a mass of absurdity the subject is involved'.

Your statement however seems tolerably complete considering the number of pages. One or two ideas should be brought in with greater pomp of entry, perhaps.

I do not understand how Verdets discovery that paramagnetic bodies produce rotation of the plane of polarization in the opposite direction to diamagnetic[5] bodies *confirms* Faradays doctrine that a diamagnetic body is only less paramagnetic than the field.[6]

It is a pretty doctrine, but I do not think Faraday thought it certain and Verdets phenomenon appears to me the strongest thing against it. I am myself sorry to part with it.[7]

Webers doctrine is that paramagnetic bodies have ready made electromagnets in them which are set in one direction by magnetic force, and therefore when they are all set parallel there is a limit to magnetization and that diamagnetics have currents set up in them by induction and that these are unopposed by resistance and these will give an opposite polarity.[8]

I do not say this theory is true[9] but if it were Thomsons revolving

---

(5) Émile Verdet, 'Recherches sur les propriétés optiques développées dans les corps transparentes par l'action du magnétisme', *Ann. Chim. Phys.*, ser. 3, **52** (1858): 129–63.

(6) Michael Faraday, 'Experimental researches in electricity. – Twenty-sixth series. Magnetic conducting power', *Phil. Trans.*, **141** (1851): 29–84 (= *Electricity*, **3**: 200–73).

(7) See Maxwell's comment on Faraday's theory in 'On Faraday's lines of force', *Trans. Camb. Phil. Soc.*, **10** (1856): 27–83, esp. 45 (= *Scientific Papers*, **1**: 180), as 'the most precise, and at the same time the least theoretic statement'. See Maxwell's further discussion in his letter to Thomson of 18 July 1868 (Number 295).

(8) Wilhelm Weber, 'Ueber die Erregung und Wirkung des Diamagnetismus nach den Gesetzen inducirter Ströme', *Ann. Phys.*, **73** (1848): 241–56 (= *Wilhelm Weber's Werke*, 6 vols (Berlin, 1892–4), **3**: 255–68), (trans.) 'On the excitation and action of diamagnetism according to the laws of induced currents', *Scientific Memoirs*, ed. R. Taylor, **5** (London, 1852): 477–88; Weber, 'Ueber der Zusammenhang der Lehre vom Diamagnetismus mit der Lehre von dem Magnetismus und der Elektricität', *Ann. Phys.*, **87** (1852): 145–89 (= *Werke*, **3**: 555–90), (trans.) 'On the connection of diamagnetism with magnetism and electricity', *Scientific Memoirs, Natural Philosophy*, ed. J. Tyndall and W. Francis (London, 1853): 163–99. See Volume I: 363n.

(9) See Maxwell's positive discussion of Weber's theory in his chapter on 'Ferromagnetism and diamagnetism explained by molecular currents' in the *Treatise*, **2**: 418–25 (§§832–45).

diamagnetic sphere would not be a prime mover[10] any more than any other electromagnetic machine consisting of coils revolving in the presence of magnets.

There is a difference between a vortex theory ascribed to Maxwell[11] at p 57, and a dynamical theory of Electromagnetics by the same author in Phil Trans 1865.[12] The former is built up to show that the phenomena are such as can be explained by mechanism. The nature of this mechanism is to the true mechanism what an orrery is to the Solar System.[13] The latter is built on Lagranges Dynamical Equation and is not wise about vortices.[14] Examine the first part which treats of the mutual actions of currents before you decide that Webers is the only hypothesis on the subject.[15]

I hope you will come to some result with your vulcanite magnet.

It will require a great speed and you will require to guard the testing magnet from direct electromagnetic action of the revolving machinery.[16]

---

(10) William Thomson, 'On the theory of magnetic induction in crystalline and non-crystalline substances', *Phil. Mag.*, ser. 4, **1** (1851): 179–86, esp. 186 (= *Electrostatics and Magnetism*: 465–80); 'a sphere of matter of any kind, placed in a uniform field of force, and set to turn round an axis fixed perpendicular to the lines of force, cannot be an inexhaustible source of mechanical effect.' See Maxwell's discussion in 'On Faraday's lines of force': 74–6 (= *Scientific Papers*, **1**: 217–19); and Volume I: 416–17, 485.

(11) J. C. Maxwell, 'On physical lines of force', *Phil. Mag.*, ser. 4, **21** (1861): 161–75, 281–91, 338–48; *ibid.*, **23** (1862): 12–24, 85–95 (= *Scientific Papers*, **1**: 451–513). Compare Maxwell's comment in Number 235.

(12) J. Clerk Maxwell, 'A dynamical theory of the electromagnetic field', *Phil. Trans.*, **155** (1865): 459–512 (= *Scientific Papers*, **1**: 526–97). See Number 238.

(13) Compare A. W. Williamson, 'On the constitution of salts', *Journal of the Chemical Society*, **4** (1852): 350–5, on 351; '[Formulae] may be used as an actual image of what we rationally suppose to be the arrangement of the constituent atoms in a compound, as an orrery is an image of what we conclude to be the arrangement of our planetary system.' This passage is cited by B. C. Brodie, 'The calculus of chemical operations; being a method for the investigation by means of symbols, of the laws of the distribution of weight in chemical change. Part I. On the construction of chemical symbols', *Phil. Trans.*, **156** (1866): 781–859, on 783n. Maxwell had participated in the Chemical Society discussion of Brodie's chemical calculus held on 6 June 1867 (Number 270).

(14) Compare the published text of Tait's *Sketch of Thermodynamics*: 74–5. Alluding to Maxwell's 'particular hypotheses as to molecular vortices... [he observed that Maxwell] seems, however, to have since discarded these hypotheses, and to rely only on the principle of energy applied to investigate the properties of the medium... [and] Lagrange's dynamical equation'.

(15) Wilhelm Weber, 'Elektrodynamische Maassbestimmungen, über ein allgemeines Grundgesetz der elektrischen Wirkung', *Abhandlung bei Begründung der Königlichen Sächsischen Gesellschaft der Wissenschaften... Leipzig* (1846): 211–378 (= *Werke*, **3**: 25–214). See Volume I: 305–6n.

(16) See Maxwell's letter to Tait of 4 December 1867 (Number 276, esp. note (3)).

You wrote me about experiments in the Laboratory. There is one which is of a high order but yet I think within the means and powers of students namely the determination of Joules coefft[17] by means of mercury.[18] Mercury is $\frac{13.57}{.033}$[19] times better than water so that about 9 feet would give 10° Fah. You have a cistern which you keep full to a certain point with mercury by proper fillers and a tube of iron with a strong iron cistern at the bottom into which is let a place to put mercury & dip a thermometer without exposing it to pressure. Out of this is a tube which enters an open cistern and out of this tube the mercury escapes either through a series of plates each having a fine hole in it or through a plug of compressed cotton or otherwise.

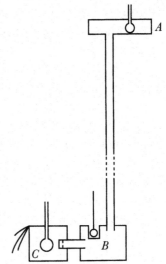

Figure 278,1

The mercury and the tube is thus heated but the heat is all communicated (in time) to the mercury for the part conducted back by the sides of the tube must be small and can be estimated.

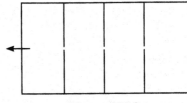

Figure 278,2

The mercury rises and pours over a notch in the open cistern below and students continually carry it up to the upper cistern mixing it with very cold mercury to keep the temperature even.

The experiments required are 1 a comparison of the temperature at A and B when the mercury flows pretty quick to determine the effect of pressure in altering temperature.

2 Rate of cooling (or heating) of B & C with given difference of temperature from air

3 difference of level at A & C. This can be done with pointed screws dipping on the surface

4 diff^e of temperature at A & C can be got within $\frac{1}{50}$°F.

I have liberty from Joule to try this experiment but though I have considered the necessaries and do not think them unattainable I have no prospect of doing it.

---

(17) The mechanical equivalent of heat: see Number 207 note (43).

(18) On this experiment see Number 235.

(19) The specific gravity and specific heat of mercury (relative to water as unity). See W. J. M. Rankine, *A Manual of the Steam Engine* (London/Glasgow, 1859): 555.

I think it a plan free from many mechanical difficulties and in a lofty room with plenty of mercury and strong iron work, and a cherub aloft to read the level & the thermometer and a monkey to carry up mercury to him (called Quicksilver Jack) the thing might go on for hours, the coefficient meanwhile converging to a value to be appreciated only by the naturalist.

Are you aware that if anything converges according to log. to a fixed value v and if $x\ y\ z$ are three equidistant values

$$v = \frac{xz - y^2}{x + z - 2y}.$$

I have sent the Secretary of the RSE an article on the arrangement of a prism and a lens of the same material for spectrum observations, as for instance when you are restricted to quartz or rock salt and cannot use achromatic lenses.[20]

I may find something else but this is the first I could lay hands on for the Proceedings.

Yours truly
J. Clerk Maxwell

---

(20) J. Clerk Maxwell, 'On the best arrangement for producing a pure spectrum on a screen', *Proc. Roy. Soc. Edinb.*, **6** (1868): 238–42 (= *Scientific Papers*, **2**: 96–100).

DRAFT ON THE PRINCIPLES OF STEREOSCOPIC VISION

circa 1867

From the original in the University Library, Cambridge[1]

STEREOSCOPIC ILLUSTRATIONS OF SOLID GEOMETRY[2]

by J. Clerk Maxwell, M.A., FRSS. L. & E.

If lines drawn from a fixed point to the several points of any figure cut a fixed plane, the several points in which these lines cut the plane are called the projections of the corresponding points of the figure.

If the centre of the pupil of the eye coincide with the fixed point then the direction of the axes of pencils entering the eye will be the same whether they come from the points of the figure or from corresponding points of the projection. Hence the positions of the images of corresponding points on the retina will be the same, and if the distance of the point and of its projection from the eye are large compared with the principal focal length of the eye, the difference of adjustment for distinct vision of the two points will be small.

Hence the appearance of the figure and that of its projection are nearly alike when viewed by an eye placed at the fixed point.

The centres of the right and left eye are about $2\frac{1}{2}$ inches apart generally in a horizontal direction. Hence the projection of a figure taken with respect to one eye will not in general be similar to the projection taken with respect to the other eye. This will be the case only when the original figure is in a plane parallel to that on which it is projected. If we look with both eyes at once at the same plane projection of a figure, we become aware of the similarity and conclude that the figure is a plane one unless the figure represented is of a form which powerfully suggests solidity.

But if each eye looks at a different plane figure, and if these figures are projections of the same solid figure with respect to the centres of the two eyes, then we become aware of the dissimilarity of the two figures and we find that in order to look at any point we have to make the same motions of both eyes as would be requisite in looking at the corresponding point of the real figure.

---

(1) ULC Add. MSS 7655, V, b/11.

(2) Very probably a preliminary and aborted draft of 'The construction of stereograms of surfaces', *Proceedings of the London Mathematical Society*, **2** (1868): 57–8 (= *Scientific Papers*, **2**: 101), presented at a meeting of the Society on 23 January 1868.

We also find that the points in the figure which are at the same distance as the point we look at are more distinct than those nearer or farther off, which appear double, and in this way while looking at the pair of projections we may probe or sound the figure so as to obtain an accurate knowledge of its depth as well as its length and breadth.

Two projections of this kind are called a Stereoscopic Pair. The complete study of the theory of binocular vision requires the consideration of the doctrine of corresponding points and of the motions of the eyes. These subjects are ably treated by Prof^r H. Helmholtz in his 'Physiological Optics' (Karsten's Cyclopädie)[3] and his Croonian Lecture on the Motions of the Eye (Proceedings of the Royal Society 186   [4]).[5]

In each eye there is a certain direction called the axis defined by a straight line drawn through the optic centre and a certain point on the retina on which the image of an object is made to fall when we look intently at it. This point may be called the centre of the retina. The centres of the two retinae are corresponding points. The other corresponding points are defined by their having equal coordinates $x\ y$ measured from axes of which that of x is horizontal in both eyes, and that of y is inclined to the vertical at an angle of about   [6] degrees measured outwards, so that the two axes of y would meet at a point about   [6] below the level of the eyes.

Each eye is acted on by three pairs of muscles one pair of which tend to turn it about a horizontal axis so as to raise or lower the axis another pair turns it about a vertical axis to the right or left while the third pair tend to turn the eye about the axis of vision. These three motions are mechanically independent but in the actual motion of the eye they are connected by the following law.

There is a certain direction, fixed with regard to the head, which may be called the normal direction of the axis of the eye. This direction is nearly parallel to the median plane of the head and nearly horizontal when the head is in its normal position. A certain position of the whole eye when the axis is in this direction is called the normal position. When the axis of the eye is turned into any other position the position of the eye with respect to rotation about the axis is such that by a simple rotation about an axis perpendicular to the optic axis it could be brought into the normal position.

---

(3) Hermann Helmholtz, *Handbuch der physiologischen Optik* (Leipzig, 1867): 457–529.

(4) Space in the MS.

(5) Hermann Helmholtz, 'On the normal motions of the human eye in relation to binocular vision', *Proc. Roy. Soc.*, **13** (1864): 186–99. Maxwell almost certainly attended Helmholtz's Croonian Lecture, read on 14 April 1864 (see Number 225).

(6) Space in the MS.

APPENDIX: EXHIBITION OF STEREOGRAMS TO THE LONDON MATHEMATICAL SOCIETY

23 JANUARY 1868

From the *Proceedings of the London Mathematical Society*[7]

[ON STEREOGRAMS OF SURFACES][8]

Mr Maxwell stated that he had prepared most of the specimens exhibited for publication. The members present were enabled, after the meeting, to examine a large number of stereograms by means of a Real Image Stereoscope constructed after Mr Maxwell's directions.[9]

There were on view stereograms of the lines of curvature of the ellipsoid, and its surface of centres; of the wave surface of Fresnel,[10] of confocal spherical ellipses, of concyclic spherical ellipses, showing the form of Laplace's coefficient of the second order, of twisted cubics, of Gordian knots of the form

$$x = a\sin pt, \quad y = b\sin qt, \quad z = c\cos rt,$$ [11]

and of 4 forms of the cyclide.[12]

---

(7) *Proceedings of the London Mathematical Society*, **2** (1868): 58.

(8) The exhibition of stereograms followed the presentation of Maxwell's paper on 'The construction of stereograms of surfaces'.

(9) See Number 272.

(10) See Numbers 274 and 275 and Plates VI, VII and VIII.

(11) See Number 277 and Plates IX and X.

(12) See Number 274 esp. note (6).

QUESTION TO THE LONDON MATHEMATICAL SOCIETY ON GOVERNORS

23 JANUARY 1868[1]

From the *Proceedings of the London Mathematical Society*[2]

Mr Maxwell asked if any member present could point out a method of determining in what cases all the possible parts of the impossible roots of an equation are negative.[3] In studying the motion of certain governors for regulating machinery,[4] he had found that the stability of the motion depended on this condition, which is easily obtained for a cubic,[5] but becomes more difficult in the higher degrees.[6]* Mr. W. K. Clifford[7] said that, by forming an equation whose roots are the sums of the roots of the original equation taken in pairs and determining the condition of the real roots of this equation being negative, we should obtain the condition required.[8]

* On Governors. Proceedings of the Royal Society, March 5, 1868.[4]

---

(1) See note (2).

(2) *Proceedings of the London Mathematical Society*, **2** (1868): 60–1; a meeting held on 23 January 1868.

(3) See Number 219 esp. note (17).

(4) See his paper 'On governors', *Proc. Roy. Soc.*, **16** (1868): 270–83 (= *Scientific Papers*, **2**: 105–20); received on 20 February 1868.

(5) For Thomson's and Jenkin's governors: see Number 219, and 'On governors': 276, 278 (= *Scientific Papers*, **2**: 111, 114).

(6) For the 'combination of governors' (combining the principles of Thomson's and Jenkin's governors) see Number 219 esp. note (9) and 'On governors': 278–9 (= *Scientific Papers*, **2**: 114–15). For the solution to the problem of establishing stability criteria for systems of fifth order, see Number 297: Appendix, esp. note (9).

(7) William Kingdon Clifford, Trinity 1863, second wrangler 1867 (Venn).

(8) For an account of Clifford's interjection see *Mathematical Papers by William Kingdon Clifford*, ed. Robert Tucker (London, 1882): xvi–xvii.

APPENDIX: FRAGMENT OF DRAFT ON GOVERNORS[9]

circa JANUARY 1868[10]

From the original in the University Library, Cambridge[11]

[ON GOVERNORS][12]

[...] or $M'\dfrac{d^2\theta'}{dt^2} + C\omega \sin 2\beta \dfrac{d\phi'}{dt} = P - R' - G'\phi' - X\dfrac{d\theta'}{dt}$.

The nature of the motion is in this case also determined by a cubic equation of which the form is

$$MBn^3 + (MY + BX)n^2 + \{(C\omega \sin 2\beta)^2 + XY\}n + GC\omega \sin 2\beta = 0.$$

The condition that the possible parts of the impossible roots of this equation should be negative is

$$(MY+BX)(\overline{C\omega \sin 2\beta}|^2 + XY) - MBGC\omega \sin 2\beta = \text{a positive quantity}.$$

This implies that X and Y must not both vanish or that a damper must be applied either to the main shaft or to the arm of the centrifugal piece. A vessel full of a viscous liquid attached to either of these moveable pieces would answer the purpose if the unavoidable resistances of the parts of the machine are not sufficient.

If we neglect the product XY the condition becomes

$$\left(\frac{X}{M} + \frac{Y}{B}\right) C\omega \sin 2\beta > G.$$

If we increase the power of the break the quantity G is increased and the governor acts more promptly, but if G is increased beyond the value given by the above equation the motion becomes unstable in the form of a continually increasing oscillation.

Instead of allowing the whole force $G \sin \phi$ to act on the break a constant part of it may be taken off by means of a spring so as to diminish the waste of power.

---

(9) Compare Maxwell's discussion of 'Sir W. Thomson's and M. Foucault's governors' in 'On governors': 276–8 (= *Scientific Papers*, **2**: 112–14).   (10) See notes (2) and (4).

(11) ULC Add. MSS 7655, V, e/7. Previously published in A. T. Fuller, 'James Clerk Maxwell's Cambridge manuscripts: extracts relating to control and stability – V', *International Journal of Control*, **43** (1986): 805–18, on 805–6.

(12) Compare Maxwell's discussion of Thomson's governor in his letter to Thomson of 11 September 1863 (Number 219).

The governor of M. Foucault[13] is identical in principle with that just described. The centrifugal force of the arm is balanced by the downward force of gravity combined with the upward force of a system of levers, the resultant effect of which is the same as that of the spring in the former case. The break instead of acting by friction acts by admitting air to a centrifugal fan so as to increase and diminish the quantity of work done by the machine. The resultant equations of motion however are of the same form as equations ([....]

---

(13) Léon Foucault, 'Expression générale des conditions d'isochronisme du pendule régulateur à force centrifuge', *Comptes Rendus*, **57** (1863): 738–40.

281

LETTER TO WILLIAM THOMSON

20 FEBRUARY 1868

From the original in the University Library, Glasgow[1]

8 Palace Gardens Terrace
London W
1868 Feb 20

Dear Thomson

Many thanks for your letter. Do not study the geometrical statics too much.[2] I have got better results which I hope to send to the R.S.E.[3]

I hope Tait will start the determination of Joules Equivalent with mercury coming down a wide tube from a cistern and flowing through a difficult passage into a lower cistern. One foot of mercury is as good as 400 of water so an experiment in a room will be much better than Niagara falls.[4]

I do not know what authority Tait has for my coming to Edinburgh in winter, as we intend always to be in London as head quarters. I have no doubt that a general reversal of all motions would lead to curious results such as the past becoming future and only part of the future past.

I see by advertisements that Mr Esson of Merton Coll Oxford[5] is going to do an Electricity for the Clarendon Press. I only know Mr Esson as an observer of the progress of chemical changes along with Mr Vernon Harcourt,[6] so I do not know whether his book will be about Greens Theorem or about the influence of electrical action on plants. If the latter I shall go on with the theorem.[7]

---

(1) Glasgow University Library, Kelvin Papers, M 21.

(2) J. Clerk Maxwell, 'On reciprocal diagrams in space, and their relation to Airy's function of stress', *Proceedings of the London Mathematical Society*, **2** (1868): 58–60 (= *Scientific Papers*, **2**: 102–4).

(3) J. Clerk Maxwell, 'On reciprocal figures, frames and diagrams of forces', *Trans. Roy. Soc. Edinb.*, **26** (1870): 1–40 (= *Scientific Papers*, **2**: 161–207). See Tait's letter to Maxwell of 13 December 1867 (Number 277 note (22)).   (4) See Number 278.

(5) William Esson, Fellow of Merton College, Oxford, 1860 (J. Foster, *Alumni Oxonienses*, 4 vols. (Oxford, 1888), **2**: 429).

(6) A. Vernon Harcourt and William Esson, 'On the laws of connexion between the conditions of a chemical change and its amount', *Phil. Trans.*, **156** (1866): 193–211; *ibid.*, **157** (1867): 117–37.

(7) Maxwell's first statement that he was writing the *Treatise on Electricity and Magnetism*. For his account there of Green's theorem see the *Treatise*, **1**: 108–13 (§100); and see George Green, *An Essay on the Application of Mathematical Analysis to the Theories of Electricity and Magnetism* (Nottingham, 1828): esp. 10 (= *Mathematical Papers of the Late George Green*, ed. N. M. Ferrers (London/Cambridge, 1871): esp. 23). See also Number 274.

I am glad to see a good deal of Spherical Harmonics in T. T'[8] which will relieve me. I do not see however the doctrine that every S. H. of the ith degree has i poles, and is formed by differentiating $\frac{1}{r}$ with respect to these i directions in any order and either leaving the result as it stands or multiplying by r^{2i+1}.[9]

This can be done only for these i poles and no others when the form of the S. H. is given but it is a trouble to find them when i is above 2. I have a stereogram of a S. H. for $i = 2$.[10] The equipotential surface which passes through the centre is of course a cone of the ith degree. I want to find out into how many regions it divides space, or a spherical surface when the i poles are at arbitrary points. It is easy when the surface is cut up into quads by meridians & parallels.

The doctrine of the whole number of points and lines of equilibrium in a field of force depends on this. I *think* that n centres of force have p points and l lines of equilibrium where $p + 2l + 1 = n$.

Yours truly
J. CLERK MAXWELL

(8) Thomson and Tait, *Natural Philosophy*: 140–60.
(9) See Numbers 277 and 388.
(10) See Numbers 277 and 279: Appendix and Plate X.

REPORT ON A PAPER BY JOSEPH DAVID EVERETT ON THE RIGIDITY OF METAL RODS

circa 25 FEBRUARY 1868[1]

From the original in the Library of the Royal Society, London[2]

REPORT ON Dr EVERETT'S THIRD PAPER ON TORSION AND FLEXURE[3]

This paper gives an account of experiments on the same plan as those described in the 2nd paper (Feb 1867)[4] but on rods of different materials, namely Wrought Iron, Cast Iron, and Copper. I have already reported on the merit of the method of the experiments and on a few defects.[5] A clearer statement is given in this paper of the relative positions of the scale, the mirrors and the telescopes, and of the optical correction required on account of the obliquity of the ray to the plane of the scale.

This might be made smaller if it were worth while by making the plane of the scale perpendicular to the rays reflected from the mirrors when they are both horizontal, and if the scale is on a flat board this is easily done by placing the back of a mirror against the centre of the scale and causing the ray to be reflected back from this mirror to the mirrors on the rod.

In making the observations of torsion I think it would be worth while to observe if any flexure takes place and vice versâ. The scale being divided in both directions, such observations would not only test the proper orientation of the scale but would indicate any inequality or ellipticity in the section of the rod and might be used as illustrations of the theory of combined torsion and flexure by Kirchhoff.[6] See Thomson & Taits Natural Philosophy §588 et seq.[7]

---

(1) According to the Royal Society's *Register of Papers Received* Everett's paper was referred to Maxwell on 20 February 1868, and to Stokes on 28 February 1868.

(2) Royal Society, *Referees' Reports*, **6**: 119.

(3) J. D. Everett, 'Account of experiments on torsion and flexure for the determination of rigidities', *Phil. Trans.*, **158** (1868): 363–9. The paper was received by the Royal Society on 13 January 1868, and read on 30 January 1868; see the abstract in *Proc. Roy. Soc.*, **16** (1868): 248.

(4) J. D. Everett, 'Account of experiments on torsion and flexure for the determination of rigidities', *Phil. Trans.*, **157** (1867): 139–53.

(5) Number 269. See also Number 261.

(6) Gustav Kirchhoff, 'Ueber das Gleichgewicht und die Bewegung eines unendlich dünnen elastischen Stabes', *Journal für die reine und angewandte Mathematik*, **56** (1859): 285–313.

(7) Thomson and Tait, *Natural Philosophy*: 437–52.

I consider the publication of the method of these researches as of scientific value. This has already been done in the second paper. I also think that the new results are very valuable and ought to be published for the use of physicists & engineers. The actual values of the observed scale readings afford a means of estimating the accuracy of the experiments and a few examples of the process of deducing the final results enables the reader to understand the course of experiments. In other respects the table of the values of $M\ n\ k$ & $\sigma^{(8)}$ for the given specimens condenses the whole substance of the paper. From this table it will be seen that the three substances Steel, Wrought Iron, and Cast Iron have the values of M, n & k in descending order, steel being stiffest in every sense. Not much however is stated about the mode of preparation and the state of annealing or temper, or previous strain of the rods.

The values of Poissons ratio[9] are also in a descending order for these three substances which seems to show that neither the stiffness and small plasticity of steel nor the high melting point of wrought iron indicate an approach to the value .250 given by a particular assumption in a molecular theory.[10]

The greater values of M & n (the observed rigidities) for copper than for brass deserves attention, as brass is generally supposed harder than copper.

If the method is applicable to lead, it would be worth trying it as Matthiessen finds that lead is remarkably uniform in its properties, to whatever strains and temperatures it has previously been subjected.[11]

Dr Everett has referred to some unpublished experiments of mine.[12] The observations of torsion in these and all other similar experiments is generally satisfactory but those of flexure were made on a plan much inferior to that of Dr Everett, and are not to be depended on.[13]

Dr Everetts experiments on a wooden rod are very interesting as showing that the rigidity which resists a shearing stress in planes perpendicular to the fibres is very much less than that in planes parallel to the fibres. The explanation of the results with fibrous substances given on p. 152 of the 2nd paper[14] does not seem to me correct as it refers the phenomenon to the

---

(8) In Everett's papers M denotes Young's modulus, n the rigidity, k the resistance to compression, and σ Poisson's ratio.

(9) See Number 261 note (6).

(10) See Number 261, esp. note (7).

(11) A. Matthiessen and M. von Bose, 'On the influence of temperature on the electric conducting power of metals', *Phil. Trans.*, **152** (1862): 1–27, on 15–16.

(12) There is no reference to Maxwell's experiments in the printed text of Everett's paper; but see Number 261, esp. notes (17) and (18).

(13) See Volume I: 180, 193–4.

(14) Everett, 'Account of experiments on torsion and flexure...', *Phil. Trans.*, **157** (1867): 152.

difference of shearing rigidity between planes parallel *or* perpendicular to the length and planes oblique to the length, whereas these last have nothing to do with it and the ratio $\frac{T}{F}$[15] is greater or less than for isotropy as the rigidity in planes parallel to the length is greater or less than in planes perpendicular to the length.

JAMES CLERK MAXWELL

---

(15) In Everett's papers T and F denote the numbers on his scale for torsion and flexure.

LETTER TO GEORGE BIDDELL AIRY

12 MARCH 1868

From the original in the Royal Greenwich Observatory Archive[1]

8 Palace Gardens Terrace
London W
1868 March 12

Dear Sir

I have neither the MS nor a copy of my paper on Governors[2] so that I cannot be certain as to every expression.

I divided the governors considered into

1   those which act by alteration of pressure
2   ——————— by alteration of position of a centrifugal piece
3   ——————— by the motion of a liquid.

After describing the general principle of the second kind and stating briefly how the conditions are fulfilled in Sir W. Thomsons and M. Foucaults governors respectively[3] I said that governors on Mr Siemens principle[4] were used in the Greenwich Observatory and that they essentially consisted of a conical pendulum slightly inclined to the vertical, the angular velocity of which is checked by means of a fan which dips into a liquid as the pendulum diverges from the vertical, and that the driving power of the pendulum and its inclination to the vertical is kept within narrow limits of variation by means of a differential system of wheelwork between the main shaft and the pendulum shaft which works a valve or a break in the prime mover.[5]

(I think it is a break in the Chronograph and a valve in the Equatoreal.)[6]

I did not enter into any detail as I had already explained the general principle and the mathematical theory so far as I understand it of the Greenwich instruments is considerably more difficult than that of some others.

I read several years ago the descriptions of the instruments in the prefaces

---

(1) Royal Greenwich Observatory Archive, ULC, Airy Papers 6/172, 447R–448R.
(2) J. Clerk Maxwell, 'On governors', *Proc. Roy. Soc.*, **16** (1868): 270–83 (= *Scientific Papers*, **2**: 105–20), read on 5 March 1868.
(3) See Number 280 note (9).
(4) See Number 219 note (10).
(5) Compare Maxwell, 'On governors': 273 (= *Scientific Papers*, **2**: 108).
(6) See the *Astronomical and Magnetical and Meteorological Observations made at the Royal Observatory, Greenwich, In the Year 1860* (London, 1862): ix–x, xv–xviii.

to the Greenwich Observations[7] and I saw them at one of the visitations of the Observatory but if you can furnish me with some of the facts related thereto which appear to you most deserving of attention I shall be greatly obliged to you, as it will enable me to make my paper fuller and more accurate with respect to those governors which have been subjected to the longest and the most accurate testing of any now existing.

I remain
Yours truly
J. CLERK MAXWELL

The Astronomer Royal

---

(7) Airy's reports, as Astronomer Royal, of *Observations made at the Royal Observatory, Greenwich*, were published annually, and were prefaced by descriptions of the instruments used at the Observatory.

= 284 =

LETTER TO PETER GUTHRIE TAIT
12 MARCH 1868
From the original in the University Library, Cambridge[1]

8 P.G.T.[2]
12 March 1868

Dr Tait

Yours received. I dispatched the proofs to you yesterday. As regards conduction of heat I have not considered it enough to know whether a deductive method like yours would predict anything about it.[3] I have come to a knowledge of my ignorance of the nature of electrical conduction in metals which is a phenomenon like that of heat, and both very easy to formulate but difficult to conceive.[4]

As regards Clausius he pointed out *gross* mistakes in M.[5] I have no doubt he has some of his own but I have not had patience to find them out, except that he stuck to uniform velocity in the molecules[6] though I proved it impossible and pointed out the only true distribution of velocity.[7] Clausius uniform velocity leads (by sound mathematics) to an expression for mean relative velocity which is unsymmetrical with respect to the components so that you need to know which is the greater of the two velocities and to put it in the right place of the formula.

With respect to Riemann for whom I have great respect and regret,[8] I only lately got either Pogg or Phil Mag[9] from the binder & wrote you a rough note for yourself. I now have him more distinct. Weber says that electrical force depends on the distance and its 1st & 2nd derivatives with respect to t.[10]

---

(1) ULC Add. MSS 7655, I, b/10. Previously published in *Molecules and Gases*: 473–4.
(2) Palace Gardens Terrace [London]. (3) See Numbers 293 esp. note (3) and 294.
(4) Compare Maxwell's discussion of the analogy in the *Treatise*, **1**: 297–8 (§§243–5).
(5) Rudolf Clausius, 'Ueber die Wärmeleitung gasförmiger Körper', *Ann. Phys.*, **115** (1862): 1–56; see Number 207 notes (9) and (39).
(6) Rudolf Clausius, 'On the dynamical theory of heat', *Phil. Mag.*, ser. 4, **19** (1860): 434–6.
(7) See Number 207 §4 and note (13), and Number 377 para. (12).
(8) Georg Friedrich Bernhard Riemann had died in 1866.
(9) Bernhard Riemann, 'Ein Beitrag zur Elektrodynamik', *Ann. Phys.*, **131** (1867): 237–43; (trans.) 'A contribution to electrodynamics', *Phil. Mag.*, ser. 4, **34** (1867): 368–72.
(10) For Wilhelm Weber's statement of his electrodynamic force law (which included terms for the relative velocity and acceleration between electric charges e, e') in the form

$$\frac{ee'}{r^2}\left(1 - \frac{1}{c^2}\left(\frac{dr}{dt}\right)^2 + \frac{2r}{c^2}\frac{d^2r}{dt^2}\right)$$

Riemann says that this is due to the fact that the potential at a point is due to the distribution of electricity elsewhere not at that instant but at times before depending on the distance.

In other words potential is propagated through space at a certain rate and he actually expresses this by a partial diff eq^n appropriate to propagation.[11]

Hence either (1) space contains a medium capable of dynamical actions which go on during transmission independently of the causes which excited them (and this is no more or less than my theory divested of particular assumptions)

or (2) if we consider the hypothesis as a fact without any etherial substratum and if A & B are two bodies each of which can vary in electrical power, say each a pair of equal magnets one of which revolves about the middle of the other so that the combination is alternately $= 2$ and $= 0$.

Now let things be so arranged that the time of propagation from A to $B = T$ then if the magnetism of A be

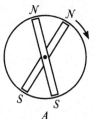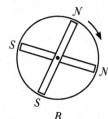

Figure 284,1

$A\cos(nt+\alpha)$ and that of B $\quad B\cos(nt+\beta)$ the action of B on A will be $A\cos(nt+\alpha)\,B\cos(nt+\beta-nT)$ into a function of the distance and that of A on B $\quad A\cos(nt+\alpha-nT)\,B\cos(nt+\beta)$ into same function. The difference of these is $F(r)\,AB\sin nT\,(\sin(nt+\beta)-\sin(nt+\alpha))$ that is, action & reaction are not equal & opposite. (I mean pushes and pulls not Hamiltonian action.)[12]

Webers action and reaction are equal but his energy is unreclaimable.[13]

---

where r is the distance between the electric charges, see his 'Elektrodynamische Maassbestimmungen, insbesondere Widerstandsmessungen', *Abhandlungen der Königlichen Sächsischen Gesellschaft der Wissenschaften, math.-phys. Klasse*, **1** (1852): 199–381, esp. 259–70 (= *Wilhelm Weber's Werke*, **3**: 301–471). On Weber's interpretation of the constant c see Volume I: 306n, 686n.

(11) Compare Maxwell's discussion of Riemann's theory of electrodynamics in the 'Note on the electromagnetic theory of light' appended to his paper 'On a method of making a direct comparison of electrostatic with electromagnetic force', *Phil. Trans.*, **158** (1868): 643–57, esp. 652 (= *Scientific Papers*, **2**: 137). The paper was received by the Royal Society on 10 June 1868 (see Number 289). Compare also the *Treatise*, **2**: 435 (§862).

(12) W. R. Hamilton, 'On a general method in dynamics', *Phil. Trans.*, **124** (1834): 247–308; *ibid.*, **125** (1835): 95–144. Hamilton's 'principle of varying action' is discussed by Thomson and Tait, *Natural Philosophy*: 231–41.

(13) A criticism originally advanced against Weber's theory by Helmholtz, who indicated that the velocity-dependent terms in Weber's force law conflicted with his own principle of

Riemanns action & reaction between the gross bodies are unequal and his energy is nowhere unless he admits a medium which he does not do explicitly. My action & reaction are equal only between things in contact not between the gross bodies till they have been in position for a sensible time, and any energy is and remains in the medium including the gross bodies which are among it.

Instead of part about A & B read as follows

$$\begin{array}{cc} X & Y \\ \bullet \longrightarrow & \bullet \longrightarrow \end{array}$$

Let X & Y be travelling to the right with velocity v at a distance a then

the force of X on Y will be $\dfrac{XY}{a^2}\left(1-\dfrac{v}{V}\right)^2$

and that of Y on X $\quad \dfrac{XY}{a^2}\left(1+\dfrac{v}{V}\right)^2$

where V is the velocity of transmission of force. If the force is an attraction and if X & Y are connected by a rigid rod X will be pulled forward more than Y is pulled back and the system will be a locomotive engine fit to carry you through space with continually increasing velocity.[14] See Gullivers Travels in Laputa.[15]

Yours truly
J. CLERK MAXWELL

'Erhaltung der Kraft' which required that forces should be functions only of the distance. See Hermann Helmholtz, *Über die Erhaltung der Kraft, eine physikalische Abhandlung* (Berlin, 1847): 63, (trans.) 'On the conservation of force', in *Scientific Memoirs, Natural Philosophy*, ed. J. Tyndall and W. Francis (London, 1853): 114–62, esp. 156. Maxwell had echoed Helmholtz's argument in his paper 'On Faraday's lines of force', *Trans. Camb. Phil. Soc.*, **10** (1856): 27–83, esp. 67 (= *Scientific Papers*, **1**: 208); and see also 'A dynamical theory of the electromagnetic field', *Phil. Trans.*, **155** (1865): 459–512, esp. 460 (= *Scientific Papers*, **1**: 527) where he alludes to the 'mechanical difficulties' of Weber's theory. See Number 389 for Maxwell's subsequent discussion of the issue.

(14) Compare the similar argument in the 'Note on the electromagnetic theory of light': 652–3 (= *Scientific Papers*, **2**: 137–8), directed not only at Riemann's electrodynamics but also at the paper by L. V. Lorenz, 'Ueber die Identität der Schwingungen des Lichts mit den elektrischen Strömen', *Ann. Phys.*, **131** (1867): 243–63, (trans.) 'On the identity of the vibrations of light with electric currents', *Phil. Mag.*, ser. 4, **34** (1867): 287–301. Compare his discussion of Lorenz in the *Treatise*, **2**: 398 (§805 note).

(15) The island floating in the air in Jonathan Swift's *Gulliver's Travels*; the members of the 'Academy' of Lagado engaged in fanciful scientific enquiries.

LETTER TO WILLIAM ROBERT GROVE[1]

27 MARCH 1868

From the *Philosophical Magazine* for May 1868[2]

8 Palace Gardens Terrace,
W.
March 27, 1868

Dear Sir,

Since our conversation yesterday on your experiment on magneto-electric induction,[3] I have considered it mathematically, and now send you the result. I have left out of the question the secondary coil, as the peculiar effect you observed depends essentially on the strength of the current in the primary coil, and the secondary sparks merely indicate a strong alternating primary current. The phenomenon depends on the magneto-electric machine, the electromagnet, and the condenser.

The machine produces in the primary wire an alternating electromagnetic force, which we may compare to a mechanical force alternately pushing and pulling at a body.

The resistance of the primary wire we may compare to the effect of a viscous fluid in which the body is made to move backwards and forwards.

The electromagnetic coil, on account of its self-induction, resists the starting and stopping of the current, just as the mass of a large boat resists the efforts of a man trying to move it backwards and forwards.

The condenser resists the accumulation of electricity on its surface, just as a railway-buffer resists the motion of a carriage towards a fixed obstacle.

---

(1) Lawyer and scientist, FRS 1840 (*DNB*).

(2) J. C. Maxwell, 'On Mr Grove's "Experiment in Magneto-electric induction". In a letter to W. R. Grove, F.R.S.', *Phil. Mag.*, ser. 4, **35** (1868): 360–3, esp. 360–1 (= *Scientific Papers*, **2**: 121–2). Maxwell's letter was communicated to the *Phil. Mag.* by Grove.

(3) W. R. Grove, 'An experiment in magneto-electric induction', *Phil. Mag.*, ser. 4, **35** (1868): 184–5. Grove investigated whether 'the ordinary effects of the Ruhmkorff-coil might be produced by applying to it a magneto-electric machine [dynamo]'. He found that: 'The result was very unexpected. The terminals of the magneto-electric coils being connected with the primary coil of the Ruhmkorff, and the contact-breaker being kept closed so as to make a completed circuit of the primary wire (a condition which would have appeared *à priori* essential to success), no effect was produced; while if the circuit was interrupted by keeping the contact-breaker open, sparks of 0.3 of an inch passed between the terminals of the secondary coil of the Ruhmkorff, and vacuum-tubes were readily illuminated. Here there was in effect no primary coil, no metallic connexion for the primary current; and yet a notable effect was produced.' For description of the Ruhmkorff coil see Gustav Wiedemann, *Die Lehre vom Galvanismus und Elektromagnetismus*, 2 vols. (Braunschweig, 1861), **2**: 836; and Fleeming Jenkin, *Electricity and Magnetism* (London, 1873): 287–8.

Now let us suppose a boat floating in a viscous fluid, and kept in its place by buffers fore and aft abutting against fixed obstacles, or by elastic ropes attached to fixed moorings before and behind. If the buffers were away, the mass of the boat would not prevent a man from pulling the boat along with a long-continued pull; but if the man were to push and pull in alternate seconds of time, he would produce very little motion of the boat. The buffers will effectually prevent the man from moving the boat far from its position by a steady pull; but if he pushes and pulls alternately, the period of alternation being not very different from that in which the buffers would cause the boat to vibrate about its position of equilibrium, then the force which acts in each vibration is due, partly to the efforts of the man, but chiefly to the resilience of the buffers, and the man will be able to move the boat much further from its mean position than he would if he had pushed and pulled at the same rate at the same boat perfectly free.

Thus, when an alternating force acts on a massive body, the extent of the displacements may be much greater when the body is attracted towards a position of equilibrium by a force depending on the displacement than when the body is perfectly free.

The electricity in the primary coil when it is closed corresponds to a free body resisted only on account of its motion; and in this case the current produced by an alternating force is small. When the primary coil is interrupted by a condenser, the electricity is resisted with a force proportional to the accumulation, and corresponds to a body whose motion is restrained by a spring; and in this case the motion produced by a force which alternates with sufficient rapidity may be much greater than in the former case. I enclose the mathematical theory of the experiment,[4] and remain,

Yours truly
J. CLERK MAXWELL

(4) Maxwell's appended 'Mathematical theory of the experiment', which forms the substance of his paper 'On Mr Grove's "Experiment in magneto-electric induction"': 361–3 (= *Scientific Papers*, **2**: 122–4), is not reproduced here. In this paper he gives an explanation of resonating alternating current circuits.

LETTER TO MARK PATTISON[1]

7 APRIL 1868

From the original in the Bodleian Library, Oxford[2]

8 Palace Gardens Terrace
London W
1868 April 7

Sir

In the Saturday Review of April 4 is an article on Science & Positivism[3] the writer of which appears to take so much interest in metaphysics science and positivism that I should be obliged if you will communicate to him the following remarks on a portion of the article.

M. Caro, according to the article (for I have not yet seen his own work),[4] uses in his argument the doctrine of the gradual conversion of all kinds of energy into the form of heat, and the ultimate uniform distribution of temperature over all matter.

As the speculation has important consequences I should like to point out to the writer of the article where he may find the data on which it is formed.

1   Fourier, in his great work on the conduction of heat,[5] has given methods by which if we know the temperature of every part of a body at any time and the temperature of the surface at all times we can determine the temperature of any point of the body at any *future* time as arising from the conduction of heat within it. (If the body be supposed to include the universe the condition about the surface is unnecessary.)

Now the formulae of Fourier for predicting the future temperature are equally applicable to determine the *former* temperature of the body in all its parts by simply making the quantity denoting the time a negative quantity.

If in this way we attempt to ascertain the state of the body previous to our observation of it, then (except in particular cases) we find that as we go back we arrive at an epoch at which the temperature varied in a discontinuous manner, and if we seek for the state of the body at any time still farther back we arrive at an impossible result.

Hence the body could not have existed as a solid body and a conductor of

---

(1) Rector of Lincoln College, Oxford; a regular contributor to the *Saturday Review* (see M. M. Bevington, *The Saturday Review 1855–1868* (New York, 1941): 26).
(2) MS Pattison 56, fols. 438ʳ–441ᵛ, Bodleian Library, Oxford.
(3) 'Science and positivism', *Saturday Review*, **25** (4 April 1868): 455–6.
(4) Elme Marie Caro, *Le Matérialisme et la Science* (Paris, 1867), reviewed in the *Saturday Review*.
(5) Joseph Fourier, *Théorie Analytique de la Chaleur* (Paris, 1822).

heat before a certain epoch. At that time or after it something must have happened, e.g. two bodies at different temperatures may have been joined together at a certain epoch and the present condition of the compound body will indicate when that was.⁽⁶⁾

This is a purely mathematical result founded however on experimental data. It has been pointed out by Sir W Thomson in several papers on the Secular Cooling of the Earth & Sun.⁽⁷⁾

2   The general doctrine of the dissipation (not the destruction) of energy was first clearly stated by Sir W. Thomson in his papers on the Dynamical Theory of Heat (Trans. Royal Society of Edinburgh 185 $\frac{1}{1345}$).⁽⁸⁾ It has also been treated at some length and with great labour by Prof. R Clausius of Zurich under the name of 'Entropy'⁽⁹⁾ which is an expression for the quantity of energy now rendered unavailable, a quantity always on the increase.⁽¹⁰⁾

The data are

1ˢᵗ   the fact that energy cannot be created or destroyed by physical agency

2ⁿᵈ   the fact that energy may change its form in two different ways

(α) in a certain class of conceivable cases the process by which the transfer takes place may be exactly reversed so that everything is at last in the same condition as at first

(β) in another class of cases the process is not reversible by any physical agency e.g. the equalization of temperature by conduction of heat in a body & the production of heat by the electric current when it meets with 'resistance'.

---

(6) The reviewer reported Caro's discussion of thermodynamics: 'We should then have to conceive of the existing order of things...as a slow but sure advance towards extinction. And, looking backward, it would...become...infinitely probable that the laws which now regulate the world had been arranged by an intelligent Cause.' The reviewer noted that 'this speculation...is at once metaphysical, and in harmony with the facts of science', and was used by Caro 'in vindication of metaphysical speculation as a form of knowledge', against the claims of positivist thinkers 'to have suppressed metaphysics'. See also Number 339.

(7) William Thomson, 'On the age of the sun's heat', *Macmillan's Magazine*, **5** (1862): 288–93 (= Thomson, *Popular Lectures and Addresses*, 3 vols. (London, 1889–94), **1**: 349–68); Thomson, 'On the secular cooling of the earth', *Phil. Mag.*, ser. 4, **25** (1863): 1–14 (= *Math. & Phys. Papers*, **3**: 295–311).

(8) William Thomson, 'On the dynamical theory of heat', *Trans. Roy. Soc. Edinb.*, **20** (1851): 261–88, 475–82; *ibid.*, **21** (1854): 123–71 (= *Math. & Phys. Papers*, **1**: 174–210, 222–32, 232–91).

(9) Rudolf Clausius, 'Ueber verschiedene für die Anwendung bequeme Formen der Hauptgleichungen der mechanischen Wärmetheorie', *Ann. Phys.*, **125** (1865): 353–400, esp. 390, 400. See Number 483 note (22).

(10) On Maxwell's interpretation of Clausius' concept of entropy see Number 483 esp. notes (19) and (20).

By no contrivance can we arrange an example of class α without introducing processes belonging to class β so that in every action in nature part of the process is not capable of reversion.

This part always tends in one direction to diminish the energy which is available for producing phenomena involving change, and to increase the energy which cannot be so used. The ultimate condition is one of uniform temperature in which everything remains at the same distance from every other thing in so far as these are sensible objects.

I speak of sensible objects because according to a certain theory the phenomena of heat are due to the intestine motion of the small parts of hot bodies.[11]

A uniformly hot body apparently at rest is not on this theory devoid of motion for if we had the means of observing the very smallest parts (I do not speak of atoms) of the body and of distinguishing the smallest intervals of time we should find at a given instant different parts moving in different ways, and if we could lay hold of these parts by machinery we might extract energy from this motion till the whole mass was reduced to stillness.

There is no evidence that this can be done either by direct manipulation or by any physical process, and therefore in the present dispensation there remain a number of irreversible processes, all of which tend in the same direction, and therefore tend of themselves to an end and by reasoning backwards (if we know enough) we should find an epoch before which the present order could not have existed.

The peculiar faith required of a positivist is in the universal validity of laws, the form of which he does not yet know, though he speculates to a certain extent on their results.

A strict materialist believes that everything depends on the motion of matter. He knows the form of the laws of motion though he does not know all their consequences when applied to systems of unknown complexity.

Now one thing in which the materialist (fortified with dynamical knowledge) believes is that if every motion great & small were accurately reversed, and the world left to itself again, everything would happen backwards the fresh water would collect out of the sea and run up the rivers and finally fly up to the clouds in drops which would extract heat from the air and evaporate and afterwards in condensing would shoot out rays of light to

---

(11) 'The Dynamical Theory of Heat...that heat consists of a motion excited among the particles of bodies'; Thomson, 'On the dynamical theory of heat', *Trans. Roy. Soc. Edinb.*, **20** (1851): 261, who attributes the theory to Humphry Davy. Maxwell subsequently listed Bacon, Boyle, Newton and Cavendish as supporters of the theory: see Number 377 para. 3.

the sun and so on. Of course all living things would regrede from the grave to the cradle and we should have a memory of the future but not of the past.⁽¹²⁾

The reason why we do not expect anything of this kind to take place at any time is our experience of irreversible processes, all of one kind, and this leads to the doctrine of a beginning & an end instead of cyclical progression for ever.

The practical relation of metaphysics to physics is most intimate. Metaphysicians differ from age to age according to the physical doctrines of the age and their personal knowledge of them. Leibnitz is in advance of Descartes Newton so far as he exposes himself is distinct. Locke Berkeley &c differ according to the degree in which they enjoyed the diffusion and dilution of the Galilean and Newtonian doctrines.

The Edinburgh & the Dublin Hamilton⁽¹³⁾ differ in their metaphysical power in the direct ratio of their physical knowledge (not the inverse as most people suppose).

On the other hand the effect of the absence of metaphysics may be traced in most physical treatises of the present century.

I have been somewhat diffuse but I happen to be interested in speculations standing on experimental & mathematical data and reaching beyond the sphere of the senses without passing into that of words and nothing more.

I am Sir
Yours truly
J. CLERK MAXWELL

---

(12) Compare Maxwell's letter to J. W. Strutt of 6 December 1870 (Number 350). Maxwell's expression of the reverse movement of the universe may perhaps echo the myth expounded in Plato's *Politicus* (269–70), of which a major edition had been published by Lewis Campbell in 1867. See *The Sophistes and Politicus of Plato*, with a revised text and English notes by Lewis Campbell (Oxford, 1867): [*Politicus*] 45–53; 'The universe is at one time turned by God, but at certain periods is relinquished by him, and turns itself in the opposite direction. ... Yet it has the least possible change of motion, when the direction of its rotation is reversed ... guided by its Divine Author, and receives from him a renewal of life and immortality. And again, being let go at the most auspicious moment, it makes countless revolutions by itself, like a huge and perfectly balanced top, revolving on the finest peg.... As the movement of the world, so the order of the ages of man is reversed. And, at the time when the world returns under the Divine care, old age is done away, and men pass through maturity and youth to childhood and infancy, and so pass away.' In his 'Introduction to the Statesman': xxviii–xli, esp. xxxiv Campbell gave a full discussion of the problems surrounding the interpretation of the myth.

(13) Sir William Hamilton, Bart and Sir William Rowan Hamilton, respectively.

287

LETTER TO MARK PATTISON
13 APRIL 1868
From the original in the Bodleian Library, Oxford[1]

8 Palace Gardens Terrace
London W
1868 April 13

Sir

I have received your letter[2] and will do my best to answer your queries. You must see that my acquaintance with positivism whether as stated by Comte,[3] Littré,[4] or Mill,[5] is but slight.

Comte certainly endeavoured to form a distinct picture of the shape, method and aim of a system of sciences, some of which he considered as in a very immature state at present. This picture he considered as a sort of matrix in which these sciences would probably be developed by future labourers and one of its uses was to prevent them from wasting their efforts on attempts of a kind which would prove abortive. In this part of his work Comte was like other philosophers who try to make their 'Principles of Human Knowledge' practically useful, and using every method – conjecture – imagination & himself for that purpose.

But when he prescribes rules for the study of sciences already formed, as Astronomy, all this part of the philosophic spirit is proscribed, and the astronomer is even forbidden to extend his views beyond the Solar System.

I say therefore that though it is quite the part of a philosopher to try to form a conception of a state of science more developed than the present, and of the methods likely to be most fertile, he who does so assumes that although he does not know *what* will be discovered he has some anticipation of the mould in which future discoveries will be cast.

The statements of certain positivists therefore about human knowledge & science in general are apt to make one think that they are convinced that new truths will fall into the old moulds, even in sciences yet unborn.

---

(1) MS Pattison 56, fols. 442^r–448^v, Bodleian Library, Oxford.

(2) Not extant.

(3) Auguste Comte, *Cours de Philosophie Positive*, 6 vols. (Paris, 1830–42). There is a copy of G. H. Lewes, *Comte's Philosophy of the Sciences: being an Exposition of the Cours de Philosophie Positive of Auguste Comte* (London, 1853) in Maxwell's library (Cavendish Laboratory, Cambridge).

(4) Émile Littré, *Auguste Comte et la Philosophie Positive* (Paris, 1863).

(5) John Stuart Mill, *Auguste Comte and Positivism* (London, 1865). Mill and Littré were mentioned in the review 'Science and positivism', *Saturday Review*, **25** (1868): 455–6, which had occasioned Maxwell's correspondence with Pattison: see Number 286, esp. notes (4) and (6).

I have no doubt however that in my last letter[6] I went astray on this subject. I go on to your 3rd query, taking them in the reverse order.

I am not sure whether the 'Matter' against which Berkeley argued has any existence now. I am little satisfied with most of the definitions of it. 'That which is perceived by the senses' is utterly wrong both in excess and defect.[7]

Lucretius says

'facere et fungi sine corpore nulla potest res'.[8] In Dynamics, the science of the motion of matter as affected by forces, matter is defined and measured solely with respect to the force required to move it in a certain manner and the force is likewise defined with respect to matter & motion.[9]

Having defined equal times equal distances and equal velocities, Force is defined to be that which produces change in a bodys velocity and is *measured* by the change which it would produce in the velocity [of] a standard body (Imperial Pound) if it acted on it for a second.

Any other mass on which the same force would produce the same effect is called an equal mass, whatever be its other properties.

This is the definition of equal quantities of matter and it is found to lead to consistent statements.

The measurement of quantity of matter by weight is a secondary method founded on the fact, which Newton and others have carefully verified, that the weight of all bodies known to us is proportional to the quantity of matter in them and independent of the *kind* of matter.

When the word Inertia is used by a physicist since Newton it generally

---

(6) Number 286.

(7) Compare Number 294: Appendix.

(8) *Titi Lucreti Cari De Rerum Natura Libri Sex*, ed. and trans. H. A. J. Munro, 2 vols. (Cambridge, $_2$1866), **1**: 57 (Book I, line 443); 'no thing can do and suffer without body', *ibid.*, **2**: 11. On Lucretius see also Maxwell's letter to H. A. J. Munro of 7 February 1866 (Number 257) and Number 377 para. 1. Fleeming Jenkin had recently published an essay reviewing Munro's edition of *De Rerum Natura*: 'The atomic theory of Lucretius', *North British Review*, **48** (1868): 211–42. Jenkin had written to Maxwell on 10 January 1868: 'I send by book post a revise of my atoms article will you write anything you please in pencil on the margin.' (ULC Add. MSS 7655, II/28). In a letter to William Thomson of 20 February Jenkin commented on Maxwell's response: 'Thank you very much for your notes on Lucretius... Munro unearthed Lesage. Maxwell says he has calculated the effect of atoms striking as he described and found that no gravitation would result if the striking atoms rebounded.' (ULC Add. MSS 7342, J 27). Maxwell commented on Lesage's theory in his manuscript for Thomson on the 'Kinetic Theory of Gases' (Number 377, see para. 5 and note (7)). Compare Jenkin's discussion of Lesage in 'The atomic theory of Lucretius': 238–9, where he alluded to the 'dynamical imperfections' of Lesage's hypothesis.

(9) Compare Number 266.

means not metaphysical passivity[10] but a measurable quantity namely the number of pounds in the body.

Suppose that a chemist asserted that the addition of a certain substance (say phlogiston) diminished the weight of a body, a physicist would say that there could not be very much of it in the Solar System or facts would be different.

But if two bodies were found to be of equal mass (by giving them equal and opposite velocities and observing them come to rest after impact) and if phlogiston added to one of them diminished its mass so *measured* then either the mechanical properties of the body and of the phlogiston are not simply added together, or the phlogiston by itself would have negative mass, that is, a force acting on it would cause it to move against the force, which is pure nonsense.

Again on the undulatory theory of light, the medium is supposed to communicate motion from one part to another by the action of elastic force which gradually changes the motion of each portion. This implies that the medium is material and that the number of pounds of it in a cubic mile might be ascertained*[11] though as yet we have no evidence of gravitation acting on it.

These examples are meant to show that the true test of matter is its relation to the force which alters its motion.

When matter is in motion it has two mathematical possessions.

1 Momentum, a directed quantity equal to Mass × Velocity and in the direction of the velocity.

2 Kinetic Energy an absolute positive quantity, without direction measured by $\frac{1}{2}$ Mass × (Velocity)^2.

This was formerly called Vis Viva and the controversy between the Newtonians & Leibnitzians was about which (1) or (2) was the more excellent measure of the Motion of a Body.

*See Thomson on the Value of a Cubic Mile of Sunlight and the density of the Aether Trans R S E 1854.[11]

---

(10) In his review of the second edition of Thomson and Tait's *Treatise on Natural Philosophy* (Cambridge, 1879), Maxwell rejected their assertion that 'matter has an innate power of resisting external influences', which he terms the 'Manichæan doctrine of the innate depravity of matter'; see J. Clerk Maxwell, 'Thomson and Tait's Natural Philosophy', *Nature*, 20 (1879): 213–16, esp. 214 (= *Scientific Papers*, 2: 779). For comment see P. M. Harman, *Metaphysics and Natural Philosophy* (Brighton, 1982): 140–5.

(11) William Thomson, 'Note on the possible density of the luminiferous medium and on the mechanical value of a cubic mile of sunlight', *Trans. Roy. Soc. Edinb.*, 21 (1854): 57–61 (= *Math. & Phys. Papers*, 2: 28–33).

The *facts* are that in *all* cases of the mutual action of a system of bodies
1 the *geometrical* sum of the momenta reckoned according to their directions remains constant.
2 In certain cases visibly, and in all cases if we could measure it the sum of the kinetic energies taken arithmetically together with the sum of certain other energies called potential energies remains constant.

Berkeley quotes (with disdain) a passage of Torricelli which seems appropriate. 'Matter is nothing but an enchanted vase of Circe, which serves for a receptacle of the force and the momenta of impulse. Power* and impulse† are such subtle abstracts, are quintessences so refined, that they cannot be enclosed in any other vessels but the inmost materiality of natural solids'.(12)

I so far agree with this, that I cannot admit any theory which considers matter as a system of points which are centres of force acting on other similar points, and admits nothing but these forces. For this does not account for the perseverance of matter in its state of motion and for the measure of matter.

I am afraid I have been tiresome on this subject but I consider it of the first importance in physics to know what we mean by matter and how to measure it, and both natural and mental science writers often go astray at the beginning about these things.

You ask about the definition of Energy. Energy is of two kinds, Kinetic and Potential.(13) Energy is the capacity which a body has of doing *work*.(14) A moving body has energy due to its motion called kinetic energy and measured by $\frac{1}{2}$ mass × (velocity)^2.

A body or system of bodies which are connected so that forces act between them tending to alter their relative position is capable of work and this capacity is called Potential Energy. Two heavenly bodies tending to approach or (say) the earth and a weight have potential energy due to gravitation. Electrified bodies have electrical potential. Elastic springs when bent &c &c are examples of potential energy.

* = Energy   † = Momentum? in modern language

(12) The passage from Torricelli's *Lezioni Accademiche* is cited in Berkeley's 'De Motu; sive de motus principio et natura, et de causa communicationis motuum', (trans.) 'Concerning motion; or the origin and nature of motion, and the cause of communicating it', in The *Works of George Berkeley, D.D., Bishop of Cloyne*, ed. G. N. Wright, 2 vols. (London, 1843), **2**: 83–103, on 86n (exactly as quoted by Maxwell). He subsequently consulted the Torricelli text itself: see Numbers 294 esp. note (29) and 437: Appendix.

(13) The term 'kinetic energy' had been introduced by Thomson and Tait, *Natural Philosophy*: 163; and 'potential energy' by W. J. M. Rankine, 'On the general law of the transformation of energy', *Phil. Mag.*, ser. 4, **5** (1853): 106–17, on 106.

(14) Compare Thomson and Tait, *Natural Philosophy*: 177–8.

Energy of both kinds is capable of exact measurement, and the progress of science at present is in the direction of measuring additional forms of energy.

Now the conception of Kinetic Energy is simply that of a moving mass which can do work till it is stopped.

Potential energy is force acting between bodies and capable of continuing to act between them while they yield to its action.

Now the conception of a body in motion is more fundamental than that of the power of producing motion in other bodies (commonly called force of attraction repulsion &c). Hence when any form of potential energy (such as the elasticity of air) can be explained by motion only, the explanation is a step in advance, and I suppose that gravitation itself will not be satisfactorily understood till it is explained in some way not involving action at a distance.

I have examined several attempts by various speculators, but the dynamics in all were faulty. I have also tried to apply to gravitation the same method which I had found useful in electromagnetism, but I have found no opening for such a theory of gravitation.[15]

I merely state this to show that there is a desire among men to explain action apparently at a distance by the intermediate action of a medium and then to explain the action of the medium as much as possible by its motion, and so to reduce Potential Energy to a form of Kinetic Energy.

Energy is never destroyed, but some of its transformations are not reversible. I have investigated the case of a multitude of molecules moving in a confined space and occasionally deflecting each other from their paths.[16] This is a question in pure dynamics but it gives results which apply with great exactness to the properties of gases.

In whatever way the motion is distributed among the particles at first, it is very quickly distributed according to a certain law according to which the number of particles having velocities between certain limits can be found. There remains always a great difference between the greatest and the least velocities and the molecules are often gaining and losing velocity but a general law of distribution prevails like that of wealth in a nation by which the proportion having so much above or below the average is calculable.

Now in a nation you can pick out the rich people as such, but in a gas you cannot pick out the swift molecules either by mechanical or chemical means.

As a simpler instance of an irreversible operation which (I think) depends on the same principle suppose so many black balls put at the bottom of a box

---

(15) See Numbers 217 esp. note (11), 238 and 309.
(16) See Number 263.

and so many white above them. Then let them be jumbled together. If there is no physical difference between the white and black balls, it is exceedingly improbable that any amount of shaking will bring all the black balls to the bottom and all the white to the top again, so that the operation of mixing is irreversible unless either the black balls are heavier than the white or a person who knows white from black picks them and sorts them.

Thus if you put a drop of water into a vessel of water no chemist can take out that identical drop again,[17] though he could take out a drop of any other liquid.

(Can you tell me without trouble what is meant by the expression 'idem *numero*' in metaphysical or theological language as when James Bernoulli calls his spiral 'carnis nostrae...post varias alterationes — ejusdem *numero* resurrecturæ symbolum'.)[18]

I think you are right in thinking that we are likely to arrive at physical indications of a beginning & an end. That end is not a destruction of matter or of energy but such a distribution of energy that no further change is possible without an intervention of an agent who need not create either matter or energy but only direct the energy into new channels.

I do not think that anyone can have a second-hand acquaintance with a physical *principle* such as the ideas of matter force, energy, motion. To every one it must either be a mere word or a true form of thought, whether he is a professional experimenter or a mathematician or a lover of wisdom. The power to understand and assimilate elementary physical ideas (such as those contained in the Definitions and Axioms in Newtons Principia) is not confined to professed mathematicians or experimenters.

Experiments are often made to illustrate these principles but not to prove them, and these illustrations help to explain what is meant, say, by Action and Reaction but no one has proved them equal, or has required any proof, after he knew the meaning of the terms.

All these things therefore, being the foundations of science are as much the property of one man as of another. The discovery of such principles is the work of eminent men like Archimedes, Galileo, Newton, Young, Faraday but when they are illustrated and explained they may be fully understood as a

---

(17) Compare Maxwell's letter to J. W. Strutt of 6 December 1870 (Number 350).

(18) '[Our curve] will be a symbol of our flesh which will arise the same in number after various changes and finally also death itself'. See Jakob Bernoulli, 'Lineae cycloidales, evolutae, anti-evolutae, causticae, anti-causticae peri-causticae. Earum usus & simplex relatio ad se invicem. Spira mirabilis', *Acta Eruditorum* (May 1692): 207–13, esp. 213 (= *Opera*, 2 vols. (Lausanne/Geneva, 1744), **2**: 491–502, esp. 502). Compare Volume I: 96.

useful mental possession by any one whose mind is sufficiently open to receive them.

At the same time it is possible to become eminent both in mathematics and experiment with a very faulty set of first principles provided they are not often appealed to and so brought to the test.

I think that Newton through himself Desaguliers[19] Bentley[20] Locke[21] Gregory[22] and others exercised a very great influence on English thought among men who were neither mathematicians nor astronomers and that Voltaires scientific writings[23] produced a very great influence on French thought, though several most important ideas in Newton have been almost lost in the process of transmission, so that I would recommend the reading of Newtons Definitions & Axioms to every scientific man who is not familiar with them ⟨and others will find there the origin of several expressions which are now part of our mother tongue⟩.

If I had taken more time I should have occupied yours less with trying to answer your queries.

I remain
Yours faithfully
J. CLERK MAXWELL

---

(19) J. T. Desaguliers, *A Course of Experimental Philosophy*, 2 vols. (London, 1734–44).

(20) Richard Bentley, *A Confutation of Atheism from the Origin and Frame of the World* (London, 1693).

(21) Interpreting John Locke's *Essay Concerning Human Understanding* (1690) as 'Newtonian' in inspiration.

(22) David Gregory, *The Elements of Astronomy, Physical and Geometrical*, 2 vols. (London, 1715).

(23) F. M. A. Voltaire, *Lettres Philosophiques* (Amsterdam, 1734).

REPORT ON PAPERS BY FRANCIS BASHFORTH,[1] JAMES ATKINSON LONGRIDGE[2] AND CHARLES WATKINS MERRIFIELD[3] ON THE MOTION OF PROJECTILES

19 MAY 1868

From the original in the Library of the Royal Society, London[4]

REPORT ON PROFESSOR BASHFORTHS PAPER ON THE RESISTANCE OF THE AIR TO THE MOTION OF ELONGATED PROJECTILES[5]

The Author has examined the theory of chronographs as applied to the investigation of the motion of artillery projectiles, and also other methods of determining their velocities.

The method of Robins' ballistic pendulum[6] has the disadvantage that it gives only one velocity for each round, and the initial velocity must be deduced from the supposition that it depends on the known weight of the projectile & that of the powder or that it is the same in successive rounds.[7]

The author therefore has adopted the method of determining the times of transit of the projectile through ten planes at equal distances from each other, thus finding the time corresponding to nine different spaces. He finds that these times may be represented with sufficient accuracy by the formula

$$t = as + bs^2 \quad [8]$$

---

(1) St John's 1840, Fellow 1843, Professor of Applied Mathematics to the Advanced Class of Artillery Officers, Woolwich 1864 (Venn, *DNB*).

(2) Trinity 1841; an engineer with interests in gunnery (Venn; and see 'Armstrong, Sir W. G.' (*DNB*)).

(3) FRS 1863, Principal of the Royal School of Naval Architecture and Marine Engineering 1867 (Boase).   (4) Royal Society, *Referees' Reports*, **6**: 17.

(5) Francis Bashforth, 'On the resistance of the air to the motion of elongated projectiles having variously formed heads', *Phil. Trans.*, **158** (1868): 417–41. The paper was received by the Royal Society on 30 January 1868, and read on 20 February 1868; see the abstract in *Proc. Roy. Soc.*, **16** (1868): 261–3.

(6) Described by Benjamin Robins in his *New Principles of Gunnery* (London, 1742); and see W. J. M. Rankine, *A Manual of Applied Mechanics* (London/Glasgow, 1858): 548–51.

(7) See Bashforth, 'On the resistance of the air to the motion of elongated projectiles': 418.

(8) Bashforth, 'On the resistance of the air to the motion of elongated projectiles': 437; s and t denote space and time.

which indicates a resistance proportional to the cube of the velocity and equal to $2bv^3$.[9]

As much labour has already been spent in the interpretation of the readings in the experiments and apparently good results have been obtained I think it worth while to point out the theoretically best value of b according to the method of least squares, supposing equal errors in each observation of time.

$$s_n = nl^{(10)}$$

and let t_n be the time of passing the $n+1^{\text{th}}$ screen then let

$$t_0 - c = \epsilon_0$$
$$t_0 - c - al - bl^2 = \epsilon_1$$
$$------$$
$$t_n - c - nal - n^2 bl^2 = \epsilon_n.$$

Let $\quad t_0 + t_1 + \&c + t_n = \sum(t), \quad (t_1 + 2t_2 + \&c + nt_n) = \sum(nt)$
$$(t_1 + 4t_2 + \&c + n^2 t_n) = \sum(n^2 t)$$

then we have the following equations to determine the best values of $a\ b\ c$

$$\sum(t) = nc + \frac{n(n+1)}{2} al + \frac{n(n+1)(2n+1)}{6} bl^2$$

$$\sum(nt) = \frac{n(n+1)}{2} c + \frac{n(n+1)(2n+1)}{6} al + \frac{n^2(n+1)^2}{4} bl^2$$

---

(9) Bashforth had noted in his 'On the resistance of the air to the motion of elongated projectiles': 417, that: 'According to Newton's law [Principia, Book II, Prop. X], the resistance of the air varies as the square of the velocity.... But in spite of grave doubts respecting the accuracy of Newton's law, it has been adopted by most of the eminent mathematicians who have written on the subject'. This was the law as stated in contemporary mechanics texts; and by Maxwell in an 1852 draft on the motion of a body in a resisting medium (see Volume I: 214–15). Bashforth however noted that 'in 1719 John Bernoulli gave equations for finding... the path &c of a projectile, when the resistance of the air was supposed to vary according to any power of the velocity.' In his *A Mathematical Treatise on the Motion of Projectiles, founded chiefly on the results of experiments made with the author's chronograph* (London, 1873): 45–9, Bashforth explained that his expressions for the path of a projectile on the supposition that the resistance varies according to any power of the velocity, from which he had derived tables on the assumption of a third power law, were based on Bernoulli's method. 'Professor Adams communicated to me the above expressions... in a letter dated Nov. 13 1866, when the few ballistic experiments I had then made seemed to indicate a cubic law of resistance. Professor Adams at the same time remarked that... "an equivalent process was given long ago by John Bernoulli".' See Johann Bernoulli, 'Responsio ad non-neminis provocationem', *Acta Eruditorum* (May 1719): 216–26, and 'Operatio analytica per quam deducta est... solutio', *ibid.* (May 1721): 228–30 (= Johann Bernoulli, *Opera Omnia*, 4 vols. (Lausanne/Geneva, 1742), 2: 393–402, 513–16).

(10) l is the distance between the screens, which are connected by an electric circuit, passed by the projectiles in Bashforth's experiments.

$$\sum (n^2 t) = \frac{n(n+1)(2n+1)}{6} c + \frac{n^2(n+1)^2}{4} al + \frac{n(n+1)}{30}(6n^3 + 9n^2 + n - 1) bl^2.$$

From these equations we find

$$bl^2 = \frac{30\{(n+1)(n+2)\sum(t) - 6(n+1)\sum(nt) + 6\sum(n^2 t)\}}{(n-2)(n-1)n(n+1)(n+2)}.$$

It is not difficult after finding b to determine the probability of a term indicating that the resistance increases faster or slower than $2bv^3$. b should be determined for each round and the weight size and kind of projectile given together with the mean velocity at which b was determined. In this way it may be ascertained whether $\dfrac{2b \cdot W^{(11)}}{d^2}$ is a quantity independent of v and dependent only on the kind of shot.

Professor Bashforth appears to have determined b by eliminating a between three observed times from the equation[12]

$$\frac{t_n}{n-1} - \frac{t_3}{2} = \overline{n-3}\, bl^2$$

or a similar equation. As he has in general nine equations for each round it is well to use the most advantageous combination of them.

The Chronograph

Most chronographs aim at producing uniform motion. Some of these attempt to make the mean motion in long periods constant others to reduce the greatest and least velocities as nearly as possible to the mean.

For the exact measurement of small portions of time the constancy of the mean rate is of small importance but the disturbances of the motion are of great importance. Hence the simpler the mechanism the simpler is likely to be the nature of the motion. A complex mechanism containing rapidly revolving parts and having several degrees of freedom is likely to be liable to a considerable number of superposed oscillations of different periods most of which are unknown and difficult of investigation.

In Mr Bashforths Chronograph the moving part may be described as a

---

(11) W is the weight of the shot, d its diameter; see Bashforth, 'On the resistance of the air to the motion of elongated projectiles': 438.

(12) Bashforth obtains the general equation $t_n/(n-1) = al + \overline{n-1}\, bl^2$; finding numerical values of $t_n/(n-1)$ for each experiment, and taking the difference of two of these quantities, he obtains $t_n/(n-1) - \tfrac{1}{2}t_3 = \overline{n-3}\, bl^2$; see Bashforth, 'On the resistance of the air to the motion of elongated projectiles': 437.

rigid body revolving round a vertical axis. If care is taken that this axis is a principal axis through the centre of gravity and vertical then the velocity of rotation is affected only by the resistance of the air and friction. If the centre of gravity is not in the axis and if the axis is not vertical there will be a disturbance having a period of one revolution which will be easily detected from the clock records.

If the axis though vertical is not a principal axis or not through the centre of gravity there will be a tendency to make the stand of the instrument oscillate or work round in a circle which also will be easily detected.

The absolute measure of time is entrusted to a pendulum clock as in the Greenwich Chronograph,[13] and as each set of observations is the result of a good deal of labour & expense it is worth while to interpolate as Mr Bashforth has done so as to find the true time of each transit on a scale of divisions which constantly increase.

The other methods enumerated are deficient in simplicity of construction and in simplicity of motion.

Electrical Arrangement

The object of the electrical arrangement is that the interval of time between the breaking of the circuit and the motion of the marker shall be the same whatever screen is broken.[14]

Let R be the resistance of the coil of the electromagnet

L its coeff^t of self-induction

C the capacity of a foot of covered wire of the connexions

Y the quantity of electricity which passes the electromagnet after the circuit is broken at S, where the distances from L are a & b feet,

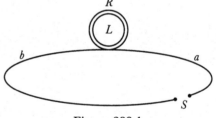

Figure 288,1

then
$$\frac{1}{c}\left(\frac{1}{a}+\frac{1}{b}\right)X + R\frac{dX}{dt} + L\frac{d^2X}{dt^2} = 0$$

whence $X = Ce^{nt}$ where $n = -\dfrac{R}{2L} \pm \sqrt{\dfrac{R^2}{4L^2} - \dfrac{1}{CL}\left(\dfrac{1}{a}+\dfrac{1}{b}\right)}.$

---

(13) See the 'Description of the galvanic chronographic apparatus', appendix to *Astronomical and Magnetical and Meteorological Observations made at the Royal Observatory, Greenwich, in the Year 1856* (London, 1858).

(14) See note (10) and Bashforth, 'On the resistance of the air to the motion of elongated projectiles': 421–3.

If the connecting wire is kept off the ground C is very small and n will be a large impossible quantity indicating a rapidly decreasing alternating current. The period of alternation will depend on $\frac{1}{a}+\frac{1}{b}$ and therefore on the position of the break, but the rate of decrease depends on $\frac{R}{2L}$ which is independent of the position of the screen. To make the electromagnets act quickly they should be made of bundles of iron wire insulated from each other, and the keepers should never be in contact with them.

Professor Bashforth has published much of the matter of his paper in the Proceedings of the Royal Artillery Institution[15] nevertheless as the methods are good and the results remarkable I think it deserving of publication in the Philosophical Transactions.[16]

II

Mr LONGRIDGE'S PAPER[17]

The author discusses several laws of velocity, and has obtained an expression for the distance in terms of the initial and final velocity when the resistance varies as the pth power of the velocity. He has applied this to the results given in the report of the Special Armstrong & Whitworth Committee[18] for the velocities at 40, 440 and 840 yards and finds $p = 8.747$.

The results were obtained by Navez electroballistic pendulum.[19] I do not know whether the different velocities are those of the same shot but in any case the value of the results must depend on the method employed which is not described.

As an example of an effort to derive working mathematical formulae from

---

(15) Francis Bashforth, 'Description of a chronograph, adapted for measuring the varying velocity of a body in motion through the air, and for other purposes', *Minutes of Proceedings of the Royal Artillery Institution*, **5** (1866): 161–92; published separately (London, 1866).

(16) In a letter to Stokes of 26 April 1868 (Royal Society, *Referees' Reports*, **6**: 16) W. J. M. Rankine stated that Bashforth's paper was a 'valuable communication, and in every respect eligible for being printed in the Philosophical Transactions'.

(17) J. A. Longridge, 'On the resistance of the air to rifled projectiles' (Royal Society, AP. 50.10). The paper was received by the Royal Society on 13 February 1868, and read on 27 February 1868; see the abstract in *Proc. Roy. Soc.*, **16** (1868): 263–6.

(18) The *Report of the Special Armstrong and Whitworth Committee. Vol. II. Minutes of Evidence, Appendix, and Index* (London, 1866): 500–3 (*Parliamentary Papers* (1866) XLII) includes results of experiments on the velocities of projectiles.

(19) This instrument is described by Bashforth, 'On the resistance of the air to the motion of elongated projectiles': 419; see also Stephen Vincent Benet, *Electro-ballistic Machines and the Schultz' Chronoscope* (New York, 1866): 10–11, 39.

a limited number of facts the paper is valuable but I doubt whether we can have much confidence in any part of the process.[20]

III Mr MERRIFIELD'S PAPER[21]

The data in this case were the elevations required for different ranges in shooting with Metfords match rifle.

If we consider the horizontal motion only and if $\dfrac{dv}{dt} = -mv^3$ [22] then

$$m = 2\frac{t.v-s}{s^2V}$$

where t is the actual time V the initial velocity and s the space.[23] If the vertical motion is unaffected by the resistance we may find t (which is not observed) as the time in vacuum for an assumed velocity with the given elevation. (This ought to be verified.) I do not know how the initial velocity was found except that it gives consistent results, but I have no doubt that the author had a method for finding it which he could explain. This paper is also an example of deduction from data which are not so complete as might be wished, but the number of experiments, the conciseness of the method and the consistency of the results incline me to believe that this paper ought to be printed in the Transactions.[24]

J. Clerk Maxwell

(a)

(a) {Maxwell} Report on Three Papers on the motion of Rifled Projectiles / J. Clerk Maxwell / 19 May 1868

(20) The paper was not printed in the *Philosophical Transactions*, despite a judgement by W. J. M. Rankine, in a letter to Stokes of 21 April 1868 (Royal Society, *Referees' Reports*, **6**: 162), that it was 'on the whole eligible for publication in the Philosophical Transactions, because it contains a useful series of investigations regarding the application of various formulae for resistance to previously published experiments.' Longridge had himself commented ('On the resistance of the air to rifled projectiles', f. 8) that: 'He was prepared to find the resistance increasing at a higher ratio than the cube of the velocity... but the ninth power staggered him, and he thought that there must be either some error of observation in the results, or that the form of the assumed function was altogether wrong.'

(21) C. W. Merrifield, 'On the law of the resistance of the air to rifled projectiles', *Phil. Trans.*, **158** (1868): 443–6. The paper was received by the Royal Society on 19 March 1868, and read on 23 April 1868; see the abstract in *Proc. Roy. Soc.*, **16** (1868): 321–2.

(22) m is 'the coefficient of resistance'. Merrifield stated that 'I found the resistance to vary as the cube of the velocity'; compare Bashforth's conclusion.

(23) See Merrifield, 'On the law of the resistance of the air to rifled projectiles': 443–4. Maxwell considers only the horizontal motion and ignores the inclination which appears in Merrifield's expression.

(24) A judgement confirmed by W. J. M. Rankine in a letter to Stokes of 26 June 1868 (Royal Society, *Referees' Reports*, **6**: 182), stating the paper to be an 'important contribution... of especial value in connection with two papers on the same subject... lately... read to the Royal Society... highly eligible for publication in the Philosophical Transactions'.

ABSTRACT OF PAPER 'ON A METHOD OF MAKING A DIRECT COMPARISON OF ELECTROSTATIC WITH ELECTROMAGNETIC FORCE; WITH A NOTE ON THE ELECTROMAGNETIC THEORY OF LIGHT'

[10 JUNE 1868][1]

From the *Proceedings of the Royal Society*[2]

ON A METHOD OF MAKING A DIRECT COMPARISON OF ELECTROSTATIC WITH ELECTROMAGNETIC FORCE; WITH A NOTE ON THE ELECTROMAGNETIC THEORY OF LIGHT[3]

By J. Clerk Maxwell, F.R.SS.L. & E.

Received June 10, 1868

(Abstract)

The experiments described in this paper[4] were made in the laboratory of Mr. Gassiot,[5] who placed his great battery of 2600 cells of bichloride of mercury at the disposal of the author. Mr. Willoughby Smith[6] lent his resistance-coils of 1,102,000 Ohms; Messrs. Forde[7] and Fleeming Jenkin lent a sensitive galvanometer, a set of resistance-coils, a bridge, and a key for

---

(1) The date the paper was received by the Royal Society. The paper was read on 18 June 1868: see note (2).

(2) *Proc. Roy. Soc.*, **16** (1868): 449–50.

(3) Published in *Phil. Trans.*, **158** (1868): 643–57 (= *Scientific Papers*, **2**: 125–43). Reporting on the paper in a letter to Stokes of 16 July 1868 (Royal Society, *Referees' Reports*, **6**: 180) Fleeming Jenkin declared the paper 'eminently suited for publication in the Transactions'; while in a letter to Stokes of 19 October 1868 (Royal Society, *Referees' Reports*, **6**: 181; printed in Wilson, *Stokes–Kelvin Correspondence*, **1**: 336) William Thomson stated that it 'ought to be published by all means in the Transactions'.

(4) Maxwell published a revised account of these 'Experiments on the value of v, the ratio of the electromagnetic to the electrostatic unit of electricity' in the 'Report of the Committee on standards of electrical resistance', *Report of the Thirty-ninth Meeting of the British Association* (London, 1870): 434–8, on 436–8.

(5) John Peter Gassiot: see Number 242 esp. note (8).

(6) Willoughby Smith, Chief Electrician to the Telegraph Construction and Maintenance Co. (Boase).

(7) Henry Charles Forde, telegraph engineer, partner of Fleeming Jenkin (Boase).

double simultaneous contacts; and Mr. C. Hockin[8] undertook the observation of the galvanometer, the adjustment of the resistances, and the

---

(8) Insight into the technical difficulties of the experiment is provided by a letter from Charles Hockin to Maxwell dated 15 May 1868 (ULC Add. MSS 7655, II/30; first published in I. B. Hopley, 'Maxwell's determination of the number of electrostatic units in one electromagnetic unit of electricity', *Annals of Science*, **15** (1959): 91–108, on 97–8). 'Dear Sir, / I tested all the coils & the galvanometer today. Becker could not let me have room so I took them to St Mary's. The results most unsatisfactory. The boxes containing Siemens were well enough the errors being not much more than I have some times found after carrying a box of coils from one place to another with all sorts of variations of temperature. But the box containing B.A. units did not at all agree, one coil marked 33,000 had a resistance 100,000 & more – the sum of all boxes being 1,100,000 (1,096,500). I shall do them again tomorrow morning. If the error arises from bad contact anywhere the result is *still not* to come out the same. This brings v from 22×10^7 to $24\frac{1}{2} \times 10^7$. / The galvanometer has been altered since I had it last the resistance 45,290 $(1 \pm 1/200)$. The shunts remaining as before. I expect to get tomorrow results true to 1/1000 the coils being together in a room like Mr Gassiotts at a pretty constant temperature. The 31 coil is right & agrees with the coils in Jenkins boxes $(\pm 1/2000)$. I made them at different times from different standards so there is no great error there. I fancy any amount of error may be expected in the absolute value of the micrometer screw. Have you any objection to my taking the screw to Mathiessen's to measure it?... / How was the contact ensured with the insulated disc? It seems to me very imperfect & I do not understand how the touching the micrometer screw produced such a deflection now I have seen the arrangement. Was this screw anyhow in *metallic* connection with the suspended system? If so one could understand it better. I find among my notes for the attraction of two uniformly electrified discs of radii c & c', $c \ll c'$ & at a distance h

$$\frac{q}{s} \cdot \frac{q'}{s'} \times 2\pi^2 c^2 \left(1 - \frac{h}{c'} + \frac{3}{8}\frac{hc^2}{c'^3} - \frac{1}{2}\frac{h^3}{c'^3}\right) \text{ or } \frac{P^2}{8v^2} \cdot \frac{c^2}{h^2} \left(1 - \frac{h}{c'} + \frac{3}{8}\frac{hc^2}{c'^3} - \frac{1}{2}\frac{h^3}{c'^3}\right)$$

but do not know if it is right. This correction is very large but the wrong way. G is of little importance. I cannot think that the errors in s & s' can be at all considerable enough to account for the difference of 1 per cent even. / You are right that the small battery (galv.) should have had two coils as well as the other as at first proposed. With one coil & one needle one is altogether free of errors arising from changes of relative sensitiveness in the two needles & a change in the magnetism of the single needle does not appear. I do not think however that an error of this kind can be the cause of the difference – I found when the galvanometer was made that when a very strong current was passed through it the correctness of the instrument was impaired slightly as a differential instrument & therefore had that little moveable coil made at the back. A very slight motion of this coil I have found sufficient to correct after using the instrument for weeks for all sorts of work the correction of the order 1/10,000 or so. / Also the reasonable agreement of the values of the two coils on different days would seem to preclude the idea of 10 or more per cent error on this account. I will make some experiments on this tomorrow. When a galv. with one needle is rendered astatic by a needle at the top so as to be 1000 times as sensitive as we had the galvanometer a strong current will double or half its sensitiveness. But this is not like the case in question. It is essential to know how a very strong current affects the ratio of the coils & how far a change in level does so this I will find out & let you know. Jenkin tells me he wants galv. as you said on 29th. I will return it in time. / Yours truly / C. Hockin.' The letters s and s' denote the areas of the discs, P the potential

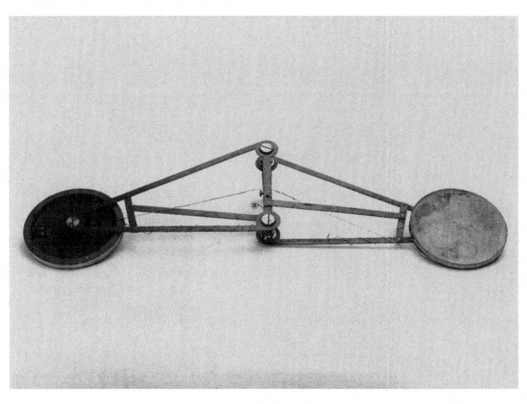

Plate XI. The torsion balance arm (1868) from Maxwell's apparatus for the determination of the ratio of the electrostatic to the electromagnetic unit of electricity (Number 289).

testing of the galvanometer, the resistance-coils and the micrometer-screw. The electrical balance itself was made by Mr. Becker.[9]

The experiments consisted in observing the equilibrium of two forces, one of which was the attraction between two disks, kept at a certain difference of potential, and the other was the repulsion between two circular coils, through which a certain current passed in opposite directions. For this purpose one of the disks, with one of the coils attached to its hinder surface, was suspended on one arm of a torsion-balance, while the other disk, with the other coil behind it, was placed at a certain distance, which was measured by a micrometer-screw.[10] The suspended disk, which was smaller than the fixed disk, was adjusted so that in its position of equilibrium its surface was in the same plane with that of a 'guard-ring', as in Sir W. Thomson's electrometers,[11] and its position was observed by means of a microscope directed on a graduated glass scale attached to the disk. In this way its position could be adjusted to the thousandth of an inch, while a motion of much smaller extent was easily detected.

An exactly similar coil was placed at the other end of the torsion-balance, so as to get rid of the effects of terrestrial magnetism.

It was found that though the suspended disk and coil weighed about half a pound, a very slight want of equality between the opposing forces could be detected, and remedied by means of the micrometer.

The difference of potential between the disks was maintained by means of Mr. Gassiot's great battery. To measure this difference of potential, it was made to produce a current through Mr. Willoughby Smith's resistance-coil, and the primary coil of the galvanometer shunted with a variable resistance.

---

difference between them. Following a notebook entry dated 'May 28th [1868]' recording data, Maxwell jotted: 'Memorandum of Improvements. / 1 object glass tube of microscope to be made longer and firmer. / 2 a guard round the suspended discs in metallic connexion with the case and the mercury cup. / 3 Hoopers compound removed. / 4 Index of micrometer put right. / 5 Selenium resistance?'. (King's College London Archives, Maxwell Note Book (3)).

(9) Carl Becker: see Number 214 note (5).

(10) See Number 243.

(11) Thomson's guard-ring electrometer measured the potential between two discs at different potentials. One disc is fixed; and a central portion of the second disc is separated from the rest to form the attracted disc, the outer ring forming the remainder of the disc being fixed and forming the guard ring. Force is measured on the central part of the discs, where it is regular. Thomson described his electrometer in his 'Report on electrometers and electrostatic measurements', *Report of the Thirty-seventh Meeting of the British Association for the Advancement of Science; held at Dundee in September 1867* (London, 1868): 489–512, esp. 497–501 and Plate 6, Fig. 11 (= *Electrostatics and Magnetism*: 281–6). The instrument is described, and Thomson's figure reproduced, in *Treatise*, 1: 266–71 (§§216–18). See also G. Green and J. T. Lloyd, *Kelvin's Instruments and the Kelvin Museum* (Glasgow, 1970): 20–1, and frontispiece, and Number 459 notes (4) and (5).

The current in the coils was maintained by a Grove's battery,[12] and was led through the secondary coil of the galvanometer.

One observer, by means of the micrometer-screw, altered the distance of the disks till the suspended disk was in equilibrium at zero. At the same time the other observer altered the shunt, till the galvanometer-needle was also in equilibrium. The micrometer reading and the resistance of the shunt were then set down as the results of the experiment.

The mean of twelve satisfactory experiments, at distances varying from .25 to .5 inch, gave for the ratio of the electromagnetic to the electrostatic unit of electricity —[13]

v = 27.79 Ohms, or B. A. units.

= 277,900,000 metres per second.

= 174,800 statute miles per second.[14]

This value is considerably lower than that found by MM. Weber and Kohlrausch by a different method, which was 310,740,000 metres per second.[15] Its correctness depends on that of the B. A. unit of resistance, which, however, cannot be very far from the truth, as it agrees so well with Dr. Joule's thermal experiments.[16]

It is also decidedly less than any estimate of the velocity of light, of which the lowest, that of M. Foucault, is 298,000,000 metres per second.[17]

In a note to this paper[18] the author gave his reasons, in as simple a form

(12) On Grove's voltaic battery (consisting of zinc and platinum plates) see W. R. Grove, 'On a small voltaic battery', *Phil. Mag.*, ser. 3, **15** (1839): 287–93.

(13) The ratio of electrical units is expressed in terms of the resistance of the British Association standard coil: see Number 235 note (3). In the 'Report of the committee on standards of electrical resistance', *Report of the Thirty-fourth Meeting of the British Association* (London, 1865): 345–67, table facing 349, the coil forming the British Association unit, denoted the 'B.A. unit or Ohmad' had a value of '10,000,000 metres/second according to experiments of Standard Committee'.

(14) In the British Association report on 'Experiments on the value of v': 438, and in the paper 'On a method of making a direct comparison of electrostatic with electromagnetic force' as published in *Phil. Trans.*, **158** (1868): 651, Maxwell corrected these values: 'Mean value of v = 28.798 Ohms, or B.A. units, or 288,000,000 metres per second, or 179,000 statute miles per second.' (*Scientific Papers*, **2**: 135).

(15) See Number 238 esp. notes (22) and (23).

(16) J. P. Joule, 'Determination of the dynamical equivalent of heat from the thermal effects of electric currents', in the 'Report of the committee on standards of electrical resistance', *Report of the Thirty-seventh Meeting of the British Association* (London, 1868): esp. 512–22. Determining the mechanical equivalent of heat by measuring the heat generated by a current flowing through a resistance, Joule provided a check on the value of the B.A. unit of resistance.

(17) See Number 238 esp. note (25).

(18) *Phil. Trans.*, **158** (1868): 652–7 (= *Scientific Papers*, **2**: 137–43).

as he could, for believing that the ratio of the electrical units, and the velocity of light, are one and the same physical quantity, pointing out the difference between his theory and those of MM. Riemann[19] and Lorenz,[20] which appear to lead to the same conclusion.

---

(19) See Maxwell's letter to Tait of 12 March 1868 (Number 284, esp. note (9)).
(20) See Number 284 note (14).

REPORT ON A PAPER BY ALFRED DES CLOISEAUX[1] ON THE OPTICAL PROPERTIES OF CRYSTALS

circa LATE MAY 1868[2]

From the original in the Library of the Royal Society, London[3]

REPORT ON A PAPER ON THE DISPERSION OF THE OPTIC AXES IN HARMOTOME AND WÖHLERITE BY M. DES CLOISEAUX[4]

On account of my ignorance of crystallography and of the recent researches on the optical properties of crystals I am not able to judge of the originality of this paper and can only form a rough estimate of its merits.

If the crystallographic axes of a mineral are all at right angles and coincide with the three principal axes of the wave surface for any kind of light they will probably coincide in direction for all kinds of light and the optic axes will be in the plane containing the extreme axes and will be equally inclined to these axes on opposite sides.[5]

If the ratio of the axes of 'elasticity' is different for different kinds of light there will be 'dispersion' of the optic axes[6] the axes, as the light is made to vary will move in their own plane through equal and opposite angles. If they meet, they will then open out in a plane at right angles to the first.

---

(1) Eminent crystallographer, author of *Manuel de Minéralogie* (Paris, 1862–93), Foreign Member of the Royal Society, 1875; see *Proc. Roy. Soc.*, **63** (1898): xxv–xxviii.

(2) According to the Royal Society's *Register of Papers Received* Des Cloiseaux's paper was referred to Maxwell on 13 May 1868, and approved for publication on 2 July 1868.

(3) Royal Society, *Referees' Reports*, **6**: 100.

(4) A. L. O. Des Cloiseaux, 'New researches upon the dispersion of the optic axes in harmotome and wöhlerite, proving these minerals to belong to the clinorhombic (oblique) system', *Phil. Trans.*, **158** (1868): 565–75. The paper was received by the Royal Society on 12 March 1868, and read on 23 April 1868; see the abstract in *Proc. Roy. Soc.*, **16** (1868): 319–21. Harmotome (baryta-harmotome or morvenite) is a barium and aluminium silicate, and wöhlerite a silicon–zirconium niobate of calcium and sodium; see Henry Watts, *A Dictionary of Chemistry*, 5 vols. (London, 1863–9), **3**: 12–13, **5**: 104.

(5) The case of orthorhombic crystals.

(6) The expression was familiar in the literature; see James MacCullagh, 'On the dispersion of the optic axes, and of the axes of elasticity, in biaxial crystals', *Phil. Mag.*, ser. 3, **21** (1842): 293–7. For a brief discussion see G. G. Stokes, 'Report on double refraction', *Report of the Thirty-second Meeting of the British Association for the Advancement of Science* (London, 1863): 253–82, esp. 271–4 (= *Papers*, **4**: 157–202). See also the bibliography in Émile Verdet, *Leçons d'Optique Physique*, 2 vols. (Paris, 1869–70), **2**: 212–16; and Verdet's discussion in *ibid.*: 180–8.

But if the crystallographic axes are not at right angles,[7] the axes of elasticity cannot coincide in direction with them but their directions as well as their ratios may depend on the kind of light.[8] As the directions of these axes remain at right angles, their motion must be one of rotation.

A rotation about the mean axis will make the bisectors of the optic axes revolve in their own plane.

This rotation is the least likely to occur on account of the difference of the extreme axes, which causes a considerable variation of optical properties to produce but a small rotation.

A rotation about an extreme axis will be shown by 'twisted dispersion' seen in the plane perpendicular to this axis, and 'horizontal dispersion'[9] that is a displacement perpendicular to the line joining the extremities of the axes as seen in the plane perpendicular to the other principal axis.

'Twisted dispersion' may be expected most frequently in plates normal to the *acute* bisector of the optic axes and 'horizontal dispersion' in plates normal to the obtuse bisector on account of a small difference of properties in directions in the plane of the first plate producing considerable rotation, the principal elasticities being nearly equal. This is the case in Harmotome but in Wöhlerite the rotation is about the obtuse bisector.

These properties show that there are not three rectangular axes of absolute symmetry in either of these bodies and the same is deduced from the action of heat on these crystals, which in one case appears to depend on the previous as well as the actual temperature.

The kind of light employed in the study of this kind of dispersion is not mentioned. A mixture of light from the extreme ends of the spectrum may be obtained by Dove's Dichrooscope[10] by the use of small blue glass of proper thickness, by the use of a flame coloured with two substances or by direct superposition of the prismatic colours. I have found a mixture of three kinds of light belonging to the red green and blue parts of the spectrum produced by a prism useful in making achromatic combinations and I should think such a mixture useful in detecting 'twisted dispersion'.

The investigation is evidently a careful one and the crystals of obscure

---

(7) As in the case, considered by Des Cloiseaux, of examples of monoclinic crystals, termed 'clinorhombic' by Des Cloiseaux, the French term being 'clinorhombique' (see Verdet, *Leçons d'Optique Physique*, **2**: 182–3).

(8) A possibility which had been noted by Stokes in his 'Report on double refraction': 274.

(9) Terms employed by Des Cloiseaux, 'New researches upon the dispersion of the optic axes in harmotome and wöhlerite': 570.

(10) H. W. Dove, 'Das Dichrooskop', *Ann. Phys.*, **110** (1860): 265–78; (trans.) 'The dichrooscope', *Phil. Mag.*, ser. 4, **20** (1860): 352–60.

characters, and I have no doubt of the propriety of publishing the paper in the Transactions if Prof^r Miller is also satisfied.[11]

J. CLERK MAXWELL

---

(11) William Hallowes Miller, Professor of Mineralogy at Cambridge, Foreign Secretary of the Royal Society, 1856–73 (Venn, *DNB*), had communicated Des Cloiseaux's paper to the Royal Society.

REPORT ON A PAPER BY ROBERT MOON[1] ON THE IMPACT OF COMPRESSIBLE BODIES

8 JULY 1868

From the original in the Library of the Royal Society, London[2]

REPORT ON Mʳ MOON'S PAPER 'ON THE IMPACT OF COMPRESSIBLE BODIES'[3]

This paper consists of three parts. The first part has already been published in the 'Proceedings'[4] and appears to contain all the essential matter of the paper. The second part consists of a translation of the first part into mathematical language, and the third part contains remarks on the equations of propagation of waves in an elastic body.

The object of the paper appears to be explained in a note at the end at least I have not been able to gather it from anything else in it. The author several years ago endeavoured to prove the existence in fluids of a force of resistance which is not taken into account in the ordinary theory of fluid motion.[5] If I recollect it right the force suggested was either of the nature of the 'rigidity' of elastic solids (a property admitted by others in the luminiferous medium) or similar to 'viscosity' in liquids. I am sorry I cannot now refer to what Mʳ Moon published and he has given no reference to it.

The investigation in this paper was undertaken 'to meet the objection of an eminent mathematician' that 'the velocities of the surfaces of contact of contiguous laminae are necessarily equal'.[6] I do not see how this objection can be overturned, or what bearing anything in the paper has on it, or how it is an objection to anything in the paper.

The case which the author has first described is that of two cylinders having the same axis one of which is initially at rest while the other has a velocity

---

(1) Queens' 1834, Fellow 1839, Inner Temple 1838 (Venn).

(2) Royal Society, *Referees' Reports*, **6**: 190.

(3) Robert Moon, 'On the impact of compressible bodies, considered with reference to the theory of pressure' (Royal Society, AP. 50.11). The paper was received by the Royal Society on 22 April 1868, and read on 28 May 1868; see *Proc. Roy. Soc.*, **16** (1868): 411–14. The paper was communicated by J. J. Sylvester.

(4) See note (3).

(5) Robert Moon, 'On the theory of internal resistance and internal friction in fluids, and on the theories of sound and of auscultation', *Proc. Roy. Soc.*, **9** (1858): 223–7.

(6) Moon, 'On the impact of compressible bodies', ff. 15–16.

which as the cylinder is compressible may be different at different points. He then takes the case in which, at the moment of contact the front end of the impinging cylinder has no velocity but the parts behind have a forward velocity increasing as we go back along the cylinder. The author has said nothing whatever about the physical properties of the cylinder and he seems carefully to avoid the use of such words as force, pressure &c substituting for them 'transference of momentum'. For anything we are informed of in the paper, the subsequent motion of the different particles of the cylinder might be unaffected by their mutual action, and the hindmost particles might go on through those in front and through the cylinder at rest without disturbing them.

In the actual case, momentum will be transferred from the hindmost particles to those in front, which is neither more nor less than saying that forces will act between certain parts of the bodies. The relation between the amount of these forces and the relative state of these parts constitutes the 'rigidity' elasticity or plasticity of the body, about which the most scrupulous silence is maintained in the paper, but which nevertheless are absolutely necessary to prevent the one body from going through the substance of the other.

It is impossible to treat the question without knowing something of these forces. If we suppose them like those of elasticity, then in the case before us we have a disturbance confined to the first cylinder which will be propagated to the second by known laws. For an excellent statement of the consequences of impact in elastic cylinders see Thomson & Taits Nat. Phil. §§ 303, 304.[7] A perusal of the statement there given will justify the authors last remark that 'the extraordinary difficulty which the subject opposes to our apprehension when approached in this direction may be entirely obviated by contemplating it from a different point of view'.[8]

If Mr Moons 'extraordinary difficulty' had arisen from the metaphysics of motion or of matter, or if he had explained his objections to the use of the words force, pressure & elasticity; or if he had shown that some received theory does not agree with experiment, I should have had some difficulty in deciding, but as it seems to me that the difficulty of solving a dynamical problem without any consideration of forces or anything equivalent is of a

---

(7) Thomson and Tait, *Natural Philosophy*: 212–13; on collision in the case of 'compressibility with perfect elasticity'.

(8) Moon, 'On the impact of compressible bodies', f. 16; for 'point of view' read 'quarter'.

kind which I should be sorry to see overcome, I think it would be well not to print the paper in the Philosophical Transactions.[9]

JAMES CLERK MAXWELL

Glenlair
Dalbeattie
1868 July 8

---

(9) A judgement echoed in a letter from Thomas Archer Hirst to Stokes of 5 October 1868 (Royal Society, *Referees' Reports*, **6**: 189): 'Apart from the fact, therefore, that I hold these views to be unsound, further publication appears to be unnecessary.'

MANUSCRIPT ON THE MEASUREMENT OF SURFACE TENSION

circa SUMMER 1868[1]

From the original in the University Library, Cambridge[2]

ON AN INSTRUMENT FOR MEASURING THE SUPERFICIAL TENSION OF LIQUIDS

by J. Clerk Maxwell, F.R.S.L. & E.

The equilibrium of a liquid at its bounding surface may be determined by assuming that the surface is in a state of tension the tension depending only on the nature of the liquid, and being equal in all directions. The agreement of this theory with phenomena in the case of liquids in capillary tubes, has been investigated by various observers. The form of the surface near a vertical solid plane has been delineated by Felici*[3] the shape of drops has been studied by Waterston†[4] & Bashforth[5] and the tension of films has been directly measured by Van der Mensbrugghe§.[6]

Without entering into any theory of the cause of this tension such as that which has been given by Laplace[7] I intend to point out a method of determining the magnitude of the force in absolute measure.[8]

---

* Nuovo Cimento[3]
† Phil Mag[4]
§ Bulletin de l'Académie Royale de Belgique ser 2 tom xxii[6]

---

(1) See Number 293.

(2) ULC Add. MSS 7655, V, e/8. Previously published in I. B. Hopley, 'Clerk Maxwell's apparatus for the measurement of surface tension', *Annals of Science*, **13** (1957): 180–7, where the microscope (Plate XII) is identified.

(3) Read: Enrico Betti, 'Teoria della capillarità', *Nuovo Cimento*, **25** (1867): 81–105, 225–37 (see *Scientific Papers*, **2**: 548n).

(4) J. J. Waterston, 'On capillarity and its relation to latent heat', *Phil. Mag.*, ser. 4, **15** (1858): 1–19.

(5) Francis Bashforth, 'On capillary attraction', *Report... of the British Association... [for] 1862* (London, 1863), part 2: 2–3.

(6) G. Van der Mensbrugghe, 'Sur la tension des lames liquides', *Bulletin de l'Académie Royale des Sciences et Belles-Lettres de Bruxelles*, ser. 2, **22** (1866): 308–28; *ibid.*, **23** (1867): 448–65; (trans.) 'On the tension of liquid films', *Phil. Mag.*, ser. 4, **33** (1867): 270–82; *ibid.*, **34** (1867): 192–202.

(7) P. S. de Laplace, *Traité de Mécanique Céleste*, 5 vols. (Paris, An VII [1799]–1825), supplements 'Sur l'action capillaire' and 'Supplément à la théorie de l'action capillaire' to Book X, Volume 4 (= *Oeuvres Complètes de Laplace*, 14 vols. (Paris, 1879–1912), **4**: 349–498).

(8) See also Maxwell's article on 'Capillary action' in *Encyclopaedia Britannica* (9th edn), **5** (Edinburgh, 1876): 56–71 (= *Scientific Papers*, **2**: 541–91).

Plate XII. Maxwell's microscope (1868) adapted for the measurement of the surface tension of liquids (Number 292).

For this purpose I take two portions of the free surface of the liquid one convex and the other concave and measure the difference of level of these surfaces and their radii of curvature.

The liquid is contained in a small vessel in the lid of which slide two vertical tubes. One of the tubes contains a simple diaphragm with a hole $\frac{1}{6}$ inch diameter. When this is dipped into the liquid and then raised above the general level the liquid adheres to the diaphragm and its upper surface within the hole becomes concave. The other tube contains a diaphragm in which is placed a short vertical tube $\frac{1}{6}$ inch diameter. When this is pressed down into the vessel the liquid rises in the short tube and forms a convex bead. To determine the position and curvature of these two surfaces the vessel is placed upon an accurately levelled plane surface above which a microscope is made to work vertically by means of a rack.

The microscope consists of an achromatic object glass of about $1\frac{1}{2}$ inch focal length and an eyeglass of about 1 inch focal length. At 7 inches from the object glass is placed a frame containing two spiders lines at right angles. Below this an opening is made in the side of the microscope in which slide the following parts – a tube at the end of which is placed a piece of parallel glass inclined 45° to the axis. Within this is another tube with a diaphragm having a slit in it along and across which are stretched fine spider lines. A mirror to reflect the light into this tube is placed outside. The tubes with the glass and the slit are so arranged that the virtual image of the cross lines in the slit formed by reflexion in one of the surfaces of the glass plate coincides accurately in position with the intersection of the cross lines in the axis of the tube. This is ensured by taking off the upper part of the instrument and examining the coincidence of the virtual image with the real cross lines by means of the microscope.

When the instrument is in use, the light enters the side tube and is reflected down the axis of the microscope by the parallel glass and after passing through the object glass falls on the surface of the liquid. It is then reflected and seen through the eye glass of the microscope. A real image of the cross lines of the slit is formed in the same place as that of the other cross lines at a definite distance below the object glass. If this point coincides either with the surface or with the centre of curvature of a spherical reflector the rays after reflexion will form an image of the cross lines of the slit coinciding in position with the real cross lines in the axis and may be examined along with them through the eye glass. When the point coincides with the surface of the fluid the image is erect and is undisturbed by slight movements of the fluid but when the point coincides with the centre of curvature the image is inverted and is rendered invisible by slight tremors of the fluid.

It is easy by means of this instrument to determine the radius of curvature of a spherical surface to .002 inch. It is necessary however that the coincidence of the virtual image of the lines in the slit with the actual lines in the axis of the microscope should be well observed. If these points instead of coinciding are distant x along the axis, the images of the points below the axis will be distant by y where $x = 13y$ in this instrument. If a and b are the scale readings when the erect and inverted image respectively are seen distinctly and if r is the radius of curvature of the reflecting surface

$$a - b = \pm \sqrt{r^2 + y^2}.$$

Since r is seldom more than $\frac{1}{3}$ inch in the experiments it is necessary to make y very small in order to be able to take $a - b$ as the true value or r.

When the instrument was first constructed I introduced the light behind the cross lines in the axis and observed their coincidence with their own reflected image. In this case when the image is erect the coincidence is perfect and the reflected image cannot be seen at all being hidden by the cross lines themselves. The method I have now adopted admits of greater optical power and is easier in working but I have yet to ascertain which method gives the most accurate results, and to determine the actual values of the superficial tension of various liquids bounded either by air or by other liquids at various temperatures.

LETTER TO PETER GUTHRIE TAIT

14 JULY 1868[1]

From the original in the University Library, Cambridge[2]

$$\left.\begin{array}{r}\text{Fixed Point}\\ \text{of Reference}\end{array}\right\} = \left\{\begin{array}{l}\text{Glenlair}\\ \text{Dalbeattie}\end{array}\right.$$

Lat 55° Long. 4 1868 .534

Dr P.G.T.

Use no more the above triliteral expression on the outside of your communications as the expression Palace Gardens Terrace will not avail in communicating with me.

Your hypothesis about the law of conductivity[3] would be a sound one if the state of steady flow of heat were not a state involving the continual dissipation of energy. It may however be *true* though unsound. Does it agree with the *general* equations of steady flow as well as with those in one dimension? that is, Is the distribution of temperature in any case of steady flow such that if it were arrested at any instant the recoverable energy would be a min:.

I have improved my machine for finding the superficial tension of liquids. I find it decreases in water with the temperature very considerably and rapidly, say about 7.7 grammes to the metre at 69° & 5.6 at 100 °F.[4]

I am trying to get the temperature correctly by immersing my machine in hot water and I have succeeded in preventing the glass from being dimmed by the steam. I shall also try soap bubbles to test the effect of the soap.

I am doing figures of equipotential surfaces & lines of force.[5] The figure for Thomson Electrical Images[6] is very pretty if well done. I am also doing a few cases of conduction &c in plane sheets (what Rankine calls plane water

---

(1) See Maxwell's date: '1868 .534', where 0.534 of the year (366 days) = day 196 = 14 July.

(2) ULC Add. MSS 7655, I, b/11.

(3) See P. G. Tait, 'On the dissipation of energy', *Proc. Roy. Soc. Edinb.*, **6** (1868): 309–11; 'If an infinite plate be kept permanently heated in layers, each of equal temperature throughout – the temperature rising gradually from one side to the other – the hypothesis is made that the temperature of any three contiguous layers (of equal thickness) so adjust themselves that the least possible energy can be restored from the system of three.' See also Numbers 284, 294 and 296.

(4) See Number 292.

(5) Compare Figs. I–V appended to the *Treatise*, **1**.

(6) See Number 301.

lines)⁽⁷⁾ and sections of the low spherical harmonics,⁽⁸⁾ and *maps* of the surface harmonic of the 6th order as given in T.T′.⁽⁹⁾

I had a letter from Joule who says he is game to do the equivalent of heat by friction of mercury.⁽¹⁰⁾ For whom do you want my vote, Jupiter I know but who is Vulcan? not he who fell on ice, is it?⁽¹¹⁾ & what the vote.⁽¹²⁾ Send me the Vortices here.⁽¹³⁾

Yours
J.C.M.

(7) W. J. M. Rankine, 'On plane water-lines in two dimensions', *Phil. Trans.*, **154** (1864): 369–91. See Number 223.

(8) Compare Figs. V–IX appended to the *Treatise*, **1**.

(9) Thomson and Tait, *Natural Philosophy*: 627–9.

(10) Maxwell's experiment described in his letter to Tait of 23 December 1867 (Number 278).

(11) William Thomson on 22 December 1860; see S. P. Thompson, *The Life of William Thomson, Baron Kelvin of Largs*, 2 vols. (London, 1910), **1**: 412.

(12) See Number 294.

(13) See Number 294 esp. note (2).

=294=

LETTER TO PETER GUTHRIE TAIT

18 JULY 1868
From the original in the University Library, Cambridge[1]

Glenlair
18 July 1868

Dr T′

I have received Thomson on Vortices[2] which I will return in a little, as I am reading it with pains. I do not see the Comptes Rendus, nor do I perceive, without the aid of Bertrand, the 'legère faute' in H^2.[3] In fact I consider it impossible to commit one at the beginning of such a theory. You must either tell a 'rousing whid'[4] or be infallible. If equations 3 & 3a have anything the matter with them, may ζ stick in H^2s throat.[5] I not only believe them myself but set them to senate house men who did them.[6] I will send T a theory of the system of ring vortices with a common axis[7] if Kissingen will find him.[8]

---

(1) ULC Add. MSS 7655, I, b/12.

(2) Thomson to Tait, 5 July 1868 (see Number 295 note (2)); note Thomson's paper 'On vortex motion', *Trans. Roy. Soc. Edinb.*, **25** (1869): 217–60 (= *Math. & Phys. Papers*, **4**: 13–66).

(3) Joseph Bertrand, 'Théorème relatif au mouvement le plus général d'un fluide', *Comptes Rendus*, **66** (1868): 1227–30 (read 22 June 1868). Bertrand had criticised the argument of Hermann Helmholtz's paper 'Über Integrale der hydrodynamischen Gleichungen, welche den Wirbelbewegungen entsprechen', *Journal für die reine und angewandte Mathematik*, **55** (1858): 25–55, which had been translated by P. G. Tait as 'On the integrals of the hydrodynamical equations, which express vortex-motion', *Phil. Mag.*, ser. 4, **33** (1867): 485–512. Bertrand claimed that '[Helmholtz] a commis, dès le début de son Mémoire, une légère inadvertance qui, en lui faisant attacher à la condition d'intégrabilité signalée plus haut une importance tout à faire exagérée, entache d'erreur tous les résultats'. Defending his treatment of the condition of rotation of a fluid element ('Sur le mouvement le plus général d'un fluide', *Comptes Rendus*, **67** (1868): 221–5) Helmholtz replied: 'Si l'expression $(udx+vdy+wdz)$ [where at a point x, y, z in a liquid $u, v\ w$ are the components of the velocity] est une différentielle exacte, il n'y a pas de rotation dans la partie du fluide correspondant. Si cette expression n'est pas une différentielle exacte, il y a rotation.' (on 222).

(4) Robert Burns, 'Death and Dr Hornbook', i (a lie) (*OED*).

(5) Helmholtz, 'On the integrals of the hydrodynamical equations, which express vortex motion': 491–2. Equations (3) and (3a) determine the variations of the angular velocities ξ, η, ζ during the motion of a fluid element. In further response to Bertrand's continued criticisms, Helmholtz pointed out (*Comptes Rendus*, **67** (1868): 754–7) that 'M. Stokes a dit, en parlant des quantités qui, dans les théorie des solides élastiques, correspondent aux quantités ξ, η, ζ de mon Mémoire: "Ces quantités expriment les rotations de l'élément du moyen..."'; see G. G. Stokes, 'On the dynamical theory of diffraction', *Trans. Camb. Phil. Soc.*, **9** (1849): 1–62, on 12 (= *Papers*, **2**: 243–327).   (6) See Numbers 254 note (1) and 275.   (7) Number 295.

(8) See S. P. Thompson, *The Life of William Thomson, Baron Kelvin of Largs*, 2 vols. (London, 1910), **1**: 526; 'Kissingen having been recommended to Lady Thomson for its waters'.

I highly approve of Vulcan as the right man for Glasgow & Aberdeen[9] but I have been in correspondence with the Registrar & find I have no right to vote. If I can do anything else for Smith, I will. If I had influence in Greenock I would help Moncrieff there.[10]

On the back of this you will see a few of the equipotential & lines of force for an electrified point acting on an uninsulated sphere.[11] These are spent lines, I have done them better.

I send you another of plane (2 dimension) lines and one of the 1st spherical harmonic,[12] and a few remarks in pencil on chap II of T & T'.

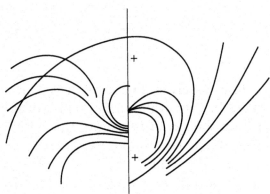

Figure 294,1

W. P. Taylor Esq[re] has sent me several diagrams of girders with their forces which I will tack to my paper on diagrams of forces for the R.S.E. W.P.T. is an independent discoverer of the method along with Rankine.[13]

I do not believe that the conductivity of a body can be found from its sp. h. & temperature by your method.[14] Your method may be expressed thus.

Given the surface temperature of a body, then its actual temperature for steady flow of heat will be so distributed that the amount of energy recoverable at any instant from *certain portions* of the body will be a minimum. Now the final temperature of a system of unequally heated bodies does not depend on their collocation neither does the recoverable energy.

But conduction essentially depends on collocation, so that in order to apply the hypothesis you must *select* certain portions of the body (3 slices &c).

For if you take the whole body with given surface temperature the recoverable energy will be least when the whole body *except the surface* is at uniform temperature.

---

(9) The Act of Parliament 31 and 32 Vict., c. 48, conferred the franchise on the General Councils of the Universities of Aberdeen and Glasgow conjointly.

(10) Archibald Smith, Glasgow University 1828, senior wrangler 1836, Hon. LL.D. Glasgow 1864 (Venn, *DNB*), as prospective Liberal candidate for the Parliamentary seat of Aberdeen and Glasgow Universities; and James Moncreiff (see Volume I: 393n), elected MP for Aberdeen and Glasgow Universities in November 1868 (*DNB*).

(11) Maxwell's fragmentary sketch is reproduced as Figure 294,1.

(12) Figures 293,4 and 3 (for which latter compare the *Treatise*, **1**: Fig. V), respectively.

(13) See Number 334.   (14) See Number 293 esp. note (3).

Your lead cylinder looks a good form of exp^t.[15] How do you find the distance of your copper–iron junctions from the axis. Do you slice the cylinder at last? or do you use optical means to find where the bottoms of your pits are. If you do the rest of the job well you will require good measures of these distances. You should also if possible distribute your pits thus so as to be distant from each other. Each pit produces a disturbance $P\frac{1}{r}\sin\theta$ in the temperature about it on neighbouring pits, so separate them well.

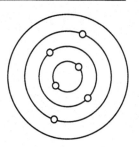

Figure 294,2

How do T & T' divide the Harmonics (Her Majestys Ships) between them. I had before getting hold of T & T' done mine for electricity but I should be delighted to get rid of the subject out of that book except in the way of reference to T & T'. My method is to treat them as the neighbourhood of singular points in potential systems, those of positive degree being p^{ts} of equilibrium and those of negative being infinite points.[16] (There is a relation between the numbers of each kind in any system.)

I then show that a complete harmonic of the ith degree has always i axes of which the directions are definite and then i poles & a constant give the $2i+1$ variable quantities of the harmonic.[17]

The complete H can also be expressed *as usual* as the sum of a set of H^s $i-s$ of whose poles are clubbed together while the other s are placed at equal distances round the equator.[18]

He may also be treated as the sum of a set of zonal H's with different poles.[19]

I have also an expression for $\Sigma Y_i Y_i'$ over the sphere where Y_i & Y_i' are of the same order but have different systems of poles.[20]

Also a prospectus of the theory as applied to closed surfaces of any form not spherical.[21]

Yours truly
J. CLERK MAXWELL

---

(15) Tait's experiments on thermo-electricity, reported in his 'First approximation to a thermo-electric diagram', *Trans. Roy. Soc. Edinb.*, **27** (1873): 125–40.

(16) See Number 281; and *Treatise*, **1**: 157–8 (§128).

(17) See *Treatise*, **1**: 160–2 (§130). (18) See *Treatise*, **1**: 163–5 (§132).

(19) See *Treatise*, **1**: 175–6 (§143) and Figs. VI–IX appended to the volume.

(20) See *Treatise*, **1**: 169–70 (§136–7). Y_i, Y_i' are surface harmonics.

(21) See *Treatise*, **1**: 178–80 (§146).

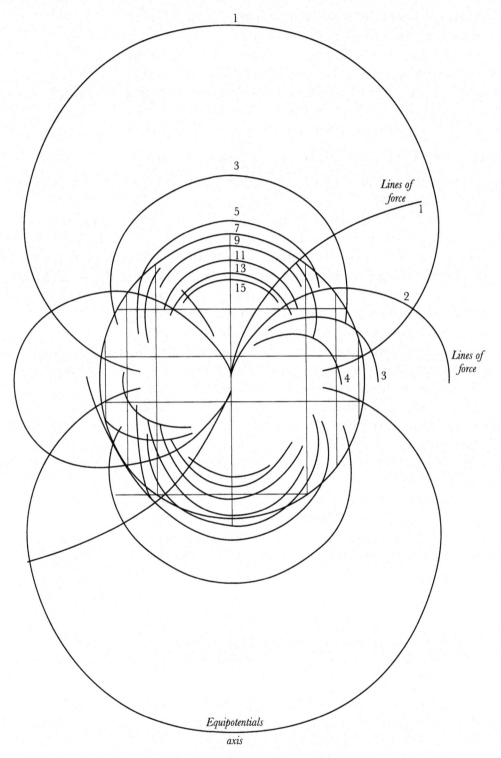

Figure 294,3. Section of 1st Harmonic Solid

APPENDIX: COMMENTS ON THOMSON AND TAIT'S *NATURAL PHILOSOPHY*, CHAPTER II
JULY 1868[22]
From the original in the University Library, Cambridge[23]

T+T′ ERRATA CHAP II[24]

§ 206 – at least in the beginning of the subject[25] – some^{tr}[26] even –
§ 207 Matter is *never* perceived by the senses.[27] According to Torricelli, quoted by Berkeley 'Matter is nothing but an enchanted vase of Circe fitted to receive Impulse and Energy, essences so subtle that nothing but the inmost nature of material bodies is able to contain them'.[28] This from memory but I mean to look up Torricelli himself when I am at a seat of learning.[29]

Be careful as to stating anything to be a direct object of sense till you know what Bain says[30] and then use your discretion.

(22) See Maxwell's reference in his letter to Tait.

(23) ULC Add. MSS 7655, V, h/12. Previously published (in part) in Knott, *Life of Tait*: 195.

(24) 'Chapter II. Dynamical laws and principles', in Thomson and Tait, *Natural Philosophy*: 161–2 (§§ 206–8).

(25) Compare *Natural Philosophy* (§ 206): 'The introduction to the *Principia* contains in a most lucid form the general foundations of Dynamics. The *Definitiones* and *Axiomata sive Leges Motûs*, there laid down require only a few amplifications and additional illustrations, suggested by subsequent developments, to suit them to the present state of science'. (26) translation.

(27) Compare *Natural Philosophy* (§ 207): 'We cannot, of course, give a definition of *Matter* which will satisfy the metaphysician, but the naturalist may be content to know matter as *that which can be perceived by the senses*'. In the second edition of their *Treatise on Natural Philosophy* (Cambridge, 1879): 219 Thomson and Tait retained this definition. On this occasion Maxwell criticised them publicly; see his review 'Thomson and Tait's Natural Philosophy', *Nature*, **20** (1879): 213–16, esp. 214 (= *Scientific Papers*, **2**: 779). See Number 287 note (10).

(28) Maxwell accurately quotes the passage, as reproduced in Berkeley's 'De Motu', in his letter to Mark Pattison of 13 April 1868 (Number 287, see esp. note (12)), here quoting from memory.

(29) In a notebook entry, probably dating from 1869 (Notebook (3), Maxwell Papers, King's College London Archives) he transcribed the passage from the *Lezioni Accademiche D'Evangelista Torricelli* (Florence, 1715): 25, from 'Della forza della percosa. Lezioni Quarta': 'Torricelli Evangelista Lezioni Accademiche Firenze 1715. En verescit Galicæus alter. L. IV p. 25. Questo è ben certo che la materia per se stessa è morta, e non serve se non per impedire, e resistere alla virtù operante. La materia altro non è, che un vaso di Circe incantato, il quale serve per ricettacolo della forza, e de' momenti dell' impeto. La forza poi, e gl'impeti sono astratti tanto sottili, son quintessenze tanto spiritose, che in altre ampolle non si posson racchindere, fuor che nell' intima corpulenza de' solidi naturali.' See Number 437: Appendix and note (48).

(30) Alexander Bain, *Mental and Moral Science. A Compendium of Psychology and Ethics* (London, 1868): 27–66 (on sensation).

§ 208 Newtons statement[31] is meant to distinguish matter from space or volume, not to explain either matter or density.

Def. The Mass of a body is that factor by which we must multiply the velocity to get the momentum of the body, and by which we must multiply the half square of the velocity to get its energy.

Hence if we take the Xchequer lb as unit of mass (which is made of platinum) and if we find a piece of copper such that when it and the Xchequer lb move with equal velocity they have the same momentum (Describe experiment) then the copper has a mass = 1 lb.

You may place the two masses in a common balance (which proves their *weights* equal) you may then cause the whole machine to move up or down. If the arm of the balance moves ∥ itself the *masses* must also be equal.

Some illustration of this sort (what you please) is good against heresy, in the doctrine of the Mass. Next show examples of things which are not matter, though they may be moved and acted on by forces. 1 The path of a body, 2 Its axis of rotation 3 the form of a steady motion 4 an undulation (sound or light) &c 5 Boscovich's centres of force.[32] Next things which are matter such as the luminiferous aether, and if there be anything capable of momentum & kinetic energy.

---

(31) Compare *Natural Philosophy* (§ 208): '*The Quantity of Matter* in a body, or, as we now call it, the *Mass* of a body, is proportional, according to Newton, to the *Volume* and the *Density* conjointly. In reality, the definition gives us the meaning of density rather than of mass'.

(32) Boscovich's theory of matter as mathematical points, or centres of force, was widely noticed by British physicists in the period, especially in Scotland (though his views were not always accurately described). A possible source for Maxwell may have been the lengthy account given by John Robison in his *A System of Mechanical Philosophy*, 4 vols. (Edinburgh, 1822), **1**: 267–368. Maxwell himself, in his article on 'Atom', in *Encyclopaedia Britannica* (9th edition), **3** (Edinburgh, 1875): 36–49, esp. 37 (= *Scientific Papers*, **2**: 448–9), later gave a good account of Boscovich's theory of matter as described in the *Theoria Philosophiæ Naturalis* (Rome, 1758; Vienna, $_2$1763); and see his comments in Numbers 287 and 437.

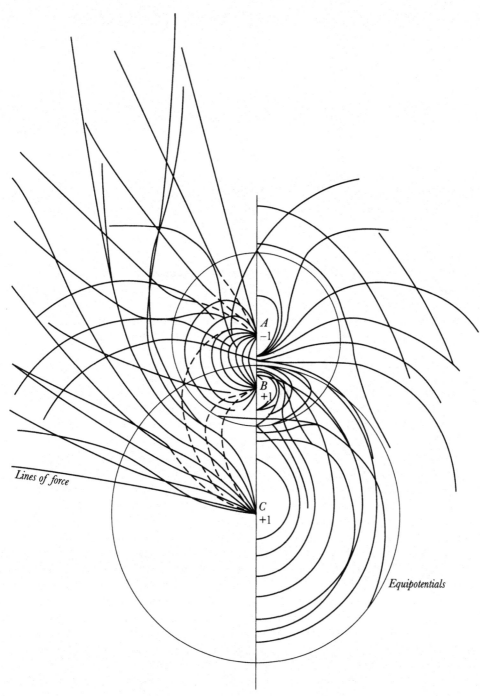

Figure 294,4. Lines in 2 dimensions. Small circle impermeable or if you please large circle perfect conductor and charged with double portion of opposite electricity to A.

295

LETTER TO WILLIAM THOMSON

18 JULY 1868

From the original in the University Library, Cambridge[1]

Glenlair
Dalbeattie
1868 July 18

(a)

Dear Thomson,
 Tait sent me a letter of yours on Vortices.[2]

(a) {Tait} See p 6 for Query from T′.

(1) ULC Add. MSS 7342, M 102.
(2) In a letter to Tait of 5 July 1868 (Glasgow University Library, Kelvin Papers T 90), which Tait had forwarded to Maxwell, Thomson had discussed Helmholtz's 1858 paper on vortex motion as well as his own current paper on the subject (see Number 294 notes (2) and (3)). The relevant portions of Thomson's long and complex letter contain the following statements: 'I proposed to begin with irrotational motion and show the reform in its theory required by the footnote of H^2 tr^n p. 488. I should have begun with division irrotational $\begin{cases} \text{non-cyclic} \\ \text{cyclic} \end{cases}$. Cyclic require a core with double or multiple continuity. Consider an infinite liquid, or one contained in a very large fixed boundary at infinitely great distance in all directions from the field of motion and having no multiple continuity. Any number of rigid, flexible, more or less imperfectly elastic solids, frictional if they rub on one another, to be in the field of mot^n.... Apply any forces to these solids.... When the forces have ceased to act what they have done is called the *impulse* of the motion that super venes. The central axis of the system, treated Poinsotically, is the line (? or axis?) of the impulse, the resultant along it is the resultant impulse: the couple round it is the impulsive couple.... *I* The resultant impulse, its line & the couple round it, remain constant for ever (i.e. as long as no new impressed forces act, and no influence is produced by the solids coming near the infinitely distant boundary)./... Going back to *I*, let the solids be asunder, and let each, being flexible, have the proper motion given to it to make the core of any desired vortex & then let all become liquid. The component impulse in any line is equal to the sum of the projections on a plane perp^1 to that line, of all infinitesimal vortex filaments of equal cyclic constants, into which the whole rotationally moving parts of the fluid may be divided. Hence *I* shows that the centre of gravity of the whole area, of projection on a plane perp^1 to the line of impulse remains fixed; & the amount of the area constant: also that the sum of the moments of positive & negative areas of proj^n on planes through the line of impulse, properly chosen to show the impulsive couple, is constant (or something to this effect). H^2's (9) expresses that the sum of the areas of proj^n on the plane $\perp$ the line of impulse is constant. I am trying for a generalisation of (9)a or (9)b which should give the law of translation of a vibrating vortex, or group of vortices, but as yet don't see through it although it looks as if it should become transparent. / If you think it worthwhile and think he would make it out, you might send the above to Maxwell, as on a recent occasion he manifested a spirit of inquiry regarding vortices. But in any case secure him for Smith as this puts me in mind he must be surely on the Aberdeen list.' Thomson was referring

I am sorry I have no vote at Aberdeen or I should support A. Smith whom I consider w^d make the best university member to be found,[3] as he would rather ascertain what is wanted and compare plans than run off on any special hobby & so lose the confidence of the House.

I have not seen Bertrands refutation of Helmholtz[4] so I will proceed as if he were still existing.

From eqn^n 9b he deduces the velocity of translation of one ring $v = \dfrac{K}{4\pi h \mathfrak{M} R^2}$.[5] Hence we must find K. This is a question in electromagnetics & done in my paper thereon[6] or as follows.[7] First find N[8] for a cylindric vortex of rotation = velocity ζ and radius b from the eq^n $\dfrac{d^2 N}{dx^2} + \dfrac{d^2 N}{dy^2} = 2\zeta$.[9]

---

to Tait's recent English translation of Helmholtz's paper on vortex motion, 'On the integrals of the hydrodynamical equations, which express vortex-motion', *Phil. Mag.*, ser. 4, **33** (1867): 485–512, esp. 488n, which reads: 'In complexly-connected spaces ϕ [the velocity potential] may have more values than one; and for multiple-valued functions which satisfy the above differential equation [Laplace's equation] Green's fundamental theorem does not hold; and hence a great number of its consequences which Gauss and Green have deduced for magnetic potential functions also fail, since the latter, from their very nature, can have but single values.' Thomson's reference to this passage and to equations (9) in Helmholtz's paper provides the context for Maxwell's response to Thomson's request.

(3) See note (2) and Number 294 notes (9) and (10).

(4) See Number 294 esp. notes (3) and (5), an issue alluded to by Thomson in his letter to Tait (see note (2)) to which Maxwell here responds. Thomson had observed that 'It is a pity that H^2 is all wrong and we all dragged so deep in the mud after him'.

(5) Helmholtz, 'On the integrals of the hydrodynamical equations, which express vortex-motion': esp. 509, his treatment of circular vortex filaments whose planes are parallel to *xy* and whose centres are symmetrical about the axis of *z*. In this equality K is the *vis viva* (kinetic energy) of the moving mass of fluid, *h* its density, *R* the mean radius of the rings, and $\mathfrak{M}$ the mass of a slice of fluid cut by a plane.

(6) J. Clerk Maxwell, 'A dynamical theory of the electromagnetic field', *Phil. Trans.*, **155** (1865): 459–512, esp. 486–91 (= *Scientific Papers*, **1**: 562–8).

(7) In his 'On the integrals of the hydrodynamical equations': 486–7 Helmholtz noted '[the] remarkable analogy between the vortex-motion of fluids and the electro-magnetic action of electric currents... the velocities of the fluid elements are represented by the forces exerted on a magnetic particle by closed electric currents which flow partly through the vortex-filaments in the interior of the fluid mass, partly on its surface, their intensity being proportional to the product of the section of the vortex-filament and the angular velocity'. Compare also Maxwell's letter to Tait of 4 December 1867 (Number 276, esp. note (8)).

(8) *L*, *M*, *N* are potential functions.

(9) Helmholtz's equation for the potential of straight vortex filaments; see his 'On the integrals of the hydrodynamical equations': 503.

Within the cylinder $\quad N = A + \tfrac{1}{2}\zeta(r^2 - b^2)$

Outside $\quad\quad\quad\quad\quad\quad N = A' + \zeta b^2 \log\dfrac{r}{b}.$

Since these coincide at the surface $A = A' =$ surface value of N.

Now $K = \dfrac{1}{2}\sum(N\zeta) = \dfrac{1}{2}l\displaystyle\int_0^b 2\pi r\,dr\left(A + \dfrac{1}{2}\zeta(r^2 - b^2)\right)\zeta \quad l =$ length

$\quad\quad = \dfrac{1}{2}l\pi\zeta b^2\left(A - \dfrac{1}{4}\zeta b^2\right).$

Now $\pi\zeta b^2$ is what H² calls $\mathfrak{M}$ and A is the surface value of N.

In the straight cylinder the N outside depends only on $\mathfrak{M}$ so that we may suppose that in a ring of nearly circular section N will, outside be nearly that due to a linear ring of equal cyclic const. (or $\mathfrak{M}$).

Now for a linear ring radius a_1, at a distance r from it measured so that the distance of this point from the axis is a_2 we have various expressions for M.

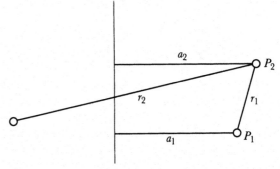

Figure 295,1

⟨Helmholtz⟩ The potential of the ring P_1 on P_2 when each carries unit electric current is

$$M = 2\pi\sqrt{aa_2}\left\{\left(c - \dfrac{2}{c}\right)F_c + \dfrac{2}{c}E_c\right\}^{(10)} \quad \text{where } c = \dfrac{2\sqrt{a_1 a_2}}{r_2}$$

or $\quad M = 4\pi\sqrt{aa_2}\,\dfrac{1}{c_1}\left(E_{c_1} - F_{c_1}\right) \quad$ where $c_1 = \dfrac{r_2 - r_1}{r_2 + r_1}$

or $\quad M = 4\pi a\log\dfrac{8a}{r}\left\{1 + \dfrac{1}{2}\dfrac{a - a_2}{a} + \dfrac{1}{16}\dfrac{3b^2(a_1 - a)^2}{a^2} - \&\mathrm{c}\right.$

$\quad\quad\quad -4\pi a\left\{2 + \dfrac{1}{2}\dfrac{a - a_2}{a} + \dfrac{1}{16}\dfrac{b^2 - 3(a - a_2)^2}{a^2} - \&\mathrm{c}\right\} \quad \left.\begin{array}{l} b = \text{distance} \\ \text{of planes.}\end{array}\right.$

The first terms of this give $M = 4\pi a\left(\log\dfrac{8a}{r} - 2\right).$

---

(10) F_c and E_c are the complete elliptic integrals of the first and second orders for the modulus c. See Number 262 note (3).

Now at the surface $r = b$ and $\mathfrak{M}M = 2\pi a N$, hence

$$A = 2\left(\log\frac{8a}{b} - 2\right)\mathfrak{M}$$

and

$$K = 2a\mathfrak{M}^2\left(\log\frac{8a}{6} - \frac{7}{4}\right).$$

Of this $2a\mathfrak{M}^2\left(\log\frac{8a}{6} - 2\right)$ is due to the irrotational motion and $2a\mathfrak{M}^2\left(\frac{1}{4}\right)$ to the rotational motion of the core itself.

If in my paper on the Electromagnetic Field you make

$$-2\pi p, \quad -2\pi q, \quad -2\pi r; \quad \alpha \; \beta \; \gamma; \quad \frac{F}{\mu} \; \frac{G}{\mu} \; \frac{H}{\mu}^{(11)}$$

$$\xi \quad \eta \quad \zeta; \quad u \; v \; w; \quad L \; M \; N^{(12)}$$

the upper line being my notation the lower line will be Helmholtz.

To generalize (9) of $H^{2\,(13)}$

Let ds & ds' be elements of two filaments the strengths of which are m & m' & direction cosines $\alpha\,\beta\,\gamma$, $\alpha'\,\beta'\,\gamma'$ then the value of L due to ds will be

$$-\frac{1}{2\pi}\frac{m\,ds\,\alpha}{r}$$

and that of u

$$\frac{m}{2\pi r^3}ds(\gamma y - \beta z).$$

Now if A' is the projection of the area of s' in the plane yz the increment of Am' per unit of time due to the motion of ds' is

$$m'(v\gamma' - w\beta')\,ds' = \frac{mm'\,ds\,ds'}{2\pi r^3}\{\alpha\gamma'z - \gamma\gamma'x - \beta\beta'x - \alpha\beta'y\}$$

$$= \frac{mm'\,ds\,ds'}{2\pi r^3}\{\alpha(\alpha'x + \beta'y + \gamma'z) - x(\alpha\alpha' + \beta\beta' + \gamma\gamma')\}.$$

---

(11) Maxwell, 'A dynamical theory of the electromagnetic field': 480–2 (= *Scientific Papers*, **1**: 554–6); p, q, r are electrical currents, α, β, γ magnetic forces, F, G, H the components of electromagnetic momentum, and μ the coefficient of magnetic induction.

(12) Helmholtz, 'On the integrals of the hydrodynamical equations': 487, 491, 496; ξ, η, ζ are the angular velocities of a fluid element, u, v, w the rectangular components of the velocity, and L, M, N potential functions.

(13) Helmholtz, 'On the integrals of the hydrodynamical equations': 508. Helmholtz's equation (9) is the integral $\iint \sigma\rho\,(d\rho/dt)\,d\rho\,d\lambda = 0$, for space filled with an infinite number of vortex rings, where σ is the angular velocity of a vortex ring, ρ its radius and λ its distance from a plane parallel to xy.

Now $(\alpha'x + \beta'y + \gamma'z)\,ds = r\,dr$ so that the integral of the first term round a closed curve is zero. If we consider the increment of mA due to ds' we shall obtain the second term with the sign of x reversed so that

$$\frac{d}{dt}mA + \frac{d}{dt}m'A' = 0 \quad \text{(This is eq}^\text{n}\text{ (8) of H}^2\text{)}^{(14)}$$

proved for filaments rings of any form, or if $A_1\ A_2\ A_3$ be the projections of the areas of rings of strength $m_1\ m_2\ m_3$ then

$$m_1 A_1 + m_2 A_2 + m_3 A_3 = \text{const.}$$

Next multiply the area ⟨swept out⟩ subtended normal to x by the element ds' by its strength m' and by its velocity u and we get

$$2\,\delta A m' u = \frac{mm'\,ds\,ds'}{2\pi r^3}(\gamma y - \beta z)(\gamma'y - \beta'z)$$

whence $$2\delta(Au + Bv + Cw)m' = mm'\,ds\,ds'\left\{\frac{\alpha\alpha' + \beta\beta' + \gamma\gamma'}{2\pi r} - \frac{(\alpha x + \beta y + \gamma z)(\alpha'x + \beta'y + \gamma'z)}{2\pi r^3}\right\}.$$

The second term disappears on integration and the first term becomes $-\int (L\alpha' + M\beta' + N\gamma')\,m'\,ds'$ or simply the energy due to the relation of m to m'.

Hence $(A'\bar{u} + B'\bar{v} + C'\bar{w})m' = \frac{1}{2}$ relative energy of m & m'

where $\bar{u}\,\bar{v}\,\bar{w}$ are the mean velocities (vel of centre of gravity) of the filament m.

This agrees with H² provided the filament moves parallel to itself but for other cases I must examine further as I have not studied it up.

Since the velocity of translation of a ring vortex is greater than that of the fluid thro its centre, the portion of fluid which travels with it is always a ring & not a simply connected body. To draw it, draw the lines of flow referred to the ring as fixed & combine with a set of lines whose distances from the axis are as $1\ \sqrt{2}\ \sqrt{3}$ &c (lines of parallel flow).

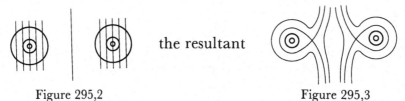

Figure 295,2   the resultant   Figure 295,3

---

(14) Helmholtz, 'On the integrals of the hydrodynamical equations': 507. Equation (8) is $m\tau\chi + m_1\tau_1 g = 0$, for two vortex filaments m and m_1 at the points χ, z and g, c; where τ, τ_1 are the velocities in the direction of the radii χ and g; and $m = \sigma d\chi\,dz$ and $m_1 = \sigma dg\,dc$ (where σ is the angular velocity of the rings).

Have I told you that Hockin & I tried exp^{ts} on electrical equilibrium$^{(15)}$ with 2600 cells of Gassiots$^{(16)}$ and get

$$v = 28.798 \text{ ohms or } 178{,}800 \text{ miles a second}^{(17)}$$

prob error $\frac{1}{6}$ per cent. on 12 exp^{ts} varying from 1000 to 2600 cells and distances from 12 to 25 fiftieths of an inch. One difficulty was in obtaining equilibrium for more than a few seconds between the effects of the great battery & those of 9 Groves$^{(18)}$ which were used for the dynamometer effect. The *observation* of the unstable equilibrium was easy enough, as is seen by the agreement of results.

Let me know when you are in the W. of Scotland again. Address Glenlair.

Correspondence between Vortices & Electric Currents$^{(19)}$	
Electric Currents	Vortices
Strength of Current $\times 2\pi$	$= -$ strength of Vortex
Magnetic intensity at a point	$=$ velocity of fluid
Coefficient of magnetic induction (μ)	$= 4\pi \times$ density $= 4\pi h$
Electromagnetic momentum at a point	$=$ resultant of $L\ M\ N$
$\dfrac{\mu}{}$	
energy of the system	$=$ energy of the system
$= \dfrac{1}{2} \sum (Fp + Gp + Hr)\, dV$	$= -\dfrac{1}{h} \sum (L\xi + M\eta + N\zeta)\, dV$
$= \dfrac{\mu}{8\pi}(\alpha^2 + \beta^2 + \gamma^2)\, dV$	$= \dfrac{1}{2} h \sum (u^2 + v^2 + w^2)\, dV.$
N^o of lines of mag force through a closed curve	$=$ quantity of fluid passing through closed curve in unit of time.
Force on a circuit resolved parallel to x due to any other system	$=$ Rate of increase of area of ring vortex projected on a plane normal to x due to the action of other vortices.

This is the equation (9) generalized, and since the forces between two circuits are such that action & reaction are equal & opposite, the sum of the areas of two vortex rings is not altered by their mutual action.

---

(15) See Number 289.
(16) See Number 289 note (5).
(17) See Number 289 note (14).
(18) See Number 289 note (12).
(19) Compare Maxwell's analogy of the flow of an incompressible fluid to lines of force in his paper 'On Faraday's lines of force', *Trans. Camb. Phil. Soc.*, **10** (1856): 27–83 (= *Scientific Papers*, **1**: 155–229). See Volume I: Numbers 83, 84, 85 and 87.

| Number of lines due to an element ds' which pass through a closed curve S | $= 6\pi \times$ | Rate at which solid space is generated by a conical surface whose base is S and vertex ds. |

Given a point P and a line S moving in any manner. Draw a conical surface with P for vertex & S for base. This surface will sweep over a certain space as S moves. If S is a closed plane curve of area A normal to x and if this plane is distant x from P then the whole space (conical) is $\frac{1}{3}Ax$ and the rate of sweeping is $\frac{1}{3}\left(A\frac{dx}{dt} - x\frac{dA}{dt}\right)$ in *this particular* case. It is less simple in other cases.

If 6 times this quantity is multiplied by the strength of the circuit in the closed curve, we get the energy due to the action of the element ds' on the closed circuit S that is

$$\left(4A\frac{dx}{dt} - \frac{x\,dA}{dt}\right)m = \text{energy of } ds' \text{ on } S.$$

Similarly
$$\left(4A'\frac{dx'}{dt} - x'\frac{dA'}{dt}\right)m' = \text{energy of } ds \text{ on } S'.$$

This is eq^n (9a) of H^2.[20] Thus in algebra.

Let the element ds move with velocity $v_1(u\,v\,w)$ which is inclined θ_1 on the right side of ds. It describes in unit time a parallelogram $v_1\,ds\sin\theta_1$. The pyramid on this base with vertex at origin is $P = \frac{1}{3}p_1 v_1 \,ds \sin\theta_1$ where p_1 is the perp. on the parallelogram & P the pyramid and if $dx\,dy\,dz$ be the components of ds

$$3P = (vz - wy)\,dx + (wx - uz)\,dy + (uy - vx)\,dz.$$

If
$$u = \frac{\gamma' y - \beta' z}{2\pi r^3} m' \quad v = \frac{\alpha' z - \gamma' x}{2\pi r^3} m' \quad w = \frac{\beta' x - \alpha' y}{2\pi r^3} m'$$

$$3P = \frac{1}{2\pi r^3}\{(\alpha' dx + \beta' dy + \gamma' dz)(x^2 + y^2 + z^2)$$
$$- (x\,dx + y\,dy + z\,dz)(\alpha' x + \beta' y + \gamma' z)\}$$
$$= \frac{1}{2\pi r}(\alpha' dx + \beta' dy + \gamma' dz) -$$

(b)

I fear I have got into a mess with the benign equation in the attempt to make it suit non-circular rings.

(b) {Tait} Wherefore I have room to say that I wish particularly to know when you will be home – as they want me in Ireland – and I may as well waste my time there as here. Price, Kitchin, & M^{c}M. are *all* dunning me about S.B, 2nd Ed. of I, and II. Everything is at a standstill – / T'.

(20) Helmholtz, 'On the integrals of the hydrodynamical equations': 508.

I want to know what you think of T' in his book on Heat §125 where he says that Verdets discovery that paramagnetics act oppositely on light from diamag^s(21) constitutes a proof that the polarity of both classes of bodies is the same.(22) This certainly requires explanation which I would be glad of, for myself & for the Heat Book.(23) He also gives your proof of the impossibility of a diamagnetic acquiring its reverse polarity gradually like a paramagnetic.(24) But Webers diamagⁿ hypothesis of induced molecular currents(25) does not lead to your absurd conclusion(26) any more than our Kings College coil could be made a perpetual motion.

T' also speaks of the 'Fact established by Faraday'(27) that a diamag. takes the same polarity as a paramag. in the same position. I cannot find that Faraday thought he had established this as a fact. He certainly showed that the lines of magnetic forces, as related to induction of currents run in the same general direction in bismuth Iron & steel (that is, not in the opposite direction)(28) but he also showed that in a steel magnet placed in the opposite direction to its natural one the lines are as in bismuth provided the dominant magnetic force is strong enough compared with the steel magnet.(29) In the Exp Res. Vol III p 528 he gives reasons against the 'magnetic fluid' theory of the reverse polarity of Bismuth(30) which I do not think apply to the

---

(21) Émile Verdet, 'Recherches sur les propriétés optiques développées dans les corps transparents par l'action du magnétisme', *Ann. Chim. Phys.*, ser. 3, **52** (1858): 129–63.

(22) Maxwell is commenting (see Number 299) on the proofs of Tait's *Sketch of Thermodynamics* (Edinburgh, 1868): 72; in the published text Tait changed the argument to read: 'It seems most probable, notwithstanding this discovery of Verdet's, that the rotations constituting the magnetic force, in a diamagnetic body, are in the same direction, but of less amount, than in the surrounding medium'. (23) See Number 278.

(24) See Tait, *Sketch of Thermodynamics*: 72–3, and W. Thomson, 'On the theory of magnetic induction in crystalline and non-crystalline substances', *Phil. Mag.*, ser. 4, **1** (1851): 179–86 (= *Electrostatics and Magnetism*: 465–80).

(25) Weber had supposed that the currents in paramagnetic molecules circulated in the opposite direction to the induced currents in diamagnetics: Wilhelm Weber, 'Ueber die Erregung und Wirkung des Diamagnetismus nach den Gesetzen inducirter Ströme', *Ann. Phys.*, **73** (1848): 241–56; Weber, 'Ueber der Zusammenhang der Lehre vom Diamagnetismus mit der Lehre von dem Magnetismus und der Elektricität', *ibid.*, **87** (1852): 145–89. See also Number 278, esp. note (8).

(26) Thomson, 'On the theory of magnetic induction': 186, and see Number 278 note (10).

(27) Deleted from the published text.

(28) Michael Faraday, 'Experimental researches in electricity. – Twenty-second series. On the crystalline polarity of bismuth (and other bodies), and on its relation to the magnetic form of force', *Phil. Trans.*, **139** (1849): 1–41 (= *Electricity*, **3**: 83–136).

(29) Michael Faraday, 'On some points of magnetic philosophy', *Phil. Mag.*, ser. 4, **9** (1855): 81–113 (= *Electricity*, **3**: 528–65, esp. 560–1 (§3357)).

(30) Faraday, 'On some points of magnetic philosophy', in *Electricity*, **3**: 534–7 (§§3309–12).

'induced current' hyp. He also gives a theory of the influence of media[31] which is first rate and Verdets discovery is the only objection which I can find against it. If you or T′ can get over Verdet I shall be much obliged to you for simplifying the theory of magnetism.[32]

I am drawing maps on stereographic projection of your tables of the 6th Harmonic (Surface of Sphere).[33] I mean to combine these so as to get some notion of the appearance of combinations of the selected terms, and the principal modifications of the general harmonic.

Any n^{th} Harmonic may be regarded as either

1° the sum of a series of not more than $2n+1$ of the zonal tesseral & sectorial forms having one axis common.

2° the sum of a number of zonal harmonics with different axes

3° A single harmonic got by differentiating $\dfrac{M}{r}$ n times in n given directions whose poles are the n poles of the harmonic.[34] It is completely defined by the const. M & the $2n$-spherical coords. of the n poles, and this be done only 1 way.

Yours
J. CLERK MAXWELL

---

(31) Faraday, 'On some points of magnetic philosophy', in *Electricity*, **3**: 537–41 (§§ 3313–17).

(32) See also Ole Knudsen, 'The Faraday effect and physical theory, 1845–1873', *Archive for History of Exact Sciences*, **15** (1976): 235–81, esp. 259–60.

(33) See Number 293 esp. note (9).

(34) M/r is the potential of a point of charge M at a distance r. See Number 277 esp. note (6).

LETTER TO PETER GUTHRIE TAIT

circa 20 JULY 1868[1]

From the original in the University Library, Cambridge[2]

Pray direct & dispatch enclosed to T.[3]

D^r T′

I do not think it necessary to explore Bertrand in the wake of H², the latter seems to me tolerably unassailable.[4] I have been transforming electromagnetic props into vortical ones, e.g. 'Two electric circuits act on one another with equal and opposite forces' becomes 'Two ring vortices of any form affect each others area so that the sum of the projection of the two areas on any plane remains constant'.[5]

/ I notice what H² says about conduction of heat & agree with him that something might be done from an investigation of irregularly distributed motion,[6] but not with you that it could be got from a maximum question, not involving the connexions of the parts.[7] But perhaps I do not understand you as you stand in print and probably you will yourself enlarge your standing ground.

Matthiessen finds general similarity between the conductivities of metals for heat & for electricity.[8] He also finds a wonderful equality in the effect of temperature on electric conductivity in all metals[9] *except* IRON & Thallium.[10]

But non metallic bodies conduct heat proportionally much better than

---

(1) See note (3); and also Numbers 293 and 295.

(2) ULC Add. MSS 7655, I, b/13.

(3) Probably Number 295.

(4) See Number 293 esp. notes (3) and (5).

(5) See Number 295.

(6) See Hermann Helmholtz, 'Über discontinuirliche Flüssigkeits-Bewegungen', *Monatsberichte der...Akademie der Wissenschaften zu Berlin* (1868): 215–28. Helmholtz noted the analogy between the discontinuous motion of fluids and the conduction of heat.

(7) P. G. Tait, 'On the dissipation of energy', *Proc. Roy. Soc. Edinb.*, **6** (1868): 309–11; see Number 293 note (3).

(8) Augustus Matthiessen, 'On the electric conducting power of the metals', *Phil. Trans.*, **148** (1858): 383–7.

(9) A. Matthiessen and M. von Bose, 'On the influence of temperature on the electric conducting power of metals', *Phil. Trans.*, **152** (1862): 1–27, esp. 24.

(10) A. Matthiessen and Carl Vogt, 'On the influence of temperature on the electric conducting-power of thallium and iron', *Phil. Trans.*, **153** (1863): 369–83. Compare *Treatise*, **1**: 416–17 (§360).

electricity and gutta percha,[11] glass &c[12] conduct electricity the better the *warmer*.

With respect to conductivity of irregular motions both Clausius & I make that of gases increase with temperature. I make it proportional to absolute T $\left(\text{you make it in solids} \propto \frac{1}{T}\right)$.[13] See dynamical theory of gases Phil Trans 1867.[14]

I will write you about your treatise[15] at earliest but

(1) I, personally, am satisfied with the book as a development of T′ and as an account of a subject where the ideas are new and as I well know almost *unknown* to the most eminent scientific men. It is a great thing to get them expressed any how and I think you have done it intelligibly as well as accurately.

But with respect to the bits of matter I sent you do you not think there are breaches of continuity between some, e.g. the statement about dynamical theories,[16] and the context, if they do not actually contradict the context at least the N.B. Review part of it.[17] If you disagree with anything of mine, out with it, for it is better to go into print having one opinion rather than with two opinions to throw the reader into perplexity.

2 I shall see what case Clausius has.[18]

3 Who is Charles[19] that I might believe in him. Is he B. Charles K & M, or is it he ycleped the Great[20] to whom Gan says of Almonte

'His sight / He kept upon the standard, and the laurels
    In fact & fairness are his earning, Charles'.[21]

I do not know where to find Charles. Give reference.

J.C.M.

---

(11) Fleeming Jenkin, 'On the insulating properties of gutta percha', *Proc. Roy. Soc.*, **10** (1860): 409–15.

(12) Heinrich Buff, 'Ueber die electrische Leitfähigkeit des erhitzten Glases', *Annalen der Chemie und Pharmacie*, **90** (1854): 257–83.

(13) See Tait, 'On the dissipation of energy': 310. (14) See Number 263.

(15) Tait's *Sketch of Thermodynamics* (Edinburgh, 1868), in proof: see Number 299.

(16) See Tait, *Sketch of Thermodynamics*: 49, on 'Dynamical theories in general'.

(17) The first two chapters of Tait's *Sketch of Thermodynamics* were based on two articles published in the *North British Review*, **40** (1864): 40–69, 337–68.

(18) See Number 278 note (2).

(19) On J. A. C. Charles see Tait, *Sketch of Thermodynamics*: iv; '[Charles] discovered that the coefficient of dilatation is nearly the same in all permanent gases.' See Number 373.

(20) Blessed Charles King and Martyr (King Charles I) and Charlemagne, respectively.

(21) Byron's translation of the first canto of the 'Morgante Maggiore di Messer Luigi Pulci', *ll.* 110–12. See Number 373.

LETTER TO JOHN TYNDALL

23 JULY 1868

From the original in the Library of Imperial College, London[1]

Glenlair
Dalbeattie
1868 July 23

Dear Tyndall

Mr C. Hockin tells me he is a candidate for your lectureship at the School of Mines. As I have worked with him for five years, I have had opportunities of forming a judgment of his scientific character. In particular, he worked at the determination of the B A unit of electrical resistance with Jenkin and me and then by himself,[2] and this spring he helped me in finding the ratio of the two electrical units (which according to me gives the velocity of light).[3]

You know the kind of difficulties which are always turning up in such investigations, the hunting for sources of discrepancies, the hitches in the working of new apparatus, the mathematical difficulties, and not least the physical difficulty of keeping up the spirit of accuracy to the end of a long and disappointing days work.[4]

I therefore need say no more to you than that I think Hockins scientific 'bottom' and patience such, that united as it is with a power of seeing the essentials of an experiment and securing *them* first, and with very extensive mathematical knowledge and an unreserved devotion to science, he is safe to do more than *any* young man I know for the promotion of natural knowledge.

Besides this he has taken care to make himself acquainted with engineering and telegraphy under Jenkin, and has studied chemistry with Matthiessen,[5] and in everything he has done he has reduced his observations and planned his experiments with a mathematical ability and a familiarity with abstract subjects, which I have seldom seen combined with actual manipulation.

If he were placed in any scientific institution like the School of Mines, I am certain that his only object would be to do honour to the institution both by

---

(1) Huxley Papers, Vol. I: letter 53, Imperial College, London.

(2) See Number 222 note (3).

(3) Number 289.

(4) Hockin's commitment is revealed in his letter to Maxwell of 15 May 1868 on his work in finding the ratio of electrical units: see Number 289 note (8). His mathematical abilities are revealed in his solution of the problem of establishing stability criteria for governors of the fifth order: see Appendix *infra* and note (9).

(5) Augustus Matthiessen was a member of the British Association electrical standards committee: see Number 245 note (8).

sound teaching, and by experimental researches, on which he seems to have set his heart.[6]

I remain
Yours truly
J. Clerk Maxwell

APPENDIX: STABILITY CRITERIA FOR GOVERNORS OF THE FIFTH ORDER

circa LATE JULY 1868[7]

From the original in the University Library, Cambridge[8]

HOCKIN ON QUINTIC EQUATION[9]

$$x^5 + px^4 + qx^3 + rx^2 + sx + t = 0.$$ [10]

That the real parts of all roots should be $-^{ve}$.
1st If all the roots are real $p\ q\ r\ s\ t$ each $+^{ve}$.

Let $\alpha, \beta, \gamma, \delta, \epsilon$ be the roots.
$\mathrm{I} = \alpha + \beta + \gamma + \delta + \epsilon = -p$ $\therefore p$ must be $+^{ve}$.
  Let $(\alpha+\beta)(\alpha+\gamma) \ldots$ 10 factors $=$ II.
II $= (pq-r)(rs-qt) - (ps-t)^2$
  $(\alpha+\beta+\gamma)(\alpha+\beta+\delta) \ldots$ 10 factors $=$ III.
III $= (pq-r)^2 pr + (pq-r)(rs-p^2 t) + p(ps+2t)(pr-s) + p^4(pt-sq) + t(rq-t)$

---

(6) In a letter to Maxwell of 27 July 1868 (ULC Add. MSS 7655, II/31), published in A. T. Fuller, 'James Clerk Maxwell's Cambridge manuscripts: extracts relating to control and stability – V', *International Journal of Control*, **43** (1986): 805–18, esp. 807–8, Hockin wrote that: 'Forde and Jenkin will be engineers to the French Atlantic cable if it is made & they offer me work.... This makes it necessary for me to make haste & find out if possible whether I have a chance of getting the appointment I wrote you about.' Hockin accepted the Atlantic cable appointment: see his letter to Maxwell of 11 March 1870 (ULC Add. MSS 7655, II/34) and Number 324 note (4).

(7) See note (9).

(8) ULC Add. MSS 7655, V, k/9, f. 12^r.

(9) Maxwell's notebook entry, a solution to the problem of establishing stability criteria for governors of the fifth order, which he had raised at a meeting of the London Mathematical Society on 23 January 1868 (Number 280), is transcribed from Hockin's letter of 27 July 1868 (see note (6)). Hockin's stability criteria are discussed and proved by Fuller, 'Maxwell's Cambridge manuscripts': 809–17.

(10) The characteristic polynomial for systems of fifth order: see Number 219 note (17).

Appendix: stability of governors, c. late July 1868

IV $= (\alpha+\beta+\gamma+\delta)(\alpha+\beta+\gamma+\epsilon)$ ∴ 5 factors
$\quad\ = -(ps-t) - p^2(pq-r)$
V $\quad \alpha\beta\gamma\delta\epsilon = t$.
    Conditions of real parts $-^{ve}$
    (II $+^{ve}$) (III $+^{ve}$) (IV $-^{ve}$) V $+^{ve}$.[11]

---

(11) In the immediately following entry in his notebook (see note (8), on f. 12^v), Maxwell drafted a problem on stability criteria for fourth-order systems: 'Shew how to find the sum of the nth powers of the roots of any equation. / Shew that the continued product of all the sums of all pairs of roots of the equation / $x^4 + px^3 + qx^2 + rx + s = 0$ / is $pqr - p^2s - r^2$ / and that if this quantity is positive and all the roots are impossible, the real parts of these roots will be of the sign of $-p$.' He subsequently set this problem (with minor changes of wording) as a question in the 1869 Mathematical Tripos: see *The Cambridge University Calendar for the Year 1869* (Cambridge, 1869): 486.

298

REPORT ON A PAPER BY GEORGE GABRIEL STOKES ON THE COMMUNICATION OF VIBRATION TO A GAS

28 JULY 1868

From the original in the Library of the Royal Society, London[1]

REPORT ON PROF. STOKES PAPER 'ON THE COMMUNICATION OF VIBRATION FROM A VIBRATING BODY TO A SURROUNDING GAS'[2]

In this paper a solution is given of the problem of wave propagation in three dimensions in an elastic fluid when the vibrations are excited either by a sphere or an indefinitely long cylinder.[3] The results are applied to the explanation of a phenomenon observed by Leslie that the sound of a bell appeared exceedingly enfeebled when the bell was struck in hydrogen gas.[4]

When a sound-wave is produced in an elastic fluid by the symmetrical expansion or contraction of a spherical surface from or to the centre, the amplitude of the excursions at any distance from the centre considerable with respect to the wave-length is nearly proportional to the reciprocal of the distance from the centre of the sphere.

If the same expansion or contraction of the spherical surface were to occur when it is surrounded by a perfectly incompressible fluid the motion would be propagated instantaneously to all parts of space but the extent of the motion would be inversely as the square of the distance from the centre.

If the expansion of the spherical surface is the same at all points it is expressed as a spherical Harmonic[5] of degree zero; if the sphere without

---

(1) Royal Society, *Referees' Reports*, **6**: 269.

(2) G. G. Stokes, 'On the communication of vibration from a vibrating body to a surrounding gas', *Phil. Trans.*, **158** (1868): 447–63 (= *Papers*, **4**: 299–324). The paper was received by the Royal Society and read on 18 June 1868; see the abstract in *Proc. Roy. Soc.*, **16** (1868): 470–1 (= *Papers*, **3**: 299–300).

(3) Compare Stokes, 'On the communication of vibration': 448–9; 'I have taken the two cases of a vibrating sphere and a long vibrating cylinder, the motion of the fluid in the latter case being supposed to be in two dimensions. The sphere is chosen as the best representative of a bell.... The cylinder is chosen as the representative of a vibrating string.'

(4) John Leslie, 'On sounds excited in hydrogen gas', *Trans. Camb. Phil. Soc.*, **1** (1821): 267–8.

(5) Following Thomson and Tait, *Natural Philosophy*: 140; see Number 277 esp. note (5). Stokes, 'On the communication of vibration': 450–1, refers to 'Laplace's Functions'.

changing its form vibrates about its mean position the motion is expressed by a harmonic of the first degree; if the diameters of the sphere expand & contract so that the sphere becomes, when vibrating, an ellipsoid the motion is expressed as a harmonic of the second degree. Any motion of the surface however complicated can be expressed by a series of such harmonics and the effect of each may be considered separately.

If the fluid is supposed incompressible, the amplitude of the vibrations is inversely proportional to the $n+2^{th}$ power of the distance supposing the vibrations of the sphere expressed by a harmonic of the nth order. The direction of this motion is radial at some points and tangential at others and regions of outward motion are separated from regions of inward motion by lines of tangential motion.

But if the fluid is elastic and if we confine our attention to those soundwaves which have advanced several wavelengths from their source we shall find them approximating to ordinary sound waves of compression & dilatation travelling with constant velocity and therefore having a common system of normals, and diverging from centres not far removed from the centre of the disturbance. The amplitude of the vibrations will in this case be inversely as the distance from the centre.

If the direction of the normal passes at a distance p from the centre of the sphere, then the radial component of the vibration at a great distance from the centre will vary as $\frac{1}{r}\frac{\sqrt{r^2-p^2}}{r}$ or as $\frac{1}{r}$ and the tangential component as $\frac{1}{r}\frac{p}{r}$ or as $\frac{1}{r^2}$. The magnitude of the vibrations at a distance from the sphere therefore depends principally on what takes place close to the sphere.[6] If the dimensions of the regions of the sphere which move in a concurrent manner are great compared with the wavelength, the case will approximate to that of the symmetrical motion and the amplitude will be as the reciprocal of the radius from the first.

If however the linear dimensions of the concurrent regions are small compared with a wave length the motion of the fluid near the sphere will be like that of an incompressible fluid, the fluid moving tangentially from the expanding to the contracting regions, so that the amplitude will diminish according to a higher inverse power of the distance till the wave has diverged so that its radius of curvature is great compared with the wave length.

Professor Stokes has applied his analysis to investigate the motion of the fluid generally so as to exhibit the whole motion when the mode of

---

(6) Stokes, 'On the communication of vibration': 452.

propagation is very different near the centre and far from it and to show that hydrogen, on account of the greater elasticity and greater length of the waves as compared with the dimensions of the sounding body will transmit disturbance to a distance in a smaller proportion than air of the same density and that when rarified air is filled up with hydrogen so as to increase its density, the amount of disturbance carried off as sound may be greatly diminished. Hence hydrogen introduced among air in the neighbourhood of a vibrating body will act as a kind of lubricator and will keep it going for a longer time. On the other hand it is said that a hot body surrounded by hydrogen cools more rapidly than in air (probably from more rapid connexion, possibly, in some much smaller degree from greater conductivity).

Professor Stokes also considers the effect of preventing the tangential motion of the fluid by radial septa,[7] and has shown how to exhibit the result by means of a tuning fork in a very simple and easily observed manner.[8]

He has also extended his calculus to the case of vibrating strings & made a practical application of the result to a phenomenon observed by himself.[9] In his investigations he has made use of various methods of treating spherical harmonics and infinite series some of which he has previously investigated in the Cambridge Transactions.[10] He has also made no account of the initial circumstances of the fluid before the vibration began.[11] He has thus avoided much trouble which in investigations about periodic disturbances is

---

(7) Stokes, 'On the communication of vibration': 452–3.

(8) Stokes, 'On the communication of vibration': 463; to exhibit 'the increase of sound produced by the stoppage of lateral motion'.

(9) Stokes, 'On the communication of vibration': 462–3; to explain 'a peculiar sound of extremely high pitch' produced when telegraph wires were 'thrown into vibration by the wind, and a number of different vibrations, having different periodic times, coexisted'.

(10) G. G. Stokes, 'On the numerical calculation of a class of definite integrals and infinite series', *Trans. Camb. Phil. Soc.*, **9** (1850): 166–87 (= *Papers*, **2**: 329–57). Stokes gave a method for calculating a definite integral discussed in a paper by G. B. Airy, 'On the intensity of light in the neighbourhood of a caustic', *Trans. Camb. Phil. Soc.*, **6** (1838): 379–402. In a letter to W. H. Miller, commenting on Stokes' result, Airy remarked that 'I am glad that Mr Stokes has made something of that unmanageable integral'. Responding to Airy's queries, raised in the letter to Miller, Stokes wrote to Airy on 12 May 1848 (see Larmor, *Correspondence*, **2**: 158–60). Stokes subsequently developed his method in a paper 'On the discontinuity of arbitrary constants which appear in divergent developments', *Trans. Camb. Phil. Soc.*, **10** (1857): 106–28 (= *Papers*, **4**: 77–109). Shortly before presenting his paper 'On the communication of vibration' to the Royal Society, he had written a 'Supplement to a paper on the discontinuity of arbitrary constants which appear in divergent developments', *Trans. Camb. Phil. Soc.*, **11** (1868): 412–25 (= *Papers*, **4**: 283–98).

(11) As Stokes had noted in 'On the communication of vibration': 449, in this respect his method differed from that employed by S. D. Poisson, 'Sur les mouvements simultanés d'un pendule et de l'air environnant', *Mémoires de l'Académie Royale des Sciences*, **11** (1832): 521–81.

invariably useless as it is in all cases of steady dissipation of energy, whether the dissipation be due to conversion of energy into heat within the system or as in this case to its propagation to an indefinite distance in its original form.

I consider this paper as an important contribution to Mathematics and to Acoustics and as worthy of being printed in the Philosophical Transactions.[12]

JAMES CLERK MAXWELL

Glenlair
28 July 1868

---

(12) In a report to 'The President and Council of the Royal Society', dated 16 July 1868 (Royal Society, *Referees' Reports*, **6**: 267), G. B. Airy strongly recommended publication: 'The fundamental equations of the theory are well known, and had been pursued to their consequences on the supposition of spherical expansion of waves, and partially on that of oscillation of spherical waves; and in a degree not quite so complete, for the corresponding cases when the movement is limited to two dimensions. Professor Stokes however has gone into the investigation with the utmost generality, so as to include not only the cases where the motions in the direction of radius vector examined at successive points through the circumference of a circle are $+ -$ (the oscillation above-mentioned), and where the motions are $+ - + -$ (the movement produced by a bell), but also the cases where the motions in any number of sectors are so divided as to produce any number of repetitions of the signs $+ - + - + -$ &c. For the successful working out of these cases, Professor Stokes is indebted to his unrivalled skill in applying abstract mathematics to physical problems; it appears here particularly in the command of Laplace's Functions, in the utilization of imaginary expressions, and in the delicate treatment of the difficulties of analysis in the cases of motion in two dimensions. The numerical results are elaborated, and the conclusion cannot be resisted, that Leslie's experiment is explained by Stokes' theoretical conclusion on the deadening effect of lateral motion of particles of gas when that gas is light and highly elastic.'

The *verso* of the first folio of Maxwell's report is endorsed: 'I recommend that Prof Stokes's paper be at once ordered for printing. W. A. Miller / I recommend that the paper by Prof Stokes be at once ordered for printing. W. H. Miller'.

299

LETTER TO PETER GUTHRIE TAIT

3 AUGUST 1868

From the original in the University Library, Cambridge[1]

Glenlair
1868 Aug 3

Dear T'

I return the letter of T and your prooves.[2] I have made a few marks on the latter which being in some measure repetition of what I did before, you may class as remarks.

But I shall remark also on what is to come. Have you given any evidence that when heat is communicated from one body to another by conduction, the one body loses as much as the other gains. This is the first axiom in measurement of a thing but especially when the thing is not a thing it requires proof.

I would put both bodies into a calorimeter and observe that the resultant effect was the same whether the one had had thermal intercourse with the other or not.

e.g. a ball at 100 °C will melt the same ultimate quantity of ice whether it be enclosed in a shell at 0 °C or not. In the first case there is conduction which is eliminated in the second.

[2] Have you a definition of temperature. *I* say 'Temperature is the thermal state of a body considered with respect to its power of exchanging heat with other bodies'.[3]

[3] In your §'What is Heat', you should eliminate the doctrine of Locke that Heat is a sensation or idea existing only in the mind and then only when it is felt.[4] The heat in your book is only found in bodies, and is detected only by thermometers. I do not think that radiant heat is heat at all as long as it is radiant.

With respect to my electrical treatise the Clarendon people have I believe accepted it.

---

(1) ULC Add. MSS 7655, I, b/14.

(2) Of Tait's *Sketch of Thermodynamics* (Edinburgh, 1868).

(3) Compare J. Clerk Maxwell, *Theory of Heat* (London, 1871): 1–4 for a development of the argument.

(4) See the text as published of the *Sketch of Thermodynamics*: 1; 'it matters not to us what... Locke and Descartes imagined, with regard to the nature of heat'; and Number 278 note (4).

I am writing out the Kinematic part (Ohms law and theory of Conduction).[5]

For electrolysis see (besides Faraday[6] Miller[7] &c) Thomson Phil Mag 1851,[8] expounded by Max & Jenk. Brit Ass. Reports 1863 §54[9] and followed up, very well for a Frenchman by Georges Salet, *Laboratory* July 7, 1867.[10] The subject looks temptingly simple but is not altogether so as yet.

My view of the energetics of magneto electric induction is to be found in the 1st part of my paper on the Field,[11] and no where else.

Rankine in a very short statement in the Phil Mag on Conservation has expressed several things very well about energy, force and effect.[12]

N.B. There are two kinds of Dissipation of E. one of which is possible in a strictly conservative universe provided it is ∞, namely the propagation of undulations to ∞ from a vibrating body.

Stokes has just sent to the R.S. a paper on a sphere, vibrating in S.H. in an elastic fluid.[13] When the elasticity of the fluid is great as in Hydrogen & the wave length therefore great as compared with the dimensions of the vibrating regions of the sphere the motion is nearly that of an incompressible fluid & little sound is sent off to ∞.

Thus a bell makes less noise in a mixture of air and H. than in the rarified air without the H., which is less dense than the mixture. The other dissipation is conversion to heat. Either kind causes a steady periodic driving power to

---

(5) Maxwell, *Treatise*, **1**: 295–306 (§§241–54).

(6) Michael Faraday, 'Experimental researches in electricity. – Fifth series. On electro-chemical decomposition', *Phil. Trans.*, **123** (1833): 675–710; Faraday, 'Seventh series. On electro-chemical decomposition', *ibid.*, **124** (1834): 77–122; and Faraday, 'Eighth series. On the electricity of the voltaic pile', *ibid.*, **124** (1834): 425–70 (= *Electricity*, **1**: 127–64, 195–258, 259–321).

(7) William Allen Miller, *Elements of Chemistry: Theoretical and Practical. Part I. Chemical Physics* (London, $_4$1867): 450–553.

(8) William Thomson, 'On the mechanical theory of electrolysis', *Phil. Mag.*, ser. 4, **2** (1851): 429–44 (= *Math. & Phys. Papers,* **1**: 472–89).

(9) J. Clerk Maxwell and Fleeming Jenkin, 'On the elementary relations between electrical measurements', *Report of the Thirty-third Meeting of the British Association for the Advancement of Science; held at Newcastle-upon-Tyne in August and September 1863* (London, 1864): 130–63, esp. 158, '§54. Electromotive force of chemical affinity' (= *Phil. Mag.*, ser. 4, **29** (1865): 436–60, 507–25).

(10) Georges Salet, 'Affinity and electricity', *Laboratory*, **1** (1867): 248–50.

(11) J. Clerk Maxwell, 'A dynamical theory of the electromagnetic field', *Phil. Trans.*, **155** (1865): 459–512, esp. 459–66 (= *Scientific Papers*, **1**: 526–36).

(12) W. J. Macquorn Rankine, 'On the phrase "potential energy" and on the definitions of physical quantities', *Phil. Mag.*, ser. 4, **33** (1867): 88–92.

(13) See Number 298.

produce a motion converging to a steady periodicity (without arbitrary functions). See a question about a vibrating disk in a tube Senate House 1867.[14]

Yours truly
J. CLERK MAXWELL

---

(14) See *The Cambridge University Calendar for the Year 1867* (Cambridge, 1867): 492; 'Form the differential equation for the propagation of sound in a uniform tube; and explain under what circumstances it may be expressed approximately in linear form. / In a uniform tube of indefinite length is placed a disc which fills it and makes n complete vibrations in a second, their amplitude being c: another disc of mass M is placed at a distance l from the first, and is supported by a spring, whose elasticity is such that the disc, if vibrating freely, would make m vibrations in a second: shew that after a sufficient time has elapsed for the excursions of the air in the tube beyond the second disc to become uniform their amplitude will be

$$c' = c \cos\beta (1 - 2\sin\beta \sin\gamma + \sin^2\beta)^{-\frac{1}{2}}$$

where $\tan\beta = \pi \dfrac{Mn}{\rho v}\left(\dfrac{m^2}{n^2} - 1\right)$ and $\gamma = \beta + 4\pi \dfrac{ln}{v}$, ρ being the density of air, and v the velocity of sound. / Find the values of l for which c' is a maximum or minimum, and shew that the maxima are greater and the minima smaller the greater the value of $\tan\beta$.'

ON THE ABSORPTION AND DISPERSION OF LIGHT[1]

circa AUGUST 1868[2]

From the original in the University Library, Cambridge[3]

[DRAFT QUESTION FOR THE MATHEMATICAL TRIPOS][4]

Shew from dynamical principles that if the elasticity [of] a medium is such that a tangential displacement η of one surface of a stratum of thickness x calls into action a force of restitution equal to $a\dfrac{\eta}{x}$ per unit of area, then the equation of propagation of waves of such tangential displacements is

$$\rho \frac{d^2\eta}{dt^2} = a\frac{d^2\eta}{dx^2}$$

and deduce the velocity of propagation.

Suppose that every particle of this medium is connected with another atom in such a manner that if the particle were kept at rest the atom would vibrate about it p times in a second. η is the displacement of the particle and $\eta + \zeta$ that of the atom a force $mp^2\zeta + mR\dfrac{d\zeta}{dt}$ acts on the particle and an equal and opposite force on the atom.

Show that if ρ and σ be the mass of the medium and of the atoms respectively in unit of volume the equations of motion are

$$\rho\frac{d^2\eta}{dt^2} - E\frac{d^2\eta}{dx^2} = \sigma p^2\zeta + \sigma R\frac{d\zeta}{dt} = -\sigma\left(\frac{d^2\eta}{dt^2} + \frac{d^2\zeta}{dt^2}\right).$$

Shew that if a disturbance of the form $\eta = e^{-lx}\cos\left(nt - \dfrac{nx}{v}\right)$ can be propagated through this medium where l is the coefficient of absorption and v is the velocity of propagation then if $1 - \dfrac{p^2}{n^2} = Q\cos\alpha$ and $\dfrac{R}{n} = Q\sin\alpha$

---

(1) Maxwell's suggestion of the mode of action of forces acting on matter in the ether may have been prompted by reading Stokes' paper 'On the communication of vibration from a vibrating body to a surrounding gas': see Number 298, and his comments in Numbers 299 and 460.

(2) See note (1) and Appendix *infra*.

(3) ULC Add. MSS 7655, V, k/9, ff. 14–15.　　　　(4) See Appendix *infra*.

and if V be the velocity in the first medium
then $QO = 1$ and $OP = \dfrac{\sigma}{\rho Q}$ and $POD = \alpha$

$$\frac{1}{v^2} = \frac{1}{2V^2}(QP+QD) \quad \text{or} \quad \frac{1}{V^2}(QP-QD)$$

and $\quad \dfrac{1}{l^2} = \dfrac{n^2}{2V^2}(QP-QD) \quad \text{or} \quad \dfrac{n^2}{V^2}(QP+QD).$

Figure 300,1

Hence there is either a velocity less than V with a small absorption or a very great velocity with a very great absorption. We must take the 1$^\text{st}$ case. Also since OP is greatest when Q is least that is when $n = p$ the absorption is then greatest and the irregularity of refraction is also greatest.

If $R = 0 \quad v^2 = V^2 \dfrac{1}{1+\dfrac{\sigma}{\rho}\dfrac{1}{1-\dfrac{p^2}{n^2}}}$. If p is small v diminishes as n increases or

refrangibility increases as wave length diminishes.[5]

APPENDIX: MATHEMATICAL TRIPOS QUESTION

circa LATE 1868

From the *Cambridge Calendar for 1869*[6]

Shew from dynamical principles that if the elasticity of a medium is such that a tangential displacement η (in the direction of y) of one surface of a stratum of thickness a calls into action a force of restitution equal to $E\dfrac{\eta}{a}$ per unit of area, then the equation of propagation of such displacements is

$$\rho\frac{d^2\eta}{dt^2} = E\frac{d^2\eta}{dx^2}.$$

Suppose that every particle of this medium is connected with an atom of other matter by an attractive force varying as the distance, and that there is also a force of resistance between the medium and the atoms varying as their

---

(5) See Maxwell's comment on the anomalous dispersion of light in his report on the paper by J. W. Strutt (Lord Rayleigh) on 'Some general theorems relating to vibrations' (Number 460). For further discussion see Number 461.

(6) *The Cambridge University Calendar for the Year 1869* (Cambridge, 1869): 502. See Number 460 note (15).

relative velocity, the atoms being independent of each other: shew that the equations of propagation of waves in this compound medium are

$$\rho \frac{d^2\eta}{dt^2} - E\frac{d^2\eta}{dx^2} = \sigma\left(p^2\zeta + R\frac{d\zeta}{dt}\right) = -\sigma\left(\frac{d^2\eta}{dt^2} + \frac{d^2\zeta}{dt^2}\right),$$

where ρ and σ are the quantity of the medium and of the atoms respectively in unit of volume, η is the displacement of the medium, and $\eta + \zeta$ that of the atoms, $\sigma p^2 \zeta$ is the attraction, and $\sigma R \dfrac{d\zeta}{dt}$ is the resistance to the relative motion per unit of volume.

If one term of the value of η be $Ce^{-\frac{x}{l}} \cos n\left(t - \dfrac{x}{v}\right)$, shew that

$$\frac{1}{v^2} - \frac{1}{l^2 n^2} = \frac{\rho + \sigma}{E} + \frac{\sigma n^2}{E} \frac{p^2 - n^2}{(p^2 - n^2)^2 + R^2 n^2},$$

$$\frac{2}{vln} = \frac{\sigma n^2}{E} \frac{Rn}{(p^2 - n^2)^2 + R^2 n^2}.$$

If σ be small, one of the values of v^2 will be less than $\dfrac{E}{\rho}$ and if R be very small v will diminish as n increases, except when n is nearly equal to p, and in the last case l will have its lowest values. Assuming these results interpret them in the language of the undulatory theory of light.

LETTER TO WILLIAM THOMSON
19 AUGUST 1868
From the original in the University Library, Glasgow[1]

Ardhallow
Dunoon
19 August 1868

Dear Thomson

I intend to be in Glasgow on Tuesday morning and will see if you are at Whites[2] and when I have got my own things done I will look you up between White and College. I shall study zero matter presently. Meantime I am doing Greens Theorem applied to conduction in bodies with 9 variable coeff^{ts} of resistance,[3] and making bodies with 6 coeff^{ts} out of linear conductors.[4] I think that the fact that you cannot produce the rotatory property by any arrangement of linear conductors ought to prove it nonexistent.[5] But it is good to be able to solve questions as if there were such a thing.

If $u\ v\ w$ be components of the current and $X\ Y\ Z$ of the electromotive force

$$u = r_1 X + p_3 Y + q_2 Z \quad X = R_1 u + Q_3 v + P_2 w$$
$$v = q_3 X + r_2 Y + p_1 Z \quad Y = P_3 u + R_2 v + Q_1 w$$
$$w = p_2 X + q_1 Y + r_3 Z \quad Z = Q_2 u + P_1 v + R_3 w$$

then $p\ q\ r$ will be conductivities
$P\ Q\ R$——— resistances.

If the ps and qs are equal there is no rotatory property and in that case the Ps & Qs are also equal.[6]

The ellipsoid of conductivity is

$$r_1 x^2 + r_2 y^2 + r_3 z^2 + (p_1+q_1) yz + (p_2+q_2) zx + (p_3+q_3) xy = \lfloor D \rfloor r^2$$

where $\lfloor D \rfloor = r_1 r_2 r_3 + 2(p_1+q_1)(p_2+q_2)(p_3+q_3)$
$$-\tfrac{1}{4}(r_1(p_1+q_1)^2 + r_2(p_2+q_2)^2 + r_3(p_3+q_3)^2).$$

The ellipsoid of resistance is got by putting big letters for little.
When there is no rotatory property these ellipsoids are polar reciprocals.
When there is rotation they are not.

---

(1) Glasgow University Library, Kelvin Papers, M 22.
(2) James White, instrument-maker in Glasgow.
(3) See Maxwell, *Treatise*, **1**: 372 (§323).   (4) See the *Treatise*, **1**: 373 (§324).
(5) See the *Treatise*, **1**: 349–50 (§303).   (6) Compare the *Treatise*, **1**: 345–6 (§§297–8).

If C is a current from the origin & V the potential

$$V = \frac{C}{4\pi r}$$

r being the quantity above.[7]

May I make use of your report on Electrometers[8] for my chapter on Instruments?[9]

Have you anything new in Electrical Imagery.[10] Betti,[11] who is otherwise good, does not seem to have got beyond the double series of images in the case of 2 spheres.[12] His method of Bicircular coordinates is very ill adapted for the purpose in 3 dimensions. It is first rate in 2.

I have a chapter on Conduction in 2 dimensions which yields neat results applicable to exp^t and capable of development ad ∞.[13]

Why do you talk of the time integral of a force.[14] Why not say Impulse and take Impulse of a Force = Momentum of a System or Body as the general eq^n of Dynamics.[15]

I have not heard Hockin lecture in other respects he is most fit.[16]

Yours truly

---

(7) Compare the *Treatise*, **1**: 348 (§301).

(8) William Thomson, 'Report on electrometers and electrostatic measurements', *Report of the Thirty-seventh Meeting of the British Association for the Advancement of Science; held at Dundee in September 1867* (London, 1868): 489–512 (= *Electrostatics and Magnetism*: 260–309).

(9) See the *Treatise*, **1**: 254–87 (§§207–29).

(10) See Number 310, and Maxwell's discussion of electric images in the *Treatise*, **1**: 191–225 (§§157–81). The theory had been developed by William Thomson and was familiar to Maxwell in 1855 (see Volume I: 321). See William Thomson, 'On the mathematical theory of electricity in equilibrium [Parts III–VI]', *Camb. & Dubl. Math. J.*, **3** (1848): 141–8, 266–74; **4** (1849): 276–84; **5** (1850): 1–9; the 'Extraits de deux lettres addressées à M. Liouville', *Journal de Mathématiques Pures et Appliquées*, **12** (1847): 256–64; and Thomson, 'On the mutual attraction or repulsion between two electrified spherical conductors', *Phil. Mag.*, ser. 4, **5** (1853): 287–97; **6** (1853): 114–15 (= *Electrostatics and Magnetism*: 52–85, 146–54, 86–97).

(11) Enrico Betti, 'Teorica delle forze che agiscono secondo la legge di Newton e sua applicazione alla elettricità statica', *Nuovo Cimento*, **18** (1863): 385–402; **19** (1863): 59–75, 77–95, 149–75, 357–77; **20** (1864): 19–39, 121–41.

(12) Betti, 'Teorica delle forze', *Nuovo Cimento*, **20** (1864): 19–39. See the *Treatise*, **1**: 215n (§172).

(13) See Part II, Chapter VI of the *Treatise*, **1**: 329–37 (§§273–84).

(14) See Thomson and Tait, *Natural Philosophy*: 207; the 'time-integral' of a force will 'measure...the whole momentum which it generates in the time in question'.

(15) See Maxwell's procedure in the *Treatise*, **2**: 184–94 (§§553–67).

(16) See Number 297.

LETTER TO WILLIAM THOMSON

5 SEPTEMBER 1868

From the original in the University Library, Glasgow[1]

Ardhallow
Dunoon
1868 Sept 5

Dear Thomson

A perfect electrical machine[2] should have a set of insulated carriers, a pair of inductors a pair of receivers and a pair of regenerators.[3]

If the coeff^{ts} of capacity of two conductors are such that

$$E_1 = (P+Q)V_1 - QV_2$$
$$E_2 = -QV_1 + (Q+R)V_2$$

then if $V_1 = V_2$, E_1 will be PV.

If the second conductor nearly surrounds the first P will be small.

If $V_1 = 0$ $E_1 = -QV_2$.

If the second conductor is not very near the first and does not surround it Q will be small.

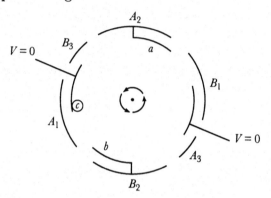

Figure 302,1

Now let A_1 be an inductor, at potential A_1 c a carrier touching an earth-spring in the middle of A_1

c will carry off a charge $= -Q_1 A_1$.

Let B_2 be a receiver, at potential B_2 opposite to A_1.

Let b be the end of a spring connected with B_2.

Let $P'_2 Q'_2 R'_2$ be the coeff^{ts} corresponding to a carrier at d the end of the spring,

---

(1) Glasgow University Library, Kelvin Papers, M 23.

(2) Thomson had described a machine he had constructed for multiplying electrical charges (in which the carriers are drops of water which charge an inductor which itself charges another stream of drops), in a paper presented to the Royal Society on 20 June 1867. See William Thomson, 'On a self-acting apparatus for multiplying and maintaining electric charges, with applications to illustrate the voltaic theory', *Proc. Roy. Soc.*, **16** (1867): 67–72 (= *Electrostatics and Magnetism*: 319–25). See also Thomson's subsequent paper 'On Mr C. F. Varley's reciprocal electrophorus', *Phil. Mag.*, ser. 4, **35** (1868): 287–9 (= *Electrostatics and Magnetism*: 337–9), where he acknowledged that Maxwell had pointed out to him Varley's priority in the principle of the regenerating instrument. See the *Treatise*, **1**: 256–60 (§§209–11).

(3) Essentially a draft of the *Treatise*, **1**: 260–2 (§§212–13).

$P_2 Q_2 R_2$ the same when the carrier is at the middle of B_2. Then if V be the potential of the carrier when just at b

$$-Q_1 A_1 = (P_2' + Q_2') V - Q_2' B_2$$

or
$$V = \frac{Q_2' B_2 - Q_1 A_1}{P_2' + Q_2'}.$$

If the spring is so arranged that $Q_1 A_1 + P_2' B_2 = 0$ then $V = B_2$ and there will be no spark at contact.

Let the carrier remain in contact with b till it comes to the middle of B_2, it will leave contact with a charge $P_2 B_2$ so that B_2 receives

$$-(Q_1 A_1 + P_2 B_2) \text{ from the carrier.}$$

Let the carrier with charge $P_2 B_2$ proceed to the middle of the regenerator A_3 and let its potential be V

then
$$P_2 B_2 = (P_3 + Q_3) V - Q_3 A_3.$$

If
$$P_2 B_2 + Q_3 A_3 = 0$$

then $V = 0$ and there will be no spark when the carrier touches the earth spring in A_3.

Let the carrier proceed to the middle of B_1 still touching the earth spring and let it leave the spring at the middle of B_1 with a charge

$$-Q_1 B_1$$

which it carries to the receiver A_2 and so on so that it can communicate to the receiver a charge
$$-(Q_1 B_1 + P_2 A_2).$$

We may suppose $A_1 A_2 A_3$ connected & at pot. V
$B_1 B_2 B_3$ ——— $-V$

then the conditions of no spark become
$$Q_1 = P_2'$$
$$P_2 = Q_3$$

and the ratio of increase of potential is

$$\frac{1}{K}(Q_1 - P_2)$$

where K is the capacity of the whole system in connexion with one electrode.

Hence Q_1 must be large, that is the inductor must closely surround the carrier and P_2 must be small, that is the receiver must closely surround the carrier.

Q_3 must be equal to P_2 and therefore small, that is the regenerator must exert a small induction on the carrier.

P'_1 must be equal to Q_1. This settles the position of the end of the springs a & b.

Now when the carrier is in the middle of A_1 its potential is 0 and if it reached the middle of B_2 without touching the spring it would be

$$-\frac{Q_1+Q_2}{P_2+Q_2}V.$$

Now since Q_1 is greater than P_2 this value is numerically greater than V. Hence there must be some place between the middle of A_1 & the middle of B_2 where the potential is $-V$ and where contact may take place without a spark.

Helmholtz' paper on Discontinuous Motion[4] has been forwarded to me. He makes an electrical application of which I shall avail myself. I had already in 2 dimensions found the good of expressing x and y in terms of ϕ & ψ the functions of potential and of flow.[5]

Betti has sent me an electromagnetic hypothesis.[6] He supposes a closed current to be like a circular magnet with a periodic variation of strength, and that the potential is propagated with a certain velocity.[7]

C Neumann has an elaborate hypothesis about emissive and receptive potentials[8] which I must study before I can understand it.[9]

Have you any easy way of calculating the case of two *unequal* spheres in contact? I get a definite integral which I suppose is connected with Euler's.[10]

---

(4) Hermann Helmholtz, 'Über discontinuirliche Flüssigkeits-Bewegungen', *Monatsberichte der ... Akademie der Wissenschaften zu Berlin* (1868): 215–28.

(5) Helmholtz, 'Über discontinuirliche Flüssigkeits-Bewegungen': 223; 'Die Curven $\psi =$ Const. sind die Strömungslinien der Flüssigkeit, und die Curven $\phi =$ Const. sind orthogonal zu ihnen. Letztere sind die Curven gleichen Potentials'. See Number 303, esp. note (15).

(6) Enrico Betti, 'Sopra elettrodinamica', *Nuovo Cimento*, **27** (1868): 402–7.

(7) For comment see the *Treatise*, **2**: 436–7 (§864).

(8) Carl Neumann, 'Resultate einer Untersuchung über die Principien der Elektrodynamik', *Nachrichten von der Königl. Gesellschaft der Wissenschaften und der Georg-August-Universität zu Göttingen* (1868): 223–35.

(9) For comment see Number 327 esp. note (12) and the *Treatise*, **2**: 435–6 (§863).

(10) See Maxwell's treatment in the *Treatise*, **1**: 219–21 (§175) of the problem of any two spheres in contact, where he remarks that the values of the integrals 'are not, so far as I know, expressible in terms of known functions'. He is referring to the Eulerian integrals: see A. M. Legendre, 'Traité des intégrales Eulériennes' in his *Traité des Fonctions Elliptiques et des Intégrales Eulériennes*, 2 vols (Paris, 1825–6), **2**: 365–530; and D. F. Gregory, *Examples of the Processes of the Differential and Integral Calculus* (Cambridge, 1841): 461–7. In the second edition of the *Treatise*, **1**: 255–7 (published posthumously in 1881) Maxwell revised §175, giving a solution using the gamma function or 'second Eulerian integral' (Gregory, *Examples*: 461; Legendre, *Traité*, **2**: 365), and making reference to Legendre's *Traité des Fonctions Elliptiques*, **2**: 438 (on the gamma function). Thomson had made use of this function in a paper 'On certain definite integrals suggested by problems in the theory of electricity', *Camb. & Dubl. Math. J.*, **2** (1847): 109–22 (= *Electrostatics and Magnetism*: 112–25).

Let $p_1 = x_{11} q_1 + x_{12} q_2 \quad + x_{1n} q_n$
$p_2 = x_{21} q_1 + x_{22} q_2 \quad + \&c$

$q_1 = y_{11} p_1 + y_{12} q_2 \quad + \&c$
$q_2 = y_{21} p_1 + y_{22} q_2 \quad + \&c$

where $p_1 \, p_2$ are the potentials and $q_1 \, q_2$ the charges of the bodies of a system then I have proved that if $2Q = p_1 q_1 + p_2 q_2 + \&c$ where Q is the electrical energy then if by the motion of the system Q change from Q_1 to Q_2 while the charges are constant the work required to move the system is $Q_2 - Q_1$.

But if the potentials are maintained constant then the work required to move it is $Q_1' - Q_2'$ and at the same time $2(Q_1' - Q_2')$ is restored to the batteries for maintaining [the] potentials. (This is true even if x_{12} is not equal to x_{21}.)

LETTER TO WILLIAM THOMSON

12 SEPTEMBER 1868

From the original in the University Library, Glasgow[1]

Ardhallow
Dunoon
1868 Sept 12

Dear Thomson

I have just made up a theory of your disk and guard ring[2] opposed to a parallel large plate.

Radius of disk $= R$

of circular aperture in guard ring $R+B$

distance of opposed surfaces $= A$.

I begin with the conjugate functions

$$x_1 = e^{\phi} \cos \psi \quad \text{and} \quad y_1 = e^{\phi} \sin \psi$$
$$\text{and} \quad x_2 = e^{-\phi} \cos \psi \quad \quad y_2 = -e^{-\phi} \sin \psi.$$

$\left(\text{Conjugate functions are such that } \dfrac{d\phi}{dx} = \dfrac{d\psi}{dy}, \dfrac{d\phi}{dy} = -\dfrac{d\psi}{dx}.\right)$[3]

Then putting

$$2x' = x_1 + x_2 = (e^{\phi} + e^{-\phi}) \cos \psi.$$
$$2y' = y_1 + y_2 = (e^{\phi} - e^{-\phi}) \sin \psi$$

x' & y' are conjugate to ϕ & ψ.

The curves of ϕ are confocal ellipses, those of ψ hyperbolas.[4]

Next let

$$x = b \log \sqrt{(x'^2 + y'^2)}$$
$$y = b \tan^{-1} \frac{y'}{x'}.$$

---

(1) Glasgow University Library, Kelvin Papers, M 24.

(2) See Number 289 note (11).

(3) See the *Treatise*, **1**: 227 (§183) for Maxwell's more explicit definition of conjugate potential functions in terms of the Cauchy–Riemann differential equations. See Bernhard Riemann, 'Allgemeine Voraussetzungen und Hülfsmittel für die Untersuchung von Functionen unbeschränkt veränderlichen Grössen', *Journal für die reine und angewandte Mathematik*, **54** (1857): 101–4; and Riemann, 'Bestimmung einer Function einer veränderlichen complexen Grösse durch Grenz- und Unstetigkeitsbedingungen', *ibid.*: 111–15.

(4) See the *Treatise*, **1**: 237–8 (§192) and Fig. X appended to the volume. The functions ϕ and ψ are the potential and stream functions. See Number 337 for further discussion.

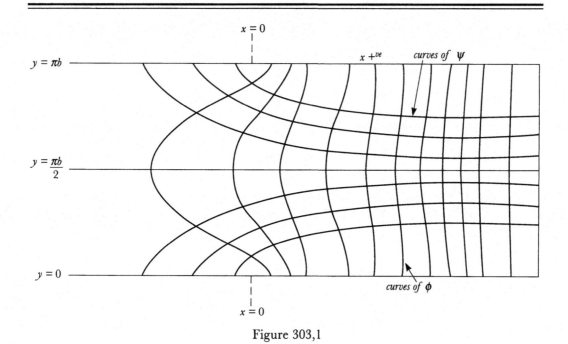

Figure 303,1

Then as you showed me in Dec 1864[5] and as I showed in my paper on Viscosity of Air in 1865[6] the curves are as shown over the page.[7]

The curves of ϕ, as ϕ increases tend to become straight lines parallel to y.

They have undulations of breadth $B = \pi b$ and depth $D = \frac{1}{2}\log\frac{e^\phi + e^{-\phi}}{e^\phi - e^{-\phi}}$ and the maximum value of x is $b\log\frac{1}{2}(e^\phi + e^{-\phi})$.

When ϕ is great this becomes $a = b\phi - b\log 2$ where $x = a$ is the equation of a plane at potential ϕ

$$b\phi = a + b\log 2.$$

Hence if a series of planes normal to y at distance $B = \pi b$ are cut off by the plane $x = 0$ and a plane $x = a$ opposed to their edges the electrical conditions are the same as those of two planes at distance $a + \frac{\log 2}{\pi} + B$.

(If instead of the set of planes there is a plate of corrugated zinc with grooves of breadth B and depth D of the shape nearly of the curves on

---

(5) See Number 240. Maxwell was calculating the friction between a rotating and fixed discs.

(6) J. Clerk Maxwell, 'On the viscosity or internal friction of air and other gases', *Phil. Trans.*, **156** (1866): 249–68, esp. 261–3 and Plate XXI, Fig. 9 (= *Scientific Papers*, **2**: 16–18, and Plate IX, Fig. 9).

(7) See the *Treatise*, **1**: 238 (§193) and Fig. XI appended to the volume.

opposite page then if A is the least distance of the opposed surfaces and

$$\alpha = \frac{B}{\pi} \log_\epsilon \frac{2}{1+e^{-\pi\frac{D}{B}}}$$

the corrected distance of the plates will be $A+\alpha$. When $D = \infty$ $\alpha = \frac{\log_\epsilon 2}{\pi} B$.)[8]

If there is only one groove, the opposed plane will be more electrified than if there were many and therefore the sides of the groove will be more electrified and there will be less diminution of effect due to the single groove. Hence if S be the flat surface and S' the surface cut away by the groove the capacity will be

$$\frac{S}{4\pi A} + \frac{S'}{4\pi(A+\alpha')}$$

where α' is less than α by a small fraction of itself.[9]

Next let us pass to the case of a system of cylinders with edges opposed to a circular disk. Let the figure revolve about one axis $y = -R$. Laplaces equation will have the form[10]

$$\frac{d^2V}{dx^2} + \frac{d^2V}{dy^2} + \frac{1}{R+y}\frac{dV}{dy} + 4\pi\rho = 0.$$

If we make $V = \phi$ we may determine ρ the volume-density required to produce this potential. Since $\frac{d\phi}{dy}$ is small except near the edges of the cylinders we may suppose this additional distribution of electricity to be an additional charge on them. If we put

$$N = \frac{2\log 2}{\pi^2} \left\{ \int_{-\infty}^{+\infty} \log(2^n + \sqrt{4^n+1})\, dn - \int_0^\infty \log(2^n + \sqrt{4^n-1})\, dn \right\} = \frac{1}{16}$$

---

(8) Compare Maxwell's discussion of Thomson's guard-ring electrometer in the *Treatise*, **1**: 245–6 (§201), for a similar argument. See also the correction (added 28 December 1868) to his paper 'On a method of making a direct comparison of electrostatic with electromagnetic force', *Phil. Trans.*, **158** (1868): 643–57, on 656n (= *Scientific Papers*, **2**: 142n).

(9) Compare the *Treatise*, **1**: 243–4 (§199).

(10) More correctly, as Maxwell states in the *Treatise*, **1**: 244 (§200), Poisson's equation. See the *Treatise*, **1**: 226–7 (§182), where he states the potential equations of Laplace and Poisson for the distribution of electricity in a space of two dimensions: 'The equation of Poisson may be written $\frac{d^2V}{dx^2} + \frac{d^2V}{dy^2} + 4\pi\rho = 0$' (where V is the potential and ρ the surface-density of the charge).

then if E is the charge on the positive outer side of one of the cylinders due to the superficial density σ that due to the volume density ρ will be

$$E \mathcal{N} \frac{B}{R}.$$

There will be a negative charge on the negative side due to the volume density.

If we now suppose these charges removed from the surrounding space and placed on the surface the change of position will be but small and the effect on the opposed plate negligible.

The capacity therefore of a disc of radius R surrounded by a guard ring with aperture radius $R+B$ and opposed by a large plate of distance A is

$$\frac{R^2}{4A} + \frac{1}{2}\frac{RB}{A+\alpha'}\left(1 + \mathcal{N}\frac{B}{R}\right). \quad (11)$$

α' is less than $\dfrac{\log_e 2}{\pi} B$ but probably little less.

$\mathcal{N}$ is a numerical quantity which I mean to calculate. The attraction is found by multiplying this by $\dfrac{V^2}{2A}$. What do you think of the lawfulness of condensing the supposed nebulous electricity on the surface of the conductor. The nebulosity is squeezed out of space by bending the field round the axis. We go to Glenlair for a week but return end of next week, 18 Sept.

I find $\mathcal{N} = \frac{1}{16}$.

I have found $\mathcal{N} = \frac{1}{16}$ (a) (12) so that the capacity of the disk is

$$\frac{R^2}{4A} + \frac{1}{2}\frac{RB + \frac{1}{16}B^2}{A + \frac{\log_e 2}{\pi}B}.$$

I also find the capacity of a thin circular disk radius R without guard ring between two infinite plates at distance B on each side of it

$$\frac{R^2}{2B} + \frac{\log_e 2}{\pi}R - \frac{1}{4}B. \quad (13)$$

(a) {Thomson} $\frac{1}{2}$

(11) Compare the *Treatise*, **1**: 244 (§200) for a revised argument.
(12) See Maxwell's correction in his next letter to Thomson (Number 306).
(13) See the *Treatise*, **1**: 245 (§200).

If the middle disk is of thickness 2β, then in the second term we must substitute for $\log_e 2$
$$\log_e\left(2\cos\frac{\pi}{2}\cdot\frac{\beta}{B+\beta}\right)$$
where $2(B+\beta)$ is the distance between the outer plates.

This I made use of for Viscosity experiments[14] but did not know how to treat the curvature of the edge.

$$\text{Helmholtz conjugate functions}\quad\begin{cases}x=\phi+e^\phi\cos\psi\\ y=\psi+e^\phi\sin\psi\end{cases}\text{[15]}$$

gives the case of *two* parallel plates not a series or of one plate opposed to another much larger.[16]

Here is a thing in conjugate functions.

If G and H are conjugate functions of x & y two other conjugate functions E & F of x & y may be found such that

$$2\left(\left|\frac{dH}{dx}\right|^2-\left|\frac{dH}{dy}\right|^2\right)=2\left(\left|\frac{dG}{dy}\right|^2-\left|\frac{dG}{dx}\right|^2\right)=\frac{d^2F}{dx^2}-\frac{d^2F}{dy^2}$$
$$=-2\frac{d^2E}{dxdy}=4\frac{dH}{dx}\frac{dH}{dy}=4\frac{dG}{dx}\frac{dG}{dy}=2\frac{d^2F}{dxdy}=\frac{d^2E}{dx^2}-\frac{d^2F}{dy^2}.$$

The question is – how to do it.

Yours truly
J. CLERK MAXWELL

---

(14) Maxwell, 'On the viscosity or internal friction of air and other gases': 263 esp. note (= *Scientific Papers*, **2**: 18), where he had remarked on the application to 'the calculation of the electrical capacity of a condenser in the form of a disk between two larger disks at equal distance from it'.

(15) Hermann Helmholtz, 'Über discontinuirliche Flüssigkeits-Bewegungen', *Monatsberichte der... Akademie der Wissenschaften zu Berlin* (1868): 215–28, esp. 224. In a notebook entry (Maxwell Notebook (3), King's College London Archives) Maxwell transcribed the equations as stated by Helmholtz: '$x=A\phi+Ae^\phi\cos\psi$ / $y=A\psi+Ae^\phi\sin\psi$'. See Number 302 esp. note (5).

(16) Helmholtz, 'Über discontinuirliche Flüssigkeits-Bewegungen': 227–8, on the distribution of electricity on two parallel infinitely long plane strips. See Maxwell's discussion in the *Treatise*, **1**: 246–7 (§202) and Fig. XII appended to the volume.

304

DRAFTS ON TOPOLOGY

circa SEPTEMBER 1868[1]

From the originals in the University Library, Cambridge[2]

[GEOMETRY OF POSITION][3]

[1] *A quantity is said to be a function of one or more variables when if the variables are given, the quantity can be determined.*

In physical questions, it is not necessary that we should be able to express the quantity as a function of a definite mathematical form applying to every value of the variables. It is sufficient if by any means, when the variables are given we can determine the quantity. Thus the function may have a certain form when the variables are within certain limits while beyond these limits the form of the function may be different. There are mathematical methods of expressing such a function by a single formula but we shall not find them necessary.

A function of the coordinates of a point is called a function of the position of the point or more simply a function of the point.

A quantity is said to be a continuous function of its variables when if the variables alter continuously from one set of values to another the quantity passes from its original to its final value through all the intermediate values.

It is not necessary that the form of the function should remain the same provided it does not pass suddenly from one value to another.

Cor. If a quantity is a continuous function of its variables its first differential coefficients with respect to these variables are finite but not necessarily continuous.

On Curves

The coordinates of a point on a curve are continuous functions of the length of the curve reckoned from a fixed point on the curve in a direction which is assumed as the positive direction along the curve.

---

(1) See Number 306.

(2) ULC Add. MSS 7655, V, d/10.

(3) The MS is endorsed 'Geometry of Position'. For this term see the *Treatise*, **1**: 16 (§18), and **2**: 41 (§421), and see Numbers 276 note (8) and 373 esp. note (10). The manuscript derives from Maxwell's reading of Riemann and Helmholtz: see note (4) and Number 305. On Maxwell's topological arguments in Numbers 304, 305 and 306, compare Number 318 and the *Treatise*, **1**: 16–17 (§18), where he refers to the work of Johann Benedict Listing.

A curve in physics may be limited by its two extremities, or it may extend to infinity in either direction or in both or it may return into itself in which case it is called a closed curve.

The different branches of a mathematical curve are not considered parts of the same physical curve because a point cannot pass along the curve from one branch to the other.

Any loop of a curve may be considered physically a closed curve.

When the position of a point on a closed curve is expressed in terms of its distance s measured along the curve from a fixed point, then if l is the whole length of the closed curve the travelling point will arrive at the same place when s becomes $s+l$ or $s+nl$ where n is any whole number.

Hence the position of the point in space is a periodic function of s and s is a function of the point of many values, these values forming an infinite arithmetical series.

On Surfaces

A Surface may either be infinite or it may be bounded by a closed curve or it may be a Closed Surface.

If a surface defined by a mathematical equation has several sheets either separate from each other or touching only at points or along lines then each sheet may be considered in physics as a separate surface.

A Closed surface is a finite surface enclosing a space so that a point cannot pass from within the surface to the space outside without passing through the surface.

A Closed surface may either be simply connected[4] like that of a sphere or complexly connected like that of a ring or of a solid body pierced with holes.

In a simply connected surface every closed curve drawn on the surface divides the surface into two parts so that a point cannot travel on the surface from the one part to the other without crossing the closed curve.

In a doubly connected surface[5] as that of a ring one closed curve may be drawn on the surface without disconnecting the surface.

---

(4) The term is taken from Riemann's expression 'einfach zusammenhangende Fläche' in his paper 'Lehrsätze aus der analysis situs für die Theorie der Integrale von zweigliedrigen vollständigen Differentialen', *Journal für die reine und angewandte Mathematik*, **54** (1857): 105–10. Riemann's expression was adopted by Helmholtz in his paper 'Über Integrale der hydrodynamischen Gleichungen, welche den Wirbelbewegungen entsprechen', *ibid.*, **55** (1858): 25–55, esp. 27. In Tait's translation of Helmholtz's paper, 'On the integrals of the hydrodynamical equations, which express vortex-motion', *Phil. Mag.*, ser. 4, **33** (1867): 485–512, esp. 486, 'simply-connected' surfaces is used as a rendition of Riemann's expression.

(5) Compare Riemann, 'Lehrsätze aus der analysis situs': 110; 'zweifach zusammenhangende Fläche'.

In the case of the ring, a closed curve drawn either longitudinally along the ring or transversely round its section does not separate one part of the surface from the other.

In a surface of n connexions $n-1$ closed curves may be drawn so that [it] may be possible to pass from any one point to any other without crossing any of these curves.[6]

Any Finite Space is bounded by one or more closed Surfaces. A Connected space is such that a point may branch from any one position within it to any other without crossing its boundary.

[2] TO DETERMINE THE COLLIGATION OF SYSTEMS OF CLOSED CURVES IN SPACE[7]

Let any system of closed curves in space be given and let them be supposed capable of having their forms changed in any continuous manner, provided that no two curves or branches of a curve ever pass through the same point of space, we propose to investigate the necessary relations between the positions of the curves and the degree of complication of the different curves of the system.

Let the system of curves as it exists at any instant be projected on a plane. Then if the different closed curves of the projected system do not intersect each other they are independent closed curves and if the projection of any one of them does not intersect itself it is a simple closed curve.

If the curves as projected on the plane appear to intersect each other we have to determine whether this indicates a real colligation of the curves or merely an overlapping or a reducible complication.

Let A, B, C &c be the different closed curves and $a\,b\,c$ &c their projections on the plane. Let a travelling point P start from a given point of a and travel completely round the curve. Let the points where the projection of A intersects the projections of itself or of other curves be called $a_1\,a_2\ldots a_n$, in the order in which the point P arrives at these points. When a intersects itself, P will arrive twice at the same point which will therefore be counted twice and have two different symbols. When a intersects another closed curve the number of intersections must be even. Hence n is always an even number for each closed curve.

---

(6) Compare Riemann, 'Lehrsätze aus der analysis situs'; and see Helmholtz, 'On the integrals of the hydrodynamical equations': 486n; 'An n-ly connected space is thus one which can be cut through by $n-1$, but no more, surfaces, without being separated into detached portions'. (7) See Number 317.

Similarly let the intersections of the curve b the projection of B with the projections of the other curves be denoted by b_1, b_2, &c and so on for the other curves.

Now let us consider any one of the intersections, say a_p and let the other symbol of this point as it is a point on the intersected curve be b_q. Then if we draw a normal to the plane from this point it will pass through a point A_p on A and a point B_q on B.

If A_p is on the positive side of B_q we shall write the symbol of the normal $\dfrac{A_p}{B_q}$ but if A_p is on the negative side of B_q we shall write it $\dfrac{B_q}{A_p}$.

If the intersection a_p is of a with itself and if its other symbol is $a_{p'}$ we should similarly have a symbol $\dfrac{A_p}{A_{p'}}$ or $\dfrac{A_{p'}}{A_p}$ according to the relative positions of A_p and $A_{p'}$.

In this way we shall find for every point of intersection of the projected curves a symbol composed of the two symbols of the point, one above the other, the upper one denoting the curve which is on the positive side of the other.

If at any point of the projection three or more curves intersect the point will count for every combination of these curves two and two, for by altering the position of the curves the multiple point will be resolved into simple intersections of every pair of curves.

We have now to determine whether the number of these intersections can be diminished by continuous motion of the curves A, B, C without one curve cutting through itself or another.

If the number of apparent intersections of the curve a can be diminished it must be by two of the intersections coalescing and disappearing. For in the continuous motion of the curves the points a_1 a_2 &c move continuously and can only disappear in one way, namely by two intersecting curves changing their position so as no longer to intersect.

Let α β γ represent the number of points on each of the closed curves and l the total number of lines, then $l = \alpha + \beta + \gamma + $ &c.

Let s be the total number of intersections $s = \frac{1}{2}(\alpha + \beta + \gamma + $&c$) = \frac{1}{2}l$.

Let f be the number of unit enclosed areas bounded by these lines $f = s + 1$.

Let n be the number of sides of any polygon. Then since every line is a side either of two finite polygons or of a finite polygon and of the part of the plane external to them all
$$2l = n_1 + n_2 + \text{&c} + n_{f+1}$$
or
$$4s = \text{sum of } s+2 \text{ integers.}$$

Hence some of the polygons must have less than four sides.

(1) Let us first consider polygons of one side, that is a curve forming a loop and intersecting itself. The symbol of the intersection is $\frac{A_p}{A_{p\pm 1}}$.

In this case the intersection may be made to disappear by uncoiling the curve without interfering with its continuity.

Hence all intersections of the form $\frac{A_p}{A_{p\pm 1}}$ may be eliminated and the symbols A_p and $A_{p\pm 1}$ may be omitted from the cycle of the curve A.

(2) Polygons of two sides are formed by the intersection of two curves or two loops of the same curve.

If the symbols of the intersections are of the form $\frac{A_p}{B_q}$ and $\frac{A_{p\pm 1}}{B_{q\pm 1}}$ as in the upper figure then the two loops may be separated and the symbols belonging to them may be cancelled but if the symbols of intersection are of the form $\frac{A_p}{B_q}$ and $\frac{B_{q\pm 1}}{A_{p\pm 1}}$ the curves are linked together and cannot be separated without moving other parts of the system. The curve B may evidently be a different part of the curve A.

Figure 304,1

(3) Polygons of three sides must be of the forms

$$\left(\frac{A_p}{B_q}, \frac{A_{p\pm 1}}{C_r}, \frac{B_{q\pm 1}}{C_{r\pm 1}}\right) \quad \text{or} \quad \left(\frac{A_{p\pm 1}}{B_q}, \frac{B_{q\pm 1}}{C_r}, \frac{C_{r\pm 1}}{A_p}\right)$$

that is either one of the curves is above or below both the others and the curves may be arranged in order of position or each curve is above one of its companions and below the other.

In the first case any one curve can be moved past the intersection of the other two without disturbing them. In the second case this cannot be done and the intersection of two curves is a bar to the motion of the third in that direction.

When in passing round the triangle in the direction of the hands of a watch each curve is nearer than the preceding and farther away than the following curve the triangle is said to be right handed. When the reverse is the case it is said to be left handed.

(4) If in a polygon of any number of sides the curve forming one of the sides lies either above both the adjacent curves or below them both the curve forming that side may be moved away and the number of sides reduced.

Hence every polygon must be such that going round it in the direction of the hands of a watch every side is either above the preceding and below the following side, in which case it is right handed or the reverse.

If a polygon is partly right handed and partly left handed it may be reduced. Every right handed polygon is bounded by left handed polygons.

DRAFTS ON CONTINUITY AND TOPOLOGY

circa SEPTEMBER 1868[1]

From the originals in the University Library, Cambridge[2]

[1]   ON PHYSICAL CONTINUITY AND DISCONTINUITY[3]

The idea of physical continuity is best conceived under the example of the continuous existence of matter in time and space.

A material particle, during the whole time of its existence must have a determinate position. Hence its path is a continuous line and its coordinates are continuous functions of the time.

We are thus led to the definition of the physical continuity of a function. A function is physically continuous within certain limits provided its differential coefficients with respect to its variables remain finite within those limits.

The idea of mathematical continuity refers rather to the form of the function than to its particular values, whereas a function may be physically continuous though its form may be different for different values of the variables.

The 'continuity' which is defined by the 'Equation of Continuity' is the continuous existence of the moving particles of a medium, not the continuity of the form of the functions expressing their velocity &c.

Most important applications of the idea of physical continuity to geometry have been made by Riemann (Crelle[4] [5]). The ideas of Riemann have been employed by Helmholtz[6] Betti[7] Thomson[8] &c in physical researches

---

(1) See Number 306.
(2) ULC Add. MSS 7655, V, d/12.   (3) An early draft of the *Treatise*, **1**: 6–7 (§7).
(4) Bernhard Riemann, 'Lehrsätze aus der analysis situs für die Theorie der Integrale von zweigliedrigen vollständigen Differentialen', *Journal für die reine und angewandte Mathematik*, **54** (1857): 105–10.   (5) Space in the MS.
(6) Hermann Helmholtz, 'Über Integrale der hydrodynamischen Gleichungen, welche den Wirbelbewegungen entsprechen', *Journal für die reine und angewandte Mathematik*, **55** (1858): 25–55.
(7) Enrico Betti, 'Teorica delle forze che agiscono secondo la legge di Newton e sua applicazione alla elettricità statica', *Nuovo Cimento*, **18** (1863): 385–402; *ibid.*, **19** (1863): 59–75, 77–95, 149–75, 357–77; *ibid.*, **20** (1864): 19–39, 121–41. See especially Betti's discussion of Green's theorem in terms of the distribution of potential in simply-connected space (*Nuovo Cimento*, **19** (1863): 59–75). Compare also Maxwell in the *Treatise*, **1**: 108–111 (§100).
(8) William Thomson, 'On vortex motion', *Trans. Roy. Soc. Edinb.*, **25** (1869): 217–60, esp. 243 (= *Math. & Phys. Papers*, **4**: 13–66), where he adapts 'the terminology of Riemann, as known to me through Helmholtz'. Thomson's paper was read to the Royal Society of Edinburgh on 29 April 1867.

and I have found it necessary for my own purposes to employ a system of nomenclature of spaces, surfaces and lines which I shall now explain.

A line, a surface, or a space is said to be continuous when a material point can travel from any one point to any other without leaving the line surface or space.

If two lines, surfaces or spaces are continuous with each other they are physically one, if they are not, they are physically distinct. Thus the two branches of an hyperbola are physically distinct, but the three sides of a triangle are physically one line.

Limits of Spaces

Spaces are limited by surfaces, surfaces by lines and lines by points. A surface which limits a space must be either closed or infinite. In either case it is called a complete surface.

If we confine ourselves to finite spaces, they are separated from infinite space by a single closed surface which we may call the *external* surface. If the space has any other limits these must be defined by closed surfaces all of which are within the external surface and are external to each other.

If the space is infinite the only condition of its limits is that they are complete surfaces excluding each other.

Continuity of Spaces

Let any closed curve be drawn on the limiting surface and let a surface be drawn within the space bounded by the closed curve then in the case of a space of simple continuity this surface will divide the space into two distinct regions so that a point cannot travel from one to the other without crossing the surface.

Any solid body without any holes through it is an example of simple continuity. Now let a hole be bored through the solid converting it into a ring, and let a surface be drawn meeting the limiting surface along one side of the hole and round one side of the solid. A point can still travel from one side of this surface to the other by going round the other [2][9] side of the hole. If n holes had been bored through the solid, n such surfaces may be drawn without separating one part of the space from the rest. Such a space would be

---

(9) There are two folios in ULC Add. MSS 7655, V, d/12 – the first draft printed here as §2, and the revise printed as an appendix to Number 308 – which present alternative versions of the argument.

called if we follow the method of Riemann, an $(n+1)$ly connected space.[10] I prefer however for reasons which will appear as we proceed to call it an *n*-cyclic space.

If a finite space bounded by a single continuous surface is *n*-cyclic the bounding surface is also *n*-cyclic and the infinite space outside the surface is also *n*-cyclic as far as that bounding surface is concerned. If we consider the finite space as solid with *n* holes in it, then the infinite space has *n* channels by which it embraces the finite space and the finite space has also *n* channels by which it embraces the infinite space.

If the expression $Xdx + Ydy + Zdz = dV$ be a complete differential at every point within the finite space then in a simply connected space which we may call acyclic V can only have one value for each point of space but in an *n*-cyclic space V may have values infinite in number of the form

$$A = V_0 + p_1 P_1 + \ldots + p_n P_n$$

where V_0 is one of the values and $p_1 \ldots p_n$ are integral numbers positive negative or zero and $P_1 \ldots P_n$ are the values of

$$\int \left(X \frac{dx}{ds} + Y \frac{dy}{ds} + Z \frac{dz}{ds} \right) ds$$

taken round a closed curve drawn round each of the *n* channels belonging to the finite space.[11] The quantities $P_1 \ldots P_n$ may be called the cyclic constants. They are important in the theory of Vortices and in Electromagnetism.[12]

If a space be bounded by several surfaces the number of cycles belonging to the space will be the sum of the number of cycles belonging to the different bounding surfaces.

[3]   ON SURFACES

A surface may be either a complete surface, or it may be bounded by lines. A finite surface, if complete must be a closed surface and if bounded its boundaries must be closed curves.

The surface of an *n*-cyclic space is an *n*-cyclic surface. On such a surface $2n$ closed curves may be drawn without separating any one part of the surface from any other. For *n* closed curves may be drawn on the inside of the surface each round one of the channels of the finite internal space without destroying

---

(10) Compare Riemann's expression '$(n+1)$fach zusammenhangende Fläche' in his 'Lehrsätze aus der analysis situs'.

(11) See Number 318.

(12) Compare Maxwell's discussion of 'Stokes' theorem' in his letters to Stokes and Tait of 11 January and 4 April 1871 (Numbers 351 and 366).

the continuity of the inner side of the surface and n closed curves may be drawn on the outside of the surface round the n channels of the infinite external space without destroying the continuity of the outside of the surface, and a point which moves in the surface itself can still pass from any one point to any other without crossing any of these $2n$ lines.

Now consider a closed n-cyclic surface and let a closed curve be drawn upon it. If the curve surrounds one of the channels say of the internal space the surface becomes $(n-1)$ cyclic. It also ceases to be a complete surface and becomes a surface with two boundaries, the two sides of the curve drawn on it.

But if the curve does not surround a channel it cuts off a portion of the surface from the rest so that we have now two surfaces, each with a single boundary of which the one may be n'-cyclic and the other $(n-n')$ cyclic n' having any value from 0 to n.

If m closed curves are drawn on an n-cyclic surface none of which surrounds a channel or cuts off a channel from the rest of the surface, the surface remains n-cyclic with m boundaries. On such a surface $2n$ closed curves may be drawn together with $m-1$ lines from one boundary to another without destroying the continuity of the surface.

LETTER TO WILLIAM THOMSON

28 SEPTEMBER 1868

From the original in the University Library, Glasgow[1]

Ardhallow
Dunoon
1868 Sept 28

Dear Thomson

Can you get me one ticket or two to see the laying of the foundation of the new College?[2]

In my last letter I made a mistake in the correction for curvature of the interval between the disk & guard-ring.[3] The capacity of the disk ought to be

$$\frac{R^2}{4A} + \frac{(R+\tfrac{1}{2}B)B}{4(A+\alpha)}$$

where R = radius of disk B = breadth of interval A = distance of opposed surfaces α a quantity less than $B\dfrac{\log_e 2}{\pi}$.

I have been making a statement about the continuity discontinuity periodicity and multiplicity of functions generally and of lines surfaces & solids. Here is the upshot in connected form.[4]

Take a solid without any hollows in it or holes through it. It is a simply connected space bounded by one simply connected closed surface. Now bore n holes right through the solid. It is now a space of n connections bounded by an n-ly connected closed surface.

The infinite space outside is also n-ly connected. Now let there be m hollow spaces within the solid and let these be bounded by closed surfaces whose connexions are $n_1\ n_2\ n_3 \ldots n_m$. Then the solid will be an $(m+1)$-ly *bounded* space and its connexions will be $n + n_1 + \&c + n_m$.[5]

---

(1) Glasgow University Library, Kelvin Papers, M 25.
(2) The new building of the University of Glasgow: see Number 308 note (2).
(3) Number 303; and see Thomson's annotation.
(4) See Numbers 304 and 305.
(5) Compare Maxwell's correction in his letter to Thomson of 7 October 1868 (Number 308).

Surfaces
are either complete or bounded

Complete surfaces are either closed or infinite. A material point cannot get from one side of a complete surface to the other without passing through it. The boundary of any space is a complete surface. The boundary of an *n*-ly connected space is an *n*-ly connected surface. Now let an *n*-ly connected surface gradually collapse till its inner surfaces meet and the closed surface becomes a double surface everywhere enclosing an infinitely small space by a finite area. Considered in its genesis this is the limit of an *n*-ly connected closed surface.

Considered in its present state it is an *n*-ly *bounded* surface, that is, a surface bounded by *n* closed curves.

We cannot call any one of these curves the external and the rest the internal boundaries as in the boundaries of solids unless we are dealing with plane surfaces only.

A spherical surface with *n* holes in it is an *n*-ly bounded surface. A pair of trousers is triply bounded. A surface may be $\overline{n\text{-ly connected and } n'\text{-ly}}$ bounded, say the electroplating of a toast rack for $\overline{n-3}$ slices with n' places worn out.

Lines are complete or bounded

Complete lines are closed or infinite. Let the holes in an *n*-ly bounded surface be enlarged till they nearly and at length quite reach each other, we shall have an *n*-ly connected line or closed line of *n* loops.

Now let *m* of these loops collapse into single lines we shall have $n-m$ loops and *m* branches with abrupt ends. Such a line is $(n-m)$-ly connected and *m*-ly bounded.

I have got a 'wheel of life' made by White[6] with concave lenses instead of slits, the focal length being equal to the diameter of the wheel. This makes each picture appear to stand still as long as it is visible.[7] The light and

---

(6) See Number 301 note (2).

(7) Maxwell's 'zoetrope' (developed from an instrument popular in the 1860s) is described in the *Life of Maxwell*: 484–5. The instrument and some of the drawings described by Maxwell are preserved in the Cavendish Laboratory, Cambridge: see Plates XIII and XIV. Alluding to the lenses with which Maxwell improved the design, Campbell referred (*Life of Maxwell*: 37n) to a question for the Cambridge Mathematical Tripos on the morning of Thursday 7 January 1869, question xx, set by Maxwell as Junior Moderator. See *The Cambridge University Calendar for the Year 1869* (Cambridge, 1869): 482; 'A lens is moving with velocity p perpendicular to its axis and an object at a distance a from the lens is moving with velocity q across the axis in the opposite

distinctness are much improved but the pictures appear half size. This may if required be corrected by holding a reading glass outside. White is now making another.

I have drawn Rankines Waves[8] in section with long plants of seaweed moving to shew the motion of the water at different depths. Also 3 Helmholtz Rings[9] threading through each other. 4th figure of Lancers[10] &c, generation and growth and final bursting of Volvox Globator,[11] dance of tadpoles in the curve $x = \sin 3\theta \quad y = \sin 2\theta$. I used to draw figures for the old disks with slits but found it was useless to draw them neatly on account of the dimness. By means of the lenses everything is quite distinct.

Yours truly
J. CLERK MAXWELL

direction. Find the focal length of the lens that to an eye on the other side of the lens the object may appear at rest'.

(8) See Number 223; and Rankine, 'On waves in liquids', *Proc. Roy. Soc.*, **16** (1868): 344–7.
(9) See Number 307 and Plate XIII.
(10) A form of quadrille (*OED*). Maxwell's drawing (see note (7)) shows dancers.
(11) A spherical green alga formed of a colony of cells in a gelatinous mass.

307
LETTER TO WILLIAM THOMSON
6 OCTOBER 1868
From the original in the University Library, Glasgow[1]

Ardhallow
Dunoon
Oct 6 1868

Dear Thomson

Many thanks for the ticket to Platform O[2] which arrived here yesterday and also for the first 6 pages of your paper on Vortex motion[3] which looks as if it was going to begin simply.

There are several curious misspellings but I suppose you have corrected them as they are scored.

In the foot notes you make an hypothesis about a mass of 20.5×10^6 grammes which I suppose to be the mass referred to by Mr Crum[4] at the Western Club, and that if the wind had been as good as on Sept 26 you could have looked us up here, and M^{rs} McCunn[5] says she would have been happy to have given you a bed and continues to keep the same at your disposal in case you should be able to make the passage.

We leave this on the 13th but I hope to see you in Glasgow on Thursday and to arrange either so or according to the other portion of your note explaining a contrary (not opposite) plan.

What you say about a uniform field of force proves that the lines of force are straight not that they are parallel. To prove them parallel you must show that a tube made of a ruled surface (otherwise a scroll) cannot be of uniform area of section unless it is prismatic or cylindric. I will look up Phil. Mag.[6]

H^2's 3 rings do as the 2 rings in his own paper that is those in front expand and go slower those behind contract and when small go faster and thread through the others.[7] I drew 3 to make the motion more slow and visible not

---

(1) Glasgow University Library, Kelvin Papers, M 26.

(2) For the laying of the foundation stones for the new building of the University of Glasgow: see Number 308 note (2).

(3) William Thomson, 'On vortex motion', *Trans. Roy. Soc. Edinb.*, **25** (1869): 217–60 (= *Math. & Phys. Papers*, **4**: 13–66).   (4) Alexander Crum, Thomson's brother-in-law.

(5) Maxwell's sister-in-law (see Volume I: 537).

(6) Thomson was probably alluding to a discussion of lines of force by G. J. Stoney, 'On the experiment of Mahomet's coffin', *Phil. Mag.*, ser. 4, **36** (1868): 188–92.

(7) Hermann Helmholtz, 'On the integrals of the hydrodynamical equations, which express

Plate XIII. Maxwell's zoetrope or 'wheel of life' (1868), showing Helmholtz's vortex rings threading through each other (Number 307).

that I have solved the case of 3 rings more than to get a rough notion about this case and to make the sum of the three areas const. I have made them fat when small and thin when big.

A binocular wheel of life would require to be on a horizontal axis, the pictures would be outside the lenses but the amount of care required to draw a presentable stereoscopic pair of pictures is about 10 times that required for a presentable wheel of life with 13 pictures so that I estimate the ratio of trouble at $\dfrac{130}{n}$ where n is the ratio of expectation of an accurate picture in a stereoscope to same in Wheel.

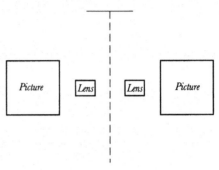

Figure 307,1

I have done a few more wheels.

1. Motion of 6 heavy balls in a vertical circle showing how the line joining opposite balls passes through a fixed point (pole of the line of height due to velocity) and how the triangle of 3 alternate balls touches a fixed circle and how lines forming opposite sides of the hexagon meet in the line of height due to velocity.

2. A fountain with a ball rolling on the top of the jet and throwing off drops which change colour as they pass through the rainbow positions.

3. Leapfrog of boys who give backs and leap alternately, cycle of 2 revolutions.

4. Acrobats male & female going opposite ways 25 positions of one and 27 of the other.

5. Growth of pines.

I am going to do uniform sliding motion ($u = Cy$) and the motion of a perfect fluid (with motes in it to make it visible) about a moving cylinder radius 1.[8]

---

vortex motion', *Phil. Mag.*, ser. 4, **33** (1867): 485–512, esp. 510, on the interaction of two circular vortex rings; 'We can now see generally how two ring-formed vortex-filaments having the same axis would mutually affect each other, since each, in addition to its proper motion, has that of its elements of fluid, as produced by the other. If they have the same direction of rotation, they travel in the same direction; the foremost widens and travels more slowly, the pursuer shrinks and travels faster, till, finally, if their velocities are not too different, it overtakes the first and penetrates it. Then the same goes on in the opposite order, so that the rings pass through each other alternately.' See Plate XIII.

(8) See Number 310 and Plate XIV.

If in this case $\phi = r\left(r - \dfrac{1}{r}\right)\sin\theta$ is the stream function[9]

$$\frac{dr}{dt} = \frac{1}{r}\frac{d\phi}{d\theta} = \frac{1}{r^2}\sqrt{r^4 - (2+\phi^2)\,r^2 + 1}$$

whence
$$t = \int \frac{r^2\,dr}{\sqrt{r^4 - (2+\phi^2)r^2 + 1}}$$

which may be done by elliptic functions. This gives the time as a function of r and ϕ the stream function so that we can find the position, say, of a row of particles after the cylinder has past, which, before, were in a straight line.

M^{rs} McCunn and Mrs Maxwell have just got tickets & I hope to see you on Thursday and arrange a meeting if possible.

Yours truly
J. CLERK MAXWELL

---

(9) Compare Helmholtz's expression 'die Strömungslinien der Flüssigkeit' (see Number 302 note (5)) and Rankine's term 'stream-line' (see Number 337 esp. note (4)); and Maxwell's definition of the 'stream function' in his paper 'On the displacement in a case of fluid motion', *Proceedings of the London Mathematical Society*, **3** (1870): 82–7, on 83n (= *Scientific Papers*, **2**: 209n). See Number 311.

308
LETTER TO WILLIAM THOMSON
7 OCTOBER 1868
From the original in the University Library, Glasgow[1]

Ardhallow
Dunoon
Oct 7 1868

Dear Thomson

The Senate sent me an invitation to Platform O for which I thank you.[2] Mrs Maxwell and M^{rs} McCunn have got tickets for platform A from Prof. Blackburn.[3] ⟨If you have a ticket for O for Mrs Maxwell she would prefer being with me but if it is not convenient she has friends in A. I will call at the Western Club early on Thursday.⟩

Yours truly
J. CLERK MAXWELL
over

I find that I made a mistake about the connectedness of hollow solids.[4]

If the solid is bounded by m surfaces of which one is external and the rest internal and if the connectedness of these are

$$n_1 \; n_2 \ldots n_m$$

Then if n_1 belongs to the external surfaces it introduces n_1 connexions into the solid, but if n_2 belongs to an internal surface it introduces only $n_2 - 1$ *new* connexions.

Hence the whole number of connexions is $n_1 + n_2 - 1 + n_3 - 1 \quad + n_m - 1$

$$= \sum(n) - m + 1.$$

If a surface is entirely composed of triangular facets then if it is singly connected, the sides of the triangles determine the form of the surface and have no conditions among themselves except limiting ones. If the surface is n-ly connected there are $6n$ conditions about the lengths of the sides.

If the sides meeting in p points are broken p degrees of freedom are introduced.

---

(1) Glasgow University Library, Kelvin Papers, M 27.
(2) For the ceremonial laying of the foundation stones, by the Prince and Princess of Wales, of the new building of the University of Glasgow at Gilmorehill, Glasgow on 8 October 1868.
(3) Hugh Blackburn, Professor of Mathematics at Glasgow University (Venn). See Volume I: 238n.
(4) See Number 306.

APPENDIX: A DRAFT REVISE ON HOLLOW SOLIDS
circa OCTOBER 1868

From the original in the University Library, Cambridge[5]

[...] side of the hole. If $n-1$ holes had been bored through the solid $n-1$ surfaces may be drawn without separating one part of the space from the rest. Such a space is said to be n-ly continuous or to have n connexions. A ring is doubly continuous, a figure of 8 triply continuous and so on.

The external surface of a space has the same degree of continuity as the space itself, and the space outside the surface has the same degree of continuity so far as that surface is concerned.

Next let us consider the continuity of a space bounded by m complete surfaces. If all the surfaces are of simple continuity the space is of simple continuity, but if any one has continuity of the nth degree, $n-1$ degrees of continuity are added to the space hence if the degrees of continuity of the m bounding surfaces are

$$n_1, n_2 \ldots n_m$$

the space bounded by them will have

$$n_1 + n_2 + \&c + n_m - m + 1 \text{ degrees of continuity.}$$

Continuity of Surfaces

A Surface is said to have n degrees of continuity when $n-1$ closed curves may be drawn upon it without destroying its continuity.

Limits of Surfaces

A finite surface can be limited by m closed curves which must exclude each other, but no one is necessarily the external limit unless the surface is plane.

If a surface of m limits is regarded as a stratum of infinitesimal thickness, the stratum is a space of m degrees of continuity.

---

(5) ULC Add. MSS 7655, V, d/12. For the first draft of this folio see Number 305 §2.

309
FROM A LETTER TO WILLIAM HUGGINS
13 OCTOBER 1868
From Campbell and Garnett, *Life of Maxwell* (2nd edn)[1]

Ardhallow
Dunoon
Oct 13/68

My dear Sir

I sympathise with you in your great sorrow. Though my own mother was only eight years with me, and my father became my companion in all things, I felt her loss for many years, and can in some degree appreciate your happiness in having so long and so complete fellowship with your mother. I have little fear, however, that the nearness to the other world which you must feel will in any way unfit you for the work on which you have been engaged, for the higher powers of the intellect are strengthened by the exercise of the nobler emotions....

Your identification of the spectrum of comet II with that of carbon is very wonderful.[2] The dynamical state of comets' tails is most perplexing,[3] but the chemistry and activity of their heads leads to new questions. With respect to the transparency of a heavenly body, I think it indicates scattered condition rather than gaseity. A cloud of large blocks of stone is much more transparent than air of the same average density. Such blocks in a nebula would never be themselves seen, but perhaps if they were often to encounter each other, the results of the collision would be incandescent gases, and might be the only visible part of the nebula.

...Any opinion as to the form in which the energy of gravitation exists in space is of great importance, and whoever can make his opinion probable will have made an enormous stride in physical speculation. The apparent universality of gravitation, and the equality of its effects on matter of all kinds are most remarkable facts, hitherto without exception; but they are purely experimental facts, liable to be corrected by a single observed exception. We

---

(1) *Life of Maxwell* (2nd edn): 260–1.

(2) William Huggins, 'Further observations on the spectra of some of the stars and nebulæ, with an attempt to determine therefrom whether these bodies are moving towards or from the earth, also observations of the spectra of the sun and of Comet II., 1868', *Phil. Trans.*, **158** (1868): 529–64, esp. 557–62. Huggins included (pp. 532–5) the text of Maxwell's letter of 10 June 1867 (Number 271).

(3) An issue discussed by Huggins, 'Further observations on the spectra of some of the stars and nebulæ': 563–4. See Maxwell's letter to G. P. Bond of 25 August 1863 (Number 217).

cannot conceive of matter with negative inertia or mass; but we see no way of *accounting* for the proportionality of gravitation to mass by any legitimate method of demonstration. If we can see the tails of comets fly off in the direction opposed to the sun with an accelerated velocity, and if we believe these tails to be matter and not optical illusions or mere tracks of vibrating disturbance, then we must admit a force in that direction, and we may establish that it is caused by the sun if it always depends upon his position and distance. I therefore admit that the proposition that the sun repels comets' tails is capable of proof; but whether he does so by his ordinary attractive power being changed into repulsion by a change of state of the matter of the tail is another question.[4] Now, it seems ascertained by simple observations with telescopes that the coma is formed by successive explosions out of the nucleus, mostly on the side of the sun, and that the formation of the tail depends on the coma, though the substance is invisible in the state of passing from the coma to the tail. Then, by your observations, the nucleus and coma have light of their own, probably due to carbon in some gaseous form; but the tail's light being polarised in the plane of the sun is due to him. Hence the head is fire and the tail smoke. The head obeys gravitation, which is exerted on it with precisely the same intensity as on all other known matter, solid or gaseous. The tail appears to be acted on in a contrary way. If the comet consisted of a mixture of gravitating and levitating matter, and is analysed by the sun, then before the emission of the tail the acceleration due to gravitation should be less than on a planet at the same distance; the more complete the discharge of tail the greater the intensity of gravitation on the remaining head.

N.B. – To understand the dynamics of the tail, the motion in space of particular portions of it must be studied.

[J. CLERK MAXWELL]

(4) In his paper 'Further observations on the spectra of some of the stars and nebulæ': 564, Huggins suggested that: 'It may be that this apparent repulsion takes place at the time of the condensation of the gaseous matter of the coma, into the excessively minute solid particles of which the tail probably consists.... Perhaps it would be too bold a speculation to suggest that, under the circumstances which attend the condensation of the gaseous matter into discrete solid particles, the division may be pushed to its utmost limit, or nearly so. If we could conceive the separate atoms to be removed beyond the sphere of their mutual attraction of cohesion, it might be that they would be affected by the sun's energy in a way altogether different from that of which we have been hitherto the witnesses upon the earth.'

LETTER TO WILLIAM THOMSON

16 OCTOBER 1868

From the original in the University Library, Glasgow[1]

Ardhallow Oct 16 1868

Dear T.

I have been trying the cap on today and have got the density at the vertex or in other words the state of the poll – as thus[2]

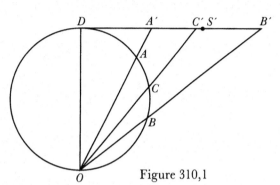

Figure 310,1

1 on a sphere $4\pi\rho = \dfrac{\text{potential}}{\text{radius}}$.

Flatten it to a disk $4\pi\rho = \dfrac{\text{potential}}{\sqrt{\text{rad}^2 - \text{dist}^2 \text{ from centre}}}$ on each side.[3]

2 Let $A'B'$ be the disk S' the centre, AB the cap C its pole.
Let $DOC = \theta$ $COA = COB = \alpha$
$DO = D$ $CO = x = D\cos\theta$ $CA = CB = a = D\sin\alpha$.
Then $DC = D\tan\theta$ $DA' = D\tan(\theta-\alpha)$ $DB' = D\tan(\theta+\alpha)$

whence $S'A' = D\dfrac{\sin\alpha\cos\alpha}{\cos(\theta+\alpha)\cos(\theta-\alpha)}$

---

(1) Glasgow University Library, Kelvin Papers, M 28.

(2) Maxwell is here considering the distribution of electricity on a portion of a spherical surface bounded by a small circle. Thomson had first communicated the results of his investigation of this problem (by his method of electric images) in a letter of 16 September 1846 to Joseph Liouville, published in the 'Extraits de deux lettres addressées à M. Liouville', *Journal de Mathématiques Pures et Appliquées*, **12** (1847): 256–65, esp. 263–4 (= *Electrostatics and Magnetism*: 152–4). Thomson's correspondence with Maxwell on his method of investigation is not extant, but he published his 'Determination of the distribution of electricity on a circular segment of plane or spherical conducting surface, under any given influence' (which is dated January 1869) in his 1872 reprint of his papers on *Electrostatics and Magnetism*: 178–91. In the *Treatise*, Maxwell's 'Application of electrical inversion to the case of a spherical bowl' (*Treatise*, **1**: 221–5 (§§176–81)), follows Thomson's published account of the problem: see Maxwell's letters to Thomson of 17 August and 1 October 1869 (Numbers 326 and 327).

(3) For this expression for the surface-density of electricity on an infinitely-thin circular disc, see George Green, 'Mathematical investigations concerning the laws of the equilibrium of fluids analogous to the electric fluid, with other similar researches', *Trans. Camb. Phil. Soc.*, **5** (1833): 1–63, esp. 61. This result is cited by Thomson in his 1869 paper on the 'Distribution of electricity on a circular segment...' (*Electrostatics and Magnetism*: 179).

and $DS' = D\dfrac{\sin\theta\cos\theta}{\cos(\theta+\alpha)\cos(\theta-\alpha)}$

and $C'S' = D\dfrac{\sin\theta\sin^2\alpha}{\cos(\theta+\alpha)\cos(\theta-\alpha)}$.

4π Density at $C' = 4\pi\rho' = \dfrac{V}{\sqrt{S'A'^2 - C'S'^2}}$

$= \dfrac{V}{D}\dfrac{\cos(\theta+\alpha)\cos(\theta-\alpha)}{\sin\alpha\sqrt{1-\sin^2\alpha\cos^2\theta}}$

$= \dfrac{V}{D}\dfrac{\dfrac{x^2-a^2}{D^2}}{\dfrac{a}{D}\sqrt{1-\dfrac{a^2x^2}{D^4}}}$

$= \dfrac{V}{aD^2}\dfrac{x^2-a^2}{\sqrt{1-\dfrac{a^2x^2}{D^4}}}$.

Density at C, on the spherical surface $\rho = \rho'\dfrac{D^3}{x^3} = \dfrac{VD}{4\pi a}\dfrac{1}{x^3}\dfrac{x^2-a^2}{\sqrt{1-\dfrac{a^2x^2}{D^4}}}$.

Potential at same point $= \dfrac{VD}{x}$. Hence a charge $-VD$ placed at O would reduce the potential of the cap to zero, and would induce the above density at C on both sides of the surface.

If CO is constant C being fixed the part cut off by the path of O is $\pi D\dfrac{x^2}{D} = \pi x^2$. Hence if there is a distribution such that the density is σ the quantity between x and $x+dx$ will be $2\pi\sigma x\,dx$. Substitute this for $-VD$ in the expression for ρ and we get

$$d\rho = -\dfrac{\sigma}{2a}\dfrac{x^2-a^2}{x^2\sqrt{1-\dfrac{a^2x^2}{D^4}}}dx$$

for the part of the density at C due to a uniform density over the sphere between x & $x+dx$.

The integral is $\quad -\dfrac{\sigma}{2}\left\{\dfrac{a}{x}\sqrt{1-\dfrac{a^2x^2}{D^4}} + \dfrac{D^2}{a^2}\sin^{-1}\dfrac{ax}{D^2}\right\}$

when $x = D$ this becomes $-\dfrac{\sigma}{2}\left\{\dfrac{a}{D}\sqrt{1-\dfrac{a^2}{D^2}} + \dfrac{D^2}{a^2}\alpha\right\}$

when $x = a$ it becomes $-\dfrac{\sigma}{2}\left\{\sqrt{1-\dfrac{a^4}{D^4}} + \dfrac{D^2}{a^2}\sin^{-1}\dfrac{a^2}{D^2}\right\}$.

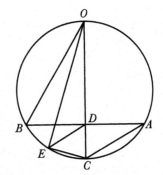

Figure 310,2. Make $EC = DC$, join OE, OB.

Whole density at poll due to induction of uniform cap

$$= \frac{\sigma}{2}\left\{\sqrt{1-\frac{a^2}{D^2}}\left(\sqrt{1+\frac{a^2}{D^2}}-\frac{a}{D}\right)-\frac{D^2}{a^2}(\text{angle } BOE)\right\} = \rho.$$

P.S. Integral from x_1 to $x_2 = -\frac{\sigma}{2}D^2\left(\frac{\sin(\gamma_1-\gamma_2)}{x_1 x_2} - \frac{\gamma_1-\gamma_2}{a^2}\right)$

where $\sin\gamma_1 = \frac{ax_1}{D^2}$ and $\sin\gamma_2 = \frac{ax_2}{D^2}.$

Now plaster the whole over to a density σ so that $4\pi\sigma = \frac{2V}{D}$ then the inductor cap will be annihilated, the induced cap will be raised to pot. V and a density σ will be added on the outside.

Hence the outside density will be $\rho+\sigma$ } at the vertex.
inside ——— ρ

ρ outside $= \frac{V}{4\pi D}\left\{\frac{D^2}{a^2}(\text{angle } BOE) - \sqrt{1-\frac{a^2}{D^2}}\left(\sqrt{1+\frac{a^2}{D^2}}-\frac{a}{D}\right)\right\} + \frac{V}{2\pi D}$

ρ inside $= \frac{V}{4\pi D}\left\{\frac{D^2}{a^2}(\text{angle } BOE) - \sqrt{1-\frac{a^2}{D^2}}\left(\sqrt{1+\frac{a^2}{D^2}}-\frac{a}{D}\right)\right\}$

$-\sin\alpha.\sin BOE$[4]

If D is very great BOE becomes $\frac{a}{D}-\frac{a^2}{D^2}$ and $\rho = \frac{V}{4\pi a}$ on both sides.

If $a = \cos\beta$ where β is a small angle $OB = D\sin\beta$
$OE = D\sin\beta\sqrt{2-\sin^2\beta}.$

ρ inside $= \frac{V}{4\pi D}\left\{\frac{1}{1-\sin^2\beta}\{\sin^{-1}(\sin\beta\sqrt{2-\sin^2\beta})-\beta\}\right.$

$\left. -\sin\beta(\sqrt{2-\sin^2\beta}-\sqrt{1-\sin^2\beta})\right\}$

$= \frac{V}{4\pi D}\left\{\frac{1}{\cos^2\beta}\{BOE-\cos\beta\sin BOE\}\right\}.$

Now BOE is a small angle equal to $(\sqrt{2}-1)\beta$ nearly and if $BOE = \gamma$

$\langle BOE-\cos\beta\sin BOE\rangle = \gamma-\cos\beta\sin\gamma = \gamma\left(\frac{\beta^2}{2}-\frac{\gamma^2}{3}\right) = \frac{4\sqrt{2}-3}{6}\beta^3$

---

(4) Compare Thomson's result stated in his letter to Liouville of 16 September 1846, proved in his 1869 'Distribution of electricity on a circular segment...' (*Electrostatics and Magnetism*: 184–5), and summarised by Maxwell in the *Treatise*, **1**: 223–4 (§180).

a result similar to Greens[5] if I recollect but exact up to the approx^n

$$\text{inside } \rho = \frac{V}{4\pi D} \frac{4\sqrt{2}-3}{6} \beta^3.$$

To get the density *anywhere* the integration is more difficult. I propose for the point P to take the point Q where PT QT are tangent planes meeting in the plane AB. Then I divide the caps by circles such that at any point R, $\dfrac{QR}{PR} = n$ and the plane PQR cuts PT in a line making an angle ϕ with PT.

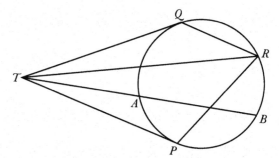

Figure 310,3

I have made some more wheels of life.[6] A harp string a fiddle string a piano wire and a sound wave also a cylinder going through a liquid sideways. There are streaks of paint in the liquid like this lapping round the successive cylinders.[7] The unlearned pronounce

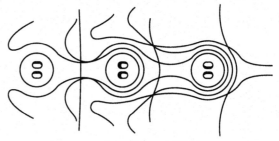

Figure 310,4

it lively. We go to Edin^h on the 20th and Glenlair 22nd.

If you are in London do not seek us at 8 Palace Gardens Terrace as we are not there. I will tell you where we are, probably Bayswater. The Moderators have just begun work.[8]

Yours truly
J. CLERK MAXWELL

I see no mistake in the result on last page at the bottom.[9] It seems not to agree with yours $f = D$ $a = a$ $r = x$?[10]

---

(5) Green, 'Mathematical investigations concerning the laws of the equilibrium of fluids': 60–3. (6) See Numbers 306 and 307.

(7) See Plate XIV and Number 311; and J. Clerk Maxwell, 'On the displacement in a case of fluid motion', *Proceedings of the London Mathematical Society*, 3 (1870): 82–7, esp. Fig. 1 (= *Scientific Papers*, 2: 211). Thomson sketched curves lapping round a cylinder on the letter.

(8) Maxwell had been appointed Moderator for the 1869 Mathematical Tripos; see *The Cambridge University Calendar for the Year 1869* (Cambridge, 1869): 472.

(9) The expression for the 'whole density at poll due to induction of uniform cap'.

(10) See Thomson's symbols in his letter to Liouville of 16 September 1846, his 1869 'Distribution of electricity on a circular segment', and Maxwell's account in the *Treatise*, 1: 221–5 (§§176–81).

Plate XIV. Maxwell's zoetrope or 'wheel of life' (1868), showing the motion of a cylinder through a liquid (Number 310).

LETTER TO WILLIAM THOMSON

30 OCTOBER 1868

From the original in the University Library, Glasgow[1]

Glenlair
Dalbeattie
1868 Oct 30

Dear Thomson

I got your letter about St Andrew's.[2] Swan[3] & Campbell[4] have also written. One great objection is the East Wind which I believe is severe in those parts. Another is that my proper line is in working not in governing, still less in reigning and letting others govern.

I have settled the case of the water through which a cylinder passes.[5]

r = distance from axis of cylinder θ angle of r

a = radius $\psi = \genfrac{}{}{0pt}{}{\langle\text{velocity}\rangle}{\text{action}}\Big\}$ potential[6] ϕ = stream potential[7]

$$u = \frac{d\psi}{dx} = \frac{d\phi}{dy} \quad v = \frac{d\psi}{dy} = -\frac{d\phi}{dx}$$

$$\psi = x\left(1+\frac{a^2}{r^2}\right) \quad \phi = y\left(1-\frac{a^2}{r^2}\right) = \left(r-\frac{a^2}{r}\right)\sin\theta$$

$$\frac{dr}{dt} = \dot{r} = \frac{1}{r}\frac{d\phi}{d\theta} = \left(1-\frac{a^2}{r^2}\right)\cos\theta = \left(1-\frac{a^2}{r^2}\right)\left(1-\frac{\phi^2}{\left(r-\frac{a^2}{r}\right)^2}\right)^{\frac{1}{2}}$$

---

(1) Glasgow University Library, Kelvin Papers, M 29. Previously published in A. T. Fuller, 'James Clerk Maxwell's Glasgow manuscripts: extracts relating to control and stability', *International Journal of Control*, **43** (1986): 1593–1612, esp. 1600–3.

(2) About the vacant post of Principal of the United College of St Salvator and St Leonard in the University of St Andrews, following the resignation of James David Forbes. See Numbers 312, 313, 314 and 315.

(3) William Swan, Professor of Natural Philosophy at St Andrews (*DNB*); see Volume I: 398n.

(4) Lewis Campbell was Professor of Greek at St Andrews.

(5) See Numbers 307 and 310; and Plate XIV. The discussion which follows is a preliminary version of Maxwell's paper 'On the displacement in a case of fluid motion', *Proceedings of the London Mathematical Society*, **3** (1870): 82–7 (= *Scientific Papers*, **2**: 208–14).

(6) In 'On the displacement in a case of fluid motion': 83 Maxwell uses the term 'velocity-potential', following Helmholtz: see Number 254 note (5).

(7) See Number 307 esp. note (9).

$$\frac{dt}{dr} = \frac{r^2}{\sqrt{r^4 - (2a^2 + \phi^2)r^2 + a^4}}.$$

Hence we can find t the time of passage along a stream line indicated by a constant value of ϕ between two values of r.

Make
$$\sqrt{4a^2 + \phi^2} + \phi = 2\beta$$
$$\sqrt{4a^2 + \phi^2} - \phi = 2c\beta$$

or
$$c = \frac{a^2}{\beta^2}$$

then $\quad t = \int \dfrac{r^2 dr}{\sqrt{r^2 - \beta^2}\sqrt{r^2 - c^2\beta^2}}.$

Put $r = \dfrac{\beta}{\sin\psi}$ [8] $\quad t = \int \dfrac{d\psi}{\sin^2\psi \sqrt{1 - c^2 \sin^2\psi}}$ [9]

$$t = \beta \cot\psi \sqrt{1 - c^2 \sin^2\psi} + \beta(E_c(\psi) - F_c(\psi))$$
$$= \frac{\sqrt{r^4 - (2a^2 + \phi^2)r^2 + a^4}}{r} + \frac{1}{2}(\sqrt{4a^2 + \phi^2} + \phi)(E_c(\psi) - F_c(\psi)).$$

After a complete passage a particle whose original distance from the plane of motion of the axis of the cylinder is y is translated forward along x a distance $2a \dfrac{1}{\sqrt{c}}(F_c - E_c)$ where $c = \dfrac{4a^2}{(\sqrt{4a^2 + y^2} + y)^2}$ & F_c & E_c are complete elliptic functions[10] (for when $r = \infty \quad \phi = y$).

Hence when the cylinder moves from $-\infty$ to $+\infty$ *every* particle moves forward. But if the fluid is in a fixed vessel a portion equal in volume to the cylinder must go backward. Hence our case must be that of an infinitely large vessel not fixed but free and having a momentum equal to that of the cylinder in its infinite mass.[11]

---

(8) ψ is here and in sequel an angular variable.

(9) Read: $-\beta d\psi$.

(10) Compare Number 295 esp. note (10).

(11) Maxwell's paper 'On the displacement in a case of fluid motion' was read to the London Mathematical Society on 10 March 1870. On 8 April 1870 Robert Tucker, Secretary of the Society, wrote to Maxwell about its publication in the *Proceedings*. 'Both referees pronounce very warmly in favour of publication – one writes we could get a little more on the subject from the author & that he could be persuaded to give a drawing of the curve for the case considered in the last page calculated from the $=^{ns}$ – by aid of Legendre's tables – it might involve, he says, too much labour, to draw accurately from the calculations. He suggests my returning it to you for the consideration of the slight pencil alterations in it – so that if you approve of the same you can make them yourself before I send the ms on to the printers (the Council on two such recommendations being sure to print). / I return the ms with this & trust you will return it to me, as soon as possible – leaving the tracing of the curve to a future occasion if it involves

N.B. Let RA be a circular ring vortex radius a P an equal ring at distance y then the quantity of fluid which flows through P in unit of time is

$4\pi \sqrt{aa'} \dfrac{1}{\sqrt{c}}(F_c - E_c)$ where

$$c = \dfrac{PR-PA}{PR+PA} = \dfrac{4a^2}{(\sqrt{4a^2+y^2}+y)^2}.$$

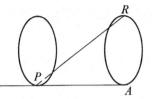

Figure 311,1

So the expression does for both cases.

Here is another electrical prop. founded on Green.[12]

Let A_1 A_2 A_3 &c be conductors, A_3 &c at potential 0. Let a charge E placed on A_1 induce a charge nE on A_2 placed in communication with the ground. Then if A_1 is insulated free of charge and A_2 is charged to potential V, the potential of A_1 will be nV where n is the same ratio as before.

I find some curious cases of unstable motion of tubes through which liquid flows.

Let A = moment of inertia of tube full of solid liquid about O.

$B = 2$ area of tube $\times \rho$.

$C = \int \rho \dfrac{ds}{k}$ where k is the section $OP = r$

$k =$ section of opening at P α angle $\widehat{OP}$ direction of stream then if $A + r^2 k^2 C - 2Brk \cos \alpha$ is negative there will be oscillations of increasing amplitude. Unfortunately this quantity is always positive which I have only just found out. It reaches zero only when the tube is a circle with centre at O, no mass of tube itself and no radial piece from O.

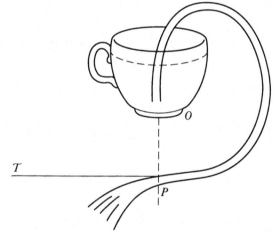

Figure 311,2

Yours truly
J. CLERK MAXWELL

---

difficulty. / Faithfully yours / R. Tucker Hon. Sec^y. / I thought this course of letting you know the referees' views would be more satisfactory to you than for you to correct the proof.' (ULC Add. MSS 7655, II/35). It seems likely that Figs. 2 and 3 of 'On the displacement in a case of fluid motion', showing the paths of particles at different distances from the cylinder, were added to the MS of the paper at the referee's suggestion.

(12) See Maxwell's discussion of the proposition in the *Treatise*, **1**: 92 (§89).

312

FROM A LETTER TO LEWIS CAMPBELL

3 NOVEMBER 1868

From Campbell and Garnett, *Life of Maxwell*[1]

Glenlair
Dalbeattie
3 November 1868

I have given considerable thought to the subject of the candidature, and have come to the decision not to stand.[2] The warm interest which you and other professors have taken in the matter has gratified me very much, and the idea of following Principal Forbes had also a great effect on my feelings, as well as the prospect of residing among friends; but I still feel that my proper path does not lie in that direction – Your affт. friend,

J. CLERK MAXWELL

---

(1) *Life of Maxwell*, 345–6.
(2) See Numbers 311, 313, 314 and 315.

313

LETTER TO WILLIAM ROBERT GROVE

7 NOVEMBER 1868

From the original in the Library of the Royal Institution, London[1]

Glenlair
Dalbeattie
7 Nov 1868

Dear Sir

I have received an invitation from two thirds of the Professors of the United College of St Salvator and St Leonard, St Andrews, to come forward as a candidate for the office of Principal of that College, of which Dr J. D. Forbes has given in his resignation.[2]

They wish a scientific man to succeed Brewster[3] and Forbes and have done me the honour to think me qualified.

I have therefore become a candidate and as far as I know there is no other professedly scientific man in the field.

If you are of the opinion that I am qualified for the situation and could bring my claims in any way before the Home Secretary or Lord Advocate, I should esteem it a great favour.

The vacancy occurs on the 11th November and Government will probably lose no time in making the appointment.[4]

I have paid so little attention to the political sympathies of scientific men that I do not know which of the scientific men I am acquainted with have the ear of the Government. If you can inform me, it would be of service to me.

I remain
Yours truly
J. CLERK MAXWELL

W. R. Grove Esqre F.R.S.

---

(1) Grove Papers, The Royal Institution, London. First published in C. Domb, 'James Clerk Maxwell in London 1860–1865', *Notes and Records of the Royal Society*, **35** (1980): 67–103, on 96–7.

(2) See Numbers 311, 312, 314 and 315.

(3) Sir David Brewster had held the office of Principal until 1860, being succeeded by Forbes; see Volume I: 623.

(4) There was an election in November 1868, Disraeli's Conservative government being replaced by Gladstone's Liberal ministry in early December.

314
LETTER TO GEORGE BIDDELL AIRY
9 NOVEMBER 1868
From the original in the Royal Greenwich Observatory Archive[1]

Glenlair
Dalbeattie
Nov 9 1868

Dear Sir

D^r J D Forbes has resigned the Principalship of the United College of St Salvator & St Leonards, St Andrews.

I have received a letter signed by two thirds of the Professors of the United College inviting me to become a candidate for the vacant office, which is in the gift of the Crown. Principal Tulloch[2] of St Mary's College, the Vice Chancellor of the University concurs in the invitation.

They are of the opinion that the successor of Sir David Brewster and of Principal Forbes should be a scientific man and they have done me the honour of assuring me that in that respect my appointment would be acceptable to them.

I have therefore become a candidate and as far as I know there is no other professedly scientific man in the field.

If you are of opinion that I am qualified for the situation you would confer on me a great favour if you could assist me in bringing my claims before the Home Secretary[3] either directly or otherwise.

The vacancy occurs on the 11th Nov. and Government will probably lose no time in making the appointment.[4]

I remain
Yours truly
J. CLERK MAXWELL

The Astronomer Royal
Greenwich

---

(1) Royal Greenwich Observatory Archive, ULC, Airy Papers 6/5, 409R–410R.

(2) John Tulloch (*DNB*).

(3) On this procedure compare Maxwell's application to Marischal College in 1856: see Volume I: 392–403.

(4) In his reply of 12 November 1868 (Airy Papers 6/5, 411R–V) Airy explained his position as Astronomer Royal: 'If it is in my power to assist you in your views regarding the office of Principal at St Andrews, I will do my best. But in this stage of the matter, there is difficulty arising from my connexion with the Government. As a general rule... I cannot suggest to the Government a name for an office.... If any Department of the Government should apply to me for an opinion, I should be free.'

315

LETTER TO WILLIAM THOMSON

9 NOVEMBER 1868

From the original in the University Library, Glasgow[1]

Glenlair
Dalbeattie
1868 Nov 9

Dear Thomson

When I last wrote I had not been at St Andrews.[2] I went last week, and have gone in for the Principalship. If you can certify my having been industrious &c since 1856, or if you can tell me what scientific men are conservative or still better if you can use any influence yourself in my favour pray do so. 6 Professors out of 9 have memorialized the Ld Adv. & Home Sec.[3] for me together with Principal Tulloch the V. Chancellor. Of the other 3, one Prof Shairp, is a candidate[4] and one, Prof. Bell[5] does not approve of memorials at all and is neutral.[6] I have written to Sabine[7] Airy[8] Stokes[9] and Grove.[10]

Yours truly
J. CLERK MAXWELL

---

(1) Glasgow University Library, Kelvin Papers M 30. Previously published in C. Domb, 'James Clerk Maxwell in London 1860–1865', *Notes and Records of the Royal Society*, **35** (1980): 67–103, on 97–8.

(2) Compare Number 311; and see Numbers 312, 313 and 314.

(3) Edward Strathearn Gordon and Gathorne Hardy (*Whitaker's Almanac*).

(4) John Campbell Shairp, Professor of Humanity, appointed Principal of the United Colleges at St Andrews in November 1868.

(5) Oswald Bell, Professor of Anatomy and Medicine.

(6) The other seven professors were: Lewis Campbell (Greek), W. L. F. Fischer (Mathematics), Thomas Spencer Baynes (Logic), Robert Flint (Moral Philosophy), William Swan (Natural Philosophy), W. McDonald (Civil History), and M. Foster (Chemistry) (*Whitaker's Almanac*).

(7) General Edward Sabine, President of the Royal Society 1861–71. This letter is not extant.

(8) Number 314.   (9) This letter is not extant.

(10) Number 313.

316

LETTER TO WILLIAM THOMSON

7 DECEMBER 1868

From the original in the University Library, Glasgow[1]

Glenlair
Dalbeattie
1868 Dec 7

Dear Thomson

If you ever see White would you ask him why he neither sends me a 'wheel of life'[2] nor answers my two letters asking him why he does not, during 7 weeks.

Can you give me a good *elementary* Thermodynamics *Problem*. I have not the opportunity of setting book work so I am trying to get in a problem which shall be thermodynamically easy. If it is mathematically difficult it will be no fault in the eyes of the Cambridge men, though I would prefer it easy myself.

I think of asking a question about the deduction of the dilatation per degree of temperature at constant pressure from the intrinsic energy expressed as a function of two variables either v & t or v and ϕ.[3]

I think it is important to insert the wedge by the thin end and to 'hold the eel of science by the tail'. Great mental inertia will be called into play if the new ideas are not fitted on to the old in a continuous manner.

If you could give me a hint of a problem I would thank you.[4]

Yours truly
J. CLERK MAXWELL

---

(1) Glasgow University Library, Kelvin Papers, M 31.

(2) See Numbers 306, esp. note (7), 307 and 310.

(3) Maxwell set a question on the compression of gases for the Cambridge Mathematical Tripos on the morning of Thursday, 21 January 1869, question (11). See *The Cambridge University Calendar for the Year 1869* (Cambridge, 1869): 499.

(4) Thomson's reply is dated 14 December 1868: 'Dear Maxwell / x(α) Experiment shows that the specific inductive capacity (electrostatic) of glass is increased by elevation and diminished by depression of temperature. Hence prove that if the charge of a charged Leyden phial be slowly increased, the glass becomes thereby cooled. / (β) Given a non-charged Leyden jar of capacity c at temperature t of absolute thermodynamic scale. Prove that when it is partially charged with a quantity Q of electricity the quantity of heat which must be given to its glass to prevent lowering of temperature is $/ \frac{1}{2}\frac{Q}{c^2} \cdot \frac{1}{c}\frac{dc}{dt} \cdot \frac{t}{J} /$ J denoting the dynam^l equivalent of the thermal unit. / (γ) Experiment gives approximately (not very, but very roughly) for the augmentation of sp. ind. capac., $\frac{1}{100}$ percent of its own amount, for a rise of temp^{re} 1° Cent. Find how much a Leyden jar weighing 200 grammes, of mean spec. heat .2 (glass and metal all included) is cooled from initial temp^{re} of 45° Cent, when it is slowly charged to potential 50 (acc^s

gramme-centimetre-second fund¹ units). The value of J in terms of corresponding units is 416000. / N.B. (α) is a *very* elementary problem (γ) a problem less elementary (β) is perhaps too transparently book work (Tait §209). / Why not also give them a liquid film? & if you don't want the 2nd Thermodyn^c law give them the ? to how thin before work is done = latent heat of evaporation. Will you not look in here on your way S & see my electrostatic thermo-multiplier 500 divisions to the 1° Cent. Yours WT'. (ULC Add. MSS 7655, II/32). In discussing example (β) Thomson refers to Tait's *Sketch of Thermodynamics* (Edinburgh, 1868): 115–16 (§209). Maxwell did not use any of Thomson's examples as examination questions.

317

MANUSCRIPT ON THE TOPOLOGY OF SURFACES

29 DECEMBER 1868

From the original in the University Library, Cambridge[1]

[ON THE GEOMETRY OF SURFACES][2]

Infinite space is divided into c cells or separate regions each of simple continuity.[3] The surface which separates two contiguous cells is called a face and each face is defined by the portions of the cells which are in contact. The boundary between two contiguous faces is called an edge. At every edge three or more cells meet. The extremities of an edge are called summits.[4] At every summit four or more edges faces and cells meet. Let c be the number of cells, f the number of faces e the number of edges and s the number of summits, then let one of the faces be destroyed so as to throw two cells into one.[5]

Let us suppose this face to have n edges and n angles and let us in the first place suppose that all these edges are formed by the meeting of three cells only. Then the destruction of this face has diminished the number of cells by one. It has also obliterated the n edges of the face and as each of these was a boundary of two faces the number of faces is thereby reduced by n, and if we include the destroyed face by $n+1$. We have also n summits obliterated,

---

(1) ULC Add. MSS 7655, V, d/12.

(2) See Number 318; and compare Maxwell's early manuscript drafts on topology: Numbers 304, 305, 306 and 308. This draft relates to a question Maxwell set for the Cambridge Mathematical Tripos, on the morning of Thursday, 21 January 1869, question (4). See *The Cambridge University Calendar for the Year 1869* (Cambridge, 1869): 497–8; 'Infinite space is divided into a number of regions, one of which encloses all the rest: every surface of contact between two distinct regions is called a face, every line in which three or more faces meet is called an edge, and every point at which four or more edges meet is called a summit; shew that if all the regions and faces have continuous boundaries and have no multiple connexions, the sum of the numbers of regions and edges will be equal to the sum of the numbers of faces and summits.' The draft also has relation to his paper on 'Topographical geometry', read to the London Mathematical Society on 10 March 1870 (see the *Proceedings*, **3** (1870): 82). The paper was presented to the Liverpool Meeting of the British Association in September 1870 (Number 345), and published as 'On hills and dales', *Phil. Mag.*, ser. 4, **40** (1870): 421–7 (= *Scientific Papers*, **2**: 233–40).

(3) Compare Maxwell's term 'simply connected', derived from Riemann: see Number 304, esp. note (4). Maxwell terms loops or closed paths 'cycles': see Number 318 note (4).

(4) A term used subsequently in 'On hills and dales': 423 (= *Scientific Papers*, **2**: 235).

(5) The terms in which Maxwell discusses the problem suggests his reading of a paper by Arthur Cayley, 'On the partitions of a close', *Phil. Mag.*, ser. 4, **21** (1861): 424–8.

466

and as each of these was a division between two edges which are now thrown into one, there are n edges.

Hence c has become $c-1$ f has become $f-n-1$ e has become $e-2n$ and s, $s-n$ but the quantity
$$c-f+e-s$$
has not been altered by the destruction of the face.

If m contiguous edges of the face belong each to more than three cells the destruction of the face will not obliterate them, or throw the faces which they separate into one.

Let us now consider infinite space as divided into R regions of which r_1 have one continuous boundary r_2 have two boundaries... and r_m have m boundaries. Also let ρ_1 of these have one cycle ρ_2 two cycles... and ρ_n n cycles.

Let the boundaries of these regions be made up of F faces of which f_0 are complete faces f_1 have one boundary f_2 two... and f_m m boundaries also let ϕ_1 be monocyclic ϕ_2 dicyclic... ϕ_n n-cyclic.

Let the boundaries of these faces consist of E edges of which η are closed curves without any divisions.

Let these edges be terminated by S points called summits.

Then if
$$\sum (mr_m) = r_1 + 2r_2 + \ldots + mr_m$$
$$\sum (n\rho_n) = \rho_1 + 2\rho_2 + \ldots + n\rho_n$$
$$\sum (mf_m) = f_1 + 2f_2 + \ldots + mf_m$$
$$\sum (n\phi_n) = \phi_1 + 2\phi_2 + \ldots + n\phi_n$$
then $\sum (mr_m) - \sum (n\rho_n) - 2F + \sum (mf_m) + 2\sum (n\phi_n) + E - \eta - S = C = 0$.

To prove this we shall first show that this quantity remains unaltered when any part of the system is destroyed or any new part added.

Let a single closed line be drawn in space. This increases E by one and also increases η by one so that C remains the same.

Let this line be divided into s parts by s points of division. We have then $E = s$ and $S = s$ and C remains unaltered.

(1) C is not altered by dividing a line into segments by points. For if the line is a complete closed one without any divisions the first division adds one to S and takes one from η and every division of a terminated line adds one to S and one to E. Hence C is not altered by adding or removing points of division.

(2) C is not altered by drawing a line upon a face. For if it is drawn between two points on the same boundary of the face it divides the face into two so that F and E are each increased by one.

If it is drawn between two points on different boundaries, it reduces the number of boundaries by one so that $\sum (mf_m)$ is diminished by one and E is increased by one and C remains the same.

If it is a closed curve not surrounding any cyclic channel then it divides the face into two and adds one to the number of boundaries of the part outside so that F and $\sum (mf_m)$ are each increased by one and so are E and η so that C still remains the same.

If a closed curve is drawn round one of the cyclic channels it adds two boundaries (the two sides of the curve) and diminishes the number of cycles, so that $\sum mf_m$ is increased by two, $2\sum (n\phi_n)$ is diminished by two and E and η are each increased by one so that C remains the same.

Hence C is not altered by drawing any lines on any faces or removing them.

(3) C is not altered by drawing a new face.

For let the new face be bounded entirely by the single boundary of a region then if it does not close a cyclic channel it divides the region into two. If the region had originally m boundaries, the sum of the boundaries of the two parts will be $m+1$ so that $\sum mr_m$ is increased by one. If the region had originally n cycles the sum of the cycles of the two parts will still be n so that $\sum (n\rho_n)$ remains the same.

At the same time $2F$ is increased by two and $\sum mf_m$ by one so that C remains the same.

Now let the new face close a cyclic channel. Then $\sum mr_m$ remains the same but $\sum n\rho_n$ is diminished by one $2F$ is increased by two and $\sum mf_m$ by one so that C is the same.

We have supposed that the new face is bounded only by the external boundary of the region. Let us examine what would be the result in either of the above cases if the new face had been also bounded by an internal boundary of the region. In this case $\sum (mr_m)$ would have been diminished by one and $\sum (mf_m)$ would have been increased by one as compared with the former cases so that C would still be the same.

Lastly let the new face be entirely disconnected from the boundaries of the region and let it be n-cyclic.

The region outside acquires one new boundary and n new cycles and the new region has one boundary and n cycles so that $\sum mr_m$ is increased by 2 and $\sum n\rho_n$ by $2n$.

At the same time $2F$ is increased by 2 $\sum (mf_m)$ remains the same and $2\sum (n\phi_n)$ is increased by $2n$ so that C remains the same.

Hence C remains the same whatever points lines or surfaces are drawn in or taken away from the system.

Now in the case of a single n cyclic surface we have two regions each with one boundary and n cycles so that $\sum mr_m = 2$ $\sum n\rho_n = 2n$ $2F = 2$, $\sum mf_m = 0$ $2\sum(n\phi_n) = 2n$ $E = 0$ $\eta = 0$ $S = 0$ so that in this case $C = 0$.

Hence C is equal to 0 in every case.

If all the regions have single boundaries $\sum(mr_m) = R$.

If they are all acyclic $\sum(n\rho_n) = 0$.

If all the faces are singly bounded and acyclic

$$2F - \sum mf_m - 2\sum(n\phi_n) = F.$$

In this case none of the edges can be closed lines so that $\eta = 0$.

Hence if all these conditions are fulfilled, the general equation becomes

$$R - F + E - S = 0.$$

If there is only one finite region bounded by an n-cyclic surface having F singly bounded faces E edges and S points

$$2 - 2n - F + E - S = 0.$$

When $n = 0$ as in acyclic figures we get the well known equation[6]

$$2 - F + E - S = 0$$

between the faces, edges and summits of a polyhedron.

Dec 29 1868

(6) Euler's equation: see Number 318 note (3).

APPENDIX

§1 The following letters, which are not extant as autograph manuscripts, have been abbreviated from the versions printed in the *Life of Maxwell*.

(1) Letter to Charles Hope Cay
 5 January 1865 (Number 240).
(2) Letter to Charles Benjamin Tayler
 2 February 1866 (Number 256).

§2 The following letters printed in extract in the *Life of Maxwell*, have not been reproduced.

(1) Letter to Lewis Campbell
 22 November 1864 (*Life of Maxwell*: 340).
(2) Letters to Charles Hope Cay
 18 November 1863, 14 October 1865 (*Life of Maxwell*: 337–8, 343–4).
(3) Letters to Katherine Mary Clerk Maxwell
 22 June 1864, 23 June 1864, 26 June 1864, 28 June 1864, December 1873 (*Life of Maxwell*: 338–40, 387).

§3 Letters written to Maxwell
Locations of the letters and details (where appropriate) of their citation and reproduction in this volume are given. Many of these letters – notably those from G. G. Stokes, P. G. Tait and William Thomson – have been reproduced *in extenso*. Letters which have been reproduced in abbreviated form are marked * below, those merely cited are marked †.

(1) Letters from George Biddell Airy
 (1) 12 November 1868, Royal Greenwich Observatory Archive, ULC, Airy Papers 6/5, 411R–V; *Number 314 note (4).
 (2) 14 October 1872, ULC, Airy Papers 6/259, 203R–V; Number 424 note (2).
 (3) 26 October 1872, ULC, Airy Papers 6/259, 205R; Number 426 note (2).
 (4) 29 October 1872, ULC, Airy Papers 6/259, 210R–V; *Number 426 note (7).
(2) Letter from John Aitken
 6 March 1873, ULC Add. MSS 7655, II/70.
(3) Letter from Jane Barnard
 20 June 1871, ULC Add. MSS 7655, II/47.

Appendix

(4) Letters from William Benson
    (1) May 1870, ULC Add. MSS 7655, II/37; † Number 341 note (6).
    (2) 13 March 1871, ULC Add. MSS 7655, II/43; † Number 358 note (3).

(5) Letter from Edward William Blore
13 February 1871, ULC Add. MSS 7655, II/38A; Number 357 note (3).

(6) Letter from George Phillips Bond
9 July 1863, Bond MSS, Harvard University Archives UAV. 630.6; * Number 217 notes (3), (4), (6) and (14).

(7) Letter from Robert E. Branston
21 October 1867, ULC Add. MSS 7655, II/27.

(8) Letter from Lewis Campbell
4 July 1872, ULC Add. MSS 7655, II/58.

(9) Letter from Arthur Cayley
20 April 1868, ULC Add. MSS 7655, II/29; Number 320 note (3).

(10) Letter from Robert Bellamy Clifton
22 November 1871, ULC Add. MSS 7655, II/53.

(11) Letter from Alexander Crum Brown
4 September 1873, ULC Add. MSS 7655, II/73; * Number 478 notes (12) and (24).

(12) Letter from V. Dwelshauvers-Dery
12 May 1872, ULC Add. MSS 7655, II/57.

(13) Letters from Joseph David Everett
    (1) 19 July 1872, ULC Add. MSS 7655, II/60; † Number 341 note (19).
    (2) 26 July 1872, ULC Add. MSS 7655, II/61; * Number 341 note (19).

(14) Letter from James David Forbes
4 June 1864, ULC Add. MSS 7655, II/22.

(15) Letter from William Francis
11 July 1873, Henry Augustus Rowland Papers MS. 6, Milton S. Eisenhower Library, The Johns Hopkins University, Baltimore; Number 467 note (2).

(16) Letter from George Griffith
27 July 1873, ULC Add. MSS 7655, II/72; † Number 470 note (25) and * Numbers 474 note (13) and 478 note (2).

(17) Letter from G. A. Hirn
25 November 1872, ULC Add. MSS 7655, II/68; † Number 426 note (7).

Appendix

(18) Letters from Charles Hockin
- (1) 15 May 1868, ULC Add. MSS 7655, II/30; *Number 289 note (8).
- (2) 27 July 1868, ULC Add. MSS 7655, II/31; *Number 297 notes (6) and (9).
- (3) 11 March 1870, ULC Add. MSS 7655, II/34; †Number 297 note (6) and *Number 378 note (9).

(19) Letters from Fleeming Jenkin
- (1) 10 January 1868, ULC Add. MSS 7655, II/28; Number 287 note (8).
- (2) 28 October 1871, ULC Add. MSS 7655, II/51; †Number 385 note (10).

(20) Letter from James Prescott Joule
n.d. [June 1871], ULC Add. MSS 7655, II/49; *Number 339 note (15).

(21) Letter from William Longman
20 June 1871, ULC Add. MSS 7655, II/48; Number 381 note (2).

(22) Letter from Arthur Luke
6 October 1868, ULC Add. MSS 7655, II/24.

(23) Letters from Cecil James Monro
- (1) 2 June 1870, Greater London Record Office, Acc. 1063/2105; *Number 341 notes (2) and (20).
- (2) 3 March 1871, GLRO, Acc. 1063/2106, 2109b, 2109c; *Number 359 notes (2) and (7).
- (3) 9 March 1871, GLRO, Acc. 1063/2107; *Number 359 notes (2), (14) and (15).
- (4) 21 March 1871, GLRO, Acc. 1063/2108; *Numbers 359 note (15) and 363 notes (2), (3) and (4).
- (5) 10 September 1871, GLRO, Acc. 1063/2109a; *Number 359 note (8).

(24) Letter from E. J. Nanson
5 December 1873, ULC Add. MSS 7655, II/75.

(25) Letter from George E. Preece
7 March 1873, ULC Add. MSS 7655, V, i/12.

(26) Letter from Bartholomew Price
4 January 1871, ULC Add. MSS 7656, P 659; *Introduction note (90) and *Number 367 note (3).

(27) Letters from Herbert Spencer
- (1) 4 December 1873, ULC Add. MSS 7655, II/74; Number 486 note (3).

Appendix

- (2) 30 December 1873, ULC Add. MSS 7655, II/76; *Number 487 note (2).
- (28) Letters from George Gabriel Stokes
  - (1) 16 February 1871, ULC Add. MSS 7655, II/40; Number 357 note (3).
  - (2) 18 February 1871, ULC Add. MSS 7655, II/41; Number 357 note (4).
  - (3) 23 February 1871, ULC Add. MSS 7655, II/42; Number 357 note (5).
  - (4) 14 March 1871, ULC Add. MSS 7655, II/44; Number 358 note (11).
- (29) Letter from John William Strutt, Lord Rayleigh
  14 February 1871, typed copy in private possession; *Numbers 355 notes (9), (10) and (12) and 357 note (3), and † Number 358 note (6).
- (30) Letter from William Swan
  11 May 1872, ULC Add. MSS 7655, II/56.
- (31) Letters and postcards from Peter Guthrie Tait
  - (1) n.d. [June 1865], ULC Add. MSS 7655, I, a/1; Number 249 note (2).
  - (2) 6 April 1866, ULC Add. MSS 7655, I, a/2; Number 262 note (15).
  - (3) 27 November 1867, ULC Add. MSS 7655, I, a/3; Number 276 note (2).
  - (4) 6 December 1867, ULC Add. MSS 7655, I, a/4; Number 277 note (2).
  - (5) 13 December 1867, ULC Add. MSS 7655, I, a/5; Number 277 note (22).
  - (6) 1 February 1871, ULC Add. MSS 7655, I, a/7; Number 353 note (11).
  - (7) 17 February 1871, ULC Add. MSS 7655, I, a/8; Number 356 note (7).
  - (8) 31 March 1871, ULC Add. MSS 7655, I, a/9; Number 365 note (5).
  - (9) 5 April 1871, ULC Add. MSS 7655, I, a/10; Number 366 note (5).
  - (10) 9 May 1871, ULC Add. MSS 7655, I, a/11; Number 368 note (6).
  - (11) 13 May 1871, ULC Add. MSS 7655, I, a/12; Number 369 note (8).
  - (12) 14 May 1871, ULC Add. MSS 7655, I, a/13; Number 371 note (8).

Appendix

(13) 1 June 1871, ULC Add. MSS 7655, I, a/14; Number 373 note (5).
(14) 5 June 1871, ULC Add. MSS 7655, I, a/15; Number 375 note (2).
(15) 7 June 1871, ULC Add. MSS 7655, I, a/16; Number 375 note (2).
(16) 13 June 1871, ULC Add. MSS 7655, I, a/17; Number 376 note (2).
(17) 14 June 1871, ULC Add. MSS 7655, I, a/18; Number 378 note (11).
(18) 20 June 1871, ULC Add. MSS 7655, I, a/20; Number 378 note (11).
(19) 9 July 1871, ULC Add. MSS 7655, I, a/21; Number 380 note (2).
(20) 10 November 1871, ULC Add. MSS 7655, I, a/22; Number 389 note (14).
(21) 2 January 1872, ULC Add. MSS 7655, I, a/23; Number 398 note (10).
(22) 6 January 1872, ULC Add. MSS 7655, I, a/25; Number 399 note (8).
(23) n.d. [January 1872], ULC Add. MSS 7655, I, a/55; Number 403 note (8).
(24) 25 January 1872, ULC Add. MSS 7655, I, a/26; Number 401 note (7).
(25) 11 June 1872, ULC Add. MSS 7655, I, a/27; Number 413 note (3).
(26) 28 June 1872, ULC Add. MSS 7655, I, a/28; Number 414 note (2).
(27) 13 July 1872, ULC Add. MSS 7655, I, a/29; Number 417 note (2).
(28) 15 July 1872, ULC Add. MSS 7655, I, a/30; Number 417 note (4).
(29) 16 July 1872, ULC Add. MSS 7655, I, a/31; Number 417 note (3).
(30) 17 July 1872, ULC Add. MSS 7655, I, a/32; Number 417 note (3).
(31) 19 July 1872, ULC Add. MSS 7655, I, a/33; Number 417 note (3).
(32) 30 June 1873, ULC Add. MSS 7655, I, a/34; Number 465 note (2).
(33) 7 July 1873, ULC Add. MSS 7655, I, a/35; Number 465 note (2).

Appendix

- (34) 31 July 1873, ULC Add. MSS 7655, I, a/36; Number 474 note (3).
- (32) Letters from James Thomson
  - (1) 21 July 1871, James Thomson Papers MS 13/22b, The Queen's University of Belfast Library; Number 382 note (2).
  - (2) 11 January 1873, James Thomson Papers MS 13/22e, Queen's University Library; *Number 421 notes (3) and (12).
- (33) Letters and postcards from Sir William Thomson
  - (1) 14 December 1868, ULC Add. MSS 7655, II/32; Number 316 note (4).
  - (2) 11 January 1871, ULC Add. MSS 7655, I, a/6; Number 350 note (14).
  - (3) 17 June 1871, ULC Add. MSS 7655, I, a/19; Number 377 note (1).
  - (4) 4 January 1872, ULC Add. MSS 7655, I, a/24; Number 393 note (7).
  - (5) 24 August 1872, ULC Add. MSS 7655, II/62; Number 420 note (8).
- (34) Letter from Coutts Trotter
  20 April [1871], ULC Add. MSS 7655, II/46; *Number 361 note (2).
- (35) Letter from Robert Tucker
  8 April 1870, ULC Add. MSS 7655, II/35; Number 311 note (11).
- (36) Letter from John Tyndall
  'Monday', *Life of Maxwell*: 381.

INDEX

Part I and Part II

Bold figures refer to text numbers. Italic figures indicate pages on which biographical details are given.

Aberdeen, University of, 249, 392
Accademia del Cimento, 648
acoustics, 412–15, 417, 538, 598–604, 605–6, 608, 856–7, 860–3, 920
Adams, John Couch, 249n, 370
Adams, William Grylls, 4, 249
   letter from Maxwell: (3 December 1873) **484**, 949–50
Adams-Reilly, A., 774n, 886n, 921n
Agassiz, Alexander, 886n
Agassiz, Louis, 886n
agitation, molecular, 959–63
Airey, J. A. L., 510n
Airy, George Biddell, 23, 33, 463, 540n, 639
   letters from Maxwell: (14 May 1863) **209**, 87; (12 March 1868) **283**, 351–2; (9 November 1868) **314**, 462; (16 October 1868) **424**, 758–9; (28 October 1868) **426**, 761–2
   letters to Maxwell: (12 November 1868), 462n; (14 October 1872), 758n; (26 October 1872), 761n; (29 October 1872), 761–2n
   letter to H. A. Faye: (26 September 1872), 758n
   letter to W. H. Miller: ([1848]), 414n
   letters to G. G. Stokes: (22 February 1863), 63–4n, 95–6n; (27 February 1863), 95n; (3 July 1872), 725n
   letters from Stokes: (12 May 1848), 414n; (26 February 1863), 64n; (18 March 1863), 95n; (10 December 1872), 718n; (13 December 1872), 718n
   report on paper by Stokes: (16 July 1868), 415n
   Royal Society papers: 'On the directive power of large steel magnets' (Maxwell's report on) **410**, 718–26; 'Magnetical observations...' (Maxwell's report on) **453**, 847; 'On the strains in the interior of beams' (Maxwell's report on) **205**, 62–9; **206**, 70–1; **212**, 95–6
   Greenwich Observatory, 351–2
   magnetisation, 718–26
   magneto-optic effect, 884
   Mathematical Tracts, 46–7n, 309n
   on Maxwell's *Saturn's Rings*, 115n, 758n, 761–2n
   stress function, 63–9, 520–1
Aitken, John, letter to Maxwell: (6 March 1873), 971
Akin, C. K., 245n
Alhazen, 629n
Ampère, André Marie, 485n, 507, 514, 654n, 678, 723–5, 767, 773, 843n, 945
Amsler, J., 874
Andrews, Thomas, 16, 277, 668, 671, 681n, 923
Ångström, A. J., 41n, 307, 311, 877n, 888–9, 897
anomalous dispersion, 11–12, 419–21, 862–3, 864–5
Appleton, R., 965
Arago, D. F., 108, 148n, 154n, 223n, 309, 713
Arago's disc, 27, 548, 704, 706, 710, 711, 712–13
Arbuthnot, John, 636n
Archimedes, 367
Argyll, Bishop of, 749n
Aristophanes, 693, 947
Aristotle, 551
Armstrong, Sir W. G., 369n
Armstrong and Whitworth Committee, 373
Athenæum Club, 6, 636, 660
Avogadro's hypothesis, 15, 135, 258, 282, 305, 657n, 892, 909

Babbage, Charles, 648, 951
Bacon, Francis, 655
Baily, Francis, 234, 657
Bain, Alexander, 395, 578
Bakerian Lecture, *see* Royal Society of London
Balfour, Evelyn, 664n
Balfour, John Hutton, *580n*, 915
   letter from Maxwell: (28 November 1870) **349**, 580–1
   letter from W. Thomson: ([1870]), 580n
Ball, W. W. Rouse, 35

Index

band (endless), 501, 872
Barclay, T., 627n
Barnard, Jane, letter to Maxwell: (20 June 1871), 971
Barrett, W. F., 551n
Bashforth, Francis, 24, *369n*, 386
   Royal Society paper: 'On the resistance of the air to the motion of...projectiles' (Maxwell's report on) **288**, 369–73
battery (standard), 734–7, 742, 866–7, 873
Baynes, T. S., 463n
beauty (rules of), 886–7
Beck, A., 936
Becker, Carl Ludwig, 98, 122, 151, 213n, 310, 377, 870
Beer, Gillian, 840n
Bell, Oswald, 463
Bell, William, 691
Belpaire, Th., 934
Benet, Stephen Vincent, 373n
Benson, William, 551, 614, 617
   letters to Maxwell: (May 1870), 551; (13 March 1871), 614n
Bentley, Richard, 368, 798
Benvenuto, E., 24n
Berkeley, George, 361, 363, 365, 395, 816
Bernoulli, Daniel, 72, 135, 250, 279, 655
Bernoulli, Jakob (James) I, 367
Bernoulli, Johann (John) I, 370n
Bernoulli equation, 242
Bernstein, H. T., 654n
Bertrand, Joseph, 391, 399, 407, 716, 745n, 945
Bessel, F. W., 752, 857
Betti, Enrico, 320n, 333, 386n, 423, 426, 439
Bible, 731
Bierhalter, G., 18n
Biot, Jean Baptiste, 559, 563, 720–1
Birkbeck, George, 5n
Birkbeck, Mrs, 5n
Bismarck, Otto, Prince von, 707
Blackburn, Hugh, 449
Blackburn's pendulum, 872
Blore, Edward William, 34, *611n*
   letter from Maxwell: (15 February 1871) **357**, 611–13
   letter to Maxwell: (13 February 1871), 611n
Boltzmann, Ludwig, 15, 18, 284n, 740n, 760n, 888, 907n, 915–16, 938, 947n
Bond, George Phillips,
   letter from Maxwell: (25 August 1863) **217**, 104–9
   letter to Maxwell: (9 July 1863), 104–7n

Bond, W. C., 105n
Bonney, T. G., 5n, 147n
Boole, George, 304
Boscovich, R. J., 396, 799–800, 812n
Bose, M. von, 211n, 349n, 407n
Bottomley, W., letter to G. G. Stokes: (26 March 1873), 867n
Bourgoin, E., 504
Boussinesq, Joseph, 19n
Bowman, William, 203
Boyle, Robert, 655, 816
Boyle's law, 673, 731
brachistochrone, 224n, 667n
   see also quickest ascent, line of
Bramah, Joseph, 869
Branston, Robert E., letter to Maxwell: (21 October 1867), 972
Brewster, Sir David, 47, 50n, 312n, 461, 462, 559
Bright, Sir Charles, 6, 735n
Bristed, Charles Astor, 228n
British Association for the Advancement of Science, 9, 466n, 489, 532n, 548, 550n, 578n, 627, 654n, 659n, 667, 671n, 677n, 749, 833, 916
   Committee on electrical standards, 6–9, 88–92, 93–4, 96, 97, 98–101, 103, 107–8, 113–14n, 122, 157, 164, 170n, 188n, 202, 207n, 211n, 214, 217, 375n, 377n, 378n, 409, 417n, 489, 548, 627, 734–7, 748, 773, 810n, 850, 871
   electrodynamometer, 627, 734–5, 738, 742, 867, 871
   Maxwell's papers, 312, 313–17, 564–5, 566–7, 898n, 911–14, 922–33, 935–6, 937–9
Brodie, Sir Benjamin Collins, Bt, 337n, 830
   chemical calculus, 304–5, 660
Bromberg, Joan, 26n
Bruhns, C., 752n
Brush, Stephen G., 12n, 15n, 17n, 81n, 128n, 138n, 250n, 280n, 900n, 902n
Buchwald, Jed Z., 11n, 26n, 37n, 485n, 559n
Buckle, Thomas Henry, 818, 932
Buff, Heinrich, 408n, 828
Bunsen, Robert, 626, 869, 874, 891
Burdon-Sanderson, J. S., *836n*
   report on paper by J. Jago: (12 May 1873), 836–7n
Burlington, Earl of, *see* Devonshire, 7th Duke of
Burns, Robert, 391n
Butler, Joseph, 834n
Butler, Samuel, 321n

Index

Byron, George Gordon, 6th Baron, 408, 646

cables (telegraph), 410n, 489, 496, 504, 517, 555
Cagniard-Latour, Charles, 670–1n
calculus of variations, 589n, 625, 787–9
calorescence, 245–8
Cambridge Philosophical Society, 37, 744n, 787n, 815n, 840, 968n
   Maxwell's report on paper by O. Fisher: **490**, 968–70
Cambridge, University of,
   Adams Prize, 8, 33, 589, 624–6
   Board of Mathematical Studies, 33, 35, 612n, 729, 839
   Cambridge Calendar, 154–5n, 239n, 241n, 251n, 277n, 293n, 411n, 418n, 420–1, 444–5n, 456n, 464n, 466n, 477n, 517n, 542n, 634n, 729n, 752n, 787n, 839, 862n, 964n
   Cavendish Laboratory, 1, 33–4, 36, 611–13, 619, 626–7, 630–1, 632–3, 634–5, 666, 681, 690, 701, 760, 840, 868–75, 876, 943
   Mathematical Tripos, 11, 33, 35, 154–5n, 227, 236n, 239–40, 241n, 248n, 251–2, 277, 293, 321, 391, 411n, 418, 419–21, 444–5n, 456, 464, 466n, 517, 542, 684, 729, 752–3, 787–9, 839, 862–3, 865
   Maxwell's lectures, 35–6, 689, 690, 760, 898n, 940–1, 942n
   Natural Sciences Tripos, 35–6, 612n, 766, 944, 961, 964
   Professorship of Experimental Physics, 33–6, 611–13, 615–16, 623
   Smith's Prize, 28, 477n, 589n, 634n
Campbell, Lewis, 1, 110n, 361n, 444n, 457, 463n, 840
   letters from Maxwell, 971: (21 April 1862), 72n, 817n; (21 November 1865) **251**, 228–9; (3 November 1868) **312**, 460; (19 October 1872) **425**, 760; (3 April 1873) **449**, 840–1
   letter to Maxwell: (4 July 1872), 972
Candolle, A. P. de, 641–2
capillary action, 386n
carbon bisulphide prisms, 607, 874
Cardwell, D. S. L., 791n
Carnot, Lazare, 646
Carnot, Sadi, 791
Carnot cycle, 36
Carnot function, 544n
Caro, Elme Marie, 358
Carpenter, W. B., 2
Carroll, Lewis (Charles Dodgson), 832

Casella's barometer, 869
Casorati, F., 936
catenary, 330
cathetometer, 631, 870
Catton, Alfred, 640n
'cat-turning', 528
Cauchy, A. L., 51n
causality, 820–3
Cavendish, Henry, 179, 655, 784n, 785–6, 800, 839, 843, 858
Cavendish Laboratory, Cambridge, 619, 666, 681
   apparatus for, 626–7, 630–1, 632–3, 634–5, 868–75, 876
   building of, 33–4, 36, 690, 701, 760, 840, 943
   plans for, 630–1, 632–3, 868–75, 876
Cay, Charles Hope, *202n*
   letters from Maxwell, 971: (5 January 1865) **240**, 202–3
Cay, Jane, 240
Cay, John, 240
Cay, Robert Dundas, *103*, 119n
   letters from Maxwell: (21 August 1863) **216**, 103; (12 July 1864) **229**, 157; (28 April 1865) **247**, 221; (8 December 1865) **253**, 240; (23 November 1871) **391**, 690; (27 May 1872) **412**, 729; (22 May 1873) **456**, 852
Cay, William Dyce, *119n*, 157, 221
Cayley, Arthur, 296n, 466n, *320n*, 566n, 589n, 687, 702, 745n
   letter from Maxwell: (12 April 1869) **320**, 476–8
   letter to Maxwell: (20 April 1868), 476n
   report on paper by N. M. Ferrers: (14 July 1869), 492n
census, 929
Challis, James, 245n, 529n, 589n, 624n, 917, 957
Chambers, Charles, 23
   Royal Society paper: 'On the nature of the sun's magnetic action' (Maxwell's report on) **220**, 117–18
charge (electric), *see* displacement (electric); electrification
Charlemagne, 408
Charles I, King of England, 408
Charles, J. A. C., 408, 646
Charles' law, 408n, 646n, 650–1n, 673, 731
Charlton, T. M., 21n, 24n
Chasles, Michel, 294, 295n, 313n, 476, 647
Chemical Society, 304–5,
chemistry, 304–5, 782

Index

Christiansen, C., 862n
chronographs, 371-2, 631, 635
Chrysostom, John, 834
Chrystal, George, 35
Church of Scotland (General Assembly), 852
circular motion, 1n, 702
Clairaut, A. C., 752
Clapeyron's theorem, 120n
Clarendon Press, 31, 636, 856, 915n
Clark, Edwin, 119
Clark, Josiah Latimer, 6, 23, 630, 734-7, 738, 742-3, 748, 872n, 873
   letter from Maxwell: (16 July 1872) **418**, 742-3
   letter to G. G. Stokes: (23 January 1873), 735n
   Royal Society papers: 'On a standard voltaic battery' (Maxwell's report on) **462**, 866-7; 'On a voltaic standard of electromotive force' (Maxwell's report on) **415**, 734-7
Clarke, Samuel, 817
Clausius, Rudolf Julius Emmanuel,
   electrolysis, 657, 922-3, 967
   entropy, 16-18, 359, 564, 672n, 710, 946-7
   kinetic theory of gases, 12-13, 72-4, 75n, 77, 83, 84n, 133, 250, 280, 305, 408, 656-8, 896, 923, 938
   light of the sky, 619
   on Maxwell, 73-5, 83n, 133, 280, 353, 658, 709, 710, 732n
   off-prints of papers, 757, 897n
   and Tait, 328n, 335n, 408, 732n, 740n
   thermodynamics, 16-18, 328n, 335n, 408, 609, 709-10, 732n, 757n, 946-7
Clifford, William Kingdon, *343, 666*, 677n, 956
Clifton, Robert Bellamy, 34, 623n, *632*, 636, 701
   letter to Maxwell: (22 November 1871), 972
   letter to G. G. Stokes: (20 January 1871), 603n
   report on paper by J. W. Strutt: (20 January 1871), 603n
colloids, 285-7
colour,
   blindness, 621-2
   boxes, 58n, 94, 146, 155-6, 551-2, 607-8, 614
   mixing, 1n, 94, 146, 155-6, 551-2, 774-5
   names, 617, 629
   vision, 1n, 58-9, 551-2, 614-15, 617-18, 704, 774-5, 781
comet II (1868), 451
comets (tails of), 105-7, 451-2
Comte, Auguste, 362

conduction of electricity, 417, 422-3, 504, 524-7
conjugate functions, 426n, 428, 487-8, 531, 546
Conservatoire des Arts et Métiers, 477
continuity, equation of, 123, 198, 262, 439, 965-7
Cookson, Henry Wilkinson, 35n, *876n*
   letter from Maxwell: (5 July 1873) **464**, 876
   letter from W. M. Fawcett: (16 December 1873), 35n
corkscrew rule, 641, 644, 679, 953-4
Cornu, Alfred, 479, 851
Corsock, 103, 202
Cotes, Roger, 510n, 799, 817, 936, 943
Coulomb, Charles Augustin, 482, 720, 800, 843
Crofton, M. W., 297n
Croonian Lecture, *see* Royal Society of London
Cross, J. J., 28n, 634n,
Crowe, M. J., 29n
Crum, Alexander, 446
Crum Brown, Alexander, 328n, 640n
   letter to Maxwell: (4 September 1873), 924-5n, 927n
crystals (optical properties of), 380-2, 559-63
Cunningham, John William,
   letters from Maxwell: (5 December 1862) **204**, 61; (24 March 1863) **208**, 86; (27 June 1863) **213**, 97; (10 August 1863) **215**, 102
curl (vector operator), 569, 574, 591, 593-4, 784, 825, 878
   see also quaternions
current (induction of), 158-9, 695-6
cyclides, 319-20, 322, 476n

Dallas, D. M., 304n
D'Almeida, J. Chr., 504
Dalton, John, 621, 909, 916
   letter from J. Herschel: (20 May 1833), 621
Daniell, John Frederic, 178n, 504
Daniell cell, 178, 196, 633n, 736
Darwin, Charles, 334n, 815n
Darwin, George Howard, 35-6, 898n, 941-2n
Daston, Lorraine J., 21n
Davies, J. P., 964
Deas, Francis, *559n*
   paper on chromatic effects of polarized light (Maxwell's comments on): **343**, 559-63
Deleuil, J. A., 869
Democritus, 654
'demon' paradox, 17-18, 331-2, 582-3, 585
Desaguliers, J. T., 368
Descartes, René, 294-7, 361, 570, 587, 656, 797, 816, 831

Index

Deschanel, A. Privat, 552n, 856–7
Des Cloiseaux, Alfred, 23, *380n*
  Royal Society paper: 'On the dispersion of the optic axes...' (Maxwell's report on) **290**, 380–2
determinism, 19, 814–23
Deville, H. Sainte-Claire, 285n, 287
Devonshire, William Cavendish, 7th Duke of, 33–4, 649, 651n, 839, 858
  letter from Maxwell: (late January–early February 1873) **435**, 785–6
  letters to John Power: (10 October 1870), 33–4; (1 June 1871), 649n
Dewar, Daniel, 552
diamagnetism, 336–7, 405–6, 781
dielectric constant, 485
  and index of refraction, 196, 543, 627–8
dielectrics,
  conduction, 497
  polarization, 484–6
differential (exact), 645
dimensions, 8, 218, 232, 270, 541
dip circle, 543, 870
Dirichlet's principle, 605n, 660, 763n
disgregation, 16, 709, 710
dispersion of optic axes, 380–2
displacement (electric), 26, 160, 190, 198, 485–6, 572, 958
Disraeli, Benjamin, 461n
Ditscheiner, L., 307,
Domb, C., 3n, 61n, 461n
Donati's comet, 105n
Donders, F. C., 203
Donkin, W. F., 856, 862n
doubly refracting crystals, 1n, 559–63
Dove, H. W., 156, 381
Droop, Henry Richmond, letters from Maxwell: (28 January 1862), 230n; (19 July 1865) **250**, 226–7
duality (principle of), 20–2, 320, 863, 899, 935, 942
Du Bois Reymond, Emil, 555, 556–7n
Dulong, P. L., 657, 910, 947
Dupin, Charles, 319n, 715, 787
Dwelshauvers-Dery, V., letter to Maxwell: (12 May 1872), 972
'dynamical method', 586, 818, 929–31
dynamics,
  collision, 383–5, 654–5
  definition of, 291, 654n, 778–9
  Hamilton on, 31, 732–3, 740n, 744–7
  instability, 19, 819–23
  Lagrange on, 31, 337, 716, 740, 744–7, 769–70
  Maxwell on, 16–19, 31, 291, 363–6, 395–6, 423, 598–9, 716, 732–3, 740, 744–7, 769–71, 777–9, 811–12
  projectiles, 369–74
  reduction to, 18, 31, 609, 769, 779–82, 947
  reversibility, 18, 359–61, 366–7, 583,
  rotating bodies, 492–5
dynamo, 298–9, 356n, 635

Earnshaw, Samuel, 540n
Edleston, Joseph, 510n, 936n
Edlund, E., 692
elasticity,
  Airy's stress function, 23–4, 63–9, 520–1
  experiments on, 269–70, 272–5, 300–3, 348–50
  mathematical theory, 64–9, 70–1, 95–6, 261–2, 270, 272–3, 282–3, 292–3
  strain/stress, 62n, 70–1, 95–6, 518
electric circuits, 158–9, 204–6, 516–17, 522–4, 678–9, 768
electric images,
  applied to magnetism, 32, 704, 706, 710, 711, 712–13
  Maxwell on, 26, 389, 423, 453–6, 479–81, 503
  W. Thomson on, 25–6, 389, 423, 453n, 479, 713
electrical atmospheres, 800
electrical resistance (standard), 6–9, 88–92, 93–4, 96, 97, 98, 100–1, 103, 107–8, 122, 157, 164, 170n, 177n, 202, 214, 217, 378n, 409, 649, 735–6, 850
electrical resistance (and temperature), 211n, 349, 407–8, 661–2
electrical standards, 6–9
  see also battery (standard); British Association, Committee on electrical standards; electrical resistance (standard)
electrical units (ratio of), 6–9, 110–11, 162–3, 172–5, 176–9, 180, 187–8, 194–5, 198, 204–6, 211, 219–20, 375–8, 403, 409, 489n, 810, 849–51
electrification,
  bowl, 25, 453–6, 489, 497, 499
  dielectrics, 484–6
  discs, 26–7, 428–32, 443, 481–2, 546–8
  generation of charge, 271, 424–6, 503, 873
  grating, 27, 487–8, 490, 496–7
  spheres, 26, 480–1
electrodynamics (continental), 26, 353–5, 426, 499–500, 686–8

Index

electrodynamometer (British Association), 627, 734–5, 738, 742, 867, 871
electrolysis, 417, 504, 657, 781, 922–3, 967
electromagnetic theory of light, 9–12, 155, 182–5, 186–8, 194–6, 199–200, 202–3, 378–9, 543n, 627, 772–3, 781, 784, 810, 849, 851
electromagnetism (theory of), 189–96, 507, 767–73, 781, 800–11
electrometers,
    attracted disc (guard ring), 209, 377, 429–30, 443, 481–2, 850, 858, 859n, 873
    portable, 828, 873
    quadrant, 482, 555, 873
    W. Thomson's 'Report' (1867), 377n, 423, 482, 555n, 736, 828, 850, 858n, 859n
    in the *Treatise*, 689
electrophorus, 424n, 503, 873
electrophysiology, 554–8
electro-tonic state, 99, 161, 192, 199n, 507
electrotonus, 557–8
Eliot, George, 840–1
Elliott Bros, 98n, 312
elliptic integrals, 276, 458n, 508–9, 550n
Ellis, R. L., 550n
Encyclopaedia Britannica, 36–7, 311n, 776–82
energy,
    conservation of, 182–4, 191–2, 335, 354–5, 359, 364–6, 417, 522, 578n, 817
    dissipation of, 359–61, 366–7, 542, 564–5, 780, 917–18, 946
    electric circuits, 516–17, 769–71, 957
    electromagnetic, 193–4, 769–71, 784
    electrostatic, 162, 485
    energetics, 291, 335, 778
    in evaporation, 672–4
    gravity, 194, 451–2
    kinetic, 75n, 364–6, 598, 657, 744–7, 769–71, 784, 864, 900–1, 916, 941n
    potential, 365–6, 784, 822, 864
    vis viva, 75, 182n, 364, 609n, 657, 888, 947
entropy, 16, 359, 564, 672n, 710, 946–7
Epicurus, 798
Eranus club, 814
ergal, 16, 609, 709, 710, 946
ergon, see work (mechanical)
errors (distribution of), 626, 938
Esson, William, *346*
ether,
    drag, 9–10, 148–53, 154–5, 306–11
    electromagnetic, 105–6, 180–1, 182–5, 186–8, 194–6, 199–200

energy, 105–6, 190, 354–5, 364
    gravity, 105–7, 194, 366, 451–2, 798–9
    luminiferous, 9–11, 23, 46–9, 50–3, 148–53, 154–5, 182–5, 189–90, 194–6, 306–11
    models of, 30–1, 180, 337
    molecular, 917–18, 919–20, 957, 959–60, 962–3
    Newton's theory, 798–9
    and refraction of light, 9–10, 147–53, 154–5, 306–11
    velocity of light in, 9, 147–53, 154–5, 306–11
Euclid, 655, 953
Euler, Leonhard, 469n, 470n, 688n
Eulerian integrals, 426
evaporation, 668–9, 670–4
Everett, Joseph David, 23, 269, 749n, 751n, 857n
    letters to Maxwell: (19 July 1872), 552n; (26 July 1872), 552n
    Royal Society papers: 'On the flexural and torsional rigidity of a glass rod' (Maxwell's report on) **261**, 272–5; 'On torsion and flexure for the determination of rigidities' (Maxwell's reports on) **269**, 300–3; **282**, 348–50
Everitt, C. W. F., 1n, 8n, 9n, 12n, 13n, 81n, 128n, 132n, 138n, 250n, 280n, 632n, 682n, 900n, 902n
Ewing, J. A., 897n, 915

Fabius Maximus, Quintus (Cunctator), 878n
factorials, 682, 684, 687, 688n, 689
farad, 736, 742–3, 748–50, 843–4
Faraday, Michael, 367, 950
    letters from Maxwell: (9 November 1857), 20n, 107n, 194n, 802n; (19 October 1861), 110n, 188n, 484n, 627n
    letter to Maxwell: (13 November 1857), 802n
    diamagnetism, 336–7, 405–6, 806
    dielectrics, 193, 958–9
    electrolysis, 417
    electromagnetic induction, 193, 507, 768
    electromagnetic rotation, 507
    electrostatic induction, 193, 829
    gold film, 181
    lines of force, 405, 507, 678–9, 802–6
    magneto-optic effect, 189–90, 336, 405–6, 781, 784n
    matter, 812n, 895
    paramagnetism, 336, 405–6
    polarity, 405
Faraday effect, *see* magneto-optic rotation

Index

Fawcett, William Milner, 35n, *701n*
  letter from Maxwell: (1 January 1872) **397**, 701
  letter to H. W. Cookson: (16 December 1873), 35n
Faye, H. A., 155, 758, 761
  letter from G. B. Airy: (26 September 1872), 758n
Felici, Riccardo, 193, 386, 710, 711, 713
Ferrers, Norman Macleod, 23, *492n*, 729n
  Royal Society paper: 'Motion of a free rigid body' (Maxwell's report on) **325**, 492–5
field equations, 160–1, 193, 514–15
figure of the earth, 98, 277, 683, 780
Fischer, W. L. F, 463n
Fisher, Osmond,
  Cambridge Philosophical Society paper: 'On the elevation of mountains by lateral pressure' (Maxwell's report on) **490**, 968–70
fish-eye lens, 752
Fizeau, Hippolyte, 9, 148–51, 154–5, 195, 311, 851, 874
Flint, Robert, 463n
fluids,
  analogy to electromagnetism, 124, 399, 401, 403, 426, 439, 485–6, 512, 524–5, 598–604, 605–7
  displacement in, 447, 456, 457–8, 551
  Helmholtz on, 124, 241–2n, 243, 391, 399–404, 426, 432, 446–7, 448n, 530, 545n, 778
  lines of motion in, 123–7, 529–34
  Maxwell on, 123–7, 236–40, 241–4, 391, 399–404, 446–8, 456, 510–12, 529–34; 730
  Rankine on, 123–7, 389, 445, 448n, 511, 529–34
  stability of, 239–40, 241–4
  Stokes on, 124, 533–4n, 778
  stream function, 123–4, 426, 428–9, 448, 457–8, 529–31, 545–6, 603
  W. Thomson on, 390, 391, 398, 778
  vena contracta, 510–12
  vortex motion, 239–40, 241–4, 391, 398–404
  vortex turbine, 236–9
fluorescence, 245n
Folie, F., 934
Fontaine's turbine, 239
Forbes, George, *228*, 886n
Forbes, James David, 1n, 2, 228n, 284, 296n, 460, 461, 462, 474, 646n, 774–5, 886n, 921n
  letter to Maxwell: (4 June 1864), 972

Forde, Henry Charles, *375*, 410n
Forrest, James, 691n
Foucault, Léon, 195, 345, 351, 378, 631, 810, 851, 871
Fourier, Charles, 542n
Fourier, Joseph, 36, 358, 541–2, 564, 941n
Fourier's theorem, 487
Fourneyron's turbine, 239
frameworks (theory of), 119–21, 313–17, 519–21, 691
Francis, William, 881
  letter to Maxwell: (11 July 1873), 881n
Fraunhofer, Joseph, 155
free will, 19, 814–23
Fresnel, Augustin Jean, 9, 46n, 47, 148, 149n, 154n, 182–4n, 187n, 309, 311
  wave surface, 319, 322, 342, 477
Fresnel rhomb, 46n
Froude, William, 532
Fuller, A. T., 98n, 112n, 128n, 139n, 236n, 239n, 344n, 410n, 624n, 783n

Galilei, Galileo, 361, 367
Galton, Francis, 815, 928n
  letter from Maxwell: (26 February 1879), 19n, 819n
galvanometers, 166–70, 204–6, 219, 375, 557–8
  mirror, 165–6, 664–5, 704n, 871–2
  sine, 735, 867
  tangent, 666, 667, 871
  in the *Treatise*, 517, 666, 667
Garber, Elizabeth, 12n, 81n, 128n, 138n, 250n, 280n, 900n, 902n
gases,
  absorption of, 24, 285–7
  Clausius on, 12–13, 72–4, 75n, 77, 83, 84n, 133, 280, 656–8
  conductivity (thermal), 13, 72–85, 133, 263–4, 268, 270, 277, 283–4, 658, 661–3, 760
  diffusion, 15, 133, 223, 271, 277, 281–2, 286–7, 564, 657, 661–2, 760, 780, 888, 890–6, 897, 926, 934
  electrical discharge in, 827–30
  equilibrium of temperature, 14–15, 16–17, 264–6, 267–9, 283, 292, 853–5, 898–910, 911–14, 916, 937–9
  force law, 13, 227, 254–6, 276–7n, 659
  kinetic theory (history of), 12–16, 19, 250–2, 279–80, 654–9
  and liquids (continuity of states), 668–9, 670–4, 923, 969
  mean free path, 12–13, 77–83, 657, 923–6

Index

relaxation time, 13, 257n, 282–3
separation of, 285–7, 344, 588
specific heats, 76–7, 259–60, 284
statistical theory, 12–15, 16–19, 133, 281, 292, 656–9, 903–10, 911–14, 915–16, 927–33, 946–7, 960
transpiration, 222–3, 224, 232–3, 283, 890–1, 926
velocity distribution function, 12–15, 17, 74–5, 133, 281, 657, 903–10, 911–14, 915–16, 938
viscosity, 13–14, 78, 96, 202, 215, 216–17, 218–19, 221, 222–3, 224–5, 230–5, 261–2, 270, 277, 282–4, 658, 780, 888, 891–4, 897
Gassiot, John Peter, 211, 375, 403, 607n
Gauss, Carl Friedrich, 654n, 809, 935
'consistent representation', 26
factorials, 689
optics, 936
potential, 399n, 843n
spherical harmonics, 330n
terrestrial magnetism, 505–6
topology, 326n, 647
Gauss' theorem, 645, 648–9n
Gay-Lussac, J. L., 135, 258, 650–1n, 657, 909, 947
generator (electrostatic), 424–7
geometry, 1n, 20–2, 702, 715, 716, 717
non-Euclidean, 618–19
projective, 21, 313–14, 647, 899, 935–6, 942
topographical, 29, 466n, 566–7
see also topology
'geometry of position', *see* geometry, projective; topology
Gibbs, J. Willard, 945
Gibson, J. C., 627n
Girard, P. S., 223n
glaciers, viscosity of, 473–5
Gladstone, J. H., 56n, 949n
Gladstone, W. E., 461n
Glaisher, J. W. L., 935
Glasgow, University of, 392, 443, 446, 449
Goethe, J. W., 578
Gonville and Caius College, Cambridge, 683
Goodeve, Thomas Minchin, 3, 668n
Gordon, Edward Strathearn, 463n
Goupillière, J. Haton de la, 717
governors, 8, 101, 107–8, 113–16, 343–5, 351–2, 410–11, 631, 635, 871
Graham, Thomas, 24, 222–3, 224, 231–3, 262n, 270, 281–3, 564n, 588, 657, 658n, 891, 926

letter from Maxwell: (1 May 1865) **248**, 222–3
Royal Society paper: 'On the absorption and dialytic separation of gases' (Maxwell's report on) **264**, 205–7
Gramme, Z. T., 872
gravity, 20, 106–9, 194, 366, 451–2, 780, 797–9, 817
and thermal equilibrium, 14, 264–6, 269, 283, 292, 853–5, 909, 916, 937–9
Gray, Charles, 251
green (colour), 629
Green, G., 377n, 665n, 871n, 873n
Green, George, 399n, 453n, 456n, 459, 683, 721–2, 843n, 859n, 880
Green's function, 320, 502
Green's reciprocity theorem, 320
Green's theorem, 24, 346, 399n, 422, 502, 532
Greenwich Observatory
chronogrraph, 351, 372
governors, 351–2
Gregory, David, 368
Gregory, D. F., 426n
Griffith, George, 753n, 895–6n
letter to Maxwell: (27 July 1873), 895n, 916n, 922n
Grove, William Robert, 6, 356n, 463
letters from Maxwell: (27 March 1868) **285**, 356–7; (7 November 1868) **313**, 461
Grove battery, 378, 403, 626, 632, 635
Grubb, Thomas, 607
Gudermann, Christoph, 550n
Gulliver's Travels, 355
Guthrie, Francis, *853*, 937
Guthrie, Frederick, 23, 513, *827n*, 949
Royal Society paper, 'On a new relation between heat and electricity' (Maxwell's report on) **442**, 827–30
Guyou, É., 528n

Haidinger's brushes, 837n
Hall, Marie Boas, 22n
Hamilton, Sir William, Bt, 335n, 361, 597
Hamilton, Sir William Rowan,
algebra, 952n
characteristic function, 224n, 667n, 935, 942, 943n
dynamics, 28, 31, 744–7
hodograph, 21, 898–900
metaphysics, 361, 952
optics, 667, 935, 942–3

Index

quaternions, 29–30, 214, 568n, 575n, 577, 580, 609, 626, 707n, 755, 951–5, 963
  spatial direction, 637, 639, 641, 643, 644
  time, 952n
  varying action, 354, 626, 757n, 947
Hamilton's operator, 30, 332–3, 568–9, 573–6, 577, 590–2, 593–7, 600–1, 609, 755, 760, 915n, 945
'Hamlet, Prince of Denmark', 610n
Hance, H. F., 642n
Hankins, Thomas L., 21n, 29n
Hanlon, George Oldham, 510–12
Hansemann, Gustav, 659, 918
Harcourt, A. Vernon, 346
Hardy, Gathorne, 463n
Harman, P. M., 12n, 20n, 28n, 618n, 686n, 746n
harmotome, 380–2
Harris, Thomas, 785, 858
Harris, Sir William Snow, 785, 858, 859n
Haughton, Samuel, 23, 46–7, 50–3
  Royal Society paper: 'On the reflexion of polarised light' (Maxwell's report on) **199**, 46–9; **200**, 50–3
  letter to G. G. Stokes: (6 November 1862), 52n
  'Remarks on Mr Stokes' Report', 52n
heat,
  conduction of, 353, 358–9, 389, 392, 416, 513–14, 541–3, 564–5, 780, 940–1, 941–2n, 962
  dynamical theory of, 266n, 269, 359, 655, 780, 957–9, 962–3
  and electricity, 353, 827–30, 940–1, 941–2n, 958–9
  radiant, 245–8, 253, 781, 962–3
  see also energy; thermodynamics; thermo-electricity
Heaviside, Oliver, 824n
Heilbron, J. L., 800n
Heimann, P. M., 26n
  see also Harman, P. M.
Helmholtz, Hermann von, 2, 22, 26, 34, 632, 681
  letter from Maxwell: (12 April 1864) **225**, 146
  acoustics, 603n, 856, 874n
  chronograph, 631
  colour vision, 775
  conservation of energy, 191–2, 335n, 354–5n, 686
  Croonian Lecture, 146n, 341, 837n
  electrodynamics, 26, 354–5n, 583, 596, 686–7, 773, 945

  geometry, 618n
  induction of currents, 191–2, 507
  optics, 146n, 341, 775, 837n, 936
  potential theory, 241–2n, 391n, 399–404, 407, 426, 432, 434n, 530, 545n, 593
  siren, 874
  topology, 434n, 439
  viscosity, 944
  vision, 341, 837n
  vortex motion, 22, 124, 241n, 242–3, 321, 391n, 399–404, 407, 434n, 445, 446–7, 530n, 533, 593, 778
Herapath, John, 280, 656
Herschel, Sir John F. W., Bt, 107, 246, 296n, 621, 856, 860
  letter to John Dalton: (20 May 1833), 621
Herschel, Sir William, 104–5n, 246n
Hicks, W. M., 35
Hirn, G. A., 761, 762n
  letter to Maxwell: (25 November 1872), 762n
Hirst, Thomas Archer, 2, 5, 6, 639, 642, 956n
  letter to G. G. Stokes: (5 October 1868), 385n
  report on paper by R. Moon: (5 October 1868), 385n
Hockin, Charles, 9, 122n, *164*, 181, 200n, 219, 376, 403, 409–10, 423, 662
  letter from Maxwell: (7 September 1864) **232**, 164
  letters to Maxwell: (15 May 1868), 376n; (27 July 1868), 410n; (11 March 1870), 410n, 662n
hodograph, 323n, 328n, 898–900
Holden, E. S., 104n
Holtz, W., 271n, 873
Home, David Milne, 580n
Home, R. W., 800n
homoeopathy, 927n
Hooke's law, 537
Hopley, I. B., 89n, 113n, 165n, 204n, 213n, 376n, 386n
Hort, F. J. A., 814n
Hudson, W. H. H., 729n
Huggins, Sir William, 6, 10, 149n, 150n, *306n*, 451–2n, 714
  letters from Maxwell: (10 June 1867) **271**, 306–11; (13 October 1868) **309**, 451–2; (2 May 1872) **406**, 714
Hunt, B. J., 11n, 824n
Hunter, John, 681
Huxley, Thomas Henry, 6, 836n

impulse (force), 423, 733, 747

index of refraction, 196, 543, 627–8
inertia, 363–4, 800, 812
   inertial effect of current, 548, 770
instruments (electrical)
   electrodynamometer, 627, 734–5, 738, 742, 867, 871
   electrometers, 209, 377, 423, 429–30, 443, 481–2, 555, 736, 828, 850, 858, 873
   galvanometers, 165–70, 204–6, 219, 375, 557–8, 664–5, 666, 667, 704n, 735, 867, 871–2
integral theorems, 28–9, 325–6, 441, 589, 634
integration (order of), 638, 639n
irreversibility, 16–19, 359–61, 366–7, 541–3, 564–5, 582, 967

Jacobi, Carl Gustav Jacob, 214
Jago, James, 23
   letter to T. H. Huxley: (11 March 1873), 836n
   Royal Society paper: 'On visible direction' (Maxwell's report on) **447**, 836–8
Jamin, Jules,
   magnetism, 883
   polarized light, 50, 51–2n, 53
   wave theory of light, 50, 155, 182–5n, 186–7
jargonium, 748n, 886
Jenkin, Henry Charles Fleeming, 6, *7n*, 8
   letters from Maxwell: (27 August 1863) **218**, 110–11; (*c.* September 1871) **385**, 678–9
   letters to Maxwell: (10 January 1868), 363n; (28 October 1871), 680n
   letters to G. G. Stokes: (16 July 1868), 375n; (27 May 1873), 830n; (30 May 1873), 850n
   letters to W. Thomson: (8 August 1860), 113n; (20 February 1868), 363n
   report on paper by Frederick Guthrie: (27 May 1873), 830n
   report on paper by D. M'Kichan: (30 May 1873), 850n
   report on paper by Maxwell: (16 July 1868), 375n
   cable, 410n, 489
   electrical measurements, 6, 88n, 92, 94, 97, 107, 110–11, 122n, 210, 214, 217, 375, 408n, 409, 417, 548n
   Electricity and Magnetism, 356n, 630n, 678n, 679n, 680, 743, 748, 842–4
   frameworks, 517, 520
   governors, 8, 101, 107–8, 113–16, 343n, 631, 871
   on Lucretius, 363n

Jochmann, E., 704n, 710, 711, 713
Jones, Henry Bence, 950
   letter from Maxwell: (4 February 1873) **438**, 813
Jordan, D. W., 879n
Joule, James Prescott, 36, 84n, 210, 390, 489
   letter to Maxwell: (n.d.), 543n
   letter to W. Thomson: (3 December 1851), 751n
   air pump, 869
   British Association (Presidency), 916
   dip circle, 543, 719n, 870
   dynamical theory of heat, 280, 333n, 656
   magnet, 810
   magnetic measurements, 499, 505, 543, 719n
   mechanical equivalent of heat, 36, 84–5, 179–80, 210n, 338–9, 346, 378, 390
Joule's equivalent, *see* mechanical equivalent of heat
Jullien, Michel, 702–3n
Jungnickel, C., 946n
Jurin, James, 510n
Juvenal, 884

Kant, I., 952n
Kelland, P., 775n, 947, 951–5
Kew Observatory, 93n, 96, 214
kinetics, 291, 654n, 778
King's College Hospital, 102
King's College London, 147
   Maxwell's appointment, 2, 61, 86, 249
   Maxwell's electrical experiments, 92n, 97, 157, 210
   Maxwell's lectures, 3–4, 60, 61, 87
   Maxwell's resignation, 4, 180, 249
Kirchhoff, Gustav,
   elasticity, 269, 272, 275, 300, 302n, 348
   electricity, 516, 704
   magnetism, 480
   spectra, 41n, 44
Klein, Martin J., 16n, 17n, 18n, 544n, 709n
Klinkerfues, Wilhelm, 152–3n
knots, 322, 325–7, 330
Knott, C. G., 17n, 328n, 335n, 568n, 577n, 593n, 667n, 677n, 699n, 731n, 755n, 756n, 763n, 825n, 831n, 915n
Knudsen, Ole, 11n, 406n
Kohlrausch, F. W. G., 230–1
Kohlrausch, R., 110–11n, 188, 195, 378, 773n, 851
Kopp, H., 895, 925
Krönig, A., 280, 656

Index

Lagout, Edouard, 887
Lagrange, Joseph Louis, 27–8, 30–2, 337, 716, 741n, 744–6, 770
Lake, Henry, 766
Lamb, Horace, 35, 123n, 730n
Lambert, J. H., 774n
Lamé, Gabriel, 70, 120n, 333, 479–80, 568, 573, 717, 825
Laplace, Pierre Simon de, 131, 277, 386, 686, 689, 751n, 818, 932
Laplace's coefficients, *see* spherical harmonic analysis
Laplace's equation, 30, 430, 480, 502, 511, 967n
Laplacian operator, 24, 30, 161, 199, 333, 569, 575, 700
Larmor, Sir Joseph, 528n, 607n
least action (principle of), 626
Legendre, A. M., 276, 278n, 426n, 458n
Leibniz, G. W., 361, 577
Leibnizians, 364
Le Sage, G. L., 250, 279, 363n, 655, 702n
Leslie, John, 412
Lévy, M., 528n
Lewes, G. H., 362n
Leyden jar, 485n, 555–7
Libri, G., 648
Lichtenberg, G. C., 774n
light,
  anomalous dispersion, 11–12, 419–21, 862–3, 864–5
  atmospheric refraction, 751–4
  blue of the sky, 614–15, 619, 666n, 919, 940n
  double refraction, 1n, 559–63
  electromagnetic theory of, 9–11, 155, 182–5, 186–8, 194–6, 199–200, 202–3, 375–9, 543n, 627, 781, 809–10, 849, 851
  emission theory, 751
  polarization of, 46–7, 50–3, 559–63, 781, 810
  refraction of, 1n, 148–53, 154–5, 224, 667, 751–4
  velocity of, 9–11, 148–53, 154–5, 187–8, 194–5, 306–11, 781, 809–10, 851
  wave theory of, 46–7, 50–3, 182–5, 186–8, 199n, 306–11, 378, 751
Lightfoot, J. B., 814n
Lindsay, James, 707n
lines of force, 125n, 192, 405, 446, 516, 666, 667, 678–9, 719–20, 802–9
Linnaeus, Carl, 641n,
Liouville, Joseph, 453n, 480, 543–4n
liquid and gaseous states (continuity of), 16, 668–9, 670–4, 923, 969

Listing, Johann Benedict, 29, 326n, 433n, 470–1, 591n, 639, 641–2, 644, 936
Littré, Émile, 362
Liveing, G. D., 833
Lloyd, Humphrey, 753
Lloyd, J. T., 377n, 665n, 871n, 873n
Locke, John, 361, 368, 416n, 816
Lockyer, J. N., 820n
logarithmic curves, 328–30
London Mathematical Society, 5, 620
  Maxwell's papers at, 318n, 340, 342, 457n, 466n, 470–1, 510–12, 570n, 715n, 716, 717, 942–3
  Maxwell's questions to, 343, 508–9, 550–1, 637, 639, 641–3, 644
  Maxwell's report on paper by J. W. Strutt, **460**, 860–3
Longman, William, 661, 710
  letter to Maxwell: (20 June 1871), 668n
Longridge, James Atkinson, 24, 369n
  Royal Society paper: 'On the resistance of the air to rifled projectiles' (Maxwell's report on) **288**, 373–4
Lorenz, L. V., 355n, 379
Loschmidt, Joseph, 15, 292n, 632, 659, 760, 888, 890–6, 897, 925–6
Loschmidt's number, 258, 892
Lowe, Robert, Viscount Sherbrooke, 704–5n
Lucretius, 19, 250–1, 291, 363, 654–5, 820, 928–9
Luke, Arthur, letter to Maxwell: (6 October 1868), 973

McCormmach, R., 946n
MacCullagh, James, 182–4n, 186–7n, 380n, 884n
McCunn, Mrs, 446, 449
McDonald, W., 463n
MacGregor, J. G., 897, 915
Mackenzie, Colin, 727, 731n
M'Kichan, Dugald, 23
  Royal Society paper: 'Determination of the number of electrostatic units...' (Maxwell's report on) **455**, 849–51
MacLaurin, Colin, 798–9, 816
MacLeod, R. M., 6n
Macmillan (publishers), 650n, 758
magnetism,
  axis of, 675–6
  coercive force, 828
  diamagnetism, 336, 405–6, 781
  effluvia, 800
  lamellar distribution of, 514n, 597, 700

Index

magnetisation, 514, 718–26, 781, 847, 879–80, 881–3, 886
  measurements, 499
  paramagnetism, 336, 405–6
  of ships, 505, 517, 781
  solar, 117–18
  solenoidal distribution of, 485, 514n, 591, 597, 700
  terrestrial, 499, 505, 549, 781
  W. Thomson on, 485n, 498n, 514n, 597n, 700, 724n
  vortices, 180, 189–90, 337, 768–9, 784
magnetometer, 870
magneto-optic rotation, 11, 180, 189–90, 336–7, 405–6, 733, 781, 784, 824, 825, 884–5
Magnus, Gustav, 504
Mance, Henry, 584n
Mansel, H. L., 335n
Marey, É. J., 528n
Marianini, S., 557
Marischal College, Aberdeen, 2
Martin Chuzzlewit, 834
materialism, 19–20, 360–1, 363–5, 654–5, 814–23
Mathison, W. C., *341*
matter (nature of), 15, 19–20, 250–1, 279–80, 291, 304–5, 360–1, 363–5, 395–6, 586–8, 654–9, 799–800, 811–12
Matthiessen, Augustus, 211, 217, 349, 376n, 407, 409, 514
Maupertuis, P. L. M., 626
Maxwell, Frances Clerk, 451
Maxwell, James Clerk,
  correspondence, 971–6; *see also* Adams, W. G.; Airy, G. B.; Aitken, J.; Balfour, J. H.; Barnard, J.; Blore, E. W.; Bond, G. P.; Branston, R. E; Campbell, L.; Cay, C. H.; Cay, R. D.; Cayley, A.; Clark, J. L.; Clifton, R. B.; Cookson, H. W.; Crum Brown, A.; Cunningham, J. W.; Devonshire, Duke of; Droop, H. W.; Dwelshauvers-Dery, V.; Everett, J. D.; Fawcett, W. M.; Forbes, J. D.; Francis, W.; Graham, T.; Griffith, G.; Grove, W. R.; Hockin, C.; Huggins, W.; Jenkin, H. C. F.; Jones, H. B.; Joule, J. P.; Longman, W.; Luke, A.; Maxwell, K. M. Clerk; Monro, C. J.; Munro, H. A. J.; Nanson, E. J.; Pattison, M.; Preece, G. E.; Price, B.; Rowland, H. A.; Sharpey, W.; Siemens, C. W.; Spencer, H.; Stokes, G. G.; Strutt, J. W.; Swan, W.; Sylvester, J. J.; Tait, P. G.; Tayler, C. B.; Thomson, J.; Thomson, W.; Tomlinson, C.; Trotter, C.; Tucker, R.; Tyndall, J.
  reports on papers: *see* Cambridge Philosophical Society; London Mathematical Society; Royal Society of London; *see also* Airy, G. B.; Bashforth, F.; Chambers, C.; Clark, J. L.; Des Cloiseaux, A.; Everett, J. D.; Ferrers, N. M.; Fisher, O.; Graham, T.; Guthrie, F.; Haughton, S.; Jago, J.; Longridge, J. A.; M'Kichan, D.; Merrifield, C. W.; Miller, W. A.; Moon, R.; Moseley, H.; Radcliffe, C. B.; Rankine, W. J. M.; Robinson, T. R.; Stokes, G. G.; Strutt, J. W.; Tarn, E. W.; Tyndall, J.
  manuscripts not reproduced as texts: 'Chief Musician upon Nabla', 577n; 'Concerning Demons', 17n, 332n; on ether drag, 154n; 'Fresnels Biaxial Wave Surface', 319n; on Heaviside, 824n; Helmholtz's conjugate functions, 432n; Helmholtz on electrodynamics, 596n; 'Instruments in the Cavendish Laboratory', 868n; 'Lines of Curvature of an Ellipsoid', 319n; 'Lines of Curvature of an Elliptic Paraboloid', 318n; line of quickest ascent, 625n; Listing's terms, 591n; 'Memorandum of Improvements', 377n; 'Oxford Physical Laboratory', 636n; notes on F. E. Neumann, 498n; 'Results of Experiments July 1850', 275, 349; 'Schröter on Steiner Surface', 477n; 'Torricelli Evangelista Lezioni Accademiche', 395n; viscosity of gases, 96n
  notebooks: 154n, 239–40, 256n, 321n, 377n, 395n, 410–11, 432n, 477n, 502–7, 625n, 630–1, 636n, 642–3, 646n, 648n, 651n, 730
  appointments: *see* Cambridge, University of; King's College London; St Andrews United College; Trinity College, Cambridge
  Bakerian Lecture, 230–5
  'Construction of stereograms of surfaces' (1868), 340n, 342n, 476n
  'On the cyclide' (1868), 312n, 319n, 476n
  'Displacement in a case of fluid motion' (1870), 448n, 456n, 457–8n, 545n
  'A dynamical theory of the electromagnetic field' (1865), 9–11, 27, 30, 99n, 112n, 158n, 160–3, 164n, 178n, 180n, 183n, 188n, 189–96, 197–201, 202–3, 337, 355n, 399, 401, 417, 773

Index

'On the dynamical theory of gases' (1867), 13–14, 250n, 254–66, 267n, 270–1n, 276–7, 279–84, 291–2, 331n, 408, 658–9, 854, 892n, 938
'On a dynamical top' (1857), 492–3n
'On the equilibrium of elastic solids' (1850), 65n, 273n, 275n
'Equilibrium and stiffness of frames' (1864), 119–21n
'On Faraday's lines of force' (1856), 21, 28, 99n, 192n, 336–7n, 355n, 484n, 527n, 529n, 530n
'Final state of a system of molecules in motion' (1873), 14–15, 898–910, 911–14, 916n, 938–9
'On governors' (1868), 8, 113–15n, 343–5, 351, 862
'Illustrations of the dynamical theory of gases' (1860), 12–13, 72–85, 133, 216, 219n, 232, 250n, 258n, 280, 331n, 657–8, 892n, 938
Keith prize, 727–8, 731n
lectures: (at Cambridge University), 35–6, 685, 689, 690, 760, 898n, 940–1, 942n; (at King's College London), 3–4, 60, 61, 87
library, 362n, 646n, 897n
'On Loschmidt's experiments on diffusion' (1873), 890–6, 926
'Mathematical classification of physical quantities' (1870), 568n, 570n, 573n, 651n, 652n
'Method of making a direct comparison of electrostatic with electromagnetic force' (1868), 9, 176–8n, 213n, 326n, 354–5n, 375–9, 484–6n, 489n, 851
'Molecules' (1873), 15, 19, 820n, 922–33
'On physical lines of force' (1861–62), 9, 27, 31, 99n, 110n, 180, 188n, 198n, 337, 484n, 627n, 769, 808n
'On reciprocal figures and diagrams of forces' (1864), 21, 60n, 313, 330
'On reciprocal figures, frames and diagrams of forces' (1870), 21, 63n, 330, 346, 392, 517–18, 519–21, 609, 946
On the Stability of the Motion of Saturn's Rings (1859), 12, 105n, 115n, 130n, 131, 758, 761
'On the theory of compound colours' (1860), 58–9n, 552n, 775n
Theory of Heat (1871), 15–16, 27, 332n, 416n, 540n, 541–3, 564–5n, 584–8, 633n, 634, 636, 645n, 646n, 648n, 651n, 661, 668, 672–4, 709, 710, 732n, 780, 853n, 946n
thermodynamic signature, 16, 543–4n, 596n, 609n, 716, 733, 740
travels (continental), 97, 98, 476
Treatise on Electricity and Magnetism (1873), 11–12, 21; (composition of), 24–33, 323n, 328n, 346, 416–17, 423, 424–7, 428–32, 453–6, 479–82, 483–6, 487–8, 489–91, 496–7, 499–500, 502–7, 508–9, 514–15, 516–17, 522–7, 589, 634, 639, 641–3, 644, 732–3; (dynamics in), 27, 30–1, 716, 732–3, 740, 744–7, 769–71; (Part II 'Electrokinematics') 27, 158n, 320n, 417, 422–3, 483, 503–4, 584n, 626n, 633n, 661–3, 699–700, 707, 765n, 828–9n, 966–7n; (Part IV 'Electromagnetism'), 27, 174n, 177n, 188n, 199n, 210n, 323n, 324–5n, 336n, 355n, 426n, 500n, 507, 508–9, 514–15, 516–17, 522–7, 549n, 572n, 583n, 597n, 627n, 666n, 679n, 686n, 695n, 704n, 706n, 725n, 732–3, 738, 742, 748–9n, 756, 770–2, 784n, 801n, 805n, 809n, 826n, 871n, 884–5n, 963n, 967n; (Part I 'Electrostatics'), 26–7, 125n, 172n, 207n, 271n, 320n, 423, 424–6, 428–32, 453–6, 459, 479–82, 484–6, 488, 489–91, 496–7, 499, 502–3, 516, 531n, 547n, 605–6n, 680n, 682, 689, 764n, 858n, 871n, 959n, 967n; (Part III 'Magnetism'), 27, 117n, 325–6n, 433n, 498–9, 505–6, 514n, 543n, 583n, 590n, 597n, 675–6, 828n, 880n, 881–2n, 966–7n; ('Preliminary'), 433n, 569n, 570n, 591n, 634n, 641n, 644, 700n, 784n; (proofs), 32, 652, 660, 676, 681, 689, 700, 707, 733, 741, 755, 757, 784n; (publication), 31–3, 416, 636, 781, 839
'On the viscosity or internal friction of air and other gases' (1866), 13, 202n, 215n, 216–17, 222n, 230–5, 262, 429, 432, 658, 891
Maxwell, John Clerk, 451
Maxwell, Katherine Mary Clerk, 446, 449, 552n
letters from Maxwell, 971; (28 January 1864) **222**, 122; (3 January 1870) **336**, 528; (20 March 1871) **361**, 623; (22 March 1871) **363**, 629
Mayer, Julius Robert, 335n
Mayer, Tobias, 774n
Mayr, O., 8n
mechanical equivalent of heat, 84–5, and British Association unit, 210n, 378, 489
experiments, 179–80, 338–9, 346, 390
mechanics (theory of), 291, 492–5, 777–9

'Memoirs of Martin Scriblerus', 636
Mensbrugghe, G. Van der, 386
Merrifield, Charles Watkins, 24, *369*
  Royal Society paper: 'Resistance of the air to rifled projectiles' (Maxwell's report on) **288**, 374
metaphysics, 19–20, 335–6, 360–1, 362–4, 367–8, 395–6, 798–800, 811–12, 814–23, 917, 952, 956–7
Meyer, Lothar, 895, 925
Meyer, O. E., 78n, 231, 234, 262n, 270, 280, 658, 891, 894
Michelson, A. A., 10
Mill, John Stuart, 335n, 362, 731
Miller, J. D., 879n
Miller, William Allen, 24, 42, 415n, 417, 504
  Royal Society paper: 'On the photographic transparency of various bodies' (Maxwell's report on) **199**, 47–9
  report on paper by T. Graham: (4 July 1866), 287n
Miller, William Hallowes, *382*, 415n, 510n, 641n
  letter from G. B. Airy: ([1848]), 414n
molecules,
  diameter of, 15, 659, 890–6, 897, 915n, 919–20, 925–6, 934
  encounters, 254–9, 898–910, 911–14,
  ether, 915–16
  gases, 15, 72–85, 230–5, 258–60, 261–4, 279–84, 291, 654–60, 888, 890–6, 922–9
  forces, 16, 668–9, 670–4
  properties, 291, 586–8, 888, 890–6, 922–7, 959–61, 962–3
Moncreiff, James, *392*
Monro, Cecil James, 58n, 614, 629
  letters from Maxwell: (6 July 1870) **341**, 550–3; (15 March 1871) **359**, 617–20
  letters to Maxwell: (2 June 1870), 550n; (3 March 1871), 617–18n; (9 March 1871), 619n; (21 March 1871), 620n, 629n; (10 September 1871), 618–19n
  letters to J. W. Strutt: (5 February 1871), 614n; (27 February 1871), 614n
Moon, Robert, 23, *383*
  Royal Society paper: 'On the impact of compressible bodies' (Maxwell's report on) **291**, 383–5
Morgan, Augustus de, 648n
Moseley, Henry, 23, 113n, *472*
  Royal Society paper: 'On the mechanical possibility of the descent of glaciers' (Maxwell's report on) **319**, 472–5

Mossotti, O. F., 193
Mott, A. J., 917
mountains (elevation of), 968–70
Muirhead, J. P., 791n
Mulcahy, John, 313n
Müller, F. Max, 617n, 840–1n
Müller, J., 246, 552
Munro, Hugh Andrew Johnstone, *250*
  letter from Maxwell: (7 February 1866) **257**, 250–2
  translation of Lucretius, 251n, 363n, 655n, 928n
Murphy, Robert, 683, 689

Nabla, 30, 568, 577, 593, 755, 760, 945
  see also Hamilton's operator
Nanson, E. J., letter to Maxwell: (5 December 1873), 973
Napier, R. D., 510n
Nature,
  letters to, 14–15, 551, 619, 853–5, 886, 917–18, 921, 937–9
  papers in, 618n, 671n, 712–13, 890–6, 898n, 913n, 922n
  poem in, 704n
  reviews in, 37, 395n, 842–4, 951–5
Navez pendulum, 373
Navier, C. L. M. H., 273n
nebular hypothesis, 956–7
nerves (electrical properties of), 554–8
Neugebauer, Otto, 98n
Neumann, Carl, 26, 320, 426, 480, 499–500, 531, 654n, 764–5
Neumann, Franz Ernst, 182–4n, 186–7n, 479–80, 498, 721n, 773, 843n, 881n, 945n
Newton, Sir Isaac, 20, 70, 297, 361, 368, 395–6, 510n, 610n, 655, 816, 936
  gravity, 20, 798, 801
  laws of motion, 31, 746, 817
Newtonians, 368, 798–800, 816–17
Newton's rings, 796, 813
Niagara, 346
Nicol's prism, 562–3, 615
Niven, William Davidson, 75n, 729n
Nobert, F. A., 874

O'Brien, Matthew, 683
Odling, William, 5n
Oersted, H. C., 193, 507, 767, 801
Ohm, Georg Simon, 516, 750
Ohm's law, 7, 417, 503, 517, 966
opacity, 180–1, 196, 200

Index

ophthalmoscope, 203
optical instruments, 21–2, 224
    see also stereoscope
optics (geometrical), 21–2, 224, 667, 751–3, 781, 899, 935–6, 942–3
orthogonal curves, 123–4, 545, 715, 825, 884
ovals, 20–1, 294–7
Oxford Physical Laboratory, 623n, 632n, 636

Paley, F. A., 840
pangenesis, 815n
paramagnetism, 336–7, 405–6
Parker, Henry Tooke, 104n
Parliament (election to), 390, 392, 399
Pattison, Mark, 18–19, *358*
    letters from Maxwell: (7 April 1868) **286**, 358–61; (13 April 1868) **287**, 362–8
Peel, Sir Robert, Bt, *212n*
Peelers, 212
Peltier, J. A. C., 483n, 765n
Peltier effect, 483–4, 692, 699–700, 765, 833
periphractic region, 591, 593–4
peripolar molecules, 555–6
perversion (topological), 637, 642, 644, 645
Petit, A. T., 657, 910
Philosophical Magazine, 446, 732, 824, 879, 881, 886
    Maxwell's letter to the editors: (12 October 1870), 566n
    Maxwell's letter to W. R. Grove: (27 March 1868) **285**, 356–7
phlogiston, 364
physical sciences, 776–82
Physical Society of London, 6, 949
Piotrowski, G. von, 944
Pirie, George, 729n
Plana, Giovanni (Jean), 479
planimeter, 874
Plato, 361n
Plücker, Julius, 41n, 214, 750
Poggendorff, J. C., 866
Poinsot, Louis, 492n, 495
Poiseuille, J. L. M., 223
Poisson, Siméon Denis,
    elasticity, 261n, 272n, 283
    electrostatics, 479, 800, 802, 843
    fluids, 241n, 540n
    integral theorems, 634
    magnetism, 117, 498, 802
    specific heats, 260n
    vibrations, 414n
Poisson's equation, 430n

Poisson's ratio, 272–5, 302, 349
polarizing prisms, 559
Pole, William, 552
Pollock, Sir Frederick, 2nd Bt, 5–6n
Pollock, Sir Frederick, 3rd Bt, *252*, 666n
polygon of forces, 519
Poncelet, J. V., 313n
Pope, Alexander, 636n
Porter, T. M., 19n
positivism, 358, 362
potential (concept of), 24, 25–7, 36, 123–4, 160–2, 392, 394, 396, 400, 424–7, 428–32, 453–6, 457–9, 479–82, 487–8, 490–1, 496, 502–4, 506–7, 508–9, 512, 516, 522–6, 529–33, 591–2, 593–7, 601–2, 606–7, 666, 667, 680, 730, 843, 941–2n, 965–6
    see also spherical harmonic analysis; stream function; velocity potential
potential (propagation of), 26, 353–5, 499–500
    see also electrodynamics (continental)
potentiometer, 630, 734
Pouillet, C. S. M., 196
Power, John, 34n
    letters from the Duke of Devonshire: (10 October 1870), 33–4; (1 June 1871), 649n
Pratt, J. H., 256n, 650n, 683
Preece, George, E., letter to Maxwell: (7 March 1873), 973
Prevost, Pierre, 250n, 279, 655, 781
Price, Bartholomew, *31*, 404n, 687, 688n, 856
    letter to Maxwell: (4 January 1871), 30n, 31n, 636n
Prior, Matthew, 619
projectiles (motion of), 24, 369–74
Ptolemy, Claudius, 797

quaternions, 25, 29–30, 32, 35, 214, 332–3, 334n, 568–9, 570–6, 577–8, 580, 590–2, 593–7, 600–1, 609, 634n, 636n, 648–9, 652, 660, 685, 700, 707, 755, 756–7, 784, 825–6, 831, 833, 877n, 878, 884–5, 915n, 947–8, 951–5, 963
Quetelet, Adolphe, 296n
quickest ascent (line of), 224n, 625, 667n, 787–9
Quincke, G., 631n

Rabelais, François, 271n
Radcliffe, Charles Bland, 23, *554*
    Royal Society paper: 'Researches on animal electricity' (Maxwell's report on) **342**, 554–8
Ramsay, A. C., 969

Rankine, William John Macquorn, 658n, 783
  letters to G. G. Stokes: (21 April 1868), 374n; (26 April 1868), 373n; (26 June 1868), 374n
  report on paper by G. B. Airy: (26 January 1863), 63n, 69n, 71n
  report on paper by F. Bashforth: (26 April 1868), 373n
  report on paper by J. A. Longridge: (21 April 1868), 374n
  report on paper by C. W. Merrifield: (26 June 1868), 374n
  report on paper by H. Moseley: (24 February 1869), 473n, 475n
  Royal Society papers: 'On the mathematical theory of stream-lines' (Maxwell's report on) **337**, 529–34; 'On plane water-lines' (Maxwell's report on) **223**, 123–7; 'On the thermodynamical theory of waves' (Maxwell's report on) **338**, 535–40
  Applied Mechanics, 60n, 63n, 65n, 70–1n, 236n, 242n, 289, 317, 369n, 520, 807
  fluids, 23, 123–7, 236n, 239n, 242n, 389, 511, 529–33
  diagrams of forces, 60n, 313, 392, 519–20
  energy, 190n, 365n, 417, 778
  specific heats of gases, 76n, 77, 260
  stream-lines, 123–7, 448n, 529–33
  stress, 71n, 807
  thermodynamics, 23, 75n, 84n, 260, 328n, 331n, 334n, 535–40, 672, 946
  waves, 23, 445, 533, 535–40
Ray Club, 949
Rayleigh, 3rd Baron, *see* Strutt, John William
reciprocal figures, 21–2, 60, 313–17, 320, 330, 346, 392, 517–18, 519–21, 609, 946
reciprocal polars, 21–2, 313, 520
Regnault, H. V., 223n, 260, 731, 791, 869
resonance, 598–604, 605–7, 856–7
Reye, Theodor, 935
Richards, Joan L., 21n
Riemann, G. F. B., 26, 605n
  Cauchy–Riemann equations, 428n
  electrodynamics, 26, 353–5, 379
  geometry, 618n
  potential theory, 320, 502
  topology, 433n, 439, 466n
Rive, A. de la, 557
Robertson, Alexander, 335
Robins, Benjamin, 369
Robinson, Thomas Romney, 24, *43*, 58, 211
  Royal Society paper: 'On the spectra of electric light' (Maxwell's reports on) **198**, 43–5; **201**, 54–7
Robison, John, 113n, 396n
Rothlauf, Kaspar, 721
Rowland, Henry Augustus, 37, 325n
  letters from Maxwell: (9 July 1873) **466**, 879–80; (12 July 1873) **467**, 881–3
Royal Institution, 3, 5, 271, 513, 614, 617n, 621–2, 628, 668, 790n, 813
Royal School of Mines, 409
Royal Society of Edinburgh, 6, 226, 328n, 330, 339, 346, 392, 517, 519–21, 580–1, 660, 675n, 700, 702, 710n, 727, 884, 897n, 915n, 946
Royal Society of London, 6, 269, 648n, 671n, 714n, 738, 785, 879
  Maxwell's papers at, 158n, 160–3; **238**, 189–96; 197–201; **252**, 230–5; 254–66, 267–9; **263**, 279–83; 291–2; 298–9; 343–5; **289**, 375–9; 706, 710, 711, 712–13
  Maxwell's reports on papers, 22–4; *see* reports on papers by G. B. Airy, **205**, 62–9; **206**, 70–1; **212**, 95–6; **410**, 718–26; **453**, 847; by F. Bashforth, **288**, 369–73; C. Chambers, **220**, 117–18; J. L. Clark, **415**, 734–7; **462**, 866–7; A. Des Cloiseaux, **290**, 380–2; J. D. Everett, **261**, 272–5; **269**, 300–3; **282**, 348–50; N. M. Ferrers, **325**, 492–5; T. Graham, **264**, 285–7; F. Guthrie, **442**, 827–30; S. Haughton, **199**, 46–7; **200**, 50–3; J. Jago, **447**, 836–8; J. A. Longridge, **288**, 373–4; D. M'Kichan, **455**, 849–51; C. W. Merrifield, **288**, 374; W. A. Miller, **199**, 47–9; R. Moon, **291**, 383–5; H. Moseley, **319**, 472–5; C. B. Radcliffe, **342**, 554–8; W. J. M. Rankine, **223**, 123–7, **337**, 529–34; **338**, 535–40; T. R. Robinson, **198**, 43–5; **201**, 54–7; G. G. Stokes, **197**, 41–2; **298**, 412–15; J. W. Strutt, **354**, 598–604; E. W. Tarn, **265**, 288–90; J. Tyndall, **255**, 245–8; **258**, 253
  Bakerian Lectures, 5, 230–5, 661, 671n
  Committee of Papers, 22, 533–4n
  Croonian Lecture, 146n, 341
  Philosophical Club, 5, 147
  Register of Papers Received, 62n, 117n, 123n, 348n, 380n, 554n, 734n, 827n, 836n, 849n
Ruhmkorff coil, 356n
Rühlmann, R., 829

Sabine, Edward, 463, 870n
Sabra, A. I., 629n

Index

Salet, Georges, 417
Salmon, George, 295n, 481n
Sang, Edward, 578, 702n
Saturday Review, 358, 362n, 812n, 921n
Saturn's rings
   Airy, 115n, 758n, 761–2n
   Bond, 105, 107n
   Maxwell, 12, 104–5, 128–45, 758–9, 761–2, 956n
   Spencer, 956n
   Struve, 130n
scalars, 29, 568–9, 570–6, 590–2, 593–7, 952
Scholz, E., 21n
Schröter, H., 477n
Schröter, J. H., 105n
Scott, M., 321
Scott, Sir Walter, Bt, 321n, 934n
Seebeck, Thomas, 765n
Seebeck effect, 765
self-induction of currents, 99–100, 112, 158–9, 200–1
Sellmeier, W., 863n
Shairp, J. C., 463, 774n, 886n, 915, 921n
Shakespeare, William, 610n, 822, 929
Sharpey, William, 22, *41*
   letter from Maxwell: (8 July 1862) **197**, 41–2
   report on paper by C. B. Radcliffe: ([1870]), 554n, 556n, 558n
ships,
   design of, 123–7, 529–34
   magnetism of, 505, 517, 543
Siegel, D. M., 9n, 11n, 26n, 161n, 198n
Siemens, Sir Charles William, 16, 114, 298, 351, 376n, 661–3
   letter from Maxwell: (23 June 1871) **378**, 661–3
Siemens, Werner, 661n
Simpson, Thomas K., 11n
Simpson's rule, 720
Simson, Robert, 816n
Smalley, George Robarts, 4, *61*, 86, 87, 249n
Smith, Archibald, *392*
Smith, C. W., 6n, 19n
Smith, Robert, 936n, 943
Smith, William Robertson, 516n, *577*
Smith, Willoughby, *375*
Somerville, Mary, 812n
Sophocles, 840
Sorby, H. C., 748n, 886
sound waves (propagation of), 412–15, 417–18, 538, 598–604, 780, 856–7, 960, 962
space (dimensions of), 618–19

space (directions in), 29, 637, 639, 641–3, 644, 953–4
spectra, 24, 41–2, 43–5, 47–9, 54–7, 58–9, 245–8, 339, 559–63, 614–15, 644n, 748n, 781, 960
Spencer, Herbert,
   letters from Maxwell: (5 December 1873) **486**, 956–61; (17 December 1873) **487**, 962–3
   letters to Maxwell: (4 December 1873), 956n; (30 December 1873), 962n
spherical harmonic analysis, 25, 26, 32, 277, 330, 347, 390, 392–4, 397, 406, 412–13, 503, 677, 682, 683–5, 688n, 689, 692, 723–5, 940–1, 942n
Spinoza, B., 618, 797
Spottiswoode, William, *5–6n*, 563n, 717
Sprengel, Hermann, 869
stability (dynamical), 625, 819–22
St Andrews (United College), 4–5, 457, 460, 461, 462, 463
'statistical method', 15, 16–18, 582–3, 818–19, 929–33
steel (manufacture of), 287
Steele, W. J., 703n, 872n
Stefan, Josef, 760, 891
Steiner, Jacob, 619
Steiner's surface, 477
Steinheil, C. A. von, 870
Stephen, Leslie, 666n
stereograms, 22, 318–20, 322, 330, 342, 476n
stereoscope (real image), 22, 312, 340–1, 342
stereoscopic vision, 340–1, 447
Stevenson, R. L., 7n
Stewart, Balfour, *6–7*, 214, 217n, 271, 277
   electrical measurements, 6–7, 88n, 92, 93–4, 103n, 122, 489n
   stability (dynamical), 819n, 820
Stewart, Dugald, 816n
Stewart, John, 816n
Stewart, Matthew, 816n
St John's College, Cambridge, 689
Stokes, Sir George Gabriel, Bt, 7, 9–10, 14, 22–4, 28, 48, 50, 463, 528n, 645, 671n, 710
   letters from Maxwell: (8 May 1857), 148n; (7 September 1858), 78n; (30 May 1859), 74n, 78n, 258n; (14 July 1862) **198**, 43–5; (16 July 1862) **199**, 46–9; (21 July 1862) **200**, 50–3; (10 September 1862) **202**, 58–9; (29 December 1862) **206**, 70–1; (9 June 1863) **212**, 95–6; (6 May 1864) **228**, 154–6; (15 October 1864) **237**, 186–8; (18 December 1866) **266**, 291–3; (27 February

Index

1867) **268**, 298–9; (26 June 1869) **323**, 487–8; (8 July 1869) **324**, 489–91; (11 January 1871) **351**, 589; (8 January 1872) **400**, 706; (12 February 1872) **404**, 711; (8 July 1872) **416**, 738; (13 May 1873) **453**, 847

letters to Maxwell: (16 February 1871), 611n; (18 February 1871), 612n; (23 February 1871), 612n; (14 March 1871), 615n

letters to G. B. Airy: (12 May 1848), 414n; (26 February 1863), 64n; (18 March 1863), 95n; (10 December 1872), 718n; (13 December 1872), 718n

letters from Airy: (22 February 1863), 63 4n, 69n, 95n, 96n; (27 February 1863), 95n; (3 July 1872), 725n

letter from W. Bottomley: (26 March 1873), 867n

letter from J. L. Clark: (23 January 1873), 735n

letter from T. A. Hirst: (5 October 1868), 385n

letters from F. Jenkin: (16 July 1868), 375n; (27 May 1873), 830n; (30 May 1873), 850n

letters from W. J. M. Rankine: (21 April 1868), 374n; (26 April 1868), 373n; (26 June 1868), 374n

letter to Lord Rayleigh: (5 June 1877), 538n

letters to W. Thomson: (22 February 1862), 230n; (25 February 1862), 230n

letters from Thomson: (2 July 1850), 589n; (10 March 1862), 230n; (19 April 1862), 98n; (8 July 1862), 98n; (29 October 1863), 117n; (17 February 1864), 125–6n; (15 March 1865), 189n; (11 April 1866), 230n; (13 October 1866), 291–3n; (19 October 1868), 375n; (7 March 1870), 537–8n; (9 May 1870), 538n; (3 March 1871), 613n; (25 May 1872), 734n; (1 January 1873), 735n; (21 January 1873), 735n; (21 April 1873), 847n

report on paper by S. Haughton: (30 June 1862), 50–2n

reports on paper by W. J. M. Rankine: ([1870]), 530n; (19 January 1871), 531n, 533–4n

report on paper by J. Tyndall: (18 January 1866), 245–8n

Royal Society papers: 'On the communication of vibrations' (Maxwell's report on) **298**, 412–15; 'On the long spectrum of electric light' (Maxwell's report on) **197**, 41–2

conduction (equations of), 527

crystal optics, 380–1n

elasticity, 262, 273n, 283n, 391n

ether, 199n

ether drag, 154, 309

fluids, 124, 241n, 242n, 529n, 530n, 533–4n, 539n, 778

fluorescence, 245n

infinite series, 487–8

periodic series, 414–15

polarized light, 155

potential, 590, 593

sound waves, 412–15, 417–18, 538

vibration, 412–15, 417–18, 419n

viscosity, 78, 218, 224, 231, 234, 262, 270, 473, 657

Stokes' theorem, 28, 441n, 589, 634

Stoney, G. J., 446n, 659, 893, 926

Strange, Alexander, 552

stream function, 123–4, 426, 428–9, 448, 457–8, 529–32, 545–7, 601, 603, 606–7

stream lines, 123–7, 456, 517, 529–34, 551

Strutt, John William, 3rd Baron Rayleigh, 18, 23–4, 623, 740

letters from Maxwell: (18 May 1870) **340**, 545–9; (6 December 1870) **350**, 582–4; (4 February 1871) **355**, 605–8; (15 March 1871) **358**, 614–16; (8 and 10 July 1871) **379**, 664–6; (26 May 1873) **458**, 856–7; (28 August 1873) **476**, 919–20; (22 November 1873) **482**, 940–3

letter to Maxwell: (14 February 1871), 607n, 608n, 611–12n, 614–15n

letters from C. J. Monro: (5 February 1871), 614n; (27 February 1871), 614n

letter from G. G. Stokes: (5 June 1877), 538n

London Mathematical Society paper: 'Theorems relating to vibrations' (Maxwell's report on) **460**, 860–3

Royal Society paper: 'On the theory of resonance' (Maxwell's report on) **354**, 598–604

anomalous dispersion, 863n

Bessel functions, 857

blue of the sky, 614, 619, 666n, 919, 940

colour mixing, 607n, 614n

dissipation function, 862, 940

echoes, 920

electromagnetism, 583–4, 599–602, 605–7

Index

marriage, 664
Theory of Sound, 856, 860n, 942
vibrations, 598–604, 605–7, 860–3, 864n, 940
Strutt, R. J., 4th Baron Rayleigh, 582n, 664n
Struve, Otto, 130n
Stuart, James, *623*, 718n, 723–5
Sturrock, George, 103
surface tension, 15, 325, 334n, 386–8, 389, 780
Sviedrys, R., 34n
Swan, William, 457, 463n
  letter to Maxwell: (11 May 1872), 974
Swift, Jonathan, 355n
Sydney Observatory, 87
Sylvester, James Joseph, 1n, 294n, 476, 492–4, 651n, 652–3, 687
  letter from Maxwell: (21 December 1866) **267**, 294–7
Szily, C., 947n

Tait, Archibald Campbell, 634–5n
Tait, Peter Guthrie, 1n, 6, 774–5n, 872n, 886n
  letters from Maxwell: (7 March 1865) **244**, 214–15; (3 April 1865) **245**, 216–17; (17 June 1865) **249**, 224–5; (4 April 1866) **262**, 276–8; (13 November 1867) **275**, 321–2; (4 December 1867) **276**, 323–7; (11 December 1867) **277**, 328–34; (23 December 1867) **278**, 335–9; (12 March 1868) **284**, 353–5; (14 July 1868) **293**, 389–90; (18 July 1868) **294**, 391–7; (c. 20 July 1868) **296**, 407–8; (3 August 1868) **299**, 416–18; (10 December 1869) **333**, 516–18; (7 November 1870) **346**, 568–9; (14 November 1870) **348**, 577–9; (23 January 1871) **352**, 590–2; (23 January 1871) **353**, 593–7; (14 February 1871) **356**, 609–10; (4 April 1871) **366**, 634–5; (3 May 1871) **367**, 636; (8 May 1871) **368**, 637; (11 May 1871) **369**, 639; (12 May 1871) **371**, 644; (25 May 1871) **372**, 645; (27 May 1871) **373**, 646–7; (27 May 1871) **374**, 648–9; (3 June 1871) **375**, 650–1; (14 June 1871) **376**, 652–3; (13 July 1871) **380**, 667; (late August 1871) **383**, 675–6; (5 September 1871) **384**, 677; (19 October 1871) **386**, 681; (23 October 1871) **387**, 682; (2 November 1871) **388**, 683–5; (7 November 1871) **389**, 686–7; (7 December 1871) **393**, 692–3; (12 December 1871) **394**, 694; (21 December 1871) **396**, 699–700; (1 January 1872) **398**, 702; (c. 4 January 1872) **399**, 704; (19 January 1872) **401**, 707; (12 February 1872) **403**, 710; (c. early May 1872) **407**, 715; (9 May 1872) **408**, 716; (14 May 1872) **409**, 717; (24 May 1872) **411**, 727–8; (c. late June 1872) **413**, 731; (29 June 1872) **414**, 732–3; (15 July 1872) **417**, 739–40; (7 August 1872) **417**, 741; (4 October 1872) **422**, 755; (9 October 1872) **423**, 756–7; (12 November 1872) **427**, 763; (late 1872–early 1873) **428**, 764–5; (c. December 1872) **429**, 766; (12 February 1873) **440**, 824; (c. early 1873) **441**, 825–6; (3 March 1873) **443**, 831; (5 March 1873) **444**, 832; (10 March 1873) **445**, 833–4; (12 March 1873) **446**, 835; (2 May 1873) **451**, 845; (7 May 1873) **452**, 846; (15 May 1873) **454**, 848; (8 July 1873) **465**, 877–8; (22 July 1873) **468**, 884–7; (24 July 1873) **469**, 888–9; (30 July 1873) **471**, 897; (c. August 1873) **474**, 915–16; (late August–early September 1873) **477**, 921; (2 September 1873) **479**, 934; (1 December 1873) **483**, 944–8; (11 November 1874), 618n
  letters to Maxwell: (n.d.), 224n; (6 April 1866), 278n; (27 November 1867), 323n; (6 December 1867), 328n; (13 December 1867), 333–4n; (1 February 1871), 596n; (17 February 1871), 610n; (31 March 1871), 633n; (5 April 1871), 634n; (9 May 1871), 637–8n; (13 May 1871), 639–40n; (14 May 1871), 644n; (1 June 1871), 646n; (5 June 1871), 650n; (7 June 1871), 650–1n; (13 June 1871), 652n; (14 June 1871), 662n; (20 June 1871), 663n; (9 July 1871), 667n; (10 November 1871), 687–8n; (2 January 1872), 702–3n; (6 January 1872), 704n; (n.d.), 710n; (25 January 1872), 707n; (11 June 1872), 731n; (28 June 1872), 732n; (13 July 1872), 739n; (15 July 1872), 740–1n; (16 July 1872), 740n; (17 July 1872), 740n; (19 July 1872), 740n; (30 June 1873), 877n; (7 July 1873), 877n; (31 July 1873), 915n
  letter to G. G. Stokes: (4 March 1865), 214n
  letters to W. Thomson: (6 January 1870), 856n; (25 April 1875), 856n
  letters from Thomson: (5 July 1868), 25, 398n; (21 August 1871), 25, 675n
  brachistochrone, 224n, 667
  and Clausius, 328n, 335n, 408, 732n, 740n
  conductivity, 389, 392, 888n
  fluids, 944n

Index

'On Green's and other allied theorems',
  29–30, 574n, 581, 590n, 660n
Keith prize, 580–1
laboratory, 634n, 636
magnetism, 824n
Maxwell's relations with, 25, 335n, 580–1, 624
pendulum motion, 702, 704
proofs of the *Treatise*, 32, 652, 660, 676, 681,
  689, 700, 733
quaternions, 29–30, 214, 332, 334n, 568–9n,
  573–5n, 577n, 580–1, 590n, 594–6n, 624,
  634n, 650–1n, 652n, 660, 704n, 707n, 825n,
  831, 833, 877n, 915n, 947–8, 951–5
Rede Lecture, 765n, 831, 833, 835, 845, 846,
  848, 852
Sketch of Thermodynamics, 16–17, 328n, 335–7,
  405, 408, 416, 465n, 543–4, 581, 646n,
  650n, 945–6
smoke rings, 321n
spatial directions, 637, 638n, 639, 640n, 641,
  644
spherical harmonics, 25, 32, 682, 684–5, 688n,
  689
and B. Stewart, 214, 217n, 271n, 277, 819n
thermo-electricity, 393, 654n, 662–3, 694,
  699–700, 707, 731, 732, 739, 740–1n, 831n
translation of Helmholtz on vortex motion,
  243n, 321, 391n, 398–9n, 434n, 446–7n,
  530n
vision, 703n, 704
Talbot, W. Fox, 333n, 702
Tarn, Edward Wyndham, 24, *288*, 291
  Royal Society paper: 'On the stability of
  domes' (Maxwell's report on) **265**, 288–90
Tatlock, John, 513
Tayler, Charles Benjamin, letter from Maxwell:
  (2 February 1866) **256**, 249
Taylor, W. P., 392, 517, 520
Teixeira, F. Gomes, 297n
Tennyson, Alfred (Lord), 294
tension (electric), 556–7
Thalén, T. R., 498, 881
Thales' eclipse, 98
thermodynamic relations (Maxwell's), 673–4
thermodynamics (second law of), 934
  Clausius on, 17, 328n, 335n, 359, 408, 564,
    609, 757n, 946
  'demon' paradox, 17–18, 331–2, 582–3,
    584–5
  gas under gravity, 14–15, 265–6, 269, 292n,
    853–5, 937–9
  irreversibility, 18, 359–60, 366–7, 583

Maxwell on, 14, 17–18, 266, 269, 359, 564–5,
  583, 585
reduction of, 609, 757n, 946–7
W. Thomson on, 17, 266n, 269, 359, 564
thermo-electricity, 32, 483–4, 527, 661–3, 692,
  694, 699–700, 707, 731, 732, 739–40,
  764–5, 833
  Tait on, 32, 393, 654n, 662, 694, 699–700,
    707, 731, 732n, 739–41n, 831n, 833
  W. Thomson on, 483, 692n, 699, 764–5
thermometer (Accademia del Cimento), 645,
  648
Thompson, S. P., 34n, 390n, 391n, 489n, 513n,
  624n, 665n, 704n, 783n, 792n, 846n, 849n,
  863n, 873n
Thompson, William Hepworth, *228*
Thomson, James, 1n, 16, 681
  letters from Maxwell: (13 July 1871), **381**,
    668–9; (24 July 1871) **382**, 670–4; (2
    September 1872) **421**, 751–4
  reference: (7 January 1873) **433**, 783
  letters to Maxwell: (21 July 1871), 670–1n;
    (11 January 1873), 751n, 753–4n
  atmospheric refraction, 751, 753
  continuity of gases and liquids, 668–9, 671,
    672n
  vortex turbine, 236, 239
Thomson, William, Lord Kelvin, 25, 34, 390,
  612, 681, 704, 751, 791–2, 839
  letters from Maxwell: (15 May 1855), 564n,
    730n; (1 August 1857), 105n; (14
    November 1857), 132n; (24 November
    1857), 18; (30 January 1858), 105n; (10
    December 1861), 110n, 188n, 484n, 548n,
    784n; (17 December 1861), 659n; (29 May
    1863) **210**, 88–92; (June 1863) **211**, 93–4;
    (31 July 1863) **214**, 98–101; (11 September
    1863) **219**, 112–16; (27 September 1864)
    234, 172–5; (15 October 1864) **235**,
    176–81; (25 February 1865) **242**, 207–12;
    (17 and 18 April 1865) **246**, 218–20; (27
    February 1866) **260**, 267–71; (14
    September 1867) **274**, 318–20; (20
    February 1868) **281**, 346–7; (18 July 1868)
    295, 398–406; (19 August 1868) **301**,
    422–3; (5 September 1868) **302**, 424–7; (12
    September 1868) **303**, 428–32; (28
    September 1868) **306**, 443–5; (6 October
    1868) **307**, 446–8; (7 October 1868) **308**,
    449; (16 October 1868) **310**, 453–6; (30
    October 1868) **311**, 457–9; (9 November
    1868) **315**, 463; (7 December 1868) **316**,

Index

464–5; (12 May 1869) **321**, 479–82; (5 June 1869) **322**, 483–6; (17 August 1869) **326**, 496–7; (1 October 1869) **327**, 498–500; (5 October 1869) **328**, 501; (16 November 1869) **332**, 513–15; (14 April 1870) **339**, 541–4; (21 March 1871) **362**, 624–8; (30 March 1871) **365**, 632–3; (Summer 1871) **377**, 654–60; (late August 1871) **383**, 675–6; (7 November 1871) **390**, 689; (8 February 1872) **402**, 708–9; (10 August 1872) **420**, 748–50; (22 January 1873) **434**, 784; (25 March 1873) **448**, 839

letters to Maxwell: (14 December 1868), 464–5n; (11 January 1871), 584n; (17 June 1871), 654n; (4 January 1872), 692–3n; (24 August 1872), 749–50n

letter to J. H. Balfour: ([1870]), 580n

letters from F. Jenkin: (8 August 1860), 113n; (20 February 1868), 363n

letters to G. G. Stokes: (2 July 1850), 589n; (10 March 1862), 230n; (19 April 1862), 98n; (8 July 1862), 98n; (29 October 1863), 117n; (17 February 1864), 124–6n; (15 March 1865), 189n; (11 April 1866), 230n; (13 October 1866), 291–3n; (16 July 1868), 375n; (7 March 1870), 537–8n; (9 May 1870), 538n; (3 March 1871), 613n; (25 May 1872), 734n; (1 January 1873), 735n; (21 January 1873), 735n; (21 April 1873), 847n

letters from Stokes: (22 February 1862), 230n; (25 February 1862), 230n

letters to P. G. Tait: (5 July 1868), 25, 398n; (21 August 1871), 25, 675n

letters from Tait: (6 January 1870), 856n; (25 April 1875), 856n

reports on papers by G. B. Airy: (10 May 1872), 719n, 725n; (21 April 1873), 847n

report on paper by C. Chambers: (28 October 1863), 118n

reports on papers by Maxwell: (15 March 1865), 189n; (11 April 1866), 230n; (13 October 1866), 291–3n; (19 October 1868), 375n

reports on papers by W. J. M. Rankine: (17 February 1864), 124–6n; (7 March 1870), 537–8n; (9 May 1870), 538n

anomalous dispersion, 863n
axis of magnet, 675n
British Association Address, 654n
cable, 496, 863, 915
on Cavendish, 786
charge (generation of), 424n, 503, 873
condenser (standard), 166, 172
conduction of heat, 542–3n, 966
conservation of energy, 191–2, 337
'demon', 17n, 332n, 582n
diamagnetism, 336–7, 405
dissipation of energy, 359–60, 542n, 564–5
elasticity, 71n, 231, 272n
electric circuits, 158n, 205–6, 584n
electric images, 389, 423n, 453n, 479, 713
electrical discharge in gases, 829
electrical standards, 6–9, 88n
electrical units (ratio of), 6–9, 110, 205–6, 810
electrification of a bowl, 25, 453n, 497, 499
electrolysis, 417
electromagnetism, 191–2, 507, 516
electrometers, 207n, 377, 423, 430–3, 443, 482, 555, 736, 750, 828, 850, 858, 859n, 871, 873
electroplatymeter, 873
Electrostatics and Magnetism, 25, 32, 455n, 482, 675n, 708, 773, 786n, 850n, 858–9n, 877
ether, 105–6, 190, 364
evaporation, 668–9
extremal conditions, 605n, 763
fluids, 390, 391, 398, 778
gamma function, 426n
governor, 101, 107–8, 113–16, 343n, 344n, 351
guard-ring (electrometer), 211, 377, 430–3, 443, 850, 858, 859n, 873
induction of currents, 192, 507
Laplacian, 199n
on Le Sage, 702n
magnetisation, 498n, 881n
magnetism (lamellar), 514n, 597n, 700
magnetism (solenoidal), 485n, 514n, 597n, 700, 724n, 877n
magneto-optic rotation, 190, 768–9, 784n
matter, 291n
on Maxwell, 25, 125n
mirror galvanometer, 665, 704n, 871
molecular size, 659, 893, 926
orthogonal curves, 124
parrot, 846
quadrant electrometer, 482, 555
spatial directions, 637–8n, 642, 644
spherical harmonic analysis, 277, 677n
suspended coil, 871
thermodynamics, 17, 75n, 84n, 266, 269, 331n, 359, 542–3n, 564–5, 946n

thermo-electricity, 483–4, 527, 692, 694n, 699, 764–5, 833
  tides, 98n, 624n
  time-reversal, 332n, 582n
  vortex atoms, 321n
  vortex motion, 321, 390, 391, 398, 439
Thomson, William (Archbishop of York), 634–5n
Thomson and Tait, *Natural Philosophy*, 325
  dynamics, 31, 654n, 716, 732, 733n, 740n, 745n, 904n
  elasticity, 348
  extremal conditions, 605n, 763
  figure of the earth, 277n
  force, 423
  Gauss' theorem, 648n
  Hamilton's principle, 354n, 947n
  impact, 384
  inertia, 364n
  kinetic energy, 75n, 365n
  kinetics, 654n
  matter, 395–6
  particle motion, 323n
  publication of, 24, 277, 330, 856n
  spatial directions, 637, 639, 641, 644
  spherical harmonics, 277n, 330, 347, 390, 412n, 677, 682, 684, 689n, 723–4, 725n
  Stokes' theorem, 589n, 635n
  viscosity, 474n
Thomson effect, 765, 833
Thomson's theorem, *see* Dirichlet's principle
tides (theory of), 98, 624n
time-reversal, 18–19, 332n, 346, 360–1, 582–3
The Times, 748n
Todd, David Peck, letter from Maxwell: (19 March 1879), 10
Todhunter, Isaac, 589n, 625n, 689n
Tomlinson, Charles, 784, 786, *858*
  letter from Maxwell: (29 May 1873) **459**, 858–9
topography, 566–7
topology, 28–9, 647
  curves, surfaces and spaces, 433–8, 439–42, 443–4, 449–50, 466–9, 470–1, 591, 594, 626
  directions in space, 637, 639, 641–3, 644, 953–4
  knots, 321–2, 325–7, 330
  topographical geometry, 29, 566–7
Torricelli, E., 20, 365, 395, 812
torsion balance (electric), 213, 377, 482, 873
Tresca, Henri Edouard, 477, 691
Trinity College, Cambridge, 624n
  Maxwell at, 528
  Maxwell's fellowship, 228
Troost, L., 285n
Trotter, Coutts, 36n, *623*
  letter to Maxwell: (20 April 1871), 623n
Tucker, Robert, 343n, 566n, 641n
  letter to Maxwell: (8 April 1870), 458–9n
Tulloch, John, 462, 463
Turner, F. M., 840n
Tyndall, John, 5–6, 24, 56, 226, 473n, 474n, 513, 578, 617, 915, 921, 956n
  letters from Maxwell: (20 April 1864) **226**, 147; (23 July 1868) **297**, 409–10
  letter to Maxwell: ('Monday'), 976
  Royal Society papers: 'On calorescence' (Maxwell's report on) **255**, 245–8; 'On radiation and absorption' (Maxwell's report on) **258**, 253

Varley, C. F., 271, 424n, 503, 873
Vaughan, Daniel, 98, 132
vaulted structures, 24, 288–90, 691
vector potential, 590, 756
vectors, 29–30, 568–9, 570–6, 577, 590–2, 593–7, 825, 831, 898, 951–3, 954, 963
  electromagnetism, 572–3, 592, 594–5, 596–7, 825, 955, 963
  see also quaternions
velocity potential, 124, 242, 426, 428, 457, 511, 530, 545
vena contracta, 510–12
Verdet, Émile, 336, 380–1n, 405–6, 646n, 651n, 826n, 885n
vibrations (theory of), 412–15, 417–18, 419n, 598–604, 605–7, 780, 856–7, 860–3, 864–5
virial, 16, 609, 709, 710, 946
viscosity of gases (experiments on), 13, 96, 202, 215, 216–17, 218–19, 221, 222–3, 224, 230–5, 270, 582, 658, 869, 888, 891, 894
vision, 23, 703n, 704, 836–8
Vogt, Carl, 407n
Volta, Alessandro, 557, 750
Voltaire, F. M. A., 368
vortex atoms, 321n, 693
vortex motion,
  Helmholtz on, 243, 321, 391, 398n, 399–404, 434n, 439n, 446–7, 533
  Maxwell on, 11, 239–40, 243, 321–2, 399–404, 407
  W. Thomson on, 321, 390, 391, 398, 439n, 446
vortex turbine, 236–9

Index

vortices (molecular), 11, 180, 337

Waltenhofen, A. von, 506
Waterston, J. J., 386
'The Waterwitch', 510n
Watson, H. W., 907n, 931n
Watt, James, 790–1
Watts, Henry, 100n, 380n, 693n, 886n
Way's mercury light, 56
Weber, Wilhelm Eduard, 736, 750
    diamagnetism, 336–7, 405, 505, 583
    electrical measurements, 7, 43–4, 211, 736, 773, 810–11
    electrical units (ratio of), 110, 171, 188, 195, 198, 378, 851
    force law, 337, 353–4, 654n, 686–7, 773, 843n
    magnetisation, 336, 498n, 583, 727
    paramagnetism, 336–7, 405, 505, 583
    terrestrial magnetism, 32, 505–6
Weierstrass, Karl, 477n
Wertheim, Guillaume, 273n, 274
Wheatstone, Sir Charles,
    reports on papers by J. L. Clark: (3 September 1872), 735n; (1 July 1873), 867n
    report on paper by W. A. Miller: (23 August 1862), 48n
    report on paper by T. R. Robinson: (22 October 1862), 45n, 57n
    report on paper by G. G. Stokes: (16 July 1862), 42n
    dynamo, 298

    polarization of light, 563
    spectra, 41n
    stereoscope, 312n
Wheatstone's bridge, 158, 193, 503, 584n, 824n, 871
Whipple, G. M., letters from Maxwell: (20 March 1874), 870n; (4 May 1874), 870n
White, James, 422, 445, 464, 498
White, Walter, 671n
Whittaker, E. T., 11n
Wiedemann, Gustav, 356n, 723, 735n, 773, 829, 866n, 871n, 888
Wilde, H., 872
Williamson, A. W., 337n, 916n
Willis, Thomas, 813
Wilson, D. B., 32n, 33n, 98n, 117n, 125–6n, 230n, 291–3n, 375n, 537–8n, 589n, 735n
Wilson, George, 621
Winstanley, D. A., 34n
Winter, Karl, 873
Wise, M. N., 6n, 19n
wöhlerite, 380
Wollaston, W. H., 751
work (mechanical), 365, 564, 609n, 710, 746
Wünsch, C. E., 775

yellow spot (of the eye), 552
Young, Thomas, 63, 367, 775
Young's modulus, 349

zoetrope ('wheel of life'), 22, 444–5, 446–7, 456, 464

CPSIA information can be obtained
at www.ICGtesting.com
Printed in the USA
LVOW06s1156180417
531173LV00002B/2/P